MATHEMATICAL
RECREATIONS AND ESSAYS

MATHEMATICAL
RECREATIONS & ESSAYS

BY

W. W. ROUSE BALL

LATE FELLOW OF TRINITY COLLEGE, CAMBRIDGE

REVISED BY

H. S. M. COXETER

PAST FELLOW OF TRINITY COLLEGE, CAMBRIDGE

NEW YORK

THE MACMILLAN COMPANY

1956

American Edition
1947

Third Printing,   1956

AUTHOR'S PREFACE

THIS book contains descriptions of various problems of the kind usually termed Mathematical Recreations, and a few Essays on some analogous questions. I have excluded all matter which involves advanced mathematics. I hasten to add that the conclusions are of no practical use, and that most of the results are not new. If therefore the reader proceeds further he is at least forewarned. At the same time I think I may say that many of the questions discussed are interesting, not a few are associated with the names of distinguished mathematicians, while hitherto several of the memoirs quoted have not been easily accessible to English readers. A great deal of new matter has 'been added since the work was first issued in 1892.

As now presented, the book contains fourteen chapters, of which the subjects are shown in the Table of Contents. Several of the questions mentioned in the first four chapters are of a somewhat trivial character, and had they been treated in any standard English work to which I could have referred the reader, I should have left them out : in the absence of such a work, I thought it better to insert them and trust to the judicious reader to omit them altogether or to skim them as he feels inclined. I may add that in discussing problems where the complete solutions are long or intricate I have been generally content to indicate memoirs or books in which the methods are set out at length, and to give a few illustrative examples. In some cases I have also stated problems which still await solution.

I have inserted detailed references, as far as I know them, to the sources of the various questions and solutions given; also, wherever I have given only the result of a theorem, I have tried to indicate authorities where a proof may be found. In general, unless it is stated otherwise, I have taken the references direct from the original works; but, in spite of considerable time spent in verifying them, I dare not suppose that they are free from all errors or misprints.

W. W. ROUSE BALL.

EDITOR'S PREFACE

IN revising Rouse Ball's delightful book, it has been my aim to preserve its spirit, adding the kind of material that he himself would have enjoyed. After consultation with several mathematicians, I have felt it desirable to strike out the fifth, eighth, and fifteenth chapters of the tenth edition. (For String Figures, the reader is referred to any previous edition, or to Rouse Ball's little book on that subject.) The twelfth chapter has been broken up and distributed among the first, third, fourth and eleventh chapters.

The present fifth chapter is new; so is most of the second and eighth chapters, and a good deal of the third and seventh. Moreover, the fourteenth, on Cryptographs and Ciphers, has been completely rewritten by Abraham Sinkov, a Cryptanalyst in the U.S. War Department. To him and many other helpers I would express my sincere thanks, especially to D. H. Lehmer, who constructively criticized the second chapter in manuscript; to J. M. Andreas, who provided a number of diagrams for the fifth chapter; and to P. S. Donchian for the photographs of his models (facing pages 130 and 134).

I shall be grateful for notices of additions or corrections which may occur to any of my readers.

H. S. M. COXETER.

University of Toronto,
Jan., 1938.

TABLE OF CONTENTS

CHAPTER I. ARITHMETICAL RECREATIONS.

PAGE

Bachet. Ozanam. Montucla 2
Elementary Questions on Numbers 3
    Determination of a number selected by someone . 4
    Prediction of the result of certain operations . . 8
    Problems involving two numbers 10
    Digit questions 11
Problems with a Series of Numbered Things . . . 16
Restorations 20
Calendar Problems 26
Medieval Problems 27
    The Josephus Problem. Decimation . . . 32
The Game of Nim 36
    Moore's Game. 38
    Wythoff's Game 38
    Kayles 39
Addendum on Solutions 40

CHAPTER II. ARITHMETICAL RECREATIONS (*continued*).

Arithmetical Fallacies 41
Paradoxical Problems 44
Probability Problems 45
Permutation Problems 48
Bachet's Weights Problem 50
The Decimal Expression for $1/n$ 53
Decimals and Continued Fractions 54
Rational Right-angled Triangles 57
Triangular and Pyramidal Numbers 59
Automorphic Numbers 60

PAGE

Finite Arithmetics 60
Lehmer's Machine 61
The Distribution of Primes 62
Mersenne's Numbers 65
Perfect Numbers 67
Fermat's Theorem on Binary Powers 68
Fermat's Last Theorem 69
Galois Arithmetics 73

CHAPTER III. GEOMETRICAL RECREATIONS.

Geometrical Fallacies 76
Paradoxical Problems 84
Continued Fractions and Lattice Points 86
Plane Dissections 87
Solid Dissections 93
Cyclotomy 94
Compass Problems 96
The Five Disc Problem 97
Besicovitch's Minimal Problem 99
Kakeya's Minimal Problem 99
Physical Configuration of a Country 101
Addendum on a Solution 103

CHAPTER IV. GEOMETRICAL RECREATIONS (continued).

Statical Games of Position 104
     Three-in-a-row. Extension to p-in-a-row . . . 105
     Tesselation with Regular Polygons 106
     Anallagmatic Pavements 108
     Tesselation with Super-Dominoes 111
     Colour-Cube Problem 112
     Tangrams 113
Dynamical Games of Position 114
     Shunting Problems 114
     Ferry-Boat Problems 116
     Geodesic Problems 118
     Problems with Counters or Pawns 119

PAGE

Paradromic Rings 125
Addendum on Solutions 127

CHAPTER V. POLYHEDRA.

Symmetry and Symmetries 129
The Five Platonic Solids 130
   Reciprocation 132
   Kepler's Mysticism 133
   Pappus, on the distribution of vertices . . . 134
   Compounds 134
The Archimedean Solids 135
   Mrs. Stott's Construction 139
Equilateral Zonohedra 140
The Kepler–Poinsot Solids 143
Solid Tesselations 146
Ball-Piling or Close-Packing 148
   The Sand by the Sea-Shore 151
Regular Sponges 151
Rotating Rings of Tetrahedra 153
The Kaleidoscope 154

CHAPTER VI. CHESS-BOARD RECREATIONS.

Chess-Board Notation 161
Relative Value of the Pieces 162
The Eight Queens Problem 165
Maximum Pieces Problem 171
Minimum Pieces Problem 171
   Analogous Problems 173
Re-Entrant Paths on a Chess-Board 174
   Knight's Re-Entrant Path 174
   King's Re-Entrant Path 185
   Rook's Re-Entrant Path 186
   Bishop's Re-Entrant Path 186
Miscellaneous Problems 187
Latin Squares 189
   Magic Card Square. Euler's Officers Problem . . 190

PAGE

Eulerian Squares 190
Latin Cubes. Eulerian Cubes 192

CHAPTER VII. MAGIC SQUARES.

Magic Squares and their History 193
Construction of Odd Magic Squares 195
Construction of Singly-Even Magic Squares . . . 196
Construction of Doubly-Even Magic Squares . . . 199
Bordered Squares 200
Number of Squares of a Given Order 202
Symmetrical and Pandiagonal Squares 202
Generalization of De la Loubère's Rule . . . 204
Arnoux's Method 207
Margossian's Method 208
Magic Squares of Non-consecutive Numbers . . . 210
Magic Squares of Primes 211
Bergholt's General Square of the Fourth Order . . 212
Doubly-Magic and Trebly-Magic Squares 212
Other Magic Problems 213
Magic Domino Squares 214
Cubic and Octahedral Dice. Interlocked Hexagons . 215
Magic Cubes 217

CHAPTER VIII. MAP-COLOURING PROBLEMS.

The Four-Colour Theorem 222
Möbius, Guthrie, De Morgan, Cayley . . . 223
Petersen, Tait 226
Heawood. Reduction to a Standard Map . . 227
Minimum Number of Districts for Possible Failure . 230
Equivalent Problem in the Theory of Numbers . . 231
Unbounded Surfaces 232
Dual Maps 234
The Seven-Colour Theorem 235
Extension to Maps of Higher Genus 236
Colouring the Icosahedron 238

CHAPTER IX. UNICURSAL PROBLEMS.

Euler's Problem 242
  Euler's General Theorems 245
Number of Ways of describing a Unicursal Figure . . 249
Mazes 254
  Rules for traversing a Maze 255
  The History of Mazes 256
Geometrical Trees 260
  Circles Inside or Outside each other 261
The Hamiltonian Game 262
  The Icosahedral Group 264

CHAPTER X. KIRKMAN'S SCHOOL-GIRLS PROBLEM.

History of the Problem 267
Solutions by One-Step Cycles 269
  Examples when $n = 3, 9, 27, 33, 51, 57, 75, 81, 99$. 270
Solutions by Two-Step Cycles 273
  Examples when $n = 15, 27, 39, 51, 63, 75, 87, 99$. 274
Solutions by Three-Step Cycles 277
  Examples when $n = 9, 21, 27, 33, 39, 45, 51, 57, 63, 69,$
    $75, 81, 87, 93, 99$ 280
Solutions by the Focal Method 283
  Examples when $n = 33, 51$ 285
Analytical Methods 286
  Application when $n = 27$ with 13 as base . . . 287
  Examples when $n = 15, 39$ 290
Number of Solutions 292
Harison's Theorem 293
Problem of n^2 Girls in n Groups (Peirce) . . . 294
  Examples when $n = 2, 3, 4, 5, 7, 8$ 294
  General Method when n is prime 296
Kirkman's Problem in Quartets, etc. 296
A Bridge Problem. Arrangements in Pairs . . . 297
Sylvester's Corollary to Kirkman's Problem . . . 297
Addendum on a Solution 298

CHAPTER XI. MISCELLANEOUS PROBLEMS.

PAGE

The Fifteen Puzzle 299
The Tower of Hanoï 303
Chinese Rings 305
    Algebraic Solution 306
    Solution in Binary Scale of Notation . . . 308
Problems connected with a Pack of Cards . . . 310
Shuffling a Pack 310
Arrangements by Rows and Columns 312
Bachet's Problem with Pairs of Cards . . . 313
The Three Pile Problem 316
    Gergonne's Generalization 317
The Window Reader 321
The Mouse Trap. Treize 324

CHAPTER XII. THREE CLASSICAL GEOMETRICAL PROBLEMS.

Statement of the Problems 326
The Duplication of the Cube. Legendary Origin of the
    Problem 327
Hippocrates's Lemma 329
Solutions by Archytas, Plato, Menaechmus, Apollonius, and
    Diocles 330
Solutions by Vieta, Descartes, Gregory of St. Vincent, and
    Newton 332
The Trisection of an Angle 333
Ancient Solutions quoted by Pappus 333
Solutions by Pappus, Descartes, Newton, Clairaut, and
    Chasles 334
The Quadrature of the Circle 335
Incommensurability of π 336
Definitions of π 337
Origin of symbol π 338
Geometrical methods of Approximation to the numerical
    value of π 338
    Results of Egyptians, Babylonians, Jews . . . 339
    Results of Archimedes and other Greek Writers . . 340

PAGE

Results of Roman Surveyors and Gerbert . . . 341
Results of Indian and Eastern Writers . . . 341
Results of European Writers, 1200–1630 . . . 342
Theorems of Wallis and Brouncker 345
Analytical methods of Approximation. Gregory's series . 346
Results of European Writers, 1699–1873 . . . 347
Geometrical Approximation 348
Approximations by the Theory of Probability . . . 348

CHAPTER XIII. CALCULATING PRODIGIES.

Calculating Prodigies. Authorities 350
John Wallis, 1616–1703 351
Buxton, circ. 1707–1772 351
Problems solved 352
Methods 353
Fuller, 1710–1790 354
Ampère, Gauss, Whately 355
Colburn, 1804–1840 355
Problems solved 356
Power of Factorizing Numbers 356
Bidder, 1806–1878 357
Career 358
Problems solved 359
The Bidder Family 362
Mondeux, Mangiamele 362
Dase, 1824–1861 363
Problems solved 363
Scientific Work 364
Safford, 1836–1901 365
Zamebone, Diamandi, Rückle 366
Inaudi, 1867– 366
Problems solved 366
Expression of Numbers by Four Squares . . . 367
Nature of Public Performances 367
Types of Memory of Numbers 368

PAGE

Bidder's Analysis of Methods used 369
    Preferably only one step at a time 370
    Multiplication 370
    Division. Digit-Terminals 372
    Digital Method for Division and Factors . . . 372
    Square Roots. Higher Roots 373
    Compound Interest 375
    Logarithms 376
Suggested Law of Rapidity of Calculation . . . 377
Requisites for Success 378

CHAPTER XIV. CRYPTOGRAPHY AND CRYPTANALYSIS.

Definitions 379
Transposition Systems 382
    The Route Method 382
    Columnar Transposition 383
    Digraphs and Trigraphs 385
    Comparison of several messages 387
    The Grille 392
Substitution Systems 393
    Tables of Frequency 396
    Polyalphabetic Systems 398
    The Vigenère Square 399
    The Playfair Cipher 402
    Code 404
Determination of Cryptographic System 406
A few final remarks 408
Addendum : References for further study . . . 410

INDEX 411

"*Les hommes ne sont jamais plus ingénieux que dans l'invention des jeux ; l'esprit s'y trouve à son aise. . . . Après les jeux qui dépendent uniquement des nombres viennent les jeux où entre la situation. . . . Après les jeux où n'entrent que le nombre et la situation viendraient les jeux où entre le mouvement. . . . Enfin il serait à souhaiter qu'on eût un cours entier des jeux, traités mathématiquement.*" (Leibniz : letter to De Montmort, July 29, 1715.)

CHAPTER I

ARITHMETICAL RECREATIONS

I COMMENCE by describing some arithmetical recreations. The interest excited by statements of the relations between numbers of certain forms has been often remarked, and the majority of works on mathematical recreations include several such problems, which, though obvious to anyone acquainted with the elements of algebra, have to many who are ignorant of that subject the same kind of charm that mathematicians find in the more recondite propositions of higher arithmetic. I devote the bulk of this chapter to these elementary problems.

Before entering on the subject, I may add that a large proportion of the elementary questions mentioned here are taken from one of two sources. The first of these is the classical *Problèmes plaisans et délectables*, by Claude Gaspar Bachet, sieur de Méziriac, of which the first edition was published in 1612 and the second in 1624 : it is to the edition of 1624 that the references hereafter given apply. Several of Bachet's problems are taken from the writings of Alcuin, Pacioli di Burgo, Tartaglia, and Cardan, and possibly some of them are of oriental origin, but I have made no attempt to add such references. The other source to which I alluded above is Ozanam's *Récréations mathématiques et physiques*. The greater portion of the original edition, published in two volumes at Paris in 1694, was a compilation from the works of Bachet, Mydorge, and Leurechon : this part is excellent, but the same cannot be said of the additions due to Ozanam. In the *Biographie Universelle* allusion is made to subsequent editions issued in 1720, 1735, 1741, 1778, and 1790 ; doubtless these references are correct, but the following editions, all of which I have seen, are the only ones of which I have any knowledge.

In 1696 an edition was issued at Amsterdam. In 1723—six years after the death of Ozanam—one was issued in three volumes, with a supplementary fourth volume, containing, among other things, an appendix on puzzles. Fresh editions were issued in 1741, 1750 (the second volume of which bears the date 1749), 1770, and 1790. The edition of 1750 is said to have been corrected by Montucla on condition that his name should not be associated with it; but the edition of 1790 is the earliest one in which reference is made to these corrections, though the editor is referred to only as Monsieur M***. Montucla expunged most of what was actually incorrect in the older editions, and added several historical notes, but unfortunately his scruples prevented him from striking out the accounts of numerous trivial experiments and truisms which overload the work. An English translation of the original edition appeared in 1708, and I believe ran through four editions, the last of them being published in Dublin in 1790. Montucla's revision of 1790 was translated by C. Hutton, and editions of this were issued in 1803, in 1814, and (in one volume) in 1840 : my references are to the editions of 1803 and 1840.

I proceed to enumerate some of the typical elementary questions connected with numbers which for nearly three centuries have formed a large part of most compilations of mathematical amusements. They are given here largely for their historical—not for their arithmetical—interest; and perhaps a mathematician may well omit this chapter.

Many of these questions are of the nature of tricks or puzzles, and I follow the usual course and present them in that form. I may note, however, that most of them are not worth proposing, even as tricks, unless either the method employed is disguised or the result arrived at is different from that expected ; but, as I am not writing on conjuring, I refrain from alluding to the means of disguising the operations indicated, and give merely a bare enumeration of the steps essential to the success of the method used. To the non-mathematician even to-day some of those results seem astonishing, but the secret is at once revealed as soon as the question is translated by symbols into mathematical language.

To Find a Number Selected by Someone

There are innumerable ways of finding a number chosen by someone, provided the result of certain operations on it is known. I confine myself to methods typical of those commonly used. Anyone acquainted with algebra will find no difficulty in framing new rules of an analogous nature.

First Method.* (i) Ask the person who has chosen the number to treble it. (ii) Enquire if the product is even or odd : if it is even, request him to take half of it ; if it is odd, request him to add unity to it and then to take half of it. (iii) Tell him to multiply the result of the second step by 3. (iv) Ask how many integral times 9 divides into the latter product : suppose the answer to be n. (v) Then the number thought of was $2n$ or $2n + 1$, according as the result of step (i) was even or odd.

The demonstration is obvious. Every even number is of the form $2n$, and the successive operations applied to this give (i) $6n$, which is even ; (ii) $\frac{1}{2}6n = 3n$; (iii) $3 \times 3n = 9n$; (iv) $\frac{1}{9}9n = n$; (v) $2n$. Every odd number is of the form $2n + 1$, and the successive operations applied to this give (i) $6n + 3$ which is odd ; (ii) $\frac{1}{2}(6n + 3 + 1) = 3n + 2$; (iii) $3(3n + 2) = 9n + 6$; (iv) $\frac{1}{9}(9n + 6) = n + a$ remainder ; (v) $2n + 1$. These results lead to the rule given above.

Second Method.† Ask the person who has chosen the number to perform in succession the following operations. (i) To multiply the number by 5.   (ii) To add 6 to the product. (iii) To multiply the sum by 4.   (iv) To add 9 to the product. (v) To multiply the sum by 5. Ask to be told the result of the last operation : if from this product 165 is subtracted, and

---

* Bachet, *Problèmes*, Lyons, 1624, problem I, p. 53.

† A similar rule was given by Bachet, problem IV, p. 74.

then the remainder is divided by 100, the quotient will be the number thought of originally.

For let n be the number selected. Then the successive operations applied to it give : (i) $5n$; (ii) $5n + 6$; (iii) $20n + 24$; (iv) $20n + 33$; (v) $100n + 165$. Hence the rule.

Third Method.* Request the person who has thought of the number to perform the following operations. (i) To multiply it by any number you like, say a. (ii) To divide the product by any number, say b. (iii) To multiply the quotient by c. (iv) To divide this result by d. (v) To divide the final result by the number selected originally. (vi) To add to the result of operation (v) the number thought of at first. Ask for the sum so found : then, if ac/bd is subtracted from this sum, the remainder will be the number chosen originally.

For, if n was the number selected, the result of the first four operations is to form nac/bd; operation (v) gives ac/bd; and (vi) gives $n + (ac/bd)$, which number is mentioned. But ac/bd is known; hence, subtracting it from the number mentioned, n is found. Of course a, b, c, d may have any numerical values it is liked to assign to them. For example, if $a = 12$, $b = 4$, $c = 7$, $d = 3$, it is sufficient to subtract 7 from the final result in order to obtain the number originally selected.

Fourth Method.† Ask someone to select a number less than 90. Request him to perform the following operations. (i) To multiply it by 10, and to add any number he pleases, a, which is less than 10. (ii) To divide the result of step (i) by 3, and to mention the remainder, say b. (iii) To multiply the quotient obtained in step (ii) by 10, and to add any number he pleases, c, which is less than 10. (iv) To divide the result of step (iii) by 3, and to mention the remainder, say d, and the third digit (from the right) of the quotient; suppose this digit is e. Then, if the numbers a, b, c, d, e are known,

---

* Bachet, problem v, p. 80.

† *Educational Times*, London, May 1, 1895, vol. XLVIII, p. 234. This example is said to have been made up by J. Clerk Maxwell in his boyhood : it is interesting to note how widely it differs from the simple Bachet problems previously mentioned.

the original number can be at once determined. In fact, if the number is $9x + y$, where $x \leqslant 9$ and $y \leqslant 8$, and if r is the remainder when $a - b + 3(c - d)$ is divided by 9, we have $x = e, y = 9 - r$.

The demonstration is not difficult. Suppose the selected number is $9x + y$. Step (i) gives $90x + 10y + a$. Let $y + a = 3n + b$, then the quotient obtained in step (ii) is $30x + 3y + n$. Step (iii) gives $300x + 30y + 10n + c$. Let $n + c = 3m + d$, then the quotient obtained in step (iv) is $100x + 10y + 3n + m$, which I will denote by Q. Now the third digit in Q must be x, because, since $y \leqslant 8$ and $a \leqslant 9$, we have $n \leqslant 5$; and since $n \leqslant 5$ and $c \leqslant 9$, we have $m \leqslant 4$; therefore $10y + 3n + m \leqslant 99$. Hence the third or hundreds digit in Q is x.

Again, from the relations $y + a = 3n + b$ and $n + c = 3m + d$, we have $9m - y = a - b + 3(c - d)$: hence, if r is the remainder when $a - b + 3(c - d)$ is divided by 9, we have $y = 9 - r$. [This is always true, if we make r positive ; but if $a - b + 3(c - d)$ is negative, it is simpler to take y as equal to its numerical value ; or we may prevent the occurrence of this case by assigning proper values to a and c.] Thus x and y are both known, and therefore the number selected, namely $9x + y$, is known.

Fifth Method.* Ask anyone to select a number less than 60. Request him to perform the following operations. (i) To divide it by 3 and mention the remainder ; suppose it to be a. (ii) To divide it by 4, and mention the remainder ; suppose it to be b. (iii) To divide it by 5, and mention the remainder ; suppose it to be c. Then the number selected is the remainder obtained by dividing $40a + 45b + 36c$ by 60.

This method can be generalized and then will apply to any number chosen. Let $a', b', c', \ldots$ be a series of numbers prime to one another, and let p be their product. Let n be any number less than p, and let $a, b, c, \ldots$ be the remainders

---

* Bachet, problem VI, p. 84 : Bachet added, on p. 87, a note on the previous history of the problem.

when n is divided by a', b', c', ... respectively. Find a number A which is a multiple of the product $b'c'd'$... and which exceeds by unity a multiple of a'. Find a number B which is a multiple of $a'c'd'$... and which exceeds by unity a multiple of b', and similarly find analogous numbers C, D, ... Rules for the calculation of A, B, C, ... are given in the theory of numbers, but in general, if the numbers a', b', c', ... are small, the corresponding numbers A, B, C, ... can be found by inspection. I proceed to show that n is equal to the remainder when $Aa + Bb + Cc + \ldots$ is divided by p.

Let $N = Aa + Bb + Cc + \ldots$, and let $M(x)$ stand for a multiple of x. Now $A = M(a') + 1$, therefore $Aa = M(a') + a$. Hence, if the first term in N—that is, Aa—is divided by a', the remainder is a. Again, B is a multiple of $a'c'd'$.... Therefore Bb is exactly divisible by a'. Similarly Cc, Dd, ... are each exactly divisible by a'. Thus every term in N, except the first, is exactly divisible by a'. Hence, if N is divided by a', the remainder is a. Also if n is divided by a', the remainder is a.

Therefore $\qquad\qquad N - n = M(a')$.

Similarly $\qquad\qquad N - n = M(b')$,

$\qquad\qquad\qquad\quad N - n = M(c')$,

. . . .

But a', b', c', ... are prime to one another. Therefore

$$N - n = M(a'b'c'\ldots) = M(p),$$

that is, $\qquad\qquad N = M(p) + n$.

Now n is less than p, hence if N is divided by p, the remainder is n.

The rule given by Bachet corresponds to the case of $a' = 3$, $b' = 4$, $c' = 5$, $p = 60$, $A = 40$, $B = 45$, $C = 36$. If the number chosen is less than 420, we may take $a' = 3$, $b' = 4$, $c' = 5$, $d' = 7$, $p = 420$, $A = 280$, $B = 105$, $C = 336$, $D = 120$.

To Find the Result of a Series of Operations Performed on Any Number (*unknown to the operator*) without Asking any Questions

All rules for solving such problems ultimately depend on
so arranging the operations that the number disappears from
the final result. Four examples will suffice.

First Example.* Request someone to think of a number.
Suppose it to be n. Ask him (i) to multiply it by any number
you please, say a; (ii) then to add, say, b; (iii) then to divide
the sum by, say, c. (iv) Next, tell him to take a/c of the
number originally chosen; and (v) to subtract this from the
result of the third operation. The result of the first three
operations is $(na + b)/c$, and the result of operation (iv) is
na/c: the difference between these is b/c and therefore is
known to you. For example, if $a = 6$, $b = 12$, $c = 4$, then
$a/c = 1\frac{1}{2}$, and the final result is 3.

Second Example.† Ask A to take any number of counters
that he pleases : suppose that he takes n counters. (i) Ask
someone else, say B, to take p times as many, where p is
any number you like to choose. (ii) Request A to give q of
his counters to B, where q is any number you like to select.
(iii) Next, ask B to transfer to A a number of counters equal
to p times as many counters as A has in his possession. Then
there will remain in B's hands $q(p + 1)$ counters : this number is known to you; and the trick can be finished either by
mentioning it or in any other way you like.

The reason is as follows. The result of operation (ii) is
that B has $pn + q$ counters, and A has $n - q$ counters. The
result of (iii) is that B transfers $p(n - q)$ counters to A :
hence he has left in his possession $(pn + q) - p(n - q)$
counters—that is, he has $q(p + 1)$.

For example, if originally A took any number of counters,
then (if you chose p equal to 2), first you would ask B to take

---

* Bachet, problem VIII, p. 102.

† Bachet, problem XIII, p. 123 : Bachet presented the above trick in a
form somewhat more general but less effective in practice.

twice as many counters as A had done; next (if you chose q equal to 3) you would ask A to give 3 counters to B; and then you would ask B to give to A a number of counters equal to twice the number then in A's possession; after this was done you would know that B had $3(2 + 1)$—that is, 9 left.

This trick (as also some of the following problems) may be performed equally well with one person, in which case A may stand for his right hand and B for his left hand.

Third Example. Ask someone to perform in succession the following operations. (i) Take any number of three digits, in which the difference between the first and last digits exceeds unity. (ii) Form a new number by reversing the order of the digits. (iii) Find the difference of these two numbers. (iv) Form another number by reversing the order of the digits in this difference. (v) Add together the results of (iii) and (iv). Then the sum obtained as the result of this last operation will be 1089.

An illustration and the explanation of the rule are given below.

(i)	237	$100a + 10b + c$
(ii)	732	$100c + 10b + a$
(iii)	495	$100(a - c - 1) + 90 + (10 + c - a)$
(iv)	594	$100(10 + c - a) + 90 + (a - c - 1)$
(v)	1089	$900 + 180 + 9$

The result depends only on the radix of the scale of notation in which the number is expressed. If this radix is r, the result is $(r - 1)(r + 1)^2$; thus if $r = 10$, the result is 9×11^2—that is, 1089. Similar problems can be made with numbers exceeding 999.

Fourth Example.* The following trick depends on the same principle. Ask someone to perform in succession the following operations. (i) To write down any sum of money

* *Educational Times Reprints*, 1890, vol. LIII, p. 78.

less than £12, in which the difference between the number of pounds and the number of pence exceeds unity. (ii) To *reverse* this sum—that is, to write down a sum of money obtained from it by interchanging the numbers of pounds and pence. (iii) To find the difference between the results of (i) and (ii). (iv) To reverse this difference. (v) To add together the results of (iii) and (iv). Then this sum will be £12 18s. 11d.

For instance, take the sum £10 17s. 5d.; we have

			£	s.	d.
(i)	.	.	10	17	5
(ii)	.	.	5	17	10
(iii)	.	.	4	19	7
(iv)	.	.	7	19	4
(v)	.	.	12	18	11

The following analysis explains the rule, and shows that the final result is independent of the sum written down initially.

				£	s.	d.
(i)	.	.	.	a	b	c
(ii)	.	.	.	c	b	a
(iii)	.	.	.	$a - c - 1$	19	$c - a + 12$
(iv)	.	.	.	$c - a + 12$	19	$a - c - 1$
(v)	.	.	.	11	38	11

Mr. J. H. Schooling has used this result as the foundation of a slight but excellent conjuring trick. The rule can be generalized to cover any system of monetary units.

PROBLEMS INVOLVING TWO NUMBERS

I proceed next to give a couple of examples of a class of problems which involve two numbers.

First Example.* Suppose that there are two numbers, one even and the other odd, and that a person A is asked to select one of them, and that another person B takes the other. It is desired to know whether A selected the even or the odd number. Ask A to multiply his number by 2, or any even number, and B to multiply his by 3, or any odd number. Request them to add the two products together and tell you the sum. If it is even, then originally A selected the odd number, but if it is odd, then originally A selected the even number. The reason is obvious.

Second Example.† The above rule was extended by Bachet to any two numbers, provided they are prime to one another and one of them is not itself a prime. Let the numbers be m and n, and suppose that n is exactly divisible by p. Ask A to select one of these numbers, and B to take the other. Choose a number prime to p, say q. Ask A to multiply his number by q, and B to multiply his number by p. Request them to add the products together and state the sum. Then A originally selected m or n, according as this result is not or is divisible by p. The numbers, $m = 7$, $n = 15$, $p = 3$, $q = 2$, will illustrate the rest.

Problems Depending on the Scale of Notation

Many of the rules for finding two or more numbers depend on the fact that in arithmetic an integral number is denoted by a succession of digits, where each digit represents the product of that digit and a power of ten, and the number is equal to the sum of these products. For example, 2017 signifies $(2 \times 10^3) + (0 \times 10^2) + (1 \times 10) + 7$—that is, the 2 represents 2 thousands, *i.e.* the product of 2 and 10^3, the 0 represents 0 hundreds, *i.e.* the product of 0 and 10^2; the 1 represents 1 ten, *i.e.* the product of 1 and 10, and the 7 represents 7 units. Thus every digit has a local value. The application to tricks connected with numbers will be understood readily from three illustrative examples.

* Bachet, problem IX, p. 107.   † Bachet, problem XI, p. 113.

First Example.* A common conjuring trick is to ask a boy among the audience to throw two dice, or to select at random from a box a domino on each half of which is a number. The boy is then told to recollect the two numbers thus obtained, to choose either of them, to multiply it by 5, to add 7 to the result, to double this result, and lastly to add to this the other number. From the number thus obtained, the conjurer subtracts 14, and obtains a number of two digits which are the two numbers chosen originally.

For suppose that the boy selected the numbers a and b. Each of these is less than ten—dice or dominoes ensuring this. The successive operations give : (i) $5a$; (ii) $5a + 7$; (iii) $10a + 14$; (iv) $10a + 14 + b$. Hence, if 14 is subtracted from the final result, there will be left a number of two digits, and these digits are the numbers selected originally. An analogous trick might be performed in other scales of notation if it was thought necessary to disguise the process further.

Second Example.† Similarly, if three numbers, say a, b, c, are chosen, then, if each of them is less than ten, they can be found by the following rule. (i) Take one of the numbers, say a, and multiply it by 2. (ii) Add 3 to the product. (iii) Multiply this by 5, and add 7 to the product. (iv) To this sum add the second number, b. (v) Multiply the result by 2. (vi) Add 3 to the product. (vii) Multiply by 5, and, to the product, add the third number, c. The result is $100a + 10b + c + 235$. Hence, if the final result is known, it is sufficient to subtract 235 from it, and the remainder will be a number of three digits. These digits are the numbers chosen originally.

Third Example.‡ The following rule for finding a person's

---

* Some similar questions were given by Bachet in problem xii, p. 117; by Oughtred or Leake in the *Mathematicall Recreations*, commonly attributed to the former, London, 1653, problem xxxiv; and by Ozanam, part i, chapter x. Probably the *Mathematicall Recreations* were compiled by Leake, but as the work is usually catalogued under the name of W. Oughtred, I shall so describe it : it is founded on the similar work by J. Leurechon, otherwise known as H. van Etten, published in 1626.

† Bachet gave some similar questions in problem xii, p. 117.

‡ Due to Royal V. Heath.

age is of the same kind. Tell him to think of a number (preferably not exceeding 10); (i) square it; (ii) subtract 1; (iii) multiply the result by the original number; (iv) multiply this by 3; (v) add his age; (vi) give the sum of the digits of the result. You then have to guess his age within nine years, knowing that it has this same digit-sum.

The algebraic proof of the rule is obvious. Let a be the age, and b the number thought of. The successive operations give (i) b^2; (ii) $b^2 - 1$; (iii) $b(b^2 - 1)$; (iv) $3b(b^2 - 1)$; (v) $a + 3b(b^2-1)$; (vi) the digit-sum of a, because $3b(b^2 - 1)$ is always a multiple of 9.

Other Examples.* Another such problem, but of more difficulty, is the determination of all numbers which are integral multiples of their reversals. For instance, among numbers of four digits, $8712 = 4 \times 2178$ and $9801 = 9 \times 1089$ possess this property.

Again, we might ask for two numbers whose product is the reversal of the product of their reversals; for example,

$$312 \times 221 = 68952, \quad 213 \times 122 = 25986.$$

The number 698896 is remarkable as being a perfect square, equal to its own reversal.

Just four numbers have the property of being equal to the sum of the cubes of their digits :† $\quad 153 = 1^3 + 5^3 + 3^3$, $370 = 3^3 + 7^3 + 0^3$, $371 = 3^3 + 7^3 + 1^3$, $407 = 4^3 + 0^3 + 7^3$.

The properties of the recurring decimal for $\frac{1}{7}$ are notorious. Troitsky has shown ‡ that 142857 and 285714 are the only numbers less than a million which become multiplied when we remove the first digit and put it after the last.

OTHER PROBLEMS WITH NUMBERS IN THE DENARY SCALE

I may mention here two or three other problems which seem to be unknown to most compilers of books of puzzles.

* *L'Intermédiaire des Mathématiciens*, Paris, vol. xv, 1908, pp. 228, 278; vol. xvi, 1909, p. 34; vol. xix, 1912, p. 128. M. Kraïtchik, *La Mathématique des Jeux*, Brussels, 1930, pp. 55, 59.

† *Sphinx*, 1937, pp. 72, 87.   ‡ *L'Echiquier*, 1930, p. 663.

First Problem. The first of them is as follows. Take any number of three digits, the first and third digits being different : reverse the order of the digits : subtract the number so formed from the original number : then, if the last digit of the difference is mentioned, all the digits in the difference are known.

For suppose the number is $100a + 10b + c$, then the number obtained by reversing the digits is $100c + 10b + a$. The difference of these numbers is equal to $(100a + c) - (100c + a)$ —that is, to $99(a - c)$. But $a - c$ is not greater than 9, and therefore the remainder can only be 99, 198, 297, 396, 495, 594, 693, 792, or 891 ; in each case the middle digit being 9 and the digit before it (if any) being equal to the difference between 9 and the last digit. Hence, if the last digit is known, so is the whole of the remainder.

Second Problem. The second problem is somewhat similar, and is as follows. (i) Take any number ; (ii) reverse the digits ; (iii) find the difference between the number formed in (ii) and the given number ; (iv) multiply this difference by any number you like to name ; (v) cross out any digit except a nought ; (vi) read the remainder. Then the sum of the digits in the remainder subtracted from the next highest multiple of nine will give the figure struck out. This is clear since the result of operation (iv) is a multiple of nine, and the sum of the digits of every multiple of nine is itself a multiple of nine. This and the previous problem are typical of numerous analogous questions.

Third Problem. If n digits are required in the pagination of a book, how many pages are contained therein—for instance, $n = 3001$?

The analysis is obvious. The first 999 pages require the use of $(9 + 180 + 2700)$ digits. But 112 additional digits are employed, and these suffice to identify 28 more pages. Therefore the total number of pages is $999 + 28$, that is, 1027.

Fourth Problem. The numbers from 1 upwards are written consecutively. What is the nth digit—for instance, $n = 500000$?

The numbers from 1 to 99999 inclusive require 488889 digits. Hence we want the 11111th digit in the series of six-digit numbers starting with 100000. We have $11111 = 6 \times 1851 + 5$. Hence we want the 5th digit in 101851, and this is 5.

Empirical Problems. There are also numerous empirical problems, such as the following. With the ten digits, 9, 8, 7, 6, 5, 4, 3, 2, 1, 0, express numbers whose sum is unity : each digit being used only once, and the use of the usual notations for fractions being allowed. With the same ten digits express numbers whose sum is 100. With the nine digits, 9, 8, 7, 6, 5, 4, 3, 2, 1, express numbers whose sum is 100. To the making of such questions there is no limit, but their solution involves little or no mathematical skill.

Four Digits Problem. I suggest the following problem as being more interesting. With the digits 1, 2, 3, 4, express the consecutive numbers from 1 upwards as far as possible : each of the four digits being used once, and only once, in the expression of each number. Allowing the notation of the denary scale (including decimals), as also algebraic sums, products, and positive integral powers, we can get to 88. If the use of the symbols for square roots and factorials (repeated if desired a finite number of times) is also permitted, we can get to 264 ; if negative integral indices are also permitted, to 276 ; and if fractional indices are permitted, to 312. Many similar questions may be proposed, such as using four out of the digits 1, 2, 3, 4, 5. With the five digits 1, 2, 3, 4, 5, each being used once and only once, I have got to 3832 and 4282, according as negative and fractional indices are excluded or allowed.

Four Fours Problem. Another traditional recreation is, with the ordinary arithmetic and algebraic notation, to express the consecutive numbers from 1 upwards as far as possible in terms of four " 4's." Everything turns on what we mean by ordinary notation. If (a) this is taken to admit only the use of the denary scale (e.g. numbers like 44), decimals, brackets, and the symbols for addition, subtraction, multiplication, and division, we can thus express every number up to 22 inclusive.* If (β) also we grant the use of the symbol for square root (repeated if desired a finite number of times), we can get to 30 ; but note that though by its use a number like 2 can be expressed by one " 4," we cannot for that reason say that ·2 is so expressible. If (γ), further, we permit the use of symbols for factorials, we can express every number to 112.† Finally, if (δ) we sanction the employment of integral indices expressible by a " 4 " or " 4's " and allow the symbol for a square root to be used an infinite number of times, we can get to 156 ; but if (ϵ) we concede the employment of integral indices and the use of sub-factorials,‡ we can get to 877. These interesting problems are typical of a class of similar questions. Thus, under conditions γ and using no indices, with four " 1's " we can get to 34, with four " 2's " to 36, with four " 3's " to 46, with four " 5's " to 36, with four " 6's " to 30, with four " 7's " to 25, with four " 8's " to 36, and with four " 9's " to 66.

Problems with a Series of Things which are Numbered

Any collection of things numbered consecutively lend themselves to easy illustrations of questions depending on elementary properties of numbers. As examples I proceed to enumerate a few familiar tricks. The first two of these are commonly shown by the use of a watch, the last four may be exemplified by the use of a pack of playing cards.

First Example.§ The first of these examples is connected with the hours marked on the face of a watch. In this puzzle some-

---

* $E.g.$, $22 = (4 + 4)/(\cdot\dot{4}) + 4$.

† $E.g.$, $99 = 4 \times 4! + \sqrt{4/(\cdot\dot{4})}$.

‡ Sub-factorial n is equal to $n!\,(1 - 1/1! + 1/2! - 1/3! + \ldots \pm 1/n!)$. On the use of this for the four " 4's " problem, see the *Mathematical Gazette*, May 1912.

§ Bachet, problem xx, p. 155; Oughtred or Leake, *Mathematicall Recreations*, London, 1653, p. 28.

one is asked to think of some hour, say m, and then to touch a number that marks another hour, say n.   Then if, beginning with the number touched, he taps each successive hour marked on the face of the watch, going in the opposite direction to that in which the hands of the watch move, and reckoning to himself the taps as m, $(m + 1)$, etc., the $(n + 12)$th tap will be on the hour he thought of.   For example, if he thinks of v and touches ix, then, if he taps successively ix, viii, vii, vi, ..., going backwards and reckoning them respectively as 5, 6, 7, 8, ..., the tap which he reckons as 21 will be on the v.

The reason of the rule is obvious, for he arrives finally at the $(n + 12 - m)$th hour from which he started.   Now, since he goes in the opposite direction to that in which the hands of the watch move, he has to go over $(n - m)$ hours to reach the hour m : also it will make no difference if, in addition, he goes over 12 hours, since the only effect of this is to take him once completely round the circle.   Now $(n + 12 - m)$ is always positive, since n is positive and m is not greater than 12, and therefore if we make him pass over $(n + 12 - m)$ hours we can give the rule in a form which is equally valid whether m is greater or less than n.

Second Example. The following is another well-known watch-dial problem.   If the hours on the face are tapped successively, beginning at vii and proceeding backwards round the dial to vi, v, etc., and if the person who selected the number counts the taps, beginning to count from the number of the hour selected (thus, if he selected x, he would reckon the first tap as the 11th), then the 20th tap as reckoned by him will be on the hour chosen.

For suppose he selected the nth hour.   Then the 8th tap is on xii and is reckoned by him as the $(n + 8)$th ; and the tap which he reckons as $(n + p)$th is on the hour $(20 - p)$.   Hence, putting $p = 20 - n$, the tap which he reckons as 20th is on the hour n.   Of course, the hours indicated by the first seven taps are immaterial : obviously also we can modify the presentation by beginning on the hour viii and making 21 consecutive taps, or on the hour IX and making 22 consecutive taps, and so on.

Third Example. The following is another simple example. Suppose that a pack of n cards is given to someone who is asked to select one out of the first m cards and to remember (but not to mention) what is its number from the top of the pack; suppose it is actually the xth card in the pack. Then take the pack, reverse the order of the top m cards (which can be easily effected by shuffling), and transfer y cards, where $y < n - m$, from the bottom to the top of the pack. The effect of this is that the card originally chosen is now the $(y + m - x + 1)$th from the top. Return to the spectator the pack so rearranged, and ask that the top card be counted as the $(x + 1)$th, the next as the $(x + 2)$th, and so on, in which case the card originally chosen will be the $(y + m + 1)$th. Now y and m can be chosen as we please, and may be varied every time the trick is performed; thus anyone unskilled in arithmetic will not readily detect the method used.

Fourth Example.* Place a card on the table, and on it place as many other cards from the pack as with the number of pips on the card will make a total of twelve. For example, if the card placed first on the table is the five of clubs, then seven additional cards must be placed on it. The court cards may have any values assigned to them, but usually they are reckoned as tens. This is done again with another card, and thus another pile is formed. The operation may be repeated either only three or four times or as often as the pack will permit of such piles being formed. If finally there are p such piles, and if the number of cards left over is r, then the sum of the number of pips on the bottom cards of all the piles will be $13(p - 4) + r$.

For, if x is the number of pips on the bottom card of a pile, the number of cards in that pile will be $13 - x$. A similar argument holds for each pile. Also there are 52 cards in the

* A particular case of this problem was given by Bachet, problem XVII, p. 138.

pack; and this must be equal to the sum of the cards in the p piles and the r cards left over. Thus we have

$$(13 - x_1) + (13 - x_2) + \ldots + (13 - x_p) + r = 52,$$
$$13p - (x_1 + x_2 + \ldots + x_p) + r = 52,$$
$$x_1 + x_2 + \ldots + x_p = 13p - 52 + r$$
$$= 13(p - 4) + r.$$

More generally, if a pack of n cards is taken, and if in each pile the sum of the pips on the bottom card and the number of cards put on it is equal to m, then the sum of the pips on the bottom cards of the piles will be $(m + 1)p + r - n$. In an écarté pack $n = 32$, and it is convenient to take $m = 15$.

Fifth Example. It may be noticed that cutting a pack of cards never alters the relative position of the cards provided that, if necessary, we regard the top card as following immediately after the bottom card in the pack. This is used in the following trick.* Take a pack, and deal the cards face upwards on the table, calling them one, two, three, etc., as you put them down, and noting in your own mind the card first dealt. Ask someone to select a card and recollect its number. Turn the pack over, and let it be cut (not shuffled) as often as you like. Enquire what was the number of the card chosen. Then, if you deal, and as soon as you come to the original first card, begin (silently) to count, reckoning this as one, the selected card will appear at the number mentioned. Of course, if all the cards are dealt before reaching this number, you must turn the cards over and go on counting continuously.

Sixth Example. Here is another simple question of this class. Remove the court cards from a pack. Arrange the remaining 40 cards, faces upwards, in suits, in four lines thus. In the first line, the 1, 2, ... 10, of suit A; in the second line, the 10, 1, 2, ... 9, of suit B; in the third line, the 9, 10, 1, ... 8, of suit C; in the last line, the 8, 9, 10, 1, ... 7, of suit

* Bachet, problem XIX, p. 152.

D. Next take up, face upwards, the first card of line 1, put below it the first card of line 2, below that the first card of line 3, and below that the first card of line 4. Turn this pile face downwards. Next take up the four cards in the second column in the same way, turn them face downwards, and put them below the first pile. Continue this process until all the cards are taken up. Ask someone to mention any card. Suppose the number of pips on it is *n*. Then if the suit is *A*, it will be the 4*n*th card in the pack; if the suit is *B*, it will be the (4*n* + 3)th card; if the suit is *C*, it will be the (4*n* + 6)th card; and if the suit is *D*, it will be the (4*n* + 9)th card. Hence by counting the cards, cyclically if necessary, the card desired can be picked out. It is easy to alter the form of presentation, and a full pack can be used if desired. The explanation is obvious.

ARITHMETICAL RESTORATIONS

I take next a class of problems dealing with the reconstruction of arithmetical sums from which various digits have been erased. Some of these questions are easy, some difficult. This kind of exercise has attracted a good deal of attention in recent years. I give examples of three kinds of restoration.

Class A. The solutions of one group of these restoration questions depend on the well-known propositions that every number

$$a + 10b + 10^2c + 10^3d + \ldots$$

is equal to any of certain expressions such as

$$M (9) + a + b + c + d + \ldots$$
$$M (11) + a - b + c - d + \ldots$$
$$M (33) + (a + 10b) + (c + 10d) + (e + 10f) + \ldots$$
$$M (101) + (a + 10b) - (c + 10d) + (e + 10f) - \ldots$$
$$M (m) + (a + 10b + 10^2c) + (d + 10e + 10^2f) + \ldots$$
$$M (n) + (a + 10b + 10^2c) - (d + 10e + 10^2f) + \ldots$$

where, in the penultimate line, $m = 27$, or 37, or 111, and in the last line, $n = 7$, or 13, or 77, or 91, or 143.

Examples, depending on such propositions, are not uncommon. Here are four easy instances of this class of questions.

(i) The product of 417 and .1 ... is 9 ... 057. Find the missing digits, each of which is represented by a dot. If the undetermined digits in the multiplier are denoted in order by a, b, c, d, and we take the steps of the multiplication in their reverse order, we obtain successively $d = 1$, $c = 2$, $b = 9$. Also the product has 7 digits, therefore $a = 2$. Hence the product is 9,141,057.

(ii) The seven-digit number 70 . . 34 . is exactly divisible by 792. Find the missing digits, each of which is represented by a dot. Since 792 is $8 \times 9 \times 11$, we can easily show that the number is 7,054,344.

(iii) The five-digit number 4 . 18 . is divisible by 101. Find the missing digits.*

Denote the two missing digits, from right to left, by x and y. Applying the theorem for 101, noting that each of the unknowns cannot exceed 9, and for convenience putting $y = 10 - z$, this equation gives $z = 1$, $x = 7$, $y = 9$. Hence the number is 49,187.

(iv) The four-digit number . 8 . . is divisible by 1287. Find the missing digits.†

Denote these digits, from right to left, by x, y, z. We have $1287 = 9 \times 11 \times 13$. Applying the suitable propositions, and noting that each of the unknowns cannot exceed 9, we get $x = 1$, $y = 6$, $z = 3$. Hence the number is 3861.

(v) As a slightly harder example of this type, suppose we know that 6 . 80 . 8 . . 51 is exactly divisible by 73 and 137. Find the missing digits.‡ The data suffice to determine the number, which is 6,780,187,951.

---

* P. Delens, *Problèmes d'Arithmétique Amusante*, Paris, 1914, p. 55.
† *Ibid.*, p. 57.
‡ *Ibid.*, p. 60.

Class B. Another and more difficult class of restoration problems is illustrated by the following examples. Their solutions involve analytical skill which cannot be reduced to rules.

(i) I begin with an easy instance, said to be of Hindoo origin, in which the problem is to restore the missing digits in the annexed division sum where a certain six-digit number when divided by a three-digit number gives a three-digit result.*

$$
\begin{array}{r}
\ldots\,)\,\ldots\ldots\,(\,\ldots \\
.\,0\,.\,. \\
\hline
.\,.\,.\,. \\
.\,5\,0\,. \\
\hline
.\,.\,. \\
.\,4\,. \\
\hline
\end{array}
$$

The solution involves no difficulty. The answer is that the divisor is 215, and the quotient 573; the solution is unique.

(ii) As a more difficult specimen I give the following problem, proposed in 1921 by Prof. Schuh of Delft. A certain seven-digit integer when divided by a certain six-digit integer gives a result whose integral part is a two-digit number and whose fractional part is a ten-digit expression of which the last nine digits form a repeating decimal, as indicated in the following work, where a bar has been put above the repeating digits. It is required to restore the working.† This problem is remarkable from the fact that not a single digit is given explicitly.

---

* *American Mathematical Monthly*, 1921, vol. XXVIII, p. 37.
† *Ibid.*, p. 278.

```
                                                    _____
        . . . . . . )  . . . . . . . . ( . .  . . . . . . . . . . . .
                      . . . . . .
                      _____
                      . . . . . .
                      . . . . . .
                      _____
                      . . . . . .
                      . . . . . .
                      . . . . . . .
                      . . . . . . .
                      . . . . . . .
                      . . . . . . .
                      _____
                      . . . . . . .
                      . . . . . . .
                      _____
                      . . . . . . .
                      . . . . . . .
                      _____
                      . . . . . . .
                      . . . . . . .
                      _____
                          . . . . . .
                          . . . . . .
                          _____
                          . . . . . .
```

The answer is that the divisor is 667334 and the dividend is 7752341.

Here are three additional examples of arithmetical restorations.* The solutions are lengthy and involve much empirical work.

(iii) The first of these Berwick questions is as follows. In the following division sum all the digits, except the seven

* All are due to W. E. H. Berwick. The " 7 " problem appeared in the *School World*, July and October 1906, vol. VIII, pp. 280, 320; the "4" problem appeared in the *Mathematical Gazette*, 1920, vol. X, pp. 43, 359—360; the " 5 " problem in the same paper, vol. X, p. 361, vol. XI, p. 8.

" 7's " shown, have been erased : each missing digit may be
1, 2, 3, 4, 5, 6, 7, 8, 9, or (except in the first digit of a line) 0.
Observe that every step in the working consists of two lines
each of which contains an equal number of digits. The problem
is to restore the whole working of the sum. The solution is
unique and gives a divisor of 125473 and a quotient of 58781.

```
. . . . 7 . ) . . 7 . . . . . . . . ( . . 7 . .
          . . . . . .
          ──────────
          . . . . . 7 .
          . . . . . . .
          ──────────
              . 7 . . . .
              . 7 . . . .
              ──────────
              . . . . . . . .
              . . . . 7 . .
              ──────────
                . . . . . .
                . . . . . .
                ──────────
```

(iv) The second problem is similar and requires the restoration of the digits in the following division sum, where the
position of four " 4's " is given,

```
. . . ) . . . . . . 4 ( . 4 . .
      . . .
      ─────
      . . 4 .
      . . . .
      ─────
          . . . .
          . 4 .
          ─────
          . . . .
          . . . .
          ─────
```

To this problem there are four solutions, the divisors being 846, 848, 943, 949; and the respective quotients 1419, 1418, 1418, 1416.

If we propound the problem (using five " 4's ") thus:

```
. . . ) . . . . . . 4 ( . 4 . . .
        . . .
        ―――
        . . 4 .
        . . . 4
        ―――――
        . . . .
         . 4 .
        ―――――
        . . . .
        . . . .
        ―――――
```

there is only one solution, and some will think this is a better form in which to enunciate it.

(v) In the last of these Berwick examples, it is required to restore the working of the following division sum where all the digits, except five " 5's," have been erased.

```
. . . ) . 5 5 . . 5 . ( . 5 .
        . . 5 . .
        ―――――
        . . . . .
        . . . . .
        ―――――
        . . . .
        . . . .
        ―――――
```

To this problem there is only one solution, the divisor being 3926 and the quotient 652.

Class C. A third class of digit problems depends on finding the values of certain symbols which represent specified numbers. Two examples will suffice.

(i) Here is a very simple illustrative specimen. The result

of multiplying bc by bc is abc, where the letters stand for certain numbers. What are the numbers ? A brief examination shows that bc stands for 25, and therefore a stands for 6.

(ii) Here is another example. The object is to find the digits represented by letters in the following sum : *

$$a\,b\,)\,c\,d\,e\,e\,b\,(\,b\,f\,b$$
$$c\,e\,b$$

$$g\,g\,e$$
$$g\,c\,h$$

$$c\,e\,b$$
$$c\,e\,b$$

A solution may be obtained thus : Since the product of b by b is a number which ends in b, b must be 1, 5, or 6. Since the product of ab by b is a number of three digits, b cannot be 1. The result of the subtraction of h from e is e, hence $h = 0$, and therefore if $b = 5$ we have f even, and if $b = 6$ we have $f = 5$. Also the result of the subtraction of c from g is c, hence $g = 2c$, and therefore c cannot be greater than 4 : from which it follows that b cannot be 6. A few trials now show that the question arose from the division of 19,775 by 35.

It is possible to frame digit restoration examples of a mixed character involving the difficulties of all the examples given above, and to increase the difficulty by expressing them in a non-denary scale of notation. But such elaborations do not add to the interest of the questions.

CALENDAR PROBLEMS

The formulae given by Gauss and Zeller, which I quoted in former editions of this work, serve to solve all questions likely to occur about dates, days of the week, Easter, etc. Here are two easy but elegant questions on the Gregorian Calendar of a somewhat different nature.

* *Strand Magazine*, September–October, 1921

The first is as follows : it is due, I believe, to E. Fourrey. In the century and a half between 1725 and 1875 the French fought and won a certain battle on 22 April of one year, and 4382 days later, also on 22 April, they gained another victory. The sum of the digits of the years is 40. Find the dates of the battles.

To solve it we notice that $4382 = 12 \times 365 + 2$. Hence the date of the second battle was 12 years after that of the first battle ; but only two leap years had intervened, and therefore the year 1800 must be within the limiting dates. Thus 1788 and 1800, 1789 and 1801, . . ., 1800 and 1812, are the only possible years. Of the years thus suggested, 1796 and 1808 alone give 40 as the sum of their digits. Hence the battles were fought on the 22 April, 1796 (Mondovi under Napoleon), and 22 April, 1808 (Eckmuhl under Davoust).

The other of these questions is to show that the first or last day of every alternate century must be a Monday. This follows from knowing any one assigned date, and the fact that the Gregorian cycle is completed in 400 years ($= 20871$ weeks). The same principle is involved in B. H. Brown's assertion * that the thirteenth day of the month is more likely to be a Friday than to be any other day of the week.

Medieval Problems in Arithmetic

Before leaving the subject of these elementary questions, I may mention a few problems which for centuries have appeared in nearly every collection of mathematical recreations, and may therefore claim what is almost a prescriptive right to a place here.

First Example. The following is a sample of one class of these puzzles. A man goes to a tub of water with two jars, of which one holds exactly 3 pints and the other 5 pints. How can he bring back exactly 4 pints of water ? The solution presents no difficulty.

---

* *American Mathematical Monthly*, 1933, vol. XL, p. 607.

Second Example.* Here is another problem of the same kind. Three men robbed a gentleman of a vase, containing 24 ounces of balsam. Whilst running away they met a glass-seller, of whom they purchased three vessels. On reaching a place of safety they wished to divide the booty, but found that their vessels contained 5, 11, and 13 ounces respectively. How could they divide the balsam into equal portions? Problems like this can be worked out only by trial.

Third Example.† The next of these is a not uncommon game, played by two people, say A and B. A begins by mentioning some number not greater than (say) six, B may add to that any number not greater than six, A may add to that again any number not greater than six, and so on. He wins who is the first to reach (say) 50. Obviously, if A calls 43, then whatever B adds to that, A can win next time. Similarly, if A calls 36, B cannot prevent A's calling 43 the next time. In this way it is clear that the key numbers are those forming the arithmetical progression 43, 36, 29, 22, 15, 8, 1; and whoever plays first ought to win.

Similarly, if no number greater than m may be added at any one time, and n is the number to be called by the victor, then the key numbers will be those forming the arithmetical progression whose common difference is $m + 1$. and whose smallest term is the remainder obtained by dividing n by $m + 1$.

The same game may be played in another form by placing p coins, matches, or other objects on a table, and directing each player in turn to take away not more than m of them. Whoever takes away the last coin wins. Obviously the key numbers are multiples of $m + 1$, and the first player who is able to leave an exact multiple of $(m + 1)$ coins can win.

* Some similar problems were given by Bachet, Appendix, problem III, p. 206; problem IX, p. 233: by Oughtred or Leake in the *Mathematicall Recreations*, p. 22: and by Ozanam, 1803 edition, vol. I, p. 174; 1840 edition, p. 79. Earlier instances occur in Tartaglia's writings. See also Kraïtchik, p. 11.

† Bachet, problem XXII, p. 170.

Perhaps a better form of the game is to make that player lose who takes away the last coin, in which case each of the key numbers exceeds by unity a multiple of $m + 1$.

Another variety * consists in placing p counters in the form of a circle, and allowing each player in succession to take away not more than m of them which are in unbroken sequence : m being less than p and greater than unity. In this case the second of the two players can always win.

These games are simple, but if we impose on the original problem the restriction that each player may not add the same number more than (say) three times, the analysis becomes by no means easy. I have never seen this extension described in print, and I will enunciate it at length. Suppose that each player is given eighteen cards, three of them marked 6, three marked 5, three marked 4, three marked 3, three marked 2, and three marked 1. They play alternately; A begins by playing one of his cards; then B plays one of his, and so on. He wins who first plays a card which makes the sum of the points or numbers on all the cards played exactly equal to 50, but he loses if he plays a card which makes this sum exceed 50. The game can be played by noting the numbers on a piece of paper, and it is not necessary to use cards.

Thus suppose they play as follows. A takes a 4, and scores 4; B takes a 3, and scores 7; A takes a 1, and scores 8; B takes a 6, and scores 14; A takes a 3, and scores 17; B takes a 4, and scores 21; A takes a 4, and scores 25; B takes a 5, and scores 30; A takes a 4, and scores 34; B takes a 4, and scores 38; A takes a 5, and scores 43. B can now win, for he may safely play 3, since A has not another 4 wherewith to follow it; and if A plays less than 4, B will win the next time. Again, suppose they play thus. A, 6; B, 3; A, 1; B, 6; A, 3; B, 4; A, 2; B, 5; A, 1; B, 5; A, 2; B, 5; A, 2; B, 3. A is now forced to play 1, and B wins by playing 1.

A slightly different form of the game has also been sug-

* S. Loyd, *Tit-Bits*, London, July 17, Aug. 7, 1897.

gested. In this there are put on the table an agreed number of cards—say, for example, the four aces, twos, threes, fours, fives, and sixes of a pack of cards—twenty-four cards in all. Each player in turn takes a card. The score at any time is the sum of the pips on all the cards taken, whether by A or B. He wins who first selects a card which makes the score equal, say to 50, and a player who is forced to go beyond 50 loses.

Thus, suppose they play as follows. A takes a 6, and scores 6; B takes a 2, and scores 8; A takes a 5, and scores 13; B takes a 2, and scores 15; A takes a 5, and scores 20; B takes a 2, and scores 22; A takes a 5, and scores 27; B takes a 2, and scores 29; A takes a 5, and scores 34; B takes a 6, and scores 40; A takes a 1, and scores 41; B takes a 4, and scores 45; A takes a 3, and scores 48; B now must take 1, and thus score 49; and A takes a 1, and wins.

In these variations the object of each player is to get to one of the key numbers, provided there are sufficient available remaining numbers to let him retain the possession of each subsequent key number. The number of cards used, the points on them, and the number to be reached can be changed at will; and the higher the number to be reached, the more difficult it is to forecast the result and to say whether or not it is an advantage to begin.

Fourth Example. The following medieval problem is some-what more elaborate. Suppose that three people, P, Q, R, select three things, which we may denote by a, e, i respectively, and that it is desired to find by whom each object was selected.*

Place 24 counters on a table. Ask P to take one counter, Q to take two counters, and R to take three counters. Next, ask the person who selected a to take as many counters as he has already, whoever selected e to take twice as many counters as he has already, and whoever selected i to take four times as many counters as he has already. Note how many counters remain on the table. There are only six ways of distributing the three things among P, Q, and R; and the number of

---

* Bachet, problem xxv, p. 187.

counters remaining on the table is different for each way. The remainders may be 1, 2, 3, 5, 6, or 7. Bachet summed up the results in the mnemonic line *Par fer* (1) *César* (2) *jadis* (3) *devint* (5) *si grand* (6) *prince* (7). Corresponding to any remainder is a word or words containing two syllables : for instance, to the remainder 5 corresponds the word *devint*. The vowel in the first syllable indicates the thing selected by P, the vowel in the second syllable indicates the thing selected by Q, and of course R selected the remaining thing.

Extension. M. Bourlet, in the course of a very kindly notice * of the second edition of this work, gave a much neater solution of the above question, and has extended the problem to the case of n people, P_0, P_1, P_2 ..., P_{n-1}, each of whom selects one object, out of a collection of n objects, such as dominoes or cards. It is required to know which domino or card was selected by each person.

Let us suppose the dominoes to be denoted or marked by the numbers 0, 1, ..., $n - 1$, instead of by vowels. Give one counter to P_1, two counters to P_2, and generally k counters to P_k. Note the number of counters left on the table. Next ask the person who had chosen the domino 0 to take as many counters as he had already, and generally whoever had chosen the domino h to take n^h times as many dominoes as he had already : thus if P_h had chosen the domino numbered h, he would take $n^h k$ counters. The total number of counters taken is $\Sigma n^h k$. Divide this by n, then the remainder will be the number on the domino selected by P_0 ; divide the quotient by n, and the remainder will be the number on the domino selected by P_1 ; divide this quotient by n, and the remainder will be the number on the domino selected by P_2 ; and so on. In other words, if the number of counters taken is expresse d in the scale of notation whose radix is n, then the $(h + 1)$th digit from the right will give the number on the domino selected by P_h.

* *Bulletin des Sciences Mathématiques*, Paris, 1893, vol. XVII, pp. 105—107.

Thus in Bachet's problem with 3 people and 3 dominoes, we should first give one counter to Q, and two counters to R, while P would have no counters; then we should ask the person who had selected the domino marked 0 or a to take as many counters as he had already, whoever had selected the domino marked 1 or e to take three times as many counters as he had already, and whoever had selected the domino marked 2 or i to take nine times as many counters as he had already. By noticing the original number of counters, and observing that 3 of these had been given to Q and R, we should know the total number taken by P, Q, and R. If this number were divided by 3, the remainder would be the number of the domino chosen by P; if the quotient were divided by 3 the remainder would be the number of the domino chosen by Q; and the final quotient would be the number of the domino chosen by R.

Exploration Problems. Another common question is concerned with the maximum distance into a desert which could be reached from a frontier settlement by the aid of a party of n explorers, each capable of carrying provisions that would last one man for a days. The answer is that the man who reaches the greatest distance will occupy $na/(n + 1)$ days before he returns to his starting-point. If in the course of their journey they may make depôts, the longest possible journey will occupy $\frac{1}{2}a(1 + \frac{1}{2} + \frac{1}{3} + \ldots + 1/n)$ days.

The Josephus Problem. Another of these antique problems consists in placing men round a circle so that if every mth man is killed, the remainder shall be certain specified individuals. Such problems can be easily solved empirically.

Hegesippus * says that Josephus saved his life by such a device. According to his account, after the Romans had captured Jotapat, Josephus and forty other Jews took refuge in a cave. Josephus, much to his disgust, found that all except himself and one other man were resolved to kill themselves, so as not to fall into the hands of their çonquerors.

---

* *De Bello Judaico*, bk. III, chaps. 16—18.

Fearing to show his opposition too openly he consented, but declared that the operation must be carried out in an orderly way, and suggested that they should arrange themselves round a circle and that every third person should be killed until but one man was left, who must then commit suicide. It is alleged that he placed himself and the other man in the 31st and 16th place respectively.

The medieval question was usually presented in the following form. A ship, carrying as passengers 15 Turks and 15 Christians, encountered a storm, and, in order to save the ship and crew, one-half of the passengers had to be thrown into the sea. Accordingly the passengers were placed in a circle, and every ninth man, reckoning from a certain point, was cast overboard. It is desired to find an arrangement by which all the Christians should be saved.* In this case we must arrange the men thus :
$C C C C T T T T T C C T C C C T C T T C C T T T C T T C C T$,
where C stands for a Christian and T for a Turk. The order can be recollected by the positions of the vowels in the following line : *From numbers' aid and art, never will fame depart*, where a stands for 1, e for 2, i for 3, o for 4, and u for 5. Hence the order is o Christians, u Turks, etc.

If every tenth man were cast overboard, a similar mnemonic line is *Rex paphi cum gente bona dat signa serena*. An oriental setting of this decimation problem runs somewhat as follows. Once upon a time, there lived a rich farmer who had 30 children, 15 by his first wife who was dead, and 15 by his second wife. The latter woman was eager that her eldest son should inherit the property. Accordingly one day she said to him, " Dear Husband, you are getting old. We ought to settle who shall be your heir. Let us arrange our 30 children in a circle, and counting from one of them, remove every tenth child until there remains but one, who shall succeed to your estate." The proposal seemed reasonable. As the process of selection went on, the farmer grew more and more astonished as he

---

* Bachet, problem xxiii, p. 174. The same problem had been previously enunciated by Tartaglia.

noticed that the first 14 to disappear were children by his first wife, and he observed that the next to go would be the last remaining member of that family. So he suggested that they should see what would happen if they began to count backwards from this lad. She, forced to make an immediate decision, and reflecting that the odds were now 15 to 1 in favour of her family, readily assented. Who became the heir ?

In the general case n men are arranged in a circle which is closed up as individuals are picked out. Beginning anywhere, we continually go round, picking out each mth man until only r are left. Let one of these be the man who originally occupied the pth place. Then had we begun with $n + 1$ men, he would have originally occupied the $(p + m)$th place when $p + m$ is not greater than $n + 1$, and the $(p + m - n - 1)$th place when $p + m$ is greater than $n + 1$. Thus, provided there are to be r men left, their original positions are each shifted forwards along the circle m places for each addition of a single man to the original group.*

Now suppose that with n men the last survivor $(r = 1)$ occupied originally the pth place, and that with $(n + x)$ men the last survivor occupied the yth place. Then, if we confine ourselves to the lowest value of x which makes y less than m, we have $y = (p + mx) - (n + x)$.

Based on this theorem we can, for any specified value of n, calculate rapidly the position occupied by the last survivor of the company. In effect, Tait found the values of n for which a man occupying a given position p, which is less than m, would be the last survivor, and then, by repeated applications of the proposition, obtained the position of the survivor for intermediate values of n.

For instance, take the Josephus problem in which $m = 3$. Then we know that the final survivor of 41 men occupied originally the 31st place. Suppose that when there had been

* P. G. Tait, *Collected Scientific Papers*, Cambridge, vol. II, 1900, pp. 432–435.

$(41 + x)$ men, the survivor occupied originally the yth place. Then, if we consider only the lowest value of x which makes y less than m, we have $y = (31 + 3x) - (41 + x) = 2x - 10$. Now, we have to take a value of x which makes y positive and less than m—that is, in this case equal to 1 or 2. This is $x = 6$, which makes $y = 2$. Hence, had there been 47 men, the man last chosen would have originally occupied the second place. Similarly had there been $(47 + x)$ men, the man would have occupied originally the yth place, where, subject to the same conditions as before, we have $y = (2 + 3x) - (47 + x) = 2x - 45$. If $x = 23$, $y = 1$. Hence, with 70 men the man last chosen would have occupied originally the first place. Continuing the process, it is easily found that if n does not exceed 2000000 the last man to be taken occupies the first place when $n = 4, 6, 9, 31, 70, 105, 355, 799, 1798, 2697, 9103, 20482, 30723, 69127, 155536, 233304, 349956, 524934,$ or 787401 ; and the second place when $n = 2, 3, 14, 21, 47, 158, 237, 533, 1199, 4046, 6069, 13655, 46085, 103691, 1181102,$ or 1771653. From these results, by repeated applications of the proposition, we find, for any intermediate values of n, the position originally occupied by the man last taken. Thus with 1000 men, the 604th place ; with 100000 men, the 92620th place ; and with 1000000 men, the 637798th place are those which would be selected by a prudent mathematician in a company subjected to trimation.

Similarly if a set of 100 men were subjected to decimation, the last to be taken would be the man originally in the 26th place. Hence, with 227 men the last to be taken would be the man originally in the first place.

Modifications of the original problem have been suggested. For instance,* let 5 Christians and 5 Turks be arranged round a circle thus, $T\ C\ T\ C\ C\ T\ C\ T\ C\ T$. Suppose that, if beginning at the ath man, every hth man is selected, all the Turks will be picked out for punishment ; but if beginning at the bth man, every kth man is selected, all the Christians will be picked out

* H. E. Dudeney, *Tit-Bits*, London, Oct. 14 and 28, 1905.

for punishment. The problem is to find a, b, h, and k. A solution is $a = 1$, $h = 11$, $b = 9$, $k = 29$.

I suggest as a similar problem, to find an arrangement of c Turks and c Christians arranged in a circle, so that if beginning at a particular man, say the first, every hth man is selected, all the Turks will be picked out, but if, beginning at the same man, every kth man is selected, all the Christians will be picked out. This makes an interesting question because it is conceivable that the operator who picked out the victims might get confused and take k instead of h, or vice versa, and so consign all his friends to execution instead of those whom he had intended to pick out. The problem is, for any given value of c, to find an arrangement of the men and the corresponding suitable values of h and k. Obviously if $c = 2$, then for an arrangement like $T C C T$ a solution is $h = 4$, $k = 3$. If $c = 3$, then for an arrangement like $T C T C C T$ a solution is $h = 7$, $k = 8$. If $c = 4$, then for an arrangement like $T C T T C T C C$ a solution is $h = 9$, $k = 5$. And generally, as first pointed out by Mr. Swinden, with $2c$ men, c of them, occupying initially the consecutive places numbered c, $c + 1$, ..., $2c - 1$, will be picked out, if h is the L.C.M. of $c + 1$, $c + 2$, ..., $2c - 1$; and the other c will be picked out if $k = h + 1$, though it may well be that there is a simpler solution for another initial arrangement. It may be impossible to arrange the men so that n specified individuals shall be picked out in a defined order.

THE GAME OF NIM *

Here is a game which has a complete mathematical analysis. Suppose that any number of counters are divided arbitrarily into several heaps. Two people play alternately. Each, when his turn comes, may select any one heap, and remove from it all the counters in it or as many of them as he pleases (but at least one). The player drawing the last counter (or counters) wins.

* C. L. Bouton, *Annals of Mathematics*, 1902, series 2, vol. III, pp. 35–39.

Suppose that the counters are dealt by the player A, and that the other player B, draws first. If A deals only one heap, B may win at once by drawing all the counters. Such a deal is thus an *unsafe combination* (*i.e.*, unsafe for A, who dealt it). On the other hand, if A deals two equal heaps, B cannot help making them unequal, and A must eventually win if at each stage he makes them equal again. Such a deal is therefore a *safe combination* for A. The fact is, that every combination is either safe or unsafe, in the sense that *every unsafe combination by a suitable draw may be made safe*, while *every safe combination by every draw is made unsafe*. Thus, if A deals a safe combination, B by drawing cannot avoid making it unsafe, A by drawing suitably makes it safe again, and so on, until finally B is obliged to leave a single heap, when A wins. On the other hand, if A deals an unsafe combination, B by drawing suitably makes it safe, and then the game proceeds as before, until B finally wins.

It is soon found that heaps containing $1, 2n, 2n + 1$ counters, or $n, 7 - n, 7$ counters, or $2, 3, 4, 5$ counters, are safe combinations; and that two separate safe combinations make a safe combination. These facts are usually sufficient for playing with a novice, but Bouton has shown them to be special cases of a general rule, enabling the Mathematician to beat the Gambler practically every time.

Suppose there are a_r counters in the rth heap. Express a_r in the binary scale, and denote the coefficient of 2^p in it by d_{rp} ($= 0$ or 1). Thus $a_r = d_{r0} + 2d_{r1} + 2^2 d_{r2} + 2^3 d_{r3} + \ldots$. Do this for each heap, and let s_p be the sum of the coefficients of 2^p thus determined, so that $s_p = d_{1p} + d_{2p} + d_{3p} + \ldots$. We shall see that the combination is safe or unsafe according as $S_0, S_1, S_2, \ldots$ are all even or not all even.

If $S_0, S_1, S_2, \ldots$ are not all even, let S_q be the last one of them that is odd. Then $d_{rq} = 1$ for at least one value of r. The next player should operate on this rth heap, reducing it in such a way as to alter d_{rp} for just those values of p which make S_p odd. This operation naturally has the effect of making S_0, S_1, S_2, ... all even. Since the other player must take at least one counter, he cannot help changing one of the S's by 1, and so making it odd.

For instance, (2, 3, 4, 5) is a safe combination, because these numbers, in the binary scale, are 10, 11, 100, 101, so that $S_2 = S_1 = S_0 = 2$. If the number of counters in the largest heap is less than 2^{10}, the computation is easily carried out with the fingers. For each a_r in turn, raise or lower those fingers which correspond to digits 1 in the binary number. (This is a kind of " addition without carrying," which I will mention again in the next chapter, page 73.)

If the rules of the game are changed to the extent of making that player *lose* who takes the last counter, the procedure is unaltered, save at the end. You merely have to remember that a number of heaps, each consisting of a single counter, makes a safe or unsafe combination according as the number is odd or even, instead of *vice versa*.

Moore's " Nim$_k$". E. H. Moore [*] has proposed the following generalization. The rules for " Nim$_k$ " are the same as for Nim itself (which is " Nim$_1$ "), save that in each draw the player may take at will from any number of heaps not exceeding k. It is clear that, if A deals fewer than $k + 1$ heaps, B may win at once by drawing all the counters. Such a deal is therefore an unsafe combination. As an instance of a safe combination, consider $k + 1$ equal heaps.

Defining a_r, d_{rp}, and S_p as before, we easily see that a given combination is safe if, and only if, S_0, S_1, S_2, ... are all divisible by $k + 1$.

Wythoff's Game. W. A. Wythoff [†] has invented a similar game, where there are just two heaps. In each draw the player may take counters at will from either one or both heaps, but in the latter case he must take the same number from each heap. That player wins who takes the last counter.

    * *Annals of Mathematics*, 1910, series 2, vol. XI, pp. 90—94.
    † *Nieuw Archief voor Wiskunde*, 1907, p. 199.

The safe combinations are now (1, 2), (3, 5), (4, 7), (6, 10), (8, 13), (9, 15), (11, 18), (12, 20), ...

The first pair of numbers differ by 1, the second by 2, the third by 3, and so on. In fact, the rth pair is $([r\tau], [r\tau^2])$, where $\tau = \frac{1}{2}(\sqrt{5} + 1)$, $\tau^2 = \frac{1}{2}(\sqrt{5} + 3)$, and $[x]$ means the greatest integer not exceeding x. It is interesting to observe that every positive integer appears just once in this list; in other words, every interval between two consecutive positive integers contains just one multiple of either τ or τ^2.

Kayles. Perhaps some of my readers will feel inspired to complete the following preliminary analysis of the game of Kayles,* which differs from Nim and Wythoff's game in that the number of heaps is apt to increase as the game progresses. Thirteen counters are arranged in a row, touching one another successively, and then the second one is removed, leaving a row of eleven and one isolated counter.

o ooooooooooo

Two people play alternately, removing any counter or any two that touch one another. The player drawing the last counter (or pair) wins. As in Nim, there are safe and unsafe combinations, two equal sets make a safe combination, and two safe combinations make a safe combination. The initial combination is unsafe; it can be made safe by removing the fourth (or eighth) of the eleven counters, so as to leave (1, 3, 7). Other safe combinations are (1, 4), (1, 8), (2, 7), (3, 6), (1, 2, 3), (2, 3, 4).

When the game is extended to more than twelve counters, the number of safe combinations may overtax one's memory. Michael Goldberg has worked out all the safe combinations that involve numbers from 1 to 20; they are exhibited in the accompanying diagram. Each circle contains one or more numbers, and the circles are joined by straight lines. The safe combinations are as follows: (i) two numbers in any circle, such as (8, 13) or (5, 12); (ii) three numbers, one from

* H. E. Dudeney, *The Canterbury Puzzles*, London, 1919, pp. 118, 220.

each of three circles which lie along a straight line, such as (8, 11, 15) or (4, 6, 7); (iii) four numbers, one from each of four circles which lie along two straight lines, excluding the circle at their intersection, such as (1, 2, 5, 15) or (1, 3, 5, 11). We must remember also that two equal sets make a safe combination, as also do two separate safe combinations.

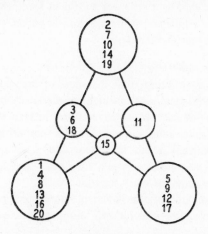

ADDENDUM

Note. Page 15. Solutions of the ten-digit problems are $35/70 + 148/296 = 1$ or $\cdot01234 + \cdot98765 = 1$, and $50 + 49 + 1/2 + 38/76 = 100$. A solution of the nine-digit problem is $1\cdot234 + 98\cdot765 = 100$ or $97 + 8/12 + 4/6 + 5/3 = 100$; but a neater solution (due to Perelman *) is $1 + 2 + 3 + 4 + 5 + 6 + 7 + 8 \times 9 = 100$, where the digits occur in their natural order.

Note. Page 28. There are several solutions of the division of 24 ounces under the conditions specified. One of these solutions is as follows :

	24 oz.	13 oz.	11 oz.	5 oz.
The vessels can contain . . .	24 oz.	13 oz.	11 oz.	5 oz.
Their contents originally are .	24 ,,	0 ,,	0 ,,	0 ,,
First, make their contents . .	0 ,,	8 ,,	11 ,,	5 ,,
Second, make their contents .	16 ,,	8 ,,	0 ,,	0 ,,
Third, make their contents . .	16 ,,	0 ,,	8 ,,	0 ,,
Fourth, make their contents .	3 ,,	13 ,,	8 ,,	0 ,,
Fifth, make their contents . .	3 ,,	8 ,,	8 ,,	5 ,,
Lastly, make their contents .	8 ,,	8 ,,	8 ,,	0 ,,

* *L'Arithmétique Récréative*, pp. 20, 44, 74. For several hundred other solutions, see *Sphinx*, 1935, pp. 95, 111, 112, 124, 125.

CHAPTER II

ARITHMETICAL RECREATIONS (*continued*)

I DEVOTE this chapter to the description of some arithmetical fallacies, a few additional problems, and notes on one or two problems in higher arithmetic.

ARITHMETICAL FALLACIES

I begin by mentioning some instances of demonstrations* leading to arithmetical results which are obviously impossible. I include algebraical proofs as well as arithmetical ones. Some of the fallacies are so patent that in preparing the first and second editions I did not think such questions worth printing, but, as some correspondents expressed a contrary opinion, I give them for what they are worth.

First Fallacy. One of the oldest of these—and not a very interesting specimen—is as follows. Suppose that $a = b$, then

$$ab = a^2. \quad \therefore ab - b^2 = a^2 - b^2. \quad \therefore b(a - b) = (a + b)(a - b).$$
$$\therefore b = a + b. \quad \therefore b = 2b. \quad \therefore 1 = 2.$$

Second Fallacy. Another example, the idea of which is due to John Bernoulli, may be stated as follows. We have

---

* Of the fallacies given in the text, the first and second are well known; the third is not new, but the earliest work in which I recollect seeing it is my *Algebra*, Cambridge, 1890, p. 430; the fourth is given in G. Chrystal's *Algebra*, Edinburgh, 1889, vol. II, p. 159; the sixth is due to G. T. Walker, and, I believe, has not appeared elsewhere than in this book; the seventh is due to D'Alembert; and the eighth to F. Galton. It may be worth recording (i) that a mechanical demonstration that $1 = 2$ was given by R. Chartres in *Knowledge*, July, 1891; and (ii) that J. L. F. Bertrand pointed out that a demonstration that $1 = -1$ can be obtained from the proposition in the Integral Calculus that, if the limits are constant, the order of integration is indifferent; hence the integral to x (from $x = 0$ to $x = 1$) of the integral to y (from $y = 0$ to $y = 1$) of a function ϕ should be equal to the integral to y (from $y = 0$ to $y = 1$) of the integral to x (from $x = 0$ to $x = 1$) of ϕ, but if $\phi = (x^2 - y^2)/(x^2 + y^2)^2$, this gives $\frac{1}{4}\pi = -\frac{1}{4}\pi$.

$(-1)^2 = 1$. Take logarithms, $\therefore$ 2 log $(-1) = \log 1 = 0$. $\therefore \log(-1) = 0$. $\therefore -1 = e^0$. $\therefore -1 = 1$.

The same argument may be expressed thus. Let x be a quantity which satisfies the equation $e^x = -1$. Square both sides,

$$\therefore e^{2x} = 1. \quad \therefore 2x = 0. \quad \therefore x = 0. \quad \therefore e^x = e^0.$$

But $e^x = -1$ and $e^0 = 1$, $\therefore -1 = 1$.

The error in each of the foregoing examples is obvious, but the fallacies in the next examples are concealed somewhat better.

Third Fallacy.   As yet another instance, we know that

$$\log(1 + x) = x - \tfrac{1}{2}x^2 + \tfrac{1}{3}x^3 - \ldots$$

If $x = 1$, the resulting series is convergent; hence we have

$$\log 2 = 1 - \tfrac{1}{2} + \tfrac{1}{3} - \tfrac{1}{4} + \tfrac{1}{5} - \tfrac{1}{6} + \tfrac{1}{7} - \tfrac{1}{8} + \tfrac{1}{9} - \ldots$$
$$\therefore 2 \log 2 = 2 - 1 + \tfrac{2}{3} - \tfrac{1}{2} + \tfrac{2}{5} - \tfrac{1}{3} + \tfrac{2}{7} - \tfrac{1}{4} + \tfrac{2}{9} - \ldots$$

Taking those terms together which have a common denominator, we obtain

$$2 \log 2 = 1 + \tfrac{1}{3} - \tfrac{1}{2} + \tfrac{1}{5} + \tfrac{1}{7} - \tfrac{1}{4} + \tfrac{1}{9} \ldots$$
$$= 1 - \tfrac{1}{2} + \tfrac{1}{3} - \tfrac{1}{4} + \tfrac{1}{5} - \ldots$$
$$= \log 2.$$

Hence $2 = 1$.

Fourth Fallacy.   This fallacy is very similar to that last given.   We have

$$\log 2 = 1 - \tfrac{1}{2} + \tfrac{1}{3} - \tfrac{1}{4} + \tfrac{1}{5} - \tfrac{1}{6} + \ldots$$
$$= (1 + \tfrac{1}{3} + \tfrac{1}{5} + \ldots) - (\tfrac{1}{2} + \tfrac{1}{4} + \tfrac{1}{6} + \ldots)$$
$$= \{(1 + \tfrac{1}{3} + \tfrac{1}{5} + \ldots) + (\tfrac{1}{2} + \tfrac{1}{4} + \tfrac{1}{6} + \ldots)\}$$
$$\quad - 2(\tfrac{1}{2} + \tfrac{1}{4} + \tfrac{1}{6} + \ldots)$$
$$= \{1 + \tfrac{1}{2} + \tfrac{1}{3} + \ldots\} - (1 + \tfrac{1}{2} + \tfrac{1}{3} + \ldots)$$
$$= 0.$$

Fifth Fallacy.   We have

$$\sqrt{a} \times \sqrt{b} = \sqrt{ab}.$$

Hence $\sqrt{-1} \times \sqrt{-1} = \sqrt{(-1)(-1)}$,

therefore, $(\sqrt{-1})^2 = \sqrt{1}$, that is, $-1 = 1$.

Sixth Fallacy. The following demonstration depends on the fact that an algebraical identity is true whatever be the symbols used in it, and it will appeal only to those who are familiar with this fact. We have, as an identity,

$$\sqrt{x - y} = i \sqrt{y - x} \ . \ . \ . \ . \ . \ \text{(i)},$$

where i stands either for $+ \sqrt{-1}$ or for $- \sqrt{-1}$. Now an identity in x and y is necessarily true whatever numbers x and y may represent. First put $x = a$ and $y = b$,

$$\therefore \sqrt{a - b} = i \sqrt{b - a} \ . \ . \ . \quad \text{(ii)}.$$

Next put $x = b$ and $y = a$,

$$\therefore \sqrt{b - a} = i \sqrt{a - b} \ . \ . \ . \quad \text{(iii)}.$$

Also since (i) is an identity, it follows that in (ii) and (iii) the symbol i must be the same, that is, it represents $+ \sqrt{-1}$ or $- \sqrt{-1}$ in both cases. Hence, from (ii) and (iii), we have

$$\sqrt{a - b} \sqrt{b - a} = i^2 \sqrt{b - a} \sqrt{a - b},$$
$$\therefore 1 = i^2,$$

that is,　　　　　　　　　$1 = -1.$

Seventh Fallacy. The following fallacy is due to D'Alembert.* We know that if the product of two numbers is equal to the product of two other numbers, the numbers will be in proportion, and from the definition of a proportion it follows that if the first term is greater than the second, then the third term will be greater than the fourth : thus, if $ad = bc$, then $a : b = c : d$, and if in this proportion $a > b$, then $c > d$. Now if we put $a = d = 1$ and $b = c = -1$ we have four numbers which satisfy the relation $ad = bc$ and such that $a > b$; hence, by the proposition, $c > d$, that is, $-1 > 1$, which is absurd.

Eighth Fallacy. The mathematical theory of probability leads to various paradoxes : of these I will give a few specimens. Suppose † three coins to be thrown up and the fact whether

---

* *Opuscules Mathématiques*, Paris, 1761, vol. I, p. 201.

† See *Nature*, Feb. 15, March 1, 1894, vol. XLIX, pp. 365—366, 413.

each comes down head or tail to be noticed. The probability that all three coins come down head is clearly $(1/2)^3$, that is, is $1/8$; similarly the probability that all three come down tail is $1/8$; hence the probability that all the coins come down alike (*i.e.* either all of them heads or all of them tails) is $1/4$. But, of three coins thus thrown up, at least two must come down alike : now the probability that the third coin comes down head is $1/2$ and the probability that it comes down tail is $1/2$, thus the probability that it comes down the same as the other two coins is $1/2$: hence the probability that all the coins come down alike is $1/2$. I leave to my readers to say whether either of these conflicting conclusions is right, and, if so, which is correct.

The Paradox of the Second Ace. Suppose that a player at bridge or whist asserts that an ace is included among the thirteen cards dealt to him, and let p be the probability that he has another ace among the other cards in his hand. Suppose, however, that he asserts that the ace of hearts is included in the thirteen cards dealt to him; then the probability, q, that he has another ace among the other cards in his hand is greater than was the probability p in the first case. For,[*] the number of hands containing an ace is $\binom{52}{13} - \binom{48}{13}$, whereas the number of hands containing two or more aces is $\binom{52}{13} - \binom{48}{13} - 4\binom{48}{12}$; therefore $p = 1 - 4\binom{48}{12}/\{\binom{52}{13} - \binom{48}{13}\} = \frac{5359}{14498}$. But the number of hands containing the ace of hearts is $\binom{51}{12}$, whereas the number of hands containing this and another ace is $\binom{51}{12} - \binom{48}{12}$; therefore $q = 1 - \binom{48}{12}/\binom{51}{12} = \frac{11686}{20825}$. Thus $p < \frac{1}{2} < q$, which at first sight appears to be absurd.

The St. Petersburg Paradox.[†] The following example is a famous one. A penny is tossed until it comes down head. If this happens at the first throw, the bank pays the player £1. Otherwise, the player throws again. If head appears at the second throw, the bank pays £2 ; if at the third throw, £4 ; and so on, doubling every time. Thus, if the coin does

---

[*] This argument is due to D. B. De Lury.

[†] Cf. E. Kamke, *Einführung in die Wahrscheinlichkeitstheorie*, Leipzig, 1932, pp. 82—89.

not come down head till the nth throw, the player then receives £2^{n-1}. What should the player pay the bank for the privilege of playing this game?

There is a probability 1/2 that the player will receive the £1, a probability 1/4 that he will receive the £2, and so on. Hence the total number of pounds that he may reasonably expect to receive is

$$\tfrac{1}{2} \cdot 1 + \tfrac{1}{4} \cdot 2 + \ldots + (\tfrac{1}{2})^n 2^{n-1} + \ldots = \tfrac{1}{2} + \tfrac{1}{2} + \tfrac{1}{2} + \ldots,$$

i.e. it is infinite.

Among various ways of modifying the problem to make the answer finite, perhaps the most satisfactory is that of T. C. Fry,[*] who supposes that the bank's wealth is limited, say to £1000000. There is then a probability $(1/2)^n$ that the player will receive £2^{n-1} at the nth throw, only as long as $2^{n-1} < 1000000$; thereafter, he will receive merely £1000000. Since

$$\sum_{1}^{20} (\tfrac{1}{2})^n 2^{n-1} + \sum_{21}^{\infty} (\tfrac{1}{2})^n 1000000 = 10 + (\tfrac{1}{2})^{20} 1000000$$
$$= 10 \cdot 9536 \ldots,$$

the player's expectation is about £10 19s. 1d.—a reasonable amount.

OTHER QUESTIONS ON PROBABILITY

Here is a result (due to H. Davenport) which many people find surprising. If you know more than 23 people's birthdays, it is more likely than not that two of them are the same (as to day and month). Consider the probability that n people's birthdays are all different, *i.e.* that in a random selection of n days out of 365 there shall be no day counted more than once. The total number of possible selections is 365^n, and the number of selections in which no day is counted more than once is $365 \cdot 364 \ldots (365 - n + 1)$. The probability is therefore †

[*] *Probability and its Engineering Uses*, New York, 1928, pp. 197—198.

† As a check on the working, note that this correctly gives 0 when $n = 366$. (For simplicity, I have ignored the possibility of a birthday falling on Feb. 29; that does not affect the result, save in this extreme case.)

$365 . 364 \ldots (365 - n + 1)/365^n$. The occurrence is as likely as not if this expression is equal to $1/2$, *i.e.* if

$$\left(1 - \frac{1}{365}\right)\left(1 - \frac{2}{365}\right) \cdots \left(1 - \frac{n-1}{365}\right) = \frac{1}{2}.$$

By taking logarithms, we obtain approximately

$$\frac{1}{365} + \frac{2}{365} + \cdots + \frac{n-1}{365} = \log_e 2,$$

or $n(n - 1) = 506$, whence $n = 23$.

Derangements. The following problem [*] is somewhat similar. Suppose you have written a letter to each of n different friends, and addressed the n corresponding envelopes. In how many ways can you make the regrettable mistake of putting *every* letter into a wrong envelope? Let X_n denote the number of ways. Suppose the first letter is placed in the ath envelope, and the bth letter in the first envelope. If $a = b$, there remain $n - 2$ letters to be placed in wrong envelopes, which can be done in X_{n-2} ways. Since $a (= b)$ may take any value from 2 to n, this possibility covers $(n - 1)X_{n-2}$ cases. In every other case, $a \neq b$. For the moment, let us fix b (and let a run over all values from 2 to n, except b). In the $n - 1$ envelopes other than the first, we have to place the $n - 1$ letters other than the bth, but the first letter must not be placed in the bth envelope. The number of ways in which this can be done is just X_{n-1}, since the situation is equivalent to that of the original problem with $n - 1$ letters, if we imagine the bth envelope to be the proper one for the first letter. Letting b vary, this accounts for $(n - 1)X_{n-1}$ cases. Hence $X_n = (n - 1)(X_{n-1} + X_{n-2})$. This relation [†] gives the successive numbers readily. Obviously $X_1 = 0$ and $X_2 = 1$; therefore $X_3 = 2$, $X_4 = 9$, $X_5 = 44$, $X_6 = 265$, and so on. The explicit formula is

[*] Cf. De Montmort, *Essai d'analyse sur les jeux de hasard*, Paris, 1713, p. 132; J. L. Coolidge, *An Introduction to Mathematical Probability*, Oxford, 1925, p. 24; Durell and Robson, *Advanced Algebra*, London, 1937, p. 459.

[†] A still simpler relation is $X_n = nX_{n-1} + (-1)^n$ $(X_1 = 0)$.

$$X_n = n! \left(1 - \frac{1}{1!} + \frac{1}{2!} - \frac{1}{3!} + \cdots \pm \frac{1}{n!}\right)$$

(" sub-factorial n ").

Since n given letters can be placed in n given envelopes in $n!$ ways altogether, the probability of this unhappy occurrence is

$$\frac{X_n}{n!} = 1 - \frac{1}{1!} + \frac{1}{2!} - \frac{1}{3!} + \cdots \pm \frac{1}{n!}.$$

Now this is the beginning of the series for $e^{-1} (= 0.367879 \ldots)$, so we may say that the probability is approximately $1/e$. The error is less than $1/(n+1)!$, which, when $n = 6$, is about 0·0002.

If we compare two packs of cards (one of them having been well shuffled), card by card, what is the probability that we shall get right through the packs without finding a single coincidence? This is merely another form of the same problem; the answer is $1/e$ (with an error of less than 10^{-69}, for packs of 52 cards). Many people are prepared to bet that no coincidence will occur, so an unscrupulous gambler might profit by knowing that $e > 2$.

Miscellaneous Problems. To the above examples I may add the following standard questions, or recreations.

The first of these questions is as follows. Two clerks, A and B, are engaged, A at a salary commencing at the rate of (say) £100 a year with a rise of £20 every year, B at a salary commencing at the same rate of £100 a year with a rise of £5 every half-year, in each case payments being made half-yearly; which has the larger income? The answer is B; for in the first year A receives £100, but B receives £50 and £55 as his two half-yearly payments and thus receives in all £105. In the second year A receives £120, but B receives £60 and £65 as his two half-yearly payments and thus receives in all £125. In fact B will always receive £5 a year more than A.

Another simple arithmetical problem is as follows. A hymn-board in a church has four grooved rows on which the numbers of four hymns chosen for the service are placed. The hymn-book in use contains 700 hymns. What is the smallest number of plates, each carrying one digit, which must be kept in stock so that the numbers of any four different hymns selected can be displayed; and how will the result be affected if an inverted 6 can be used for a 9? The answers are 86 and 81. What are the answers if a digit is painted on each side of each plate?

As another question take the following. A man bets $1/n$th of his money on an even chance (say tossing heads or tails with a penny): he repeats this again and again, each time betting $1/n$th of all the money then in his possession. If, finally, the number of times he has won is equal to the number of times he has lost, has he gained or lost by the transaction? He has, in fact, lost.

Here is another simple question to which I have frequently received incorrect answers. One tumbler is half-full of wine, another is half-full of water: from the first tumbler a tea-spoonful of wine is taken out and poured into the tumbler containing the water: a teaspoonful of the mixture in the second tumbler is then transferred to the first tumbler. As the result of this double transaction, is the quantity of wine removed from the first tumbler greater or less than the quantity of water removed from the second tumbler? In my experience the majority of people will say it is greater, but this is not the case.

PERMUTATION PROBLEMS

Many of the problems in permutations and combinations are of considerable interest. As a simple illustration of the very large number of ways in which combinations of even a few things can be arranged, I may note that there are 500,291833 different ways in which change for a sovereign can be given in current coins,* including therein the obsolescent double-florin, and crown; also that as many as 19,958400

* *The Tribune*, September 3, 1906.

distinct skeleton cubes can be formed with twelve differently coloured rods of equal length ; * while there are no less than $(52!)/(13!)^4$, that is, 53644,737765,488792,839237,440000 possible different distributions of hands at bridge or whist with a pack of fifty-two cards.

Voting Problems. As a simple example on combinations I take the cumulative vote as affecting the representation of a minority. If there are p electors each having r votes of which not more than s may be given to one candidate, and n men are to be elected, then the least number of supporters who can secure the election of a candidate must exceed $pr/(ns + r)$.

The Knights of the Round Table. A far more difficult permutation problem consists in finding as many arrangements as possible of n people in a ring so that no one has the same two neighbours more than once. It is a well-known proposition that n persons can be arranged in a ring in $(n-1)!/2$ different ways. The number of these arrangements in which all the persons have different pairs of neighbours on each occasion cannot exceed $(n-1)(n-2)/2$, since this gives the number of ways in which any assigned person may sit between every possible pair selected from the rest. But in fact it is always possible to determine $(n-1)(n-2)/2$ arrangements in which no one has the same two neighbours on any two occasions.

Solutions for various values of n have been given. Here, for instance $(n = 8)$, are 21 arrangements † of eight persons. Each arrangement may be placed round a circle and no one has the same two neighbours on any two occasions.

---

* *Mathematical Tripos*, Cambridge, Part I, 1894.

† Communicated to me by Mr. E. G. B. Bergholt, May, 1906, see *The Secretary* and *The Queen*, August, 1906. Mr. Dudeney had given the problem for the case when $n = 6$ in 1905, and informs me that the problem has been solved by Mr. E. D. Bewley when n is even, and that he has a general method applicable when n is odd. Various memoirs on the subject have appeared in the mathematical journals.

1.2.3.4.5.6.7.8;   1.2.5.6.8.7.4.3;   1.2.7.8.4.3.5.6;
1.3.5.2.7.4.8.6;   1.3.7.4.6.8.2.5;   1.3.8.6.2.5.7.4;
1.4.2.6.3.8.5.7;   1.4.3.8.7.5.6.2;   1.4.5.7.6.2.3.8;
1.5.6.4.3.7.8.2;   1.5.7.3.8.2.6.4;   1.5.8.2.4.6.3.7;
1.6.2.7.5.3.8.4;   1.6.3.5.8.4.2.7;   1.6.4.8.2.7.3.5;
1.7.4.2.5.8.6.3;   1.7.6.3.2.4.5.8;   1.7.8.5.6.3.4.2;
1.8.2.3.7.6.4.5;   1.8.4.5.3.2.7.6;   1.8.6.7.4.5.2.3.

The methods of determining these arrangements are lengthy, and far from easy.

The Ménage Problem.* Another difficult permutation problem is concerned with the number x of possible arrangements of n married couples, seated alternately man and woman, round a table, the n wives being in assigned positions, and the n husbands so placed that a man does not sit next to his wife.

The solution involves the theory of discordant permutations,† and is far from easy. I content myself with noting the results when n does not exceed 10. When $n = 3$, $x = 1$; when $n = 4$, $x = 2$; when $n = 5$, $x = 13$; when $n = 6$, $x = 80$; when $n = 7$, $x = 579$; when $n = 8$, $x = 4738$; when $n = 9$, $x = 43387$; and when $n = 10$, $x = 439792$.

BACHET'S WEIGHTS PROBLEM ‡

It will be noticed that a considerable number of the easier problems given in the last chapter either are due to Bachet or were collected by him in his classical *Problèmes*. Among the more difficult problems proposed by him was the determination of the least number of weights which would serve to weigh any integral number of pounds from 1 lb. to 40 lbs. inclusive. Bachet gave two solutions : namely, (i) the series of weights of 1, 2, 4, 8, 16, and 32 lbs. ; (ii) the series of weights of 1, 3, 9, and 27 lbs.

If the weights may be placed in only one of the scale-pans,

* *Théorie des Nombres*, by E. Lucas, Paris, 1891, pp. 215, 491—495.

† See P. A. MacMahon, *Combinatory Analysis*, vol. i, Cambridge, 1915, pp. 253—256.

‡ Bachet, Appendix, problem v, p. 215.

the first series gives a solution, as had been pointed out in 1556 by Tartaglia.*

Bachet, however, assumed that any weight might be placed in either of the scale-pans.   In this case the second series gives the least possible number of weights required.   His reasoning is as follows.   To weigh 1 lb. we must have a 1-lb. weight. To weigh 2 lbs. we must have in addition either a 2-lb. weight or a 3-lb. weight; but, whereas with a 2-lb. weight we can weigh 1 lb., 2 lbs., and 3 lbs., with a 3-lb. weight we can weigh 1 lb., $(3 - 1)$ lbs., 3 lbs., and $(3 + 1)$ lbs.   Another weight of 9 lbs. will enable us to weigh all weights from 1 lb. to 13 lbs.; and we get thus a greater range than is obtainable with any weight less than 9 lbs.   Similarly weights of 1, 3, 9, and 27 lbs. suffice for all weights up to 40 lbs., and weights of 1, 3, 3^2, . . ., 3^{n-1} lbs. enable us to weigh any integral number of pounds from 1 lb. to $(1 + 3 + 3^2 + \ldots 3^{n-1})$ lbs.—that is, to $\frac{1}{2}(3^n - 1)$ lbs.

To determine the arrangement of the weights to weigh any given mass we have only to express the number of pounds in it as a number in the ternary scale of notation, except that in finding the successive digits we must make every remainder either 0, 1 or -1: to effect this a remainder 2 must be written as $3 - 1$—that is, the quotient must be increased by unity, in which case the remainder is -1.   This is explained in most text-books on algebra.

Bachet's argument does not prove that his result is unique or that it gives the least possible number of weights required. These omissions have been supplied by Major MacMahon, who has discussed the far more difficult problem (of which Bachet's is a particular case) of the determination of all possible sets of weights, not necessarily unequal, which enable us to weigh any integral number of pounds from 1 to n inclusive, (i) when the weights may be placed in only one scale-pan, and (ii) when any weight may be placed in either scale-pan.   He

* *Trattato de' numeri e misure,* Venice, 1556, vol. II, bk. I, chap. XVI, art. 32.

has investigated also the modifications of the results which are necessary when we impose either or both of the further conditions (a) that no other weighings are to be possible, and (b) that each weighing is to be possible in only one way, that is, is to be unique.*

The method for case (i) consists in resolving $1 + x + x^2 + \ldots + x^n$ into factors, each factor being of the form $1 + x^a + x^{2a} + \ldots + x^{ma}$; the number of solutions depends on the composite character of $n + 1$. The method for case (ii) consists in resolving the expression $x^{-n} + x^{-n+1} + \ldots + x^{-1} + 1 + x + \ldots + x^{n-1} + x^n$ into factors, each factor being of the form $x^{-ma} + \ldots + x^{-a} + 1 + x^a + \ldots + x^{ma}$; the number of solutions depends on the composite character of $2n + 1$.

Bachet's problem falls under case (ii), $n = 40$. Mac-Mahon's analysis shows that there are eight such ways of factorizing $x^{-40} + x^{-39} + \ldots + 1 + \ldots + x^{39} + x^{40}$. First, there is the expression itself in which $a = 1$, $m = 40$. Second, the expression is equal to $(1 - x^{81})/x^{40}(1 - x)$, which can be resolved into the product of $(1 - x^3)/x(1 - x)$ and $(1 - x^{81})/x^{39}(1 - x^3)$; hence it can be resolved into two factors of the form given above, in one of which $a = 1$, $m = 1$, and in the other $a = 3$, $m = 13$. Third, similarly, it can be resolved into two such factors, in one of which $a = 1$, $m = 4$, and in the other $a = 9$, $m = 4$. Fourth, it can be resolved into three such factors, in one of which $a = 1$, $m = 1$, in another $a = 3$, $m = 1$, and in the other $a = 9$, $m = 4$. Fifth, it can be resolved into two such factors, in one of which $a = 1$, $m = 13$, and in the other $a = 27$, $m = 1$. Sixth, it can be resolved into three such factors, in one of which $a = 1$, $m = 1$, in another $a = 3$, $m = 4$, and in the other $a = 27$, $m = 1$. Seventh, it can be resolved into three such factors, in one of which $a = 1$, $m = 4$, in another $a = 9$, $m = 1$, and in the other $a = 27$, $m = 1$. Eighth, it can be resolved into four

---

* See his article in the *Quarterly Journal of Mathematics*, 1886, vol. XXI, pp. 367—373. An account of the method is given in *Nature*, Dec. 4, 1890, vol. XLII, pp. 113—114.

such factors, in one of which $a = 1$, $m = 1$, in another $a = 3$, $m = 1$, in another $a = 9$, $m = 1$, and in the other $a = 27$, $m = 1$.

These results show that there are eight possible sets of weights with which any integral number of pounds from 1 to 40 can be weighed subject to the conditions (ii), (a), and (b). If we denote p weights each equal to w by w^p, these eight solutions are 1^{40}; 1, 3^{13}; 1^4, 9^4; 1, 3, 9^4; 1^{13}, 27; 1, 3^4, 27; 1^4, 9, 27; 1, 3, 9, 27. The last of these is Bachet's solution : not only is it that in which the least number of weights are employed, but it is also the only one in which all the weights are unequal.

THE DECIMAL EXPRESSION FOR $1/n$

E. Schiffner has invented a remarkable technique for expressing certain fractions $1/n$ as recurring decimals. The first few digits have to be calculated in the ordinary way, say by long division; but after a certain stage we pass from division by n to division by a power of 2 or of 5. The ordinary division is continued until the remainder happens to be of the form 5^m or 2^m (mod n). (Such a remainder will always arise when the decimal has the longest possible period, namely $n - 1$ digits; also in many other cases.) Suppose that at this stage k digits have been found. We write the first $m + 1$ of these in a row from left to right, and the rest in a column below the $(m + 1)$th. The new divisor (for the rest of the process) is 2^m or 5^m, according as the above-mentioned remainder is 5^m or 2^m. By this we divide the number formed by the first $m + 1$ digits, placing the quotient * below the kth digit (since it is in fact the $(k + 1)$th), and the remainder to the left of the $(m + 2)$th digit. Then we divide the number so formed, placing the quotient below the $(k + 1)$th digit, and the remainder beside the $(m + 3)$th. The successive quotients and remainders can now be written down quite rapidly.

When $n = 7$, for example, we find a remainder 2 after obtaining (by ordinary division) the digits 14. Thus $m = 1$,

---

* If this quotient $\geqslant 10$, we write only its unit-digit.

and the new divisor is 5. Dividing 14 by 5, we obtain the
quotient 2, which we place below the 4, and the remainder 4,
which we place to the left of the 2. We next divide 42 by 5,
and so on.

14	011	0212
42	4	47
28	9	76
35	4	45
07	2	9
21	5	...

Again, when $n = 87$, we find a remainder 25 after obtaining
the digits 01149425. Thus $m = 2$, and the new divisor is 4.
Accordingly, we arrange the digits in a column, as above,
and divide 11 by 4, placing the quotient (2) below the 5, and
the remainder (3) beside the first 4. We then divide 34 by 4,
placing the quotient below the 2 and the remainder beside the
9. By this means, the period

    0 1 1 4 9 4 2 5 2 8 7 3 5 6 3 2 1 8 3 9 0 8 0 4 5 9 7 7

can be written down in a few seconds.

When $n = 47$, after obtaining the digits 0 2 1 2 7 we find
a remainder 31, which is congruent to 125. The next digit is
6, since this is the unit-digit of the quotient when 212 is divided
by 8.

For an explanation, see Schiffner's article.*

DECIMALS AND CONTINUED FRACTIONS

Every positive number can be expressed in just one way
as a decimal. If the number is rational (*i.e.*, expressible
as a vulgar fraction), its decimal expression will either terminate or (after a certain stage) recur. Otherwise, as in the
case of $\sqrt{2} = 1\cdot41421356\ldots$, or of $\pi = 3\cdot14159265\ldots$,
it will neither terminate nor recur. If another scale of notation is used, the sequence of digits will, of course, be quite

---

* *Sphinx*, 1937, p. 115. For a modified form of this method, see *Sphinx*,
1938, p. 206.

different. The " decimal " for a rational number may terminate in one scale and recur in another; thus, in the scale of seven, $\frac{1}{7} = 0\cdot1$, instead of the familiar $0\cdot\dot{1}4285\dot{7}$. Given an integer, expressed in the ordinary (denary) scale, we can express it in the scale of p by dividing by p again and again, noting the successive remainders. These remainders, when read backwards, are the digits of the required new expression. The rule for a fraction is different. There we *multiply* by p again and again, operating only on the fractional part at each stage. The successive integral parts are the digits of the required new expression (in their proper order). For instance, in the binary scale,

$$\sqrt{2}\ (=\sqrt{10}) = 1\cdot0\ 1\ 1\ 0\ 1\ 0\ 1\ 0\ 0\ 0\ 0\ 0\ 1\ 0\ 0\ 1\ 1\ 1\ 1\ 0\ 0\ \ldots,$$
$$\pi = 1\ 1\cdot0\ 0\ 1\ 0\ 0\ 1\ 0\ 0\ 0\ 0\ 1\ 1\ 1\ 1\ 1\ 1\ 0\ 1\ 1\ 0\ 1\ \ldots.$$

The actual computation proceeds thus :

1·41421356	3·14159265
0·82842712	0·28318530
1·65685424	0·56637060
1·3137085	1·1327412
0·6274170	0·2654824
1·2548340	0·5309648
0·509668	1·061930
etc.	etc.

The sequence of five zeros makes $1\cdot0110101$ a particularly good approximation for $\sqrt{2}$. In fact, working in the binary scale, we easily find that $(1\cdot0110101)^2 = 1\cdot11111111111001$. As a good approximation for π, we note $11\cdot00\dot{1} = 3\frac{1}{7}$.

Somewhat analogously, every positive number can be expressed in just one way as a *regular continued fraction*

$$a_0 + \cfrac{1}{a_1 + \cfrac{1}{a_2 + \cfrac{1}{a_3 + \ldots}}} = a_0 + \frac{1}{a_1} + \frac{1}{a_2} + \frac{1}{a_3} + \ldots.$$

where the a's are positive integers, save that a_0 may be zero. Thus *

$$\sqrt{2} = 1 + \frac{1}{2} + \frac{1}{2} + \frac{1}{2} + \cdots,$$

$$e = 2 + \frac{1}{1} + \frac{1}{2} + \frac{1}{1} + \frac{1}{1} + \frac{1}{4} + \frac{1}{1} + \frac{1}{1} + \frac{1}{6} + \frac{1}{1} + \frac{1}{1} + \frac{1}{8} + \frac{1}{1} + \cdots,$$

$$\pi = 3 + \frac{1}{7} + \frac{1}{15} + \frac{1}{1} + \frac{1}{292} + \frac{1}{1} + \frac{1}{1} + \frac{1}{1} + \frac{1}{2} + \frac{1}{1} + \frac{1}{3} + \frac{1}{1} + \cdots.$$

This kind of expression excels the decimal in three respects : (i) the continued fraction terminates whenever the number is rational, and recurs whenever it is quadratically irrational; (ii) it does not depend on any particular scale of notation (except trivially, in writing the a's); (iii) it leads to rational approximations which are " best possible " in a sense that will be illustrated geometrically in the next chapter (page 87).

The rational approximations

$$\frac{b_1}{c_1} = \frac{a_0}{1}, \frac{b_2}{c_2} = \frac{1 + a_0 a_1}{a_1}, \frac{b_3}{c_3} = \frac{a_0 + a_0 a_1 a_2 + a_2}{1 + a_1 a_2}, \cdots,$$

obtained by stopping the continued fraction at each successive stage, are called *convergents*, and have many remarkable properties. They are given successively by the formulae

$$b_{n+1} = b_{n-1} + a_n b_n, \quad c_{n+1} = c_{n-1} + a_n c_n.$$

For instance, the first half-dozen convergents to $\sqrt{2}$, e and π are $\frac{1}{1}, \frac{3}{2}, \frac{7}{5}, \frac{17}{12}, \frac{41}{29}, \frac{99}{70}$; $\frac{2}{1}, \frac{3}{1}, \frac{8}{3}, \frac{11}{4}, \frac{19}{7}, \frac{87}{32}$; $\frac{3}{1}, \frac{22}{7}, \frac{333}{106}, \frac{355}{113}, \frac{103993}{33102}, \frac{104348}{33215}$.

The simplest of all irrational continued fractions is

$$\tau = 1 + \frac{1}{1} + \frac{1}{1} + \frac{1}{1} + \cdots,$$

which satisfies the equation $\tau = 1 + 1/\tau$, whence, being

---

* Although the " partial quotients " (a_1, a_2, ...) for $\sqrt{2}$ and e obey simple laws, no law has yet been found for π. The fourth quotient 292 is still the largest known, the runner-up being $a_{73} = 161$. According to D. H. Lehmer, the arithmetic mean of the first hundred quotients is 10·2; 41 of them are equal to unity. See *Sphinx*, 1938, pp. 185—187.

obviously positive, $\tau = \frac{1}{2}(\sqrt{5}+1)$. (Cf. Wythoff's Game, on page 38.) Its convergents are $\frac{1}{1}$, $\frac{2}{1}$, $\frac{3}{2}$, $\frac{5}{3}$, $\frac{8}{5}$, $\frac{13}{8}$, ..., both numerators and denominators being formed from the sequence of *Fibonacci numbers*

$$1, 1, 2, 3, 5, 8, 13, 21, 34, 55, 89, 144, 233, 377, \ldots.$$

Each of these numbers is equal to the sum of the preceding two. The ratios of alternate Fibonacci numbers are said * to measure the fraction of a turn between successive leaves on the stalk of a plant: $\frac{1}{2}$ for grasses, $\frac{1}{3}$ for sedges, $\frac{2}{5}$ for the apple, cherry, etc., $\frac{3}{8}$ for the common plantain, $\frac{5}{13}$ for the leek, and so on. These are the convergents to

$$\frac{1}{\tau^2} = \frac{1}{2} + \frac{1}{1} + \frac{1}{1} + \frac{1}{1} + \cdots.$$

The number τ is intimately connected with the metrical properties of the pentagon, decagon, dodecahedron and icosahedron, since it is equal to $2 \cos \frac{1}{5}\pi$. A line-segment is said to be divided according to the *golden section* if one part is τ times the other, or $1/\tau$ of the whole. The nth Fibonacci number is

$$\{\tau^n - (-\tau)^{-n}\}/\sqrt{5}.$$

RATIONAL RIGHT-ANGLED TRIANGLES

If the sides of a right-angled triangle are in rational ratios, we may take them to be integers without a common factor. By Pythagoras' Theorem, the sides, x, y, z, of such a " primitive " triangle satisfy the equation $x^2 + y^2 = z^2$, z being the hypotenuse. The general solution (apart from the obvious possibility of interchanging x and y) is †

$$x = b^2 - c^2, \quad y = 2bc, \quad z = b^2 + c^2,$$

where b and c are arbitrary co-prime integers, one even and one odd, with $b > c$. The values $b = 2$, $c = 1$ give the familiar 3, 4, 5 triangle.‡ The numbers x and z are always odd, and

---

* H. E. Licks, *Recreations in Mathematics*, New York, 1936, p. 107.

† G. Chrystal, *Algebra*, Edinburgh, 1889, vol. II, p. 531.

‡ E. T. Bell, *Numerology*, Baltimore, 1933, p. 26 ff.

y is divisible by 4. Either x or y is divisible by 3, and one of x, y, z by 5. Consequently, xy is divisible by 12, and xyz by 60.

b	c	x	y	z	$\begin{aligned}x+y+z\\=2b(b+c)\end{aligned}$	b	c	x	y	z	$\begin{aligned}x+y+z\\=2b(b+c)\end{aligned}$
2	1	3	4	5	12	5	4	9	40	41	90
3	2	5	12	13	30	7	2	45	28	53	126
4	1	15	8	17	40	6	5	11	60	61	132
4	3	7	24	25	56	8	1	63	16	65	144
5	2	21	20	29	70	7	4	33	56	65	154
6	1	35	12	37	84	8	3	55	48	73	176

The first twelve primitive triangles are tabulated above. These are all that have $z < 80$, and all that have $x + y + z < 180$. D. N. Lehmer has proved * that the number of primitive triangles with hypotenuse less than X is approximately $X/2\pi$, and that the number with perimeter less than X is approximately $(X \log 2)/\pi^2$. We observe that $80/2\pi = 12\cdot73 \ldots$, while $(180 \log 2)/\pi^2 = 12\cdot64. \ldots$

If $b - c = 1$, then $z - y = 1$, as in the first, second, fourth, seventh and ninth of the above triangles. If c and b are consecutive terms of the sequence 1, 2, 5, 12, 29, 70, $\ldots$, i.e.† if b/c is a convergent to the continued fraction

$$\sqrt{2} + 1 = 2 + \frac{1}{2} + \frac{1}{2} + \frac{1}{2} + \cdots,$$

then $|x - y| = 1$, as in the first and fifth triangles.

F. Hoppenot has pointed out that the sum of the squares of $n + 1$ consecutive integers, of which the greatest is $2n(n + 1)$, is equal to the sum of the squares of the next n integers; thus $10^2 + 11^2 + 12^2 = 13^2 + 14^2$, $21^2 + 22^2 + 23^2 + 24^2 = 25^2 + 26^2 + 27^2$, and so on. As another analogue of the identity $3^2 + 4^2 = 5^2$, observe that $3^3 + 4^3 + 5^3 = 6^3$. The equation $x^3 + y^3 = z^3$ has no solutions in integers; nor

---

* *American Journal of Mathematics*, 1900, vol. XXII, p. 38.

† M. Kraïtchik, *La Mathématique des Jeux*, Brussels, 1930, p. 106.

has $x^4 + y^4 = z^4$. Euler * has conjectured a corresponding result for the equation $x^4 + y^4 + z^4 = v^4$; if any solution exists, v must exceed 1040. On the other hand, $x^4 + y^4 = z^4 + v^4$ has infinitely many solutions.†

TRIANGULAR AND PYRAMIDAL NUMBERS ‡

The *triangular numbers*

$$1, 3, 6, 10, 15, 21, 28, 36, 45, 55, 66, \ldots, \tfrac{1}{2}n(n+1), \ldots$$

are the sums of consecutive integers, beginning with 1.   Hence, as their name indicates, they are the numbers of dots (or equal circles) that can be arranged in triangular formation : one at the top, two below it, three below them, and so on. The numbers 1, 36, 1225, 41616, 1413721, 48024900, ... are simultaneously triangular and square ; the general formula for such a number is b^2c^2, where b/c is any convergent to the continued fraction for $\sqrt{2}$.

The sums of consecutive triangular numbers are the *tetrahedral numbers*

$$1, 4, 10, 20, 35, 56, 84, 120, \ldots, \tfrac{1}{6}n(n+1)(n+2), \ldots.$$

These are the numbers of equal spheres that can be piled in tetrahedral formation. Similarly, the sums of consecutive squares are the *pyramidal numbers*

$$1, 5, 14, 30, 55, 91, 140, 204, \ldots, \tfrac{1}{6}n(n+1)(2n+1), \ldots.$$

The sums of consecutive cubes (from 1 up) are the squares of the triangular numbers; the sums of consecutive *pairs* of triangular numbers are the square numbers, and the sums of consecutive pairs of tetrahedral numbers are the pyramidal numbers.

* *Commentationes Arithmeticae Collectae*, Petrograd, 1849, vol. I, pp. 473—476; vol. II, pp. 450—456. A somewhat similar unproved theorem is that the sum of n numbers of the form x^k cannot be of the form u^k if n is less than k.

† See *Sphinx*, 1937, p. 98.

‡ Cf. H. E. Dudeney, *Amusements in Mathematics*, London, 1917, pp. 26, 167.

The *only* number (> 1) which is simultaneously square and pyramidal is 4900. This result * was conjectured by Lucas in 1875, and proved by Watson in 1918. The proof is by no means elementary.

AUTOMORPHIC NUMBERS †

If two numbers, x and y, differ by a multiple of p, we say that they are congruent modulo p, and write

$$x \equiv y \;(\text{mod } p), \text{ or } x - y \equiv 0 \;(\text{mod } p).$$

If these numbers are expressed in the scale of p, they will have the same unit-digit.

A number is said to be *automorphic* if its n digits are the last n digits of its square, and consequently of its cube and higher powers too. Thus 25 and 76 are automorphic (in the denary scale), since $25^2 = 625$ and $76^2 \equiv 5776$. In the scale of p, a number x is automorphic if $x^2 \equiv x \;(\text{mod } p^n)$. The numbers 0 and 1 are trivially automorphic, and need hardly be mentioned; but if p is a prime, or a power of a prime, there are no others. Thus $p = 6$ and $p = 10$ are the first significant cases. In the scale of six, the last seven digits of an automorphic number must be either 1350213 or 4205344. (The last six digits of the former are the same as the last six digits of 3^{16}.) In the scale of ten, the last sixteen digits of an automorphic number must be either

6259918212890625 or 3740081787109376.

(The last five digits of the former are the same as the last five digits of $5^8 = 390625$.)

FINITE ARITHMETICS

The numbers 0, 1, 2, ..., $p - 1$ are called *residues* modulo p; every integer is congruent to just one of them. There is an arithmetic of residues, closely analogous to the arithmetic

---

* E. Lucas, *Nouvelles Annales de Math.* (2), vol. XIV, p. 336.   G. N Watson, *Messenger of Mathematics* (new series), vol. XLVIII, pp. 1—22.

† Kraïtchik, p. 66.   *Sphinx*, 1935, pp. 1—4.

of ordinary numbers. In it, we can obviously add, subtract and multiply. Thus, when $p = 6$, we have $3 + 4 = 1$, $3 - 4 = 5$, $3 \times 4 = 0$. If p is a *prime* number (as we shall suppose, for the rest of this chapter), we can also divide (by any residue except 0). Thus, when $p = 7$, we have $\frac{3}{4} = 3 \times \frac{1}{4} = 3 \times \frac{8}{4} = 6$; or, briefly, $3/4 = 24/4 = 6$.

It follows that every numerical problem whose solutions are rational leads to a corresponding problem in the finite arithmetic modulo p, with solutions which are congruent to those of the original problem. For instance, the equation $x^2 - x - 2 = 0$ has the roots 2, -1, and the congruence $x^2 - x - 2 \equiv 0 \pmod{p}$ has the roots 2, $p - 1$. If we can solve a problem in the finite arithmetic for each of a number of different moduli p, then the solutions of the corresponding unrestricted problem are known to within a multiple of the product of all the moduli.

Lehmer's Machine

This is the underlying principle of D. H. Lehmer's Photo-electric Number-Sieve,[*] which factorizes large numbers with almost miraculous rapidity. (It took only three seconds to factorize

$$2^{93} + 1 = 3^2 \times 529{,}510939 \times 715{,}827883 \times 2903{,}110321.)$$

This wonderful machine consists essentially of thirty parallel cog-wheels, which, in certain positions, allow a beam of light to pass through small holes in all of them. Their numbers of cogs are convenient multiples of the primes from 2 to 113, respectively; and there is a hole opposite each cog, at a uniform distance from the periphery. These holes are numbered from 0 to $p - 1$; and a problem (such as that of finding a positive integer x for which $4787532864x^2 + 171576027618912x + 10553711710905$ is a square[†]) is presented to the machine by plugging up, in each wheel, all the holes except those which give solutions of the corresponding

[*] *American Mathematical Monthly*, 1933, vol. XL, pp. 401—406.
[†] This problem arises quite naturally in seeking to factorize $2^{93} + 1$.

problem in the arithmetic modulo p. The wheels are made to turn rapidly, all with the same peripheral speed, *i.e.* so that the number of holes that pass the beam of light in a second is the same for all and is about 5000. The beam can pass through all the holes only when their positions correspond to a number which is congruent to a solution in every one of the finite arithmetics. When this happens, the light actuates a photo-electric cell, and the induced current (after enormous amplification) stops the machine.

THE DISTRIBUTION OF PRIMES

A *prime* (or *prime number*) is a positive integer which has no divisors save 1 and itself.* The twenty-six primes less than 100 are 1, 2, 3, 5, 7, 11, 13, 17, 19, 23, 29, 31, 37, 41, 43, 47, 53, 59, 61, 67, 71, 73, 79, 83, 89, 97. Euclid † proved that there are infinitely many primes, arguing somewhat as follows. Consider the product $P = 2 . 3 . 5 . 7 \ldots p$ of all the primes up to a particular one. Clearly, $P + 1$ is not divisible by any of these primes. Therefore it has a prime divisor greater than p (including, as a possibility, itself). Thus there is a prime greater than any given prime.

The best attempt that has ever been made towards an explicit formula for primes is Euler's ‡ quadratic form $x^2 + x + 41$, which represents primes for $x = 0, 1, 2, 3, \ldots,$ 39. D. H. Lehmer has shown § that if there is a form $x^2 + x + A$, with $A > 41$, which represents primes for $A - 1$ consecutive values of x, then A must exceed 1250,000000, and there is at most one such form.

It is clearly desirable to be able to tell whether a given number N is prime or composite without having to test every prime less than $\sqrt{N}$ as a possible divisor. I will mention two criteria.

---

* Some authors prefer to exclude 1 from the list of primes. See, for instance, A. E. Ingham, *The Distribution of Prime Numbers*, Cambridge, 1932

† *Elementa*, IX, 20.

‡ *Nouveaux Mémoires de l'Académie Royale des Sciences*, Berlin, 1772, p. 36.

§ *Sphinx*, 1936, pp. 212—214.

Sir J. Wilson discovered (1770) and Lagrange proved (1773) that N is prime *if, and only if*, $(N - 1)! + 1$ is divisible by N. For instance, $(7 - 1)! + 1 = 721$ is divisible by 7, but $(9 - 1)! + 1 = 40321$ is not divisible by 9. Wilson's Theorem is a theoretical rather than practical test for primality, since, if N is large enough for its primality to be in doubt, it is more laborious to find whether $(N - 1)! + 1$ is or is not divisible by N than to test every prime less than $\sqrt{N}$ as a possible factor of N.

Fermat discovered (1640) and Euler proved (1736) that, if p is prime and a is not divisible by p, then $a^{p-1} - 1$ is divisible by p. The case when $a = 2$ was known to the Chinese as early as 500 B.C.; they stated also the converse proposition: if N divides $2^{N-1} - 1$ then N is a prime. This proposition was rediscovered and " proved " by Leibniz in 1680. However, it is false; it fails for $N = 341 = 11 \times 31$ and for an infinity of other N's. Modern tests for primality are based on the following converse of Fermat's Theorem, due to Lucas : * if $a^x - 1$ is divisible by N when $x = N - 1$, but not when x is a proper divisor of $N - 1$, then N is a prime. Modifications of this converse both as to hypothesis and conclusion are necessary before the actual modern tests emerge.†

The numbers up to 10^7 have all been factorized.‡ They include 664580 primes. In order to see how larger numbers behave, Hoppenot and Kraïtchik § have tabulated the smallest prime factor of every number from $10^{12} - 10^4$ to $10^{12} + 10^4$. By an ingenious process, due to Meissel,‖ it is possible to calculate the number of primes less than X without finding the primes themselves and counting them.

* *Théorie des Nombres*, Paris, 1891, pp. 423, 441. For an interesting discussion of Fermat's Theorem, see E. T. Bell's *Numerology*, Baltimore, 1933, pp. 182—185.

† See *Bulletin of the American Mathematical Society*, 1927, vol. XXXIII, pp. 327—340.

‡ D. N. Lehmer, *Factor Table for the First Ten Millions*, Washington, 1909.

§ *Sphinx*, 1936, p. 164; 1938, p. 84.

‖ *Mathematische Annalen*, 1870, vol. II, p. 636; 1871, vol. III, p. 523.

If X is large, and x is comparatively small, the number of primes between X and $X + x$ (or between $X - x$ and X) is approximately * $x/\log X$. For the number of primes between 10,000000 and 10,005000, this formula gives $5000/(7 \log 10)$ $= \frac{5000}{7} \log_{10} e = 310\cdot210\ldots$; the exact number is known to be 305. Again, according to the Hoppenot–Kraïtchik table, there are exactly 336 primes between $10^{12} - 10^4$ and 10^{12}, whereas the approximate formula gives $10^4/(12 \log 10)$ $= 361\cdot912\ldots$

For the number of primes less than X, Riemann has given an approximate formula (too complicated to reproduce here †) which is so close that its error is only 24 when $X = 10^9$. (According to Meissel, the number of primes less than 10^9 is exactly 50,847479.)

A. de Polignac ‡ has conjectured that every even number is the difference of two consecutive primes in infinitely many ways. Taking the even number to be 2, this means that there are infinitely many pairs of primes that are consecutive odd numbers, such as 5, 7; 11, 13; 17, 19; 29, 31; 41, 43; 59, 61; 71, 73. This conjecture has not been proved or disproved. As evidence in its favour, the Hoppenot–Kraïtchik table shows that the interval from $10^{12} - 10^4$ to 10^{12} contains fifteen such pairs,§ of which the largest is the pair $999999,999960 \pm 1$. Since $10^4/(12 \log 10)^2 = (3\cdot61912\ldots)^2$ $= 13\cdot097\ldots$, we may guess that the number of prime pairs between $X - x$ and X is approximately $x/(\log X)^2$.

It can be proved quite easily that the sum of the reciprocals of all the primes less than X increases without limit as X increases. If, however, we consider only the sum of the reciprocals of those primes less than X which differ by 2, then this sum remains bounded as X increases. This fact, due to Brun,

* De la Vallée Poussin, *Mémoires Couronnés de l'Académie Royale de Belgique*, 1889, vol. LIX, pp. 1—74.

† See the fascinating Introduction to D. N. Lehmer's *List of Prime Numbers from 1 to 10,006721*, Washington, 1914.

‡ *Nouvelles Annales de Math.*, 1849, vol. VIII, p. 428.

§ There are also twenty pairs in the interval from 10^{12} to $10^{12} + 10^4$.

shows that there are not "too many" primes which differ
by 2.

A somewhat similar conjecture is *Goldbach's Theorem*,
that every even number can be expressed as the sum of two
primes. Haussner has verified this for all even numbers up
to 10000, and others have verified it for small ranges of very
large numbers and for many isolated large numbers.* Vinogradoff † has proved that every sufficiently large odd number
is the sum of three primes, and Estermann ‡ has made precise
the statement that *almost all* even numbers are sums of two
primes.

MERSENNE'S NUMBERS

A curious assertion (only partially correct) about the prime
or composite character of numbers of the form $2^p - 1$ is to be
found in Mersenne's *Cogitata Physico-Mathematica*, published
in 1644. In the preface to that work a statement is made
about perfect numbers, which implies that the only values of
p not greater than 257 which make $2^p - 1$ prime are 1, 2, 3,
5, 7, 13, 17, 19, 31, 67, 127, and 257. Some years ago I gave
reasons for thinking that 67 was a misprint for 61. Until
1911, no error in this corrected statement was established,
and it was gradually verified for all except sixteen values of p.
In 1911 and 1914, however, R. E. Powers § discovered that
$2^{89} - 1$ and $2^{107} - 1$ are prime; and in 1922, M. Kraïtchik ‖
found $2^{257} - 1$ to be composite: three facts at variance with
Mersenne's statement.

The modern technique was established by Lucas ¶ in 1877,

* For the latest work on the verification of Goldbach's Theorem, see
Pipping, *Finska Vetenskaps Societeten, Commentationes Physico-Math.*,
1927, vol. IV, Nos. 4, 10, 25.

† *C. R. Acad. Sci., U.R.S.S.*, 1937, pp. 169—172.

‡ *Proceedings of the London Mathematical Society* (Second Series), 1938,
vol. XLIV, pp. 307—314.

§ *American Mathematical Monthly*, 1911, vol. XVIII, pp. 195—197.
Proceedings of the London Mathematical Society, 1919, Ser. 2, vol. XIII, p. 39.

‖ See *Sphinx*, 1931, p. 31.

¶ *American Journal of Mathematics*, 1878, vol. I, p. 316.

and used by him to verify Mersenne's assertion that $2^{127} - 1$

$$(= 170{,}141183{,}460469{,}231731{,}687303{,}715884{,}105727)$$

is prime. (This still remains the largest known prime, in spite of eight attempts to find a larger one.) Lucas considered the sequences

$$3,\ 7,\ 47,\ 2207,\ 4870847,\ \ldots,\ u_n,\ \ldots;$$
$$4,\ 14,\ 194,\ 37634,\ 1416317954,\ \ldots,\ v_n,\ \ldots;$$

in which each term is the square of the preceding term, diminished by 2. His rule is that $2^p - 1$ is prime if it divides u_{p-1} ($p = 4k - 1$) or v_{p-1} ($p = 4k + 1$). D. H. Lehmer * has recently shown that the sequence v_n could be used in both cases, and that $2^p - 1$ is composite if it fails to divide v_{p-1}. For instance, $2^{257} - 1$ is composite, since the division of v_{256} by $2^{257} - 1$ leaves a remainder †

21044,788566,116177,742020,115097,384196,442185,967503,-
553765,065760,419861,415332,100776.

The most recent results have supported Mersenne's conjecture. Lehmer and Powers,‡ respectively, have shown $2^{149} - 1$ and $2^{241} - 1$ to be composite. The present state of knowledge is as follows. §

$2^p - 1$ is known to be prime in thirteen cases :
$p = 1, 2, 3, 5, 7, 13, 17, 19, 31, 61, 89, 107, 127.$

The complete factorization is known in thirteen cases :
$p = 11, 23, 29, 37, 41, 43, 47, 53, 59, 67, 71, 73, 79.$

Two or more prime factors are known in five other cases :
$p = 113, 151, 179, 239, 251.$

One prime factor is known in eleven other cases :
$p = 83, 97, 131, 163, 173, 181, 191, 197, 211, 223, 233.$

The composite character has been established, although no factor is known, in eight cases :
$p = 101, 103, 109, 137, 139, 149, 241, 257.$

---

* *Sphinx*, 1931, p. 164. † *Sphinx*, 1931, p. 32.
‡ *Sphinx*, 1931, p. 163; 1935, p. 57.
§ Cf. the ninth edition of this book, p. 336, and R. C. Archibald, *Scripta Mathematica*, 1935, vol. III, pp. 112—119.

There remain six cases in which nothing is yet known :
$p = 157, 167, 193, 199, 227, 229.$

PERFECT NUMBERS *

The theory of *perfect numbers* depends directly on that of
Mersenne's Numbers. A number is said to be perfect if it
is equal to the sum of all its proper divisors. Thus 6
and 28 are perfect numbers, since $6 = 1 + 2 + 3$ and
$28 = 1 + 2 + 4 + 7 + 14.$ These numbers have had a
strong appeal for mystics, since the Creation took 6 days,
and there are 28 days in a lunar month.

Euclid proved that $2^{p-1}(2^p - 1)$ is perfect whenever $2^p - 1$
is prime. In fact, the divisors of $2^{p-1}(2^p - 1)$ (including
itself) are then 2^n and $2^n(2^p - 1)$, for $n = 0, 1, \ldots, p - 1$;
and we know that $1 + 2 + 2^2 + \ldots + 2^{p-1} = 2^p - 1.$

Euler showed that this formula includes all *even* perfect
numbers. The following simplified proof has been given
by Dickson.† Let $2^n q$ be perfect, where q is odd and $n > 0.$
Then $2^{n+1} q = (2^{n+1} - 1)s$, where s is the sum of all the divisors
of q. Thus $s = q + d$, where $d = q/(2^{n+1} - 1).$ Hence d
is a divisor of q, so that q and d are the only divisors of q.
Hence $d = 1$ and $q = 2^{n+1} - 1$ is a prime.

There is reason to believe—though a rigid demonstration
is wanting—that an odd number cannot be perfect; at any
rate no odd number less than 2,000000 can be perfect. According to J. J. Sylvester,‡ an odd perfect number must have at
least six distinct prime factors.

The values $p = 2, 3, 5, 7, 13, 17, 19, 31$ give the Mersenne
primes 3, 7, 31, 127, 8191, 131071, 524287, 2147483647, and

* On the theory of perfect numbers, see bibliographical references by
H. Brocard, *L'Intermédiaire des Mathématiciens*, Paris, 1895, vol. II, pp. 52—
54; and 1905, vol. XII, p. 19. The first volume of the second edition of the
French translation of this book contains (pp. 280—294) a summary of the
leading investigation on Perfect Numbers, as also some remarks on Amicable
Numbers. See also L. E. Dickson, *History of the Theory of Numbers*, vol. I,
Washington, 1919.

† *American Mathematical Monthly*, 1911, vol. XVIII, p. 109.
‡ *Collected Mathematical Papers*, 1912, vol. IV, p. 588.

the perfect numbers 6, 28, 496, 8128, 33550336, 8589869056, 137438691328, 2305843008139952128.   It is easy to show that the two final digits of an even perfect number are necessarily either 28 or (apart from 6 itself) 6 preceded by an *odd* digit. Of the twelve known perfect numbers, six end in 28, and the rest (after 6 itself) end in 96, 36, 56, 76, 16, respectively.

FERMAT'S THEOREM ON BINARY POWERS

Fermat enriched mathematics with a multitude of new propositions.   With one exception all these have been proved or are believed to be true.   This exception is his *theorem on binary powers*, in which he asserted that all numbers of the form $2^m + 1$, where $m = 2^n$, are primes,* but he added that, though he was convinced of the truth of this proposition, he could not obtain a valid demonstration.

It may be shown that $2^m + 1$ is composite if m is not a power of 2, but of course it does not follow that $2^m + 1$ is a prime if m is a power of 2, say 2^n.   As a matter of fact the theorem is not true.   In 1732 Euler † showed that if $n = 5$ the formula gives 4294,967297, which is equal to $641 \times 6,700417$: curiously enough, these factors can be deduced at once from Fermat's remark on the possible factors of numbers of the form $2^m \pm 1$, from which it may be shown that the prime factors (if any) of $2^{32} + 1$ must be primes of the form $64k + 1$.

Kraïtchik ‡ has shown how the divisibility of $2^{32} + 1$ by 641 may be verified without actual division. We have $641 = 2^4 + 5^4 = 1 + 5 . 2^7$, whence, in the finite arithmetic modulo 641,

$$2^7 \equiv - \tfrac{1}{5}, \ 2^8 \equiv - \tfrac{2}{5}, \ 2^{32} \equiv (- \tfrac{2}{5})^4 \equiv 2^4/5^4 \equiv - 1.$$

* Letter of Oct. 18, 1640, *Opera*, Toulouse, 1679, p. 162 : or Brassinne's *Précis*, p. 143.

† *Commentarii Academiae Scientiarum Petropolitanae*, Petrograd, 1738, vol. VI, p. 104; see also *Novi Comm. Acad. Sci. Petrop.*, Petrograd, 1764, vol. IX, p. 101 : or *Commentationes Arithmeticae Collectae*, Petrograd, 1849, vol. I, pp. 2, 357.

‡ *Théorie des Nombres*, vol. II, p. 221.

G. T. Bennett has suggested a variant of this proof, which has the advantage of giving both factors. Let $a = 2^7$ and $b = 5$, so that $a - b^3 = 3$ and $ab - b^4 = 3b = 2^4 - 1$. Then

$$2^{32} + 1 = 2^4 a^4 + 1 = (ab - b^4 + 1)a^4 + 1$$
$$= (ab + 1)\{a^4 - (ab - 1)(a^2 b^2 + 1)\}$$
$$= (ab + 1)(3a^3 + a^2 b^2 - ab + 1).$$

Let $F_n = 2^{2^n} + 1$, so that $F_0 = 3$, $F_1 = 5$, $F_2 = 17$, $F_3 = 257$, $F_4 = 65537$ (all primes) and $F_5 = 641 \times 6700417$. In 1880, F. Landry showed that $F_6 = 274177 \times 67{,}280421{,}310721$. In 1909, Morehead and Western proved that F_7 and F_8 are composite (although no factors have yet been found).[*] By that time, it was already known that F_9 is divisible by $37 . 2^{16} + 1$, F_{11} by $(39 . 2^{13} + 1)(119 . 2^{13} + 1)$, F_{12} by $(7 . 2^{14} + 1)(397 . 2^{16} + 1)(973 . 2^{16} + 1)$, F_{18} by $13 . 2^{20} + 1$, F_{23} by $5 . 2^{25} + 1$, F_{36} by $5 . 2^{39} + 1$, F_{38} by $3 . 2^{41} + 1$, and F_{73} by $5 . 2^{75} + 1$. (F_{73} is one of the largest numbers that have ever been investigated. Its digits are so numerous that, if it were printed in full with the type and number of pages used in this book, many more volumes would be required than are contained in all the public libraries in the world.) More recently, Kraïtchik showed that F_{15} is divisible by $579 . 2^{21} + 1$. Thus it may well be true that Fermat was *completely* wrong, *i.e.*, that F_n is in fact composite whenever $n > 4$.

FERMAT'S LAST THEOREM

I pass now to another assertion made by Fermat which hitherto has not been proved. This, which is sometimes known as *Fermat's Last Theorem*, is to the effect † that no in-

---

[*] For bibliographical references, see A. J. C. Cunningham and A. E. Western, *Transactions of the London Mathematical Society*, 1903, series 2, vol. I, p. 175; and J. C. Morehead and A. E. Western, *Bulletin of the American Mathematical Society*, 1909, vol. XVI, pp. 1—6.

† Fermat's enunciation will be found in his edition of *Diophantus*, Toulouse, 1670, bk. II, qu. 8, p. 61; or Brassinne's *Précis*, Paris, 1853, p. 53. For bibliographical references, see L. E. Dickson, *History of the Theory of Numbers*, Washington, 1920, vol. II, ch. 26; see also L. J. Mordell, *Fermat's Last Theorem*, Cambridge, 1921.

tegral values of x, y, z can be found to satisfy the equation $x^n + y^n = z^n$, if n is an integer greater than 2. This proposition has acquired extraordinary celebrity from the fact that no general demonstration of it has been given, but there is no reason to doubt that it is true.

Fermat seems to have discovered its truth first * for the case $n = 3$, and then for the case $n = 4$. His proof for the former of these cases is lost, but that for the latter is extant,† and a similar proof for the case of $n = 3$ was outlined by Euler.‡ These proofs depend upon showing that, if three integral values of x, y, z can be found which satisfy the equation, then it will be possible to find three other and smaller integers which also satisfy it : in this way finally we show that the equation must be satisfied by three values which obviously do not satisfy it. Thus no integral solution is possible. This method is inapplicable to the general case.

Fermat's discovery of the general theorem was made later. A proof can be given on the assumption that every number can be resolved into the product of powers of primes in only one way. The assumption is true of rational integers, but is not necessarily true for algebraic integers—an algebraic integer being defined as a root of an equation

$$x^n + a_1 x^{n-1} + \ldots + a_n = 0,$$

whose coefficients, a, are arithmetical integers; for instance, $a + b\sqrt{-m}$, where a, b, and m are arithmetical integers, is an algebraic integer. Thus, admitting the use of these generalized integers, 21 can be expressed in three ways as the product of primes, namely, of 3 and 7, or of $4 + \sqrt{-5}$ and $4 - \sqrt{-5}$, or of $1 + 2\sqrt{-5}$ and $1 - 2\sqrt{-5}$; and similarly, there are values of n for which Fermat's equation leads to expressions which can be factorized in more than one way. It is possible

* See a Letter from Fermat quoted in my *History of Mathematics*, London, chapter xv.

† Fermat's *Diophantus*, note on p. 339; or Brassinne's *Précis*, p. 127.

‡ Euler's *Algebra* (English trans. 1797), vol. II, chap. xv, p. 247: one point was overlooked by Euler, but the omission can be supplied.

that Fermat's argument rested on the above erroneous supposition, but this is an unsupported conjecture. At any rate he asserted definitely that he had a valid proof—*demonstratio mirabilis sane*—and the fact that no theorem on the subject which he stated he had proved has been subsequently shown to be false must weigh strongly in his favour; the more so because in making the one incorrect statement in his writings (namely, that about binary powers) he added that he could not obtain a satisfactory demonstration of it.

It must be remembered that Fermat was a mathematician of quite the first rank who had made a special study of the theory of numbers. The subject is in itself one of peculiar interest and elegance, but its conclusions have little practical importance, and for long it was studied by only a few mathematicians. This is the explanation of the fact that it took more than a century before some of the simpler results which Fermat had enunciated were proved, and thus it is not surprising that a proof of the theorem which he succeeded in establishing only towards the close of his life should involve great difficulties.

In 1823 Legendre * obtained a proof for the case of $n = 5$; in 1832 Lejeune Dirichlet † gave one for $n = 14$; and in 1840 Lamé and Lebesgue ‡ gave proofs for $n = 7$.

To prove the proposition when $n > 4$, obviously it is sufficient to confine ourselves to cases where n is a prime. In 1849, Kummer § proved it for all "regular" primes. (A prime p is said to be regular if it does not divide any of the numerators of the Bernoulli numbers ‖ $B_1, B_2, \ldots, B_{\frac{1}{2}(p-3)}$.)

* Reprinted in his *Théorie des Nombres*, Paris, 1830, vol. II, pp. 361—368: see also pp. 5, 6.

† *Crelle's Journal*, 1832, vol. IX, pp. 390—393.

‡ *Liouville's Journal*, 1841, vol. V, pp. 195—215, 276—279, 348—349.

§ References to Kummer's Memoirs are given by H. S. Vandiver, *Transactions of the American Mathematical Society*, 1929, vol. XXXI, pp. 613—642.

‖ The Bernoulli numbers appear in the series

$$\frac{x}{2} \cot \frac{x}{2} = 1 - \frac{B_1}{2!} x - \frac{B_2}{4!} x^4 - \frac{B_3}{6!} x^6 - \ldots$$

The values of the first eight are $\frac{1}{6}$, $\frac{1}{30}$, $\frac{1}{42}$, $\frac{1}{30}$, $\frac{5}{66}$, $\frac{691}{2730}$, $\frac{7}{6}$, $\frac{3617}{510}$.

Kummer found that 37, 59, 67, 101, 103, 131, 149, 157 are the only " irregular " primes less than 164, and H. S. Vandiver * found that 233, 257, 263, 271, 283, 293, 307, 311, 347, 353, 379, 401, 409, 421, 433, 461, 463, 467, 491, 523, 541, 547, 557, 577, 587, 593, 607 are the only irregular primes between 164 and 616. The theorem can, by other arguments,* be proved for these thirty-five cases. Other tests have been established ; for instance, A. Wieferich † has shown that if the equation is soluble in integers prime to n, where n is an odd prime, then $2^{n-1} - 1$ is divisible by n^2. This restricted problem has been pushed as far as $n = 41,000000$ and $250,000000$ by J. B. Rosser and D. H. Lehmer,‡ respectively. A prize § of 100,000 marks has been offered for a general proof, to be given before 2007. (Of course this is now worthless, on account of the German inflation.)

Even though Fermat's problem remains unsolved, it has been of great importance for the theory of numbers, because many of the modern methods have been developed in connection with it, and the theories which have arisen in this connection are perhaps more important than a proof of the theorem itself would have been. Naturally there has been much speculation as to how Fermat arrived at the result. Such of his proofs as are extant involve nothing more than elementary geometry and algebra, and indeed some of his arguments do not involve any symbols. This has led some writers to think that Fermat used none but elementary algebraic methods. This may be so, but the following remark, which I believe is not generally known, rather points to the opposite conclusion. He had proposed, as a problem to the English mathematicians, to show that there was only one integral solution of the equation $x^2 + 2 = y^3$: the solution evidently being $x = 5$, $y = 3$. On this he has a note ‖ to the

---

* *Duke Mathematical Journal*, 1937, vol. III, pp. 569—584.

† *Crelle's Journal*, 1909, vol. CXXXVI, pp. 293—302.

‡ *Bulletin of the American Mathematical Society*, 1940, vol. XLVI, p. 299.

§ *L'Intermédiaire des Mathématiciens*, vol. XV, pp. 217–218.

‖ Fermat's *Diophantus*, bk. VI, prop. 19, p. 320; or Brassinne's *Précis*, p. 122.

effect that there was no difficulty in finding a solution in
rational fractions, but that he had discovered an entirely new
method—*sane pulcherrima et subtilissima*—which enabled him
to solve such questions in integers. It was his intention to
write a work * on his researches in the theory of numbers, but
it was never completed, and we know but little of his methods
of analysis. I venture, however, to add my private suspicion
that continued fractions played a not unimportant part in his
researches, and as strengthening this conjecture I may note
that some of his more recondite results—such as the theorem
that a prime of the form $4n + 1$ is expressible as the sum of
two squares †—may be established with comparative ease by
properties of such fractions.

GALOIS ARITHMETICS ‡

In analysing the game of Nim (page 36), we considered the
numbers of counters in the various heaps, expressed in the
scale of 2, and added all the unit-digits, then all the next
digits, and so on, noting whether each sum was even or odd.
This process is essentially the same as writing the binary
numbers below one another, as in an ordinary addition-sum,
and adding them (in the scale of 2) *without carrying*. In other
words, we add each column of digits as in the finite arithmetic
modulo 2. The given numbers of counters form a " safe
combination " if the result is 0 (in every column), as in the
second of the following examples.

10	10
10	11
11	100
101	101
—	—
110	000

* Fermat's *Diophantus*, bk. IV, prop. 31, p. 181; or Brassinne's *Précis*,
p. 82.

† Fermat's *Diophantus*, bk. III, prop. 22, p. 127; or Brassinne's *Précis*,
p. 65.

‡ Cf. L. E. Dickson, *History of the Theory of Numbers*, vol. I, Washington,
1919, p. viii.

In Moore's " Nim_k," we write out the binary numbers as before, and add them without carrying, but in the scale of $k + 1$ instead of the scale of 2. The process is familiar in the addition of polynomials by the method of detached coefficients; the only new feature is that the coefficients (or " digits ") now belong to a finite arithmetic.

10	x
11	$x + 1$
100	x^2
110	$x^2 + x$
111	$x^2 + x + 1$
012 (mod 3)	$x + 2$

The notion of adding without carrying has many other applications. The entities which are added, not being ordinary numbers, may be called " marks." Their digits belong to a finite arithmetic whose modulus (previously denoted by $k + 1$) is most usefully taken to be a prime, p. The rules for svbtraction, and for multiplication by an ordinary number (of the finite arithmetic), are immediate consequences of the rule for addition, namely that the digits of each rank are added modulo p. If we restrict consideration to the p^n marks that have not more than n digits, these operations will not take us outside that field.

But the multiplication of one mark by another might increase the number of digits. In order to avoid this complication, we introduce a second modulus, namely a particular mark of $n + 1$ digits which is " prime " (or irreducible) in the sense of not being the product of two marks, each of more than one digit. (It is always possible to find such a " prime " mark.) Two marks are then regarded as identical if they differ by a multiple of this particular mark. For instance, if $p^n = 3^3$, we take the second modulus 1021, and a typical multiplication-sum proceeds as follows : $112 \times 21 \equiv 2210 + 112 \equiv 2022 \equiv 2022 + 1021 \equiv 10$. Division is possible too, since in fact every mark has a reciprocal.

Most properties of the ordinary finite arithmetics continue to hold in these " Galois Arithmetics." In the ordinary arithmetic modulo 7, every number except 0 is a power of 3, since $3^2 \equiv 2$, $3^3 \equiv 6$, $3^4 \equiv 4$, $3^5 \equiv 5$, and $3^6 \equiv 1$. Analogously, in the Galois arithmetic with moduli 2 and 1011 ($p^n = 2^3$), every mark except 0 is a power of 10, since $10^2 \equiv 100$, $10^3 \equiv 11$, $10^4 \equiv 110$, $10^5 \equiv 111$, $10^6 \equiv 101$, and $10^7 \equiv 1$. Again, in the arithmetic modulo 7 (or any other odd prime), just half the numbers other than 0 are squares. Thus $1^2 \equiv 6^2 \equiv 1$, $2^2 \equiv 5^2 \equiv 4$, and $3^2 \equiv 4^2 \equiv 2$ (mod 7). It is the same in any Galois arithmetic with $p > 2$. For instance, if $p^n = 3^2$ and the second modulus is 101, we have $1^2 \equiv 2^2 \equiv 1$, $10^2 \equiv 20^2 \equiv 2$, $11^2 \equiv 22^2 \equiv 20$, and $12^2 \equiv 21^2 \equiv 10$.

CHAPTER III

GEOMETRICAL RECREATIONS

In this chapter and the next one I propose to enumerate certain geometrical questions, puzzles, and games, the discussion of which will not involve necessarily any considerable use of algebra or arithmetic. Most of this chapter is devoted to questions which are of the nature of formal propositions : the next chapter contains a description of various amusements.

In accordance with the rule I laid down for myself in the preface, I exclude the detailed discussion of theorems which involve advanced mathematics. Moreover (with one or two exceptions) I exclude any mention of the numerous geometrical paradoxes which depend merely on the inability of the eye to compare correctly the dimensions of figures when their relative position is changed. This apparent deception does not involve the conscious reasoning powers, but rests on the inaccurate interpretation by the mind of the sensations derived through the eyes, and I do not consider such paradoxes as coming within the domain of mathematics.

GEOMETRICAL FALLACIES

Most educated Englishmen are acquainted with the series of logical propositions in geometry associated with the name of Euclid, but it is not known so generally that these propositions were supplemented originally by certain exercises. Of such exercises Euclid issued three series : two containing easy theorems or problems, and the third consisting of geometrical fallacies, the errors in which the student was required to find.

The collection of fallacies prepared by Euclid is lost, and

tradition has not preserved any record as to the nature of the
erroneous reasoning or conclusions; but, as an illustration of
such questions, I append a few demonstrations, leading to
obviously impossible results. Perhaps they may amuse anyone
to whom they are new. I leave the discovery of the errors to
the ingenuity of my readers.

First Fallacy.* *To prove that a right angle is equal to an angle
which is greater than a right angle.* Let *ABCD* be a rectangle.
From *A* draw a line *AE* outside the rectangle, equal to *AB* or
DC and making an acute angle with *AB*, as indicated in the

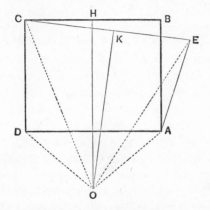

diagram. Bisect *CB* in *H*, and through *H* draw *HO* at right
angles to *CB*. Bisect *CE* in *K*, and through *K* draw *KO*
at right angles to *CE*. Since *CB* and *CE* are not parallel
the lines *HO* and *KO* will meet (say) at *O*. Join *OA*, *OE*,
OC, and *OD*.

The triangles *ODC* and *OAE* are equal in all respects.
For, since *KO* bisects *CE* and is perpendicular to it, we have
OC = *OE*. Similarly, since *HO* bisects *CB* and *DA* and is
perpendicular to them, we have *OD* = *OA*. Also, by construction, *DC* = *AE*. Therefore the three sides of the triangle

---

* I believe that this and the fourth of these fallacies were first published
in this book. They particularly interested Mr. C. L. Dodgson; see the
Lewis Carroll Picture Book, London, 1899, pp. 264, 266, where they appear
in the form in which I originally gave them.

ODC are equal respectively to the three sides of the triangle OAE. Hence, by Euc. I. 8, the triangles are equal; and therefore the angle ODC is equal to the angle OAE.

Again, since HO bisects DA and is perpendicular to it, we have the angle ODA equal to the angle OAD.

Hence the angle ADC (which is the difference of ODC and ODA) is equal to the angle DAE (which is the difference of OAE and OAD). But ADC is a right angle, and DAE is necessarily greater than a right angle. Thus the result is impossible.

Second Fallacy.* *To prove that a part of a line is equal to the whole line.* Let ABC be a triangle; and, to fix our ideas, let us suppose that the triangle is scalene, that the angle B

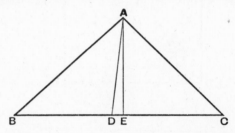

is acute, and that the angle A is greater than the angle C. From A draw AD making the angle BAD equal to the angle C, and cutting BC in D. From A draw AE perpendicular to BC.

The triangles ABC, ABD are equiangular; hence, by Euc. VI. 19,

$$\triangle ABC : \triangle ABD = AC^2 : AD^2.$$

Also the triangles ABC, ABD are of equal altitude; hence by Euc. VI. 1,

$$\triangle ABC : \triangle ABD = BC : BD,$$
$$\therefore AC^2 : AD^2 = BC : BD.$$
$$\therefore \frac{AC^2}{BC} = \frac{AD^2}{BD}.$$

* See a note by M. Coccoz in *L'Illustration*, Paris, Jan. 12, 1895.

Hence, by Euc. II. 13,

$$\frac{AB^2 + BC^2 - 2BC \cdot BE}{BC} = \frac{AB^2 + BD^2 - 2BD \cdot BE}{BD};$$

$$\therefore \frac{AB^2}{BC} + BC - 2BE = \frac{AB^2}{BD} + BD - 2BE.$$

$$\therefore \frac{AB^2}{BC} - BD = \frac{AB^2}{BD} - BC.$$

$$\therefore \frac{AB^2 - BC \cdot BD}{BC} = \frac{AB^2 - BC \cdot BD}{BD}.$$

$$\therefore BC = BD,$$

a result which is impossible.

Third Fallacy.* *To prove that the sum of the lengths of two sides of any triangle is equal to the length of the third side.*

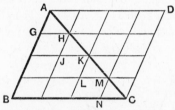

Let ABC be a triangle. Complete the parallelogram of which AB and BC are sides. Divide AB into $n + 1$ equal parts, and through the points so determined draw n lines parallel to BC. Similarly, divide BC into $n + 1$ equal parts, and through the points so determined draw n lines parallel to AB. The parallelogram $ABCD$ is thus divided into $(n + 1)^2$ equal and similar parallelograms.

I draw the figure for the case in which n is equal to 3, then, taking the parallelograms of which AC is a diagonal, as indicated in the diagram, we have

$$AB + BC = AG + HJ + KL + MN$$
$$+ GH + JK + LM + NC.$$

A similar relation is true however large n may be. Now let n increase indefinitely. Then the lines AG, GH, etc. will

* *The Canterbury Puzzles*, by H. E. Dudeney, London, 1907, pp. 26—28.

get smaller and smaller. Finally the points G, J, L, ... will approach indefinitely near the line AC, and ultimately will lie on it; when this is the case the sum of AG and GH will be equal to AH, and similarly for the other similar pairs of lines. Thus, ultimately,

$$AB + BC = AH + HK + KM + MC$$
$$= AC,$$

a result which is impossible.

Fourth Fallacy. *To prove that every triangle is isosceles.* Let ABC be any triangle. Bisect BC in D, and through D draw DO perpendicular to BC. Bisect the angle BAC by AO.

First. If DO and AO do not meet, then they are parallel. Therefore AO is at right angles to BC. Therefore $AB = AC$.

Second. If DO and AO meet, let them meet in O. Draw OE perpendicular to AC. Draw OF perpendicular to AB. Join OB, OC.

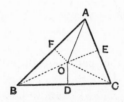

Let us begin by taking the case where O is inside the triangle, in which case E falls on AC and F on AB.

The triangles AOF and AOE are equal, since the side AO is common, angle $OAF =$ angle OAE, and angle $OFA =$ angle OEA. Hence $AF = AE$. Also, the triangles BOF and COE are equal. For since OD bisects BC at right angles, we have $OB = OC$; also, since the triangles AOF and AOE are equal, we have $OF = OE$; lastly, the angles at F and E are right angles. Therefore, by Euc. I. 47 and I. 8, the triangles BOF and COE are equal. Hence $FB = EC$.

Therefore $AF + FB = AE + EC$, that is, $AB = AC$.

The same demonstration will cover the case where DO and AO meet at D, as also the case where they meet outside BC but so near it that E and F fall on AC and AB and not on. AC and AB produced.

Next take the case where *DO* and *AO* meet outside the triangle, and *E* and *F* fall on *AC* and *AB* produced. Draw *OE* perpendicular to *AC* produced. Draw *OF* perpendicular to *AB* produced. Join *OB, OC*.

Following the same argument as before, from the equality of the triangles *AOF* and *AOE*, we obtain *AF = AE* ; and, from the equality of the triangles *BOF* and *COE*, we obtain *FB = EC*. Therefore *AF — FB = AE — EC*, that is, *AB = AC*.

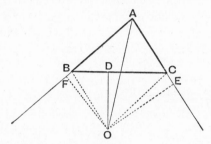

Thus in all cases, whether or not *DO* and *AO* meet, and whether they meet inside or outside the triangle, we have *AB = AC* : and therefore every triangle is isosceles, a result which is impossible.

Fifth Fallacy.* *To prove that π/4 is equal to π/3.* On the hypotenuse, *BC*, of an isosceles right-angled triangle, *DBC*, describe an equilateral triangle *ABC*, the vertex *A* being on the same side of the base as *D* is. On *CA* take a point *H* so that *CH = CD*. Bisect *BD* in *K*. Join *HK* and let it cut *CB* (produced) in *L*. Join *DL*. Bisect *DL* at *M*, and through *M* draw *MO* perpendicular to *DL*. Bisect *HL* at *N*, and through *N* draw *NO* perpendicular to *HL*. Since *DL* and *HL* intersect, therefore *MO* and *NO* will also intersect; moreover, since *BDC* is a right angle, *MO* and *NO* both slope away from *DC* and therefore they will meet on the side of *DL* remote from *A*. Join *OC, OD, OH, OL.*

* This ingenious fallacy is due to Captain Turton : it appeared for the first time in the third edition of this work.

G

The triangles *OMD* and *OML* are equal, hence $OD = OL$. Similarly the triangles *ONL* and *ONH* are equal, hence $OL = OH$. Therefore $OD = OH$. Now in the triangles *OCD* and *OCH*, we have $OD = OH$, $CD = CH$ (by construction), and *OC* common, hence (by Euc. I. 8) the angle *OCD* is equal to the angle *OCH*. Hence the angle *BCD* is equal to the angle *BCH*, that is, $\pi/4$ is equal to $\pi/3$, which is absurd.

Sixth Fallacy.* *To prove that, if two opposite sides of a quadrilateral are equal, the other two sides must be parallel.* Let *ABCD* be a quadrilateral such that *AB* is equal to *DC*. Bisect *AD* in *M*, and through *M* draw *MO* at right angles to *AD*. Bisect *BC* in *N*, and draw *NO* at right angles to *BC*.

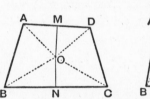 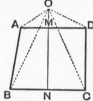

If *MO* and *NO* are parallel, then *AD* and *BC* (which are at right angles to them) are also parallel.

If *MO* and *NO* are not parallel, let them meet in *O*; then *O* must be either inside the quadrilateral as in the left-hand diagram or outside the quadrilateral as in the right-hand diagram. Join *OA*, *OB*, *OC*, *OD*.

Since *OM* bisects *AD* and is perpendicular to it, we have $OA = OD$, and the angle *OAM* equal to the angle *ODM*. Similarly $OB = OC$, and the angle *OBN* is equal to the angle *OCN*. Also by hypothesis $AB = DC$, hence, by Euc. I. 8, the triangles *OAB* and *ODC* are equal in all respects, and therefore the angle *AOB* is equal to the angle *DOC*.

Hence in the left-hand diagram the sum of the angle *AOM*, *AOB* is equal to the sum of the angles *DOM*, *DOC*; and in the right-hand diagram the difference of the angles *AOM*, *AOB* is equal to the difference of the angles *DOM*,

* *Mathesis*, October, 1893, series 2, vol. III, p. 224.

DOC; and therefore in both cases the angle *MOB* is equal to the angle *MOC*, *i.e. OM* (or *OM* produced) bisects the angle *BOC*. But the angle *NOB* is equal to the angle *NOC*, *i.e. ON* bisects the angle *BOC*; hence *OM* and *ON* coincide in direction. Therefore *AD* and *BC*, which are perpendicular to this direction, must be parallel. This result is not universally true, and the above demonstration contains a flaw.

Seventh Fallacy. The following argument is taken from a text-book on electricity, published in 1889 by two distinguished mathematicians, in which it was presented as valid. A given vector *OP* of length *l* can be resolved in an infinite number of ways into two vectors *OM*, *MP*, of lengths *l′*, *l″*, and we can make *l′/l″* have any value we please from nothing to infinity. Suppose that the system is referred to rectangular axes *Ox*, *Oy*; and that *OP*, *OM*, *MP* make respectively angles θ, θ', θ'' with *Ox*. Hence, by projection on *Oy* and on *Ox*, we have

$$l \sin \theta = l' \sin \theta' + l'' \sin \theta'',$$
$$l \cos \theta = l' \cos \theta' + l'' \cos \theta''.$$
$$\therefore \tan \theta = \frac{n \sin \theta' + \sin \theta''}{n \cos \theta' + \cos \theta''},$$

where $n = l'/l''$. This result is true whatever be the value of *n*. But *n* may have any value (*e.g.*, $n = \infty$, or $n = 0$), hence $\tan \theta = \tan \theta' = \tan \theta''$, which obviously is impossible.

Eighth Fallacy.* Here is a fallacious investigation of the value of π: it is founded on well-known quadratures. The area of the semi-ellipse bounded by the minor axis is (in the usual notation) equal to $\frac{1}{2}\pi ab$. If the centre is moved off to an indefinitely great distance along the major axis, the ellipse degenerates into a parabola, and therefore in this particular limiting position the area is equal to two-thirds of the circumscribing rectangle. But the first result is true whatever be the dimensions of the curve.

$$\therefore \tfrac{1}{2}\pi ab = \tfrac{2}{3}a \times 2b,$$
$$\therefore \pi = 8/3,$$

a result which obviously is untrue.

* This was communicated to me by Mr. R. Chartres.

Ninth Fallacy. *Every ellipse is a circle.* The focal distance of a point on an ellipse is given (in the usual notation) in terms of the abscissa by the formula $r = a + ex$. Hence $dr/dx = e$. From this it follows that r cannot have a maximum or minimum value. But the only closed curve in which the radius vector has not a maximum or minimum value is a circle. Hence, every ellipse is a circle, a result which obviously is untrue.

GEOMETRICAL PARADOXES

To the above examples I may add the following questions, which, though not exactly fallacious, lead to results which at a hasty glance appear impossible.

First Paradox. The first is a problem sent to me by Mr. W. Renton, to rotate a plane lamina (say, for instance, a sheet of paper) through four right angles so that the effect is equivalent to turning it through only one right angle.

Second Paradox. As in arithmetic, so in geometry, the theory of probability lends itself to numerous paradoxes. Here is a very simple illustration. A stick is broken at random into three pieces. It is possible to put them together into the shape of a triangle provided the length of the longest piece is less than the sum of the other two pieces (*cf.* Euc. I. 20), that is, provided the length of the longest piece is less than half the length of the stick. But the probability that a fragment of a stick shall be less than half the original length of the stick is 1/2. Hence the probability that a triangle can be constructed out of the three pieces into which the stick is broken would appear to be 1/2. This is not true, for actually the probability is 1/4.

Third Paradox. The following example illustrates how easily the eye may be deceived in demonstrations obtained by actually dissecting the figures and re-arranging the parts. In fact proofs by superposition should be regarded with considerable distrust unless they are supplemented by mathematical reasoning. The well-known proofs of the propositions Euclid I. 32 and Euclid I. 47 can be so supplemented and are valid.

On the other hand, as an illustration of how deceptive a non-mathematical proof may be, I here mention the familiar paradox that a square of paper, subdivided like a chessboard into 64 small squares, can be cut into four pieces which being put together form a figure containing 65 such small squares.* This is effected by cutting the original square into four pieces in the manner indicated by the thick lines in the first figure. If these four pieces are put together in the shape of a rectangle in the way shown in the second figure it will appear as if this rectangle contains 65 of the small squares.

This phenomenon, which in my experience non-mathematicians find perplexing, is due to the fact that the edges of

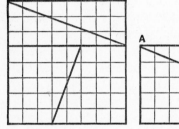

the four pieces of paper, which in the second figure lie along the diagonal AB, do not coincide exactly in direction. In reality they include a small lozenge or diamond-shaped figure, whose area is equal to that of one of the 64 small squares in the original square, but whose length AB is much greater than its breadth. The diagrams show that the angle between the two sides of this lozenge which meet at A is $\tan^{-1}\frac{2}{5} - \tan^{-1}\frac{3}{8}$, that is, is $\tan^{-1}\frac{1}{46}$, which is less than $1\frac{1}{4}°$. To enable the eye to distinguish so small an angle as this the dividing lines in the first figure would have to be cut with extreme accuracy and the pieces placed together with great care.

* I do not know who discovered this paradox. It is given in various books, but I cannot find an earlier reference to it than one in the *Zeitschrift für Mathematik und Physik*, Leipzig, 1868, vol. XIII, p. 162. Some similar paradoxes were given by Ozanam, 1803 edition, vol. I, p. 299.

This paradox depends upon the relation $5 \times 13 - 8^2 = 1$. Similar results can be obtained from the formulae

$$13 \times 34 - 21^2 = 1, \ 34 \times 89 - 55^2 = 1, \ldots;$$

or from the formulae

$$5^2 - 3 \times 8 = 1, \ 13^2 - 8 \times 21 = 1, \ 34^2 - 21 \times 55 = 1, \ldots.$$

These relations connect sets of three consecutive Fibonacci numbers (see p. 57). The general formula

$$b_n c_{n+1} - c_n b_{n+1} = (-1)^n$$

holds for two adjacent convergents to any continued fraction.

CONTINUED FRACTIONS AND LATTICE POINTS *

Consider a board, divided into a large number of equal squares, with small pegs sticking up at the vertices of all the squares. Let us regard the lines of pegs nearest to two

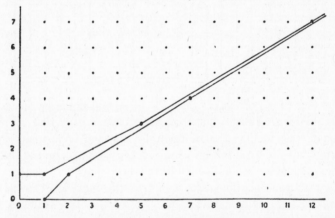

adjacent edges of the board as axes of co-ordinates, so that every peg has co-ordinates which are non-negative integers. If y/x is a fraction in its lowest terms, a stretched string joining the pegs $(0, 0)$ and (x, y) will not touch any other pegs. This string being fastened at (x, y), let us move it from the other end without allowing it to jump over any pegs. If the string is

* Cf. F. Klein, *Elementary Mathematics*, New York, 1932, p. 44.

stretched taut, with its free end at (1, 0), it will, in general, press against certain pegs (x_1, y_1), (x_2, y_2), ... between (1, 0) and (x, y). If its free end is held at (0, 1) instead of (1, 0), it will press against other pegs (x_1', y_1'), (x_2', y_2'), ... It can be proved that the fractions y_1/x_1, y_2/x_2, ... are alternate convergents to y/x, while y_1'/x_1', y_2'/x_2', ... are the remaining convergents. (The convergent y_r'/x_r' comes just before or just after y_r/x_r according as y/x is less or greater than 1.)

This construction shows clearly the manner in which the convergents approximate to y/x, alternately by excess and defect. The fraction y/x measures the *gradient* of the string in its original position. There is no difficulty in extending these notions to the case of a string of irrational gradient, firmly attached " at infinity." The case when the gradient is

$$\frac{1}{e-1} = \frac{1}{1} + \frac{1}{1} + \frac{1}{2} + \frac{1}{1} + \frac{1}{1} + \frac{1}{4} + \cdots$$

is shown above. Observe that the string from (1, 1) to (5, 3) touches (without " pressing against ") the peg (3, 2). The fraction $\frac{2}{3}$ is one of the *intermediate convergents* which, together with the ordinary or *principal* convergents ($\frac{0}{1}$, $\frac{1}{1}$, $\frac{1}{2}$, $\frac{3}{5}$, $\frac{4}{7}$, $\frac{7}{12}$, ...), make up the set of fractions of best approximation.

If b_{n-1}/c_{n-1}, b_n/c_n, b_{n+1}/c_{n+1} are three consecutive (principal) convergents to any continued fraction, we know that

$$b_n/c_n = (b_{n+1} - b_{n-1})/(c_{n+1} - c_{n-1}).$$

Geometrically, this means that the line from (0, 0) to (c_n, b_n) is parallel to the line from (c_{n-1}, b_{n-1}) to (c_{n+1}, b_{n+1}).

GEOMETRICAL DISSECTIONS

Problems requiring the division by straight lines of a given plane rectilinear figure into pieces which can be put together in some other assigned form are well known. A class of geometrical recreations is concerned with such constructions.

Pythagorean Extension. A familiar instance is found in many text-books in a dissection proof of the Pythagorean property of a right-angled triangle.   In fact, however, if we are given any two squares we can always by three cuts divide them into five pieces which can be put together to make a square. There are various solutions.   Here are two which answer the purpose.*

The first of these is as follows : Place the larger and smaller squares AG and CE side by side as in figure i below, and take AB equal to CD.   Then a cut BH and a cut BE (*i.e.* a cut BJ on the larger square and another cut JE on the smaller square) will divide the squares into five pieces which can be put together to make one square of which BH and BE are sides.

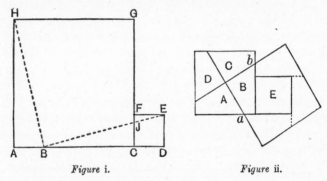

Figure i.   *Figure* ii.

A more symmetrical, though less simple, five-part solution (made up of the smaller square together with a four-part division of the larger square) can be effected as follows.   Place the larger square (denoted by the letters A, B, C, D) next the smaller square (denoted by E), as in figure ii, with their bases in the same line.   Bisect this line in one point a, and on their common side take another point b whose distance above their bases is half the sum of their sides.   Through these points draw lines perpendicular to each other, crossing in the centre of the larger square, and terminating in its sides.   This divides the larger square into four equal parts A, B, C, D.   Produce the two lines drawn through a and b for half their length

* H. Perigal, *Messenger of Mathematics*, 1873, vol. II, N.S., pp. 103—106; H. E. Dudeney, *Amusements*, London, 1917, p. 32.

beyond the common base and side of the squares, and through their extremities draw two other lines perpendicular to them. These four lines will form another square inclosing the small square within four segments equal and similar to the four quarters of the larger of the given squares, and consequently equal in area to the two together.

Montucla's Dissection. Demonstrations of a few similar propositions had long been current, but towards the close of the eighteenth century attention was recalled to this kind of solution by Montucla, who proposed and solved the problem of dividing a rectangle so that the parts could be put together in the form of a square; he also solved the converse problem. Later, other solutions of this problem were given by P. Busschop and de Coatpont who made respectively eight-part and seven-part dissections. The former also had constructions for making a square from a five-part division of a regular hexagon, and from a seven-part division of a regular pentagon.*

Polygonal Dissections. The more general problem of the dissection of a given polygon of any number of sides, and the rearrangement of the parts in the form of another polygon of equal area, had been raised by Bolyai, and a method of solution indicated by Gerwien. The question continued to attract occasional attention. In particular a solution for the case of a polygon and a triangle was given by Euzet in 1854, and the wider problem of two polygons was discussed by E. Guitel in 1895, by E. Holst in 1896,† and more recently by A. Mineur.‡

Consider first the dissection of a given triangle to form a rectangle of given base. In figure iii, a line *DE*, parallel to the

* G. G. F. Montucla, Ozanam's *Récréations Mathématiques*, 1803, English edition, vol. I, pp. 292—298; 1840 edition, pp. 127—129; Paul Busschop, *Nouvelle Correspondance Mathématique*, Brussels, 1875, vol. II, p. 83; de Coatpont, *ibid.*, 1876, vol. III, p. 116.

† P. Gerwien, *Crelle's Journal*, 1833, p. 228; M. Euzet, *Nouvelles Annales de Mathématiques*, 1854, vol. XIII, pp. 114—115; E. Guitel, *Association Française pour l'Avancement des Sciences*, 1895, pp. 264—267; E. Holst, *L'Intermédiaire des Mathématiciens*, 1896, vol. III, pp. 91—92.

‡ See *Mathesis*, 1931, pp. 150—152. The following treatment is due to Michael Goldberg.

base *BC* of the given triangle *ABC* and bisecting the sides, cuts the triangle into two parts which may be assembled into a parallelogram *BCFD*. Now with *B* as centre and with the

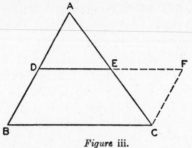

Figure iii.

given base as radius draw an arc. Make a cut *CH* tangent to this arc and a cut *BG* perpendicular to *CH*. The point *G* may fall inside the parallelogram, as in figure iv, or outside, as in

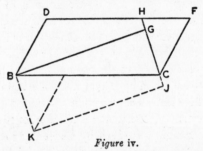

Figure iv.

figure v. In the latter case, locate *J* (on *CH*) so that *CJ = HG*, and make the cut *JL* parallel to *BG*. Then the pieces may be

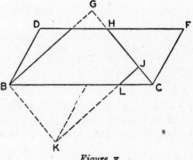

Figure v.

assembled into the desired rectangle $BGJK$. If the base BG is too long or too short to follow this procedure directly, it will be necessary first to change the proportions of the parallelogram $BCFD$ by cutting it into three pieces and rearranging these as in figure vi (where $E'F = BC' \geqslant \frac{1}{2}BC$). Of course, if the

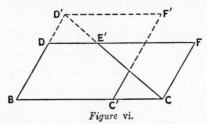

Figure vi.

base of the rectangle had been chosen to be the side of the square equivalent to the triangle, the given triangle would have been converted into a square.

Every polygon can be cut into triangles by drawing a sufficient number of diagonals. Therefore every polygon can be transformed into a square or rectangle by transforming the component triangles into rectangles all having the same base and then stacking the rectangles into a column.

We can always use a rectangle as an intermediate stage in the transformation of one polygon into another. Given the dissections which transform the given polygon and the desired polygon each into the same rectangle, we go from the given polygon to the rectangle by using the first transformation and then to the desired polygon by reversing the second transformation.

Minimum Dissections. The above-mentioned writers aimed only at finding a solution, and did not in general trouble themselves with considering the smallest number of pieces required. In 1905, the special cases of a four-part dissection of a pair of triangles, a four-part dissection of a triangle and parallelogram, and dissections of a pair of parallelograms were given by H. M. Taylor,* and he recognized the desirability of finding the smallest necessary number of cuts.

* *Messenger of Mathematics*, vol. xxxv, pp. 81—101.

Henceforth the explicit determination of the number of pieces in which a figure has to be cut to give a solution was regarded as an essential feature of the problem, and it is accepted that that solution is to be preferred in which the number of pieces is smallest. I have no doubt that Taylor's solutions do in fact give the minimum number of pieces required in those cases.

Puzzle Dissections. Of late years H. E. Dudeney has propounded various ingenious puzzles of this kind, in all cases the number of parts being specified.* His reputation has served to attract attention to this class of problems. As illustrating his results and as geometrical recreations of this

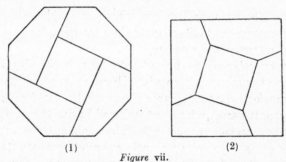

(1)   (2)

Figure vii.

type, I pick out his problems, (*a*) to divide, by two straight lines, a Greek cross, that is, one made up of five equal squares, into four pieces all of the same shape and size which can be put together to make a square; (*b*) to divide an isosceles right-angled triangle into four pieces which can be put together to make a Greek cross; (*c*) to divide a regular pentagon into six pieces which can be put together to make a square; (*d*) to divide an equilateral triangle into four pieces which can be put together to make a square. The reader interested in the subject will like to compare Dudeney's solution of the last question with that given by Taylor already mentioned, and that by Macaulay referred to below.

* For instance, see his *Amusements in Mathematics*, London, 1917, p. 27 *et seq.*

A. H. Wheeler has divided a regular pentagon into six pieces which can be put together to make an equilateral triangle; and J. Travers * has divided a regular octagon into five pieces which can be put together to make a square. (See figure vii.)

Macaulay's Four-part Dissections. The theory of four-part dissections of pairs of rectilinear figures of equal area has been discussed by W. H. Macaulay.† He has treated four-part dissections of pairs of triangles, of a triangle and a parallelogram, of pairs of quadrilaterals, of pairs of pentagons each with two sides equal and parallel, and of pairs of certain related hexagons. His results are projective and all of them are deducible from his hexagon dissections. This is an interesting generalization.

Dissecting a Square into Different Squares. Z. Moroń ‡ has observed that nine different squares can be fitted together to make a rectangle 32 × 33. A general theory of such arrangements has been developed,§ whereby W. T. Tutte has solved the problem of fitting together 26 different squares to make a *square*.

Volume Dissections. It is natural to ask whether every polyhedral solid can be divided, by a finite number of plane cuts, into pieces which will fit together to form any other polyhedral solid of the same volume. The answer is No; it was proved by M. Dehn ‖ that it is impossible to transform any tetrahedron by dissections into a prism. This annihilates any hopes for a general method of volume dissections analogous to polygonal dissections, although special volume dissections are quite possible.

The Duplication of the Cube. Here is a variant of the " Delian Problem " (which we shall consider in Chapter XII) :

---

* *Education Outlook*, 1933, p. 145.

† *Mathematical Gazette*, 1914, vol. VII, p. 381; vol. VIII, 1915, pp. 72, 109; *Messenger of Mathematics*, vol. XLVIII, 1919, p. 159; vol. XLIX, 1919, p. 111.

‡ *Przeglad Mat.-Fiz.*, 1925, vol. III, pp. 152—153.

§ By R. L. Brooks, C. A. B. Smith, A. H. Stone, and W. T. Tutte, *Duke Mathematical Journal*, 1940, vol. VI.

‖ *Nachr. der k. Gesellschaft der Wissensch. zu Göttingen*, 1900.

given a line of length $2^{1/3}$ (or $\sqrt[3]{2}$), divide two cubes of unit edge, by plane cuts, into pieces which can be assembled into a single cube. This problem can be solved by two applications of the transformation of a given rectangle into a rectangle of given base. The " minimum " dissection is obtained by using the method of figure vi, rather than that of figure iv.

First place the two equal cubes together to form a square prism $2 \times 1 \times 1$. Then mark on one of the rectangular faces (2×1) the cuts necessary to transform it into a rectangle of base $2^{1/3}$, which is equal to the edge of the duplicated cube. Through these lines pass planes perpendicular to this face, cutting the prism into three parts.

Assemble these parts to form the new prism $2^{1/3} \times 2^{2/3} \times 1$. Then, on either of the faces $2^{2/3} \times 1$, mark the cuts necessary to transform this rectangle into a square of side $2^{1/3}$. Through these lines pass planes perpendicular to this face, and assemble the three parts into the desired cube. The original prism $2 \times 1 \times 1$ has been divided into seven irregular solids by these cuts. If the pieces are disarranged, the task of assembling them to form the cube or the prism is not an easy puzzle.

This problem was proposed by W. F. Cheney, Jr., and solved thus by A. H. Wheeler.*

CYCLOTOMY

At the age of nineteen, Gauss † proved that the solution of the " cyclotomic equation " $x^p = 1$, where p is a prime, can be reduced to the solution of a succession of quadratic equations if, and only if, $p - 1$ is a power of 2. So far as we know, the only such primes (greater than 2) are the first five Fermat Numbers : 3, 5, 17, 257, 65537 (see page 69). Since the roots of the cyclotomic equation are

$$\cos (2r\pi/p) + i \sin (2r\pi/p) \quad (r = 0, 1, \ldots, p-1),$$

it follows that a regular n-gon, where n is odd, can be drawn by

* American Mathematical Monthly, 1935, vol. XLII, p. 509.
† Disquisitiones Arithmeticae, 1801.

a Euclidean construction (*i.e.* with ruler and compasses) if, and only if, n is such a prime, or a product of several such primes without repetition. It is sufficient to consider odd values of n, since the construction of a $(2^k n)$-gon involves that of an n-gon followed by k angle-bisections.

If we assume that all Fermat Numbers after F_4 are composite, it follows * that n must be a divisor of $3 . 5 . 17 . 257 . 65537 = 2^{32} - 1 = 4294,967295$. If a polygon with a larger odd number of sides can be drawn with ruler and compasses, this larger number must have at least 309 digits, since the first Fermat Number whose composite character is in doubt is F_{10} ($= 2^{1024} + 1$).

Constructions for the triangle and pentagon are familiar. A construction for the 15-gon follows immediately, since $\frac{4}{5}\pi - \frac{2}{3}\pi = \frac{2}{15}\pi$; you merely have to inscribe in one circle both a triangle and a pentagon. The following construction for the 17-gon is due to H. W. Richmond, who gave also an analogous construction for the pentagon to compare with it.

The problem is to inscribe, in a given circle, a regular 17-gon with one vertex at P_0 (see figure viii). Let OB be a radius,

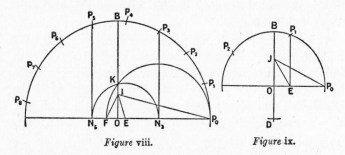

Figure viii.   *Figure* ix.

perpendicular to the diameter through P_0. Find a point I on OB so that $OI = \frac{1}{4}OB$. Join IP_0, and find points E, F on OP_0 so that angle $OIE = \frac{1}{4}OIP_0$ and angle $FIE = \frac{1}{4}\pi$. Let the circle on FP_0 as diameter cut OB in K, and let the circle with centre E and radius EK cut OP_0 in N_3 (between O and P_0)

* Kraïtchik, *La Mathématique des Jeux*, Brussels, 1930, p. 99.

and N_5. Let lines N_3P_3, N_5P_5, parallel to OB, cut the original circle in P_3, P_5. Then the arcs P_0P_3, P_0P_5 will be $\frac{3}{17}$ and $\frac{5}{17}$ of the circumference.

The proof * involves repeated application of the principle that the roots of the equation $x^2 + 2x \cot 2C = 1$ are $\tan C$ and $-\cot C$.

For the pentagon † (figure ix), define B as before, bisect OB at J, and find E on OP_0 so that JE bisects the angle OJP_0. If the line through E parallel to OB cuts the circle in P_1 the arc P_0P_1 will be $\frac{1}{5}$ of the circumference.

Constructions for polygons of 51, 85 and 255 sides follow immediately ; so do constructions for polygons whose numbers of sides are these numbers multiplied by any power of 2.

COMPASS PROBLEMS

It is well known that Euclid in his *Elements* confined his constructions to those which could be made with ungraduated rulers and compasses. The use of a ruler is, however, unnecessary.‡ Mascheroni § established a connected series of propositions by constructions made with compasses alone. Of course, the logical sequence is very different from that with which we are familiar.

As an instance which will illustrate the subject, I select the problem to find a point midway between two given points A and B. Of this fundamental proposition Mascheroni gave five solutions (prop. 66). Here are two of them : they rest on the assumption that we can draw a semicircle whose centre and one extremity are given, a result he had previously established.

* *Quarterly Journal of Mathematics*, 1893, vol. XXVI, p. 206.

† A slightly simpler construction for the pentagon has been suggested by H. E. Dudeney, *Amusements in Mathematics*, p. 38. With centre J and radius JP_0, draw an arc to cut BO (produced) in D. Then an arc with centre P_0 and radius P_0D will cut the original circle in P_1.

‡ Michael Goldberg, *School Science and Mathematics*, 1925, vol. XXV, pp. 961—965.

§ His work was published at Pavia in 1797. However, it has recently become known that he was largely anticipated by G. Mohr, whose *Euclides Danicus* was published at Amsterdam in 1672 (and at Copenhagen in 1928).

In each case the demonstration is straightforward. Other solutions of this proposition have been given, some of which evade the use of a semicircle.

One of his constructions is as follows. With B as centre, and a radius BA, describe a semicircle of which A and C are the extremities. With centres A and C, and radii AB and CA, describe circles which cut in P and Q. With centres P and Q, and a radius equal to AB, describe circles. These will cut in a point midway between A and B.

Here is another of his solutions, which for some purposes he preferred. With B as centre, and radius BA, describe a semicircle of which A and C are the extremities. With A and C as centres, and a radius equal to AB, describe circles which cut the semicircle in H and K respectively. With A and C as centres, and a radius equal to AC, describe circles which cut the last-mentioned circles (above AC) in Q and P respectively. With centres P and C, and radii PA and PQ, describe circles. These will cut in a point midway between A and B.

Numerous geometrical recreations of this kind can be made by any one, for all that is necessary is to select at random one of Euclid's propositions, and see how it can be established by using only circles. As instances, I select the construction on a given line of a triangle similar to a given triangle (prop. 125); and the construction of a regular pentagon of given dimensions (prop. 137). Whatever be the solution obtained, it is always interesting to turn to Mascheroni's book, and see how the question is tackled there.

THE FIVE DISC PROBLEM

The problem of completely covering a fixed red circular space by placing over it, one at a time, five smaller equal circular tin discs is familiar to frequenters of English fairs. Its effectiveness depends on making the tin discs as small as possible, and therefore leads to the interesting geometrical question of finding the size of the smallest tin discs which can be used for the purpose.

The problem is soluble if the radius of each tin disc is just greater than three-fifths of the radius of the red circle. Of course, in a show the visitor is not allowed to move the discs when once he has put them down, and it is only rarely, very rarely, that he succeeds empirically in placing them correctly.

The rule works out thus. If O is the centre of the red circle, a its radius, and AOB a diameter of it, we take on OA a point P such that approximately $OP = a/40$. We then place the first tin disc with its centre on OB, and so that P is on its edge : suppose that its edge meets the edge of the red circle in C and C', points on opposite sides of AB. Place the next two discs so that in each case AP is a chord of the disc. Suppose that these discs meet the edge of the red circle in D and D' respectively, C and D being on the same side of AB. Then if we place the two remaining discs so that CD and $C'D'$ are chords of them, the problem will be solved. The minimum discs are not obtained, as one might at first guess, by the overlapping of five discs placed at the vertices of an inscribed pentagon.

In practice and for simplicity it is desirable to make the tin discs a trifle larger than the theory requires, and to treat P as coincident with O.

The mathematical discussion on this problem is too technical and long to insert here. Probably a bare statement of the results such as is given above is all that most readers will want. Should closer approximations be desired, here they are.* If the radius of the red circle be taken as one foot, the critical radius for the discs, below which the problem is impossible, is ·609418 foot. Also $OP = ·028545$ foot, hence O lies very near but not quite on the circumference of the first disc which is put down. If three of the discs are placed so that their edges pass through O, the radius of each of them must exceed ·6099578 foot, a length practically indistinguishable from that of the radius of the minimum disc. If the discs are

* See *Solutions of Numerical Functional Equations*, by E. H. Neville, *Proceedings of the London Mathematical Society*, 1915, second series, vol. XIV, pp. 308—326.

put with their centres at the vertices of an inscribed pentagon and their edges passing through O, the radius of each of them must exceed ·6180340 foot. It follows that unless the discs are cut with extreme accuracy the problem may be solved by making the circumference of each disc pass through O; the possibility of using this inaccurate rule is a serious defect in the problem when used as the foundation of a puzzle.

I believe that the discs used in fairs are generally large enough to allow of the employment of the inaccurate rule, though even then it is safer to use the correct method. In an example made for myself I put a minute faint mark near the centre of the red circle but just far enough away to ensure failure for those who make that point lie on the edge of each disc. Notwithstanding their neglect or ignorance of the correct rule showmen seem to find that the game is profitable, and obviously this is an excellent test of its merits from their point of view.

BESICOVITCH'S MINIMAL PROBLEM

Here is an unsolved problem about covering an area. The *diameter* of any figure may be defined as the longest straight line that can be drawn so as to join two points of the figure. Besicovitch's problem is the determination of *the plane lamina of least area which, when suitably oriented, will cover any given plane figure of unit diameter*.

A circle of unit diameter is too small, since, although it will cover a square of unit diagonal, it will not cover an equilateral triangle of unit side. On the other hand, a square of unit side is unnecessarily large. Thus the required area is greater than $\frac{1}{4}\pi$ but less than 1. Its precise value, and the shape, have never been determined. Of course, there is no reason to expect any kind of symmetry.

KAKEYA'S MINIMAL PROBLEM

A somewhat similar problem * is the determination of the least area swept over by a straight line of unit length which is

* S. Kakeya, *Tôhoku Science Reports*, 1917, vol. VI, pp. 71—78; G. D. Birkhoff, *The Origin, Nature, and Influence of Relativity*, 1925, p. 4.

reversed in direction by a continuous motion during which it takes every possible orientation in the plane. Kakeya's problem had assumed the proportions of a famous unsolved problem although its complete solution was published only ten years after it was proposed. Osgood and Kubota suggested the deltoid (or three-cusped hypocycloid) as a possible solution, the area in this case being just half that of the circle of unit diameter. (See figure x.)

Besicovitch showed * that there is no smallest area, that the area can be made as small as we please ! This astounding fact is difficult to believe, so I proceed to give a very brief outline of his elegant demonstration.

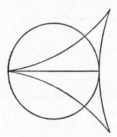

Figure x.

Consider a right-angled isosceles triangle whose hypotenuse is of length 2. Then it is obvious that the line of unit length can be rotated continuously through a right angle within this triangle of unit area. Besicovitch cuts up the triangle into a large number of small pieces, certain sets of which he shifts by translation, making them overlap. He thus obtains a number of regions, of rather complicated shape, in each of which the line can be rotated through a definite small angle. On account of the overlapping, the sum of the areas of these regions is less than $1/k$ for any value of k, previously assigned. He then shows how the line may be moved from each one of these regions into the next in such a way that the total area swept out in such processes can be

* A. S. Besicovitch, *Mathematische Zeitschrift*, 1928, vol. XXVII, p. 312.

made as small as we please. Finally, since the given line has
been moved continuously through a right angle, we can just
as readily repeat the process through another right angle
(thus reversing the direction of the line) and still make the
total area as small as we please.

PHYSICAL CONFIGURATION OF A COUNTRY

The theory of the representation of the physical configuration
of a country by means of lines drawn on a map was discussed
by Cayley and Clerk Maxwell.* They showed that a certain
relation exists between the number of hills, dales, passes, etc.
which can co-exist on the earth or on an island. I proceed to
give a summary of their nomenclature and conclusions.

All places whose heights above the mean sea level are equal
are on the same level. The locus of such points on a map is
indicated by a *contour-line*. Roughly speaking, an island is
bounded by a contour-line. It is usual to draw the successive
contour-lines on a map so that the difference between the
heights of any two successive lines is the same, and thus the
closer the contour-lines the steeper is the slope; but the
heights are measured dynamically by the amount of work to
be done to go from one level to the other, and not by linear
distances.

A contour-line in general will be a closed curve. This
curve may enclose a region of elevation : if two such regions
meet at a point, that point will be a crunode (*i.e.* a real double
point) on the contour-line through it, and such a point is
called a *pass*. The contour-line may enclose a region of depression : if two such regions meet at a point, that point will
be a crunode on the contour-line through it, and such a
point is called a *fork* or bar. As the heights of the corresponding level surfaces become greater, the areas of the regions

* Cayley on ' Contour and Slope Lines,' *Philosophical Magazine*, London,
October, 1859, series 4, vol. xviii, pp. 264—268; *Collected Works*, vol. iv,
pp. 108—111. J. Clerk Maxwell on ' Hills and Dales,' *Philosophical Magazine*,
December, 1870, series 4, vol. xi, pp. 421—427; *Collected Works*, vol. ii,
pp. 233—240.

of elevation become smaller, and at last become reduced to points : these points are the *summits* of the corresponding mountains. Similarly as the level surface sinks the regions of depression contract, and at last are reduced to points : these points are the *bottoms*, or immits, of the corresponding valleys.

Lines drawn so as to be everywhere at right angles to the contour-lines are called *lines of slope*. If we go up a line of slope generally we shall reach a summit, and if we go down such a line generally we shall reach a bottom : we may come, however, in particular cases either to a pass or to a fork. Districts whose lines of slope run to the same summit are *hills*. Those whose lines of slope run to the same bottom are *dales*. A *watershed* is the line of slope from a summit to a pass or a fork, and it separates two dales. A *watercourse* is the line of slope from a pass or a fork to a bottom, and it separates two hills.

If $n + 1$ regions of elevation or of depression meet at a point, the point is a multiple point on the contour-line drawn through it ; such a point is called a pass or a fork of the nth order, and must be counted as n separate passes (or forks). If one region of depression meets another in several places at once, one of these must be taken as a fork and the rest as passes.

Having now a definite geographical terminology we can apply geometrical propositions to the subject. Let h be the number of hills on the earth (or an island), then there will be also h summits ; let d be the number of dales, then there will be also d bottoms ; let p be the whole number of passes, p_1 that of single passes, p_2 of double passes, and so on ; let f be the whole number of forks, f_1 that of single forks, f_2 of double forks, and so on ; let w be the number of watercourses, then there will be also w watersheds. Hence, by the theorems of Cauchy and Euler,

$$h = 1 + p_1 + 2p_2 + \ldots,$$
$$d = 1 + f_1 + 2f_2 + \ldots,$$
and
$$w = 2(p_1 + f_1) + 3(p_2 + f_2) + \ldots$$

ADDENDUM

Note. Page 84. The required rotation of the lamina can be effected thus. Suppose that the result is to be equivalent to turning it through a right angle about a point O. Describe on the lamina a square $OABC$. Rotate the lamina successively through two right angles about the diagonal OB as axis and through two right angles about the side OA as axis, and the required result will be attained.

Note. Page 93. The sides of Tutte's twenty-six squares are: 1, 5, 7, 11, 20, 27, 34, 41, 42, 43, 44, 61, 85, 95, 108, 113, 118, 123, 136, 168, 172, 183, 194, 205, 209, 231. These make a single square of side 608. To solve this unusual jigsaw puzzle, use the packer's rule of placing the largest parts first. The arrangement is not quite unique, since certain blocks of squares form rectangles which can be turned around or reflected.

CHAPTER IV

GEOMETRICAL RECREATIONS (*continued*)

LEAVING now the question of formal geometrical propositions, I proceed to enumerate a few games or puzzles which
depend mainly on the relative position of things, but I postpone
to Chapter X the discussion of such amusements of this
kind as necessitate any considerable use of arithmetic or
algebra. Some writers regard draughts, solitaire, chess, and
such-like games as subjects for geometrical treatment in the
same way as they treat dominoes, backgammon, and games
with dice in connection with arithmetic : but these discussions
require too many artificial assumptions to correspond with the
games as actually played or to be interesting.

The amusements to which I refer are of a more trivial
description, and it is possible that a mathematician may like to
omit this chapter. In some cases it is difficult to say whether
they should be classified as mainly arithmetical or geometrical,
but the point is of no importance.

STATICAL GAMES OF POSITION

Of the innumerable statical games involving geometry of
position I shall mention only three or four.

Three-in-a-row. First, I may mention the games of three-
in-a-row, of which noughts and crosses, one form of merrilees,
and go-bang are well-known examples. These games are
played on a board—generally in the form of a square containing n^2 small squares or cells. The common practice is for
one player to place a white counter or piece or to make a cross
on each small square or cell which he occupies : his opponent
similarly uses black counters or pieces or makes a nought on
each cell which he occupies. Whoever first gets three (or any

other assigned number) of his pieces in three adjacent cells and in a straight line wins. There is no difficulty in giving the complete analysis for boards of 9 cells and of 16 cells : but it is lengthy, and not particularly interesting. Most of these games were known to the ancients,* and it is for that reason I mention them here.

Three-in-a-row. Extension. I may, however, add an elegant but difficult extension which has not previously found its way, so far as I am aware, into any book of mathematical recreations. The problem is to place n counters on a plane so as to form as many rows as possible, each of which shall contain three, and only three, counters.†

It is easy to arrange the counters in a number of rows equal to the integral part of $(n-1)^2/8$. This can be effected by the following construction. Let P be any point on a cubic. Let the tangent at P cut the curve again in Q. Let the tangent at Q cut the curve in A. Let PA cut the curve in B, QB cut it in C, PC cut it in D, QD cut it in E, and so on. Then the counters must be placed at the points $P, Q, A, B. \ldots$ Thus 9 counters can be placed in 8 such rows ; 10 counters in 10 rows ; 15 counters in 24 rows ; 81 counters in 800 rows ; and so on.

Sylvester found that, by a suitable choice of the initial point P, the number of rows can be increased to the integral part of $(n-1)(n-2)/6$. Thus 9 counters can be arranged in 9 rows ; 10 counters in 12 rows ; 15 counters in 30 rows ; 81 counters in 1053 rows ; and so on.

These, however, are inferior limits, and may be exceeded— for instance, Sylvester stated that 9 counters can be placed in 10 rows, each containing three counters ; I do not know how he placed them, but one way of so arranging them is by putting them at points whose co-ordinates are (2, 0), (2, 2), (2, 4), (4, 0), (4, 2), (4, 4), (0, 0), (3, 2), (6, 4) ; another way

---

* Becq de Fouquières, *Les Jeux des Anciens*, second edition, Paris, 1873, chap. XVIII.

† *Educational Times Reprints*, 1868, vol. VIII, p. 106 ; *ibid.*, 1886, vol. XLV, pp. 127—128.

is by putting them at the points (0, 0), (0, 2), (0, 4), (2, 1), (2, 2), (2, 3), (4, 0), (4, 2), (4, 4); more generally, the angular points of a regular hexagon and the three points (at infinity) of intersection of opposite sides form such a group, and therefore any projection of that figure will give a solution. At present it is not possible to say what is the maximum number of rows of three which can be formed from n counters placed on a plane.

Extension to p-in-a-row. The problem mentioned above at once suggests the extension of placing n counters so as to form as many rows as possible, each of which shall contain p and only p counters. Such problems can be often solved immediately by placing at infinity the points of intersection of some of the lines, and (if it is so desired) subsequently projecting the diagram thus formed so as to bring these points to a finite distance. One instance of such a solution is given above.

As examples I may give the arrangement of 10 counters in 5 rows, each containing 4 counters; the arrangement of 16 counters in 15 rows, each containing 4 counters; the arrangement of 18 counters in 9 rows, each containing 5 counters; and the arrangement of 19 counters in 10 rows, each containing 5 counters. These problems I leave to the ingenuity of my readers (see p. 127).

Tessellation. Another of these statical recreations is known as tessellation, and consists in the formation of geometrical designs or mosaics covering a plane area by the use of tiles of given geometrical forms.

If the tiles are regular polygons, the resulting forms can be found by analysis. For instance, if we confine ourselves to the use of like tiles, each of which is a regular polygon of n sides, we are restricted to the use of equilateral triangles, squares, or hexagons. For suppose that to fill the space round a point where one of the angles of the polygon is situated we require m polygons. Each interior angle of the polygon is equal to $(n-2)\pi/n$. Hence $m(n-2)\pi/n = 2\pi$. Therefore $(m-2)(n-2) = 4$. Now, from the nature of the problem m is greater than 2, and so is n. If $m = 3$, $n = 6$. If $m > 3$, then $n < 6$, and since $n > 2$, we have in this case only to consider the values $n = 3$, $n = 4$, and $n = 5$. If $n = 3$ we have $m = 6$. If $n = 4$ we have $m = 4$. If $n = 5$, m is non-integral, and this is impossible. Thus the only solutions are $m = 3$ and $n = 6$, $m = 4$ and $n = 4$, $m = 6$ and $n = 3$.* It is convenient to use the symbols 6^3, 4^4, 3^6 to denote these regular tessellations.

If, however, we allow the use of unlike regular tiles (triangles, squares, etc.), we can construct numerous geometrical designs covering a plane area. If at each point the same number and kind of polygons are used, in the same (or the

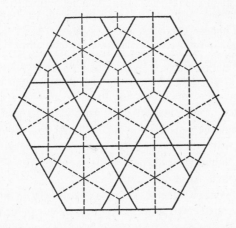

opposite) cyclic order, analysis similar to the above† shows that we can get eight possible arrangements—namely,

$$3.12^2, \quad 4.6.12, \quad 4.8^2, \quad (3.6)^2, \quad 3.4.6.4, \quad 3^3.4^2, \quad 3^2.4.3.4, \quad 3^4.6.$$

The tessellation $3^4.6$ (with four triangles and a hexagon at each vertex) has the peculiarity of existing in two enantio-

---

* The analogous problem for polygons covering the surface of a sphere is equivalent to the construction of regular polyhedra (see page 130). For an application of 6^3 to the voting system known as Proportional Representation, see G. Pólya, *L'Enseignement Mathématique*, 1918, vol. xx, p. 367.

† See Kraïtchik, pp. 272—282, Figs. 421—423, 425, 426, 432, 433, 440.

morphous forms; *i.e.*, it is not superposable with its image in a mirror (unless we allow the whole plane to be turned over).

When every edge of such a tessellation is replaced by a perpendicular line, joining the centres of two adjacent tiles, we obtain a *reciprocal* tessellation, whose tiles are all alike (though not necessarily regular). In this sense, 6^3 is reciprocal to 3^6 (and *vice versa*), while 4^4 is self-reciprocal (or rather, reciprocal to another equal 4^4). The tessellation $(3.6)^2$ and its reciprocal are drawn above.

Anallagmatic Pavements. The use of colours introduces new considerations. One formation of a pavement by the employment of square tiles of two colours is illustrated by the common chess-board; in this the cells are coloured alternately white and black. Another variety of a pavement made with square tiles of two colours was invented by Sylvester,* who termed it anallagmatic. In the ordinary chess-board, if any two rows or any two columns are placed in juxtaposition, cell to cell, the cells which are side by side are either all of the same colour or all of different colours. In an anallagmatic arrangement the cells are so coloured (with two colours) that when any two columns or any two rows are placed together side by side, half the cells next to one another are of the same colour and half are of different colours.

Anallagmatic pavements composed of m^2 cells or square tiles cannot be constructed if m is odd or oddly-even. It has been conjectured that they exist whenever m is a multiple of 4. The first doubtful case is when $m = 92$.

If solutions when $m = a$ and when $m = b$ are known, a solution when $m = ab$ can be deduced at once; we merely have to replace every black cell of the a-pavement by the whole b-pavement, and every white cell of the a-pavement by the b-pavement with its colours reversed. Repeated application of this principle gives a solution whenever m is a power

---

* See *Mathematical Questions from the Educational Times*, London, vol. x, 1868, pp. 74—76; vol. LVI, 1892, pp. 97—99. The results are closely connected with theorems in the theory of equations.

of 2. The case when $m = 8$ is shown in the first of the following drawings.

∞	∞	∞	∞	∞	∞	∞	∞
6	0	1	2	3	4	5	∞
5	6	0	1	2	3	4	∞
4	5	6	0	1	2	3	∞
3	4	5	6	0	1	2	∞
2	3	4	5	6	0	1	∞
1	2	3	4	5	6	0	∞
0	1	2	3	4	5	6	∞

When $m = p + 1$, where p is a prime (of the form $4k - 1$), an anallagmatic tessellation can be derived from the addition-table for the finite arithmetic modulo p (see page 60). In the bottom row and left-hand column of this table we write the numbers $0, 1, \ldots, p - 1$, and ∞, the last of these being an artificially introduced "number" which is unchanged when any number is added to it. The rest of the table is completed by adding (mod p) the numbers which thus define the columns and rows. Each cell is then coloured white or black according as its number is or is not a square, with the (somewhat artificial*) convention that ∞ is *not* a square. The case when $p = 7$ is illustrated above; the squares are then $0, 1, 2 \ (\equiv 9)$ and 4.

When $m = p^n + 1$ (where p^n is of the form $4k - 1$), we make a precisely analogous use of the addition-table for a Galois arithmetic of p^n marks (page 74), with an extra mark ∞ (which is unchanged when any mark is added to it). The case when $m = 28$ (and the two moduli are 3 and 1021) is illustrated below. In the bottom row and left-hand column of the addition-table we write the 28 marks $0, 1, 2, 10, 11, 12, 20, \ldots, 221, 222, \infty$. The squares are $0, 1, 20, 21, 22, 100, 102, 110, 111, 120, 121, 202, 211, 221$. These (apart from 0) are most easily calculated as being alternate terms in the sequence of powers of 10 (namely $1, 10, 100, 12, 120, \ldots, 201$).

* One would naturally expect ∞ to be its own square, like 0. I avoid using the words "quadratic residues," because 0 is undeniably a square, although it is not included among the quadratic residues.

The underlying theory is due to H. Davenport and R. E. A. C. Paley.* The latter gave also a more complicated rule to cover the case when $m = 2(p^n + 1)$ where p^n is of the form $4k + 1$. By combining these methods, he showed how an anallagmatic tessellation of m^2 cells can be constructed whenever m is divisible by 4 and of the form $2^k(p^n + 1)$, where p

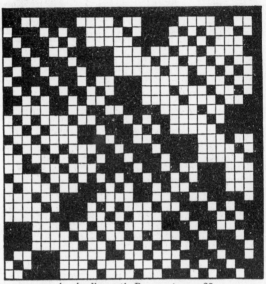

An Anallagmatic Pavement, m = 28.

is an odd prime.   (The first multiple of 4 which is not of this form is 92.)

In all these cases the pavement has one completely black row and column; consequently every other row or column is half black and half white.   When m is a power of 4, it is possible† to construct an anallagmatic pavement which is

---

* *Journal of Mathematics and Physics* (Cambridge, Mass.), 1933, vol. XII, pp. 311—320. Actually, Paley used subtraction instead of addition; but the consequent changes are quite trivial. An interesting application of this theory (to m-dimensional geometry) has been made by J. A. Barrau, *Nieuw Archief voor Wiskunde*, series 2, vol. VII. He gives tessellations, different from Paley's, for the cases $m = 16, 28$ and 36.

† *Mathematical Questions from the Educational Times*, 1868, vol. X, p. 112.

" isochromatic " in the sense that half the rows (and columns) have $\sqrt{m}$ more black than white tiles, while the rest have $\sqrt{m}$ more white than black. Previous editions of this book show such a pavement with $m = 16$.

Tessellation with Super-Dominoes. A novel form of tessellation problem was suggested in 1921 by Major MacMahon.* The object is to fill, according to certain rules, a prescribed area with wood or cardboard super-dominoes. The shape of an ordinary domino is a rectangle, the breadth of which is immaterial, with two ends or faces on which numbers or pips can be inscribed, and, if we like, each number may be taken to

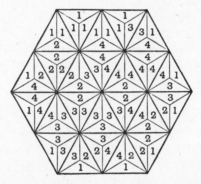

indicate a particular colour; by using n numbers we can get $n(n + 1)/2$ different linear dominoes. If our dominoes are triangular in shape, and from the centres of the triangles we draw lines to the angular points, we get dominoes with three faces on each of which numbers or pips can be inscribed, and, as before, each number may be taken to indicate a particular colour: by using n colours we can get $n(n^2 + 2)/3$ different triangular dominoes. Similarly, by using n colours we can get $n(n + 1)(n^2 - n + 2)/4$ different square dominoes, $n(n^4 + 1)/5$ different pentagonal dominoes, and so on. With each of these sets we can make up puzzles.

A particular case will illustrate the kind of questions

* P. A. MacMahon, *New Mathematical Pastimes*, Cambridge, 1921.

treated. Take the case of equilateral triangular dominoes. If four colours are used we get a set of twenty-four different dominoes, and these can be put together (preferably in a shallow box cut to the right size) to make a regular hexagon. Innumerable conditions may be imposed. For example, we may suppose that it is required to fit the dominoes into the box so that the colours of adjoining faces of the dominoes shall be the same, as also those of all the exterior faces. Here is the solution of this problem. A consideration of what conditions may be imposed naturally arises, and leads to various other problems. If our dominoes are right-angled triangles we get a hexagonal arrangement of a different shape. Further, we can play with sets selected from a particular full set and arranged in other geometrical figures. Similar problems arise from the use of square dominoes, hexagonal dominoes, etc.

Colour-Cube Problem. As an example of a recreation analogous to tessellation I will mention the colour-cube problem.* Stripped of mathematical technicalities the problem may be enunciated as follows. A cube has six faces, and if six colours are chosen we can paint each face with a different colour. By permuting the order of the colours we can obtain thirty such cubes, no two of which are coloured alike. Take any one of these cubes, K, then it is desired to select eight out of the remaining twenty-nine cubes, such that they can be arranged in the form of a cube (whose linear dimensions are double those of any of the separate cubes) coloured like the cube K, and placed so that where any two cubes touch each other the faces in contact are coloured alike.

Only one collection of eight cubes can be found to satisfy these conditions. These eight cubes can be determined by the following rule. Take any face of the cube K : it has four angles, and at each angle three colours meet. By permuting the colours cyclically we can obtain from each angle two other

---

* P. A. MacMahon, *London Mathematical Society Proceedings*, vol. XXIV, 1893, pp. 145—155; and *New Mathematical Pastimes*, Cambridge, 1921, pp. 42—46. See also F. Winter, *Die Spiele der 30 bunten Würfel*, Leipzig, 1934.

cubes, and the eight cubes so obtained are those required. A little consideration will show that these are the required cubes, and that the solution is unique.

For instance, suppose that the six colours are indicated by the letters a, b, c, d, e, f. Let the cube K be put on a table, and to fix our ideas suppose that the face coloured f is at the bottom, the face coloured a is at the top, and the faces coloured b, c, d, and e front respectively the east, north, west, and south points of the compass. I may denote such an arrangement by $(f; a; b, c, d, e)$. One cyclical permutation of the colours which meet at the north-east corner of the top face gives the cube $(f; c; a, b, d, e)$, and a second cyclical permutation gives the cube $(f; b; c, a, d, e)$. Similarly cyclical permutations of the colours which meet at the north-west corner of the top face of K give the cubes $(f; d; b, a, c, e)$ and $(f; c; b, d, a, e)$. Similarly from the top south-west corner of K we get the cubes $(f; e; b, c, a, d)$ and $(f; d; b, c, e, a)$: and from the top south-east corner we get the cubes $(f; e; a, c, d, b)$ and $(f; b; e, c, d, a)$.

The eight cubes being thus determined, it is not difficult to arrange them in the form of a cube coloured similarly to K, and subject to the condition that faces in contact are coloured alike; in fact they can be arranged in two ways to satisfy these conditions. One such way, taking the cubes in the numerical order given above, is to put the cubes 3, 6, 8, and 2 at the SE, NE, NW, and SW corners of the bottom face; of course, each placed with the colour f at the bottom, while 3 and 6 have the colour b to the east, and 2 and 8 have the colour d to the west: the cubes 7, 1, 4, and 5 will then form the SE, NE, NW, and SW corners of the top face; of course, each placed with the colour a at the top, while 7 and 1 have the colour b to the east, and 5 and 4 have the colour d to the west. If K is not given, the difficulty of the problem is increased. Similar puzzles in two dimensions can be made.

Tangrams. The formation of designs by means of seven pieces of wood—namely, a square, a rhombus, and five triangles, known as tans, of fixed traditional shapes—is one of the oldest amusements in the East. Many hundreds of figures representing men, women, birds, beasts, fish, houses, boats, domestic objects, designs, etc., can be made, but the recreation is not mathematical, and I reluctantly content myself with a bare mention of it.

Dynamical Games of Position

Games which are played by moving pieces on boards of various shapes—such as merrilees, fox and geese, solitaire, backgammon, draughts, and chess—present more interest. In general, possible movements of the pieces are so numerous that mathematical analysis is not practicable, but in a few games the possible movements are sufficiently limited as to permit of mathematical treatment; one or two of these are given later : here I shall confine myself mainly to puzzles and simple amusements.

Shunting Problems. The first I will mention is a little puzzle which I bought some years ago, and which was described as the " Great Northern Puzzle." It is typical of a good many problems connected with the shunting of trains, and though it rests on a most improbable hypothesis, I give it as a specimen of its kind.

The puzzle shows a railway, *DEF*, with two sidings, *DBA* and *FCA*, connected at *A*. The portion of the rails at *A*

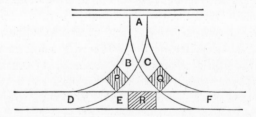

which is common to the two sidings is long enough to permit of a single wagon, like *P* or *Q*, running in or out of it; but is too short to contain the whole of an engine, like *R*. Hence, if an engine runs up one siding, such as *DBA*, it must come back the same way.

Initially a small block of wood, *P*, coloured to represent a wagon, is placed at *B*; a similar block, *Q*, is placed at *C*; and a longer block of wood, *R*, representing an engine, is placed at *E*. The problem is to use the engine *R* to interchange the wagons *P* and *Q*. without allowing any flying shunts.

Another shunting puzzle, on sale in the streets in 1905, under the name of the " Chifu-Chemulpo Puzzle," is made as follows. A loop-line *BGE* connects two points *B* and *E* on a railway track *AF*, which is supposed blocked at both ends, as shown in the diagram. In the model, the track *AF* is 9 inches long, $AB = EF = 1\frac{5}{8}$ inches, and $AH = FK = BC = DE = \frac{1}{4}$ inch.

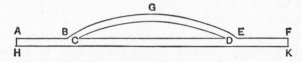

On the track and loop are eight wagons, numbered successively 1 to 8, each 1 inch long and one-quarter of an inch broad, and an engine, *e*, of the same dimensions. Originally the wagons are on the track from *A* to *F* and in the order 1, 2, 3, 4, 5, 6, 7, 8, and the engine is on the loop. The construction and the initial arrangement ensure that at any one time there cannot be more than eight vehicles on the track. Also if eight vehicles are on it, only the penultimate vehicle at either end can be moved on to the loop, but if less than eight are on the track, then the last two vehicles at either end can be moved on to the loop. If the points at each end of the loop-line are clear, it will hold four, but not more than four, vehicles. The object is to reverse the order of the wagons on the track, so that from *A* to *F* they will be numbered successively 8 to 1 : and to do this by means which will involve as few transferences of the engine or a wagon to or from the loop as is possible.

Twenty-six moves are required, and there is more than one solution in 26 moves (see p. 127).

Other shunting problems are not uncommon, but these two examples will suffice.

Ferry-Boat Problems. Everybody is familiar with the story of the showman who was travelling with a wolf, a goat, and a basket of cabbages; and for obvious reasons was unable to leave the wolf alone with the goat, or the goat alone with the cabbages. The only means of transporting them across a river was a boat so small that he could take in it only one of them at a time. The problem is to show how the passage could be effected.*

A somewhat similar problem is to arrange for the passage of a river by three men and three boys who have the use of a boat which will not carry at one time more than one man or two boys. Fifteen passages are required.†

Problems like these were proposed by Alcuin, Tartaglia, and other medieval writers. The following is a common type of such questions. Three ‡ beautiful ladies have for husbands three men, who are young, gallant, and jealous. The party are travelling, and find on the bank of a river over which they have to pass, a small boat which can hold no more than two persons. How can they cross the river, it being agreed that, in order to avoid scandal, no woman shall be left in the society of a man unless her husband is present ? Eleven passages are required. With two married couples five passages are required. The similar problem with four married couples is insoluble.

Another similar problem is the case of n married couples who have to cross a river by means of a boat which can be rowed by one person and will carry $n - 1$ people, but not more, with the condition that no woman is to be in the society of a man unless her husband is present. Alcuin's problem given

* Ozanam, 1803 edition, vol. I, p. 171; 1840 edition, p. 77.

† H. E. Dudeney, *The Tribune*, October 4, 1906.

‡ Bachet, Appendix, problem IV, p. 212.

above is the case of $n = 3$. Let y denote the number of passages from one bank to the other which will be necessary. Then it has been shown that if $n = 3$, $y = 11$; if $n = 4$, $y = 9$; and if $n > 4$, $y = 7$.

The following analogous problem is due to E. Lucas.* To find the smallest number x of persons that a boat must be able to carry in order that n married couples may by its aid cross a river in such a manner that no woman shall remain in the company of any man unless her husband is present; it being assumed that the boat can be rowed by one person only. Also to find the least number of passages, say y, from one bank to the other which will be required. M. Delannoy has shown that if $n = 2$, then $x = 2$, and $y = 5$. If $n = 3$, then $x = 2$, and $y = 11$. If $n = 4$, then $x = 3$, and $y = 9$. If $n = 5$, then $x = 3$, and $y = 11$. And finally if $n > 5$, then $x = 4$, and $y = 2n - 1$.

M. De Fonteney has remarked that, if there was an island in the middle of the river, the passage might be always effected by the aid of a boat which could carry only two persons. If there are only two or only three couples, the island is unnecessary, and the case is covered by the preceding method. His solution, involving $8n - 8$ passages, is as follows. The first nine passages will be the same, no matter how many couples there may be: the result is to transfer one couple to the island and one couple to the second bank. The result of the next eight passages is to transfer one couple from the first bank to the second bank; this series of eight operations must be repeated as often as necessary until there is left only one couple on the first bank, only one couple on the island, and all the rest on the second bank. The result of the last seven passages is to transfer all the couples to the second bank. It would, however, seem that if n is greater than 3, we need not require more than $6n - 7$ passages from land to land.†

M. G. Tarry has suggested an extension of the problem,

* *Récréations Mathématiques*, Paris, 1883, vol. I, pp. 15—18, 237—238; hereafter I shall refer to this work by the name of the author.

† See H. E. Dudeney, *Amusements in Mathematics*, London, 1917, p. 237.

which still further complicates its solution.   He supposes that
each husband travels with a harem of m wives or concubines;
moreover, as Mohammedan women are brought up in seclusion,
it is reasonable to suppose that they would be unable to row a
boat by themselves without the aid of a man.   But perhaps the
difficulties attendant on the travels of one wife may be deemed
sufficient for Christians, and I content myself with merely
mentioning the increased anxieties experienced by Moham-
medans in similar circumstances.

Geodesics.   Geometrical problems connected with finding
the shortest routes from one point to another on a curved
surface are often difficult, but geodesics on a flat surface or
flat surfaces are in general readily determinable.

I append one instance,* though I should have hesitated to
do so had not experience shown that some readers do not
readily see the solution.   It is as follows.   A room is 30 feet
long, 12 feet wide, and 12 feet high.   On the middle line of one
of the smaller side walls and 1 foot from the ceiling is a wasp.
On the middle line of the opposite wall and 11 feet from the
ceiling is a fly.   The wasp catches the fly by crawling all the
way to it: the fly, paralysed by fear, remaining still.   The
problem is to find the shortest route that the wasp can
follow.

To obtain a solution we observe that we can cut a sheet of
paper so that, when folded properly, it will make a model to
scale of the room.   This can be done in several ways.   If, when
the paper is again spread out flat, we can join the points representing the wasp and the fly by a straight line lying wholly on
the paper, we shall obtain a geodesic route between them.
Thus the problem is reduced to finding the way of cutting out
the paper which gives the shortest route of the kind.

Here is the diagram corresponding to a solution of the
above question, where A represents the floor, B and D the
longer side-walls, C the ceiling, and W and F the positions on

* This is due to Mr. H. E. Dudeney.   I heard a similar question propounded at Cambridge in 1903, but I first saw it in print in the *Daily Mail*,
London, February 1, 1905.

the two smaller side-walls occupied initially by the wasp and fly. In the diagram the square of the distance between W and F is $(32)^2 + (24)^2$; hence the distance is 40 feet.

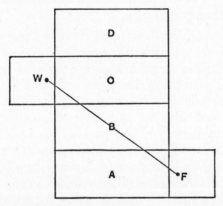

Problems with Counters placed in a Row. Numerous dynamical problems and puzzles may be illustrated with a box of counters, especially if there are counters of two colours. Of course, coins or pawns or cards will serve equally well. I proceed to enumerate a few of these played with counters placed in a row.

First Problem with Counters. The following problem must be familiar to many of my readers. Ten counters (or coins) are placed in a row. Any counter may be moved over two of those adjacent to it on the counter next beyond them. It is required to move the counters according to the above rule so that they shall be arranged in five equidistant couples.

If we denote the counters in their initial positions by the numbers 1, 2, 3, 4, 5, 6, 7, 8, 9, 10, we proceed as follows. Put 7 on 10, then 5 on 2, then 3 on 8, then 1 on 4, and lastly 9 on 6. Thus they are arranged in pairs on the places originally occupied by the counters 2, 4, 6, 8, 10.

Similarly by putting 4 on 1, then 6 on 9, then 8 on 3, then 10 on 7, and lastly 2 on 5, they are arranged in pairs on the places originally occupied by the counters 1, 3, 5, 7, 9.

If two superposed counters are reckoned as only one, solutions analogous to those given above will be obtained by putting 7 on 10, then 5 on 2, then 3 on 8, then 1 on 6, and lastly 9 on 4; or by putting 4 on 1, then 6 on 9, then 8 on 3, then 10 on 5, and lastly 2 on 7.*

There is a somewhat similar game played with eight counters, but in this case the four couples finally formed are not equidistant. Here the transformation will be effected if we move 5 on 2, then 3 on 7, then 4 on 1, and lastly 6 on 8. This form of the game is applicable equally to $(8 + 2n)$ counters, for if we move 4 on 1, we have left on one side of this couple a row of $(8 + 2n - 2)$ counters. This again can be reduced to one of $(8 + 2n - 4)$ counters, and in this way finally we have left eight counters which can be moved in the way explained above.

A more complete generalization would be the case of n counters, where each counter might be moved over the m counters adjacent to it on to the one beyond them. For instance, we may place twelve counters in a row and allow the moving a counter over three adjacent counters. By such movements we can obtain four piles, each pile containing three counters. Thus, if the counters be numbered consecutively, one solution can be obtained by moving 7 on 3, then 5 on 10, then 9 on 7, then 12 on 8, then 4 on 5, then 11 on 12, then 2 on 6, and then 1 on 2. Or again we may place sixteen counters in a row and allow the moving a counter over four adjacent counters on to the next counter available. By such movements we can get four piles, each pile containing four counters. Thus, if the counters be numbered consecutively, one solution can be obtained by moving 8 on 3, then 9 on 14, then 1 on 5, then 16 on 12, then 7 on 8, then 10 on 7, then 6 on 9, then 15 on 16, then 13 on 1, then 4 on 15, then 2 on 13, and then 11 on 6.

Second Problem with Counters. Another problem,† of a

---

* Note by J. Fitzpatrick to a French translation of the third edition of this work, Paris, 1898.

† *Bibliotheca Mathematica*, 1896, series 3, vol. VI, p. 323; P. G. Tait, *Philosophical Magazine*, London, January, 1884, series 5, vol. XVII, p. 39; or *Collected Scientific Papers*, Cambridge, vol. II. 1890, p. 93.

somewhat similar kind, is of Japanese origin. Place four
florins (or white counters) and four halfpence (or black counters) alternately in a line in contact with one another. It is
required in four moves, each of a pair of two contiguous
pieces, without altering the relative position of the pair, to
form a continuous line of four halfpence followed by four
florins.

This can be solved as follows. Let a florin be denoted by a
and a halfpenny by b, and let x x denote two contiguous blank
spaces. Then the successive positions of the pieces may be
represented thus :

Initially	x x $a\,b\,a\,b\,a\,b\,a\,b$.
After the first move . . .	$b\,a\,a\,b\,a\,b\,a$ x x b.
After the second move . .	$b\,a\,a\,b$ x x $a\,a\,b\,b$.
After the third move. . .	b x x $b\,a\,a\,a\,a\,b\,b$.
After the fourth move . .	$b\,b\,b\,b\,a\,a\,a\,a$ x x.

The operation is conducted according to the following rule.
Suppose the pieces to be arranged originally in circular order,
with two contiguous blank spaces, then we always move to the
blank space for the time being that pair of coins which occupies
the places next but one and next but two to the blank space on
one assigned side of it.

A similar problem with $2n$ counters—n of them being white
and n black—will at once suggest itself, and, if n is greater
than 4, it can be solved in n moves. I have, however, failed to
find a simple rule which covers all cases alike, but solutions, due
to M. Delannoy, have been given * for the four cases where n is
of the form $4m$, $4m + 2$, $4m + 1$, or $4m + 3$; in the first two
cases the first $\frac{1}{2}n$ moves are of pairs of dissimilar counters and
the last $\frac{1}{2}n$ moves are of pairs of similar counters; in the last
two cases the first move is similar to that given above—namely,
of the penultimate and antepenultimate counters to the beginning of the row—the next $\frac{1}{2}(n-1)$ moves are of pairs of
dissimilar counters, and the final $\frac{1}{2}(n-1)$ moves are of similar
counters.

* *La Nature*, June, 1887, p. 10.

The problem is also capable of solution if we substitute the restriction that at each move the pair of counters taken up must be moved to one of the two ends of the row instead of the condition that the final arrangement is to be continuous.

Tait suggested a variation of the problem by making it a condition that the two coins to be moved shall also be made to interchange places; in this form it would seem that five moves are required; or, in the general case, $n + 1$ moves are required.

Problems on a Chess-board with Counters or Pawns. The following three problems require the use of a chess-board as well as of counters or pieces of two colours. It is more convenient to move a pawn than a counter, and if therefore I describe them as played with pawns, it is only as a matter of convenience, and not that they have any connection with chess. The first is characterized by the fact that in every position not more than two moves are permitted; in the second and third problems not more than four moves are permitted in any position. With these limitations, analysis is possible. I shall not discuss the similar problems in which more moves are permitted.

*First Problem with Pawns.** On a row of seven squares on a chess-board 3 white pawns (or counters), denoted in the diagram by " a "s, are placed on the 3 squares at one end, and 3 black pawns (or counters), denoted by " b "s, are placed on the 3 squares at the other end—the middle square being left vacant. Each piece can move only in one direction; the " a " pieces can move from left to right, and the " b " pieces from right to left. If the square next to a piece is unoccupied, it can move on

| a | a | a | | b | b | b |

to that; or if the square next to it is occupied by a piece of the opposite colour and the square beyond that is unoccupied, then it can, like a queen in draughts, leap over that piece on to the unoccupied square beyond it. The object is to get all the

* Lucas, vol. II, part 5, pp. 141—143.

white pawns in the places occupied initially by the black pawns and *vice versa*.

The solution requires 15 moves. It may be effected by moving first a white pawn, then successively two black pawns, then three white pawns, then three black pawns, then three white pawns, then two black pawns, and then one white pawn. We can express this solution by saying that if we number the cells (a term used to describe each of the small squares on a chess-board) consecutively, then initially the vacant space occupies the cell 4, and in the successive moves it will occupy the cells 3, 5, 6, 4, 2, 1, 3, 5, 7, 6, 4, 2, 3, 5, 4. Of these moves, six are simple and nine are leaps.

More generally, if we have m white pawns at one end of a row of $m + n + 1$ cells, and n black pawns at the other end, the arrangement can be reversed in $mn + m + n$ moves, of which $m + n$ are simple and mn are leaps.

*Second Problem with Pawns.** A similar game may be played on a rectangular or square board. The case of a square board containing 49 cells, or small squares, will illustrate this sufficiently : in this case the initial position is shown in the annexed diagram where the " a "s denote the pawns or pieces

a	a	a	a	b	b	b
a	a	a	a	b	b	b
a	a	a	a	b	b	b
a	a	a		b	b	b
a	a	a	b	b	b	b
a	a	a	b	b	b	b
a	a	a	b	b	b	b

of one colour, and the " b "s those of the other colour. The " a " pieces can move horizontally from left to right or vertically down, and the " b " pieces can move horizontally from right to left or vertically up, according to the same rules as before.

* Lucas, vol. II, part 5, p. 144.

The solution reduces to the preceding case. The pieces in the middle column can be interchanged in 15 moves. In the course of these moves every one of the seven cells in that column is at some time or other vacant, and whenever that is the case, the pieces in the row containing the vacant cell can be interchanged. To interchange the pieces in each of the seven rows will require 15 moves. Hence to interchange all the pieces will require $15 + (7 \times 15)$ moves—that is, 120 moves.

If we place $2n(n + 1)$ white pawns and $2n(n + 1)$ black pawns in a similar way on a square board of $(2n + 1)^2$ cells, we can transpose them in $2n(n + 1)(n + 2)$ moves : of these $4n(n + 1)$ are simple and $2n^2(n + 1)$ are leaps.

Third Problem with Pawns. The following analogous problem is somewhat more complicated. On a square board of 25 cells, place eight white pawns or counters on the cells

a	b	c		
d	e	f		
g	h	*	H	G
		F	E	D
		C	B	A

denoted by small letters in the annexed diagram, and eight black pawns or counters on the cells denoted by capital letters, the cell marked with an asterisk (*) being left blank. Each pawn can move according to the laws already explained—the white pawns being able to move only horizontally from left to right or vertically downwards, and the black pawns being able to move only horizontally from right to left or vertically upwards. The object is to get all the white pawns in the places initially occupied by the black pawns and *vice versa*. No moves outside the dark line are permitted.

Since there is only one cell on the board which is unoccupied, and since no diagonal moves and no backward moves are permitted, it follows that at each move not more than two pieces of either colour are capable of moving. There are, however, a very large number of empirical solutions. The following, due to Mr. H. E. Dudeney, is effected in 46 moves :

$$H\,hg* Ffc* CBHh* GDFfehbag* GABHEFfdg* Hhbc* CFf* GHh*$$

the letters indicating the cells from which the pieces are successively moved. It will be noticed that the first twenty-three moves lead to a symmetrical position, and that the next twenty-two moves can be at once obtained by writing the first twenty-two moves in reverse order and interchanging small and capital letters. Similar problems with boards of various shapes can be easily constructed.

Probably, were it worth the trouble, the mathematical theory of games such as that just described might be worked out by the use of Vandermonde's notation, described later in Chapter VI, or by the analogous method employed in the theory of the game of solitaire.*

Problems on a Chess-board with Chess-pieces. There are several mathematical recreations with chess-pieces, other than pawns. Some of these are given later in Chapter VI.

Paradromic Rings. The difficulty of mentally realizing the effect of geometrical alterations in certain simple figures is illustrated by the familiar experiment of making *paradromic rings* by cutting a paper ring prepared in the following manner.

Take a strip of paper or piece of tape, say, for convenience, an inch or two wide, and at least 9 or 10 inches long, rule a line in the middle down the length AB of the strip, gum one end over the other end B, and we get a ring like a section of a cylinder. If this ring is cut by a pair of scissors along the ruled line, we obtain two rings exactly like the first, except that they are only half the width. Next suppose that the end A is twisted through two right angles before it is gummed to B (the result of which is that the back of the strip at A is gummed

---

* On the theory of the solitaire, see Reiss, ' Beiträge zur Theorie des Solitär-Spiels,' *Crelle's Journal*, Berlin, 1858, vol. LIV, pp. 344—379; and Lucas, vol. I, part v, pp. 89—141.

over the front of the strip at B), then a cut along the line will produce only one ring.   Next suppose that the end A is twisted once completely round (*i.e.* through four right angles) before it is gummed to B, then a similar cut produces two interlaced rings.   If any of my readers think that these results could be predicted off-hand, it may be interesting to them to see if they can predict correctly the effect of again cutting the rings formed in the second and third experiments down their middle lines in a manner similar to that above described.

The theory is due to J. B. Listing,* who discussed the case when the end A receives m half-twists—that is, is twisted through $m\pi$—before it is gummed to B.

If m is even, we obtain a surface which has two sides and two edges.   If the ring is cut along a line midway between the edges, we obtain two rings, each of which has m half-twists, and which are linked together $\frac{1}{2}m$ times.

If m is odd, we obtain a surface having only one side and one edge.   If this ring is cut along its mid-line, we obtain only one ring, but it has $2m + 2$ half-twists, and if m is greater than unity it is knotted.   If the ring, instead of being bisected, is trisected,† we obtain two interlocked rings: one like the original ring (coming from the middle third), and one like the bisected ring.   The manner in which these two rings are interlocked is illustrated by the following diagrams (of the cases $m = 3$ and $m = 5$).

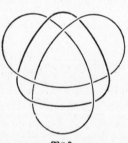
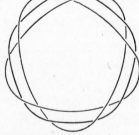

m=3   m=5

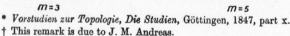

* *Vorstudien zur Topologie, Die Studien,* Göttingen, 1847, part x.
† This remark is due to J. M. Andreas.

ADDENDUM

Note. *Page* 106. One method of arranging 16 counters in 15 lines, as stated in the text, is as follows. Draw a regular re-entrant pentagon, vertices A_1, A_2, A_3, A_4, A_5, and centre O. The sides intersect in five points B_1, ... B_5. These latter points may be joined so as to form a smaller regular re-entrant pentagon whose sides intersect in five points C_1, ... C_5. The 16 points indicated are arranged as desired (*The Canterbury Puzzles*, 1907, p. 140).

An arrangement of 18 counters in 9 rows, each containing 5 counters, can be obtained thus. From one angle, A, of an equilateral triangle $AA'A''$, draw lines AD, AE inside the triangle making any angles with AA'. Draw from A' and A'' lines similarly placed in regard to $A'A''$ and $A''A$. Let $A'D'$ cut $A''E''$ in F, and $A'E'$ cut $A''D''$ in G. Then AFG is a straight line. The 3 vertices of the triangle and the 15 points of intersection of AD, AE, AF, with the similar pencils of lines drawn from A', A'', will give an arrangement as required.

An arrangement of 19 counters in 10 rows, each containing 5 counters, can be obtained by placing counters at the 19 points of intersection of the 10 lines $x = \pm a$, $x = \pm b$, $y = \pm a$, $y = \pm b$, $y = \pm x$: of these points two are at infinity.

As a further example, consider the problem of arranging 28 counters in 36 rows, each containing 4 counters. Such an arrangement can be obtained by joining certain vertices of a regular enneagon $A_1A_2 \ldots A_9$. We determine two other enneagons, $B_1B_2 \ldots B_9$, $C_1C_2 \ldots C_9$, concentric with the first. B_1 is the point of intersection of A_3A_6 with A_5A_8, while C_1 is the point of intersection of A_2A_6 with A_5A_9. The line B_4B_7 contains C_5 and C_6. The twenty-eighth point is the centre, which lies on nine lines such as $A_1B_1C_1$.

Note. *Page* 114. The Great Northern Shunting Problem is effected thus. (i) R pushes P into A. (ii) R returns, pushes Q up to P in A, couples Q to P, draws them both out to F, and then pushes them to E. (iii) P is now uncoupled, R takes Q back to A, and leaves it there. (iv) R returns to P, takes P back to C, and leaves it there. (v) R running successively through F, D, B comes to A, draws Q out, and leaves it at B.

Note. *Page* 115. One solution of the Chifu-Chemulpo Puzzle is as follows. Move successively wagons 2, 3, 4 up, *i.e.*, on to the loop line. [Then push 1 along the straight track close to 5; this is not a " move."] Next, move 4 down, *i.e.* on to the straight track and push it along to 1. Next, move 8 up, 3 down to the end of the track and keep it there temporarily, 6 up, 2 down, e down, 3 up, 7 up. [Then push 5 to the end of the track and keep it there temporarily.] Next, move 7 down, 6 down, 2 up, 4 up. [Then push e along to 1.] Next, move 4 down to the end of the track and keep it there temporarily, 2 down, 5 up, 3 down, 6 up, 7 up, 8 down to the end of the track, e up, 5 down, 6 down, 7 down. In this solution we moved e down to the track at one end, then shifted it along the track, and finally moved it up to the loop from the other end of the track. We might equally well move e down to the track at one end, and finally move it back to the loop from the same end.   In this solution the pieces successively moved are 2, 3, 4, 4, e, 8, 7, 3, 2, 6, 5, 5, 6, 3, 2, 7, 2, 5, 6, 3, 7, e, 8, 5, 6, 7

CHAPTER V

POLYHEDRA

" Although a Discourse of Solid Bodies be an uncommon and neglected Part of Geometry, yet that it is no inconsiderable or unprofitable Improvement of the Science will (no doubt) be readily granted by such, whose Genius tends as well to the Practical as Speculative Parts of it, for whom this is chiefly intended." *

A POLYHEDRON is a solid figure† with plane faces and straight edges, so arranged that every edge is both the join of two vertices and a common side of two faces. Familiar instances are the pyramids and prisms. (A pentagonal pyramid has six vertices, ten edges, and six faces; a pentagonal prism has ten, fifteen, and seven. See figure 7 on Plate I.) I would mention also the *antiprism*,‡ whose two bases, though parallel, are not similarly situated, but each vertex of either corresponds to a side of the other, so that the lateral edges form a zig-zag. (Thus a pentagonal antiprism has ten vertices, twenty edges, and twelve faces. See figure 9 on Plate I.)

The tessellations described on page 107 may be regarded as infinite polyhedra.

SYMMETRY AND SYMMETRIES

It is convenient to say that a figure is *reflexible* § if it is superposable with its image in a plane mirror (*i.e.* if it is, in

* Abraham Sharp, *Geometry Improv'd*, London, 1717, p. 65.

† More precisely, it is the *surface* of such a solid figure.

‡ Or " prismoid." See the *Encyclopaedia Britannica* (XIVth Edition), article " Solids."

§ Or " self-reflexible."

the most elementary sense, " symmetrical "). A figure which is not reflexible forms, with its mirror-image, an *enantio-morphous* pair. (The obvious example is a pair of shoes.) A reflexible figure has at least one *plane of symmetry*; the operation of reflecting in such a plane leaves the figure unchanged as a whole. A figure may also be symmetrical by rotation about an *axis of symmetry*. The vague statement that a figure has a certain amount of " symmetry " can be made precise by saying that the figure has a certain number of *symmetries*, a symmetry * being defined as any combination of motions and reflections which leaves the figure unchanged as a whole.

For a regular polygon $ABC \ldots X$, there is a symmetry (in fact, a rotation) which changes A into B, B into C, and so on.

THE FIVE PLATONIC SOLIDS

Let $ABC \ldots X$ and $CBE \ldots Y$ be two adjacent faces of a polyhedron. The polyhedron is said to be *regular* if it admits two particular symmetries : one which changes A into B, and B into C, and one which changes A into C, and C into E. It follows that all the faces are regular and equal, all the edges are equal, and all the vertices are surrounded alike. If each vertex is surrounded by m n-gons, we may denote the polyhedron by the symbol n^m (as on page 107).

If the polyhedron is finite, the faces at one vertex form a solid angle. The internal angle of each face being $(n-2)\pi/n$, we now have $m(n-2)\pi/n < 2\pi$. Therefore $(m-2)(n-2) < 4$. This inequality has to be solved in integers greater than 2, and then in each case the polyhedron can be built up, face by face. Letting V, E, F denote the number of vertices, edges, faces, the results are as follows. (See Plate I, figures 1, 3, 2, 5, 4).

---

* Or "symmetry operation." (Any rotation or translation may be regarded as a combination of two reflections.)

PLATE I

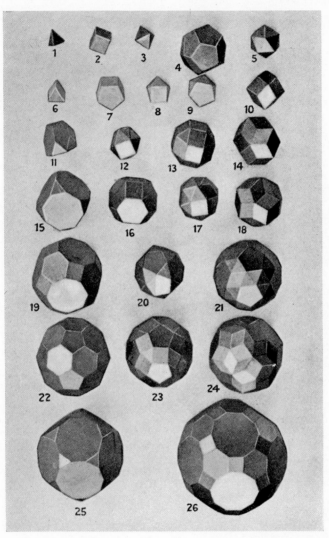

n^m	V	E	F	Name
3^3	4	6	4	Regular Tetrahedron
3^4	6	12	8	Octahedron
4^3	8	12	6	Cube
3^5	12	30	20	Icosahedron
5^3	20	30	12	Dodecahedron

Clearly, $mV = 2E = nF$. A less obvious relation is $E = 2mn/\{4 - (m - 2)(n - 2)\}$. This is a consequence of Euler's Theorem, $V - E + F = 2$, which will be proved in Chapter VIII, on page 233.

In four ways the tetrahedron can be regarded as a triangular pyramid, and the octahedron as a triangular antiprism. In three ways the octahedron can be regarded as a square double-pyramid, and the cube as a square prism. In six ways the icosahedron can be regarded as a pentagonal antiprism with two pentagonal pyramids stuck on to its bases. The faces of the dodecahedron consist of two opposite pentagons (in parallel planes), each surrounded by five other pentagons.

An icosahedron can be inscribed in an octahedron, so that each vertex of the icosahedron divides an edge of the octahedron according to the " golden section." * A cube can be inscribed in a dodecahedron so that each edge of the cube lies in a face of the dodecahedron (and joins two alternate vertices of that face).

These five figures have been known since ancient times. The earliest thorough investigation of them is probably that of Theaetetus.† It has been suggested that Euclid's *Elements* were originally written, not as a general treatise on geometry, but in order to supply the necessary steps for a full apprecia-

* See page 57.
† T. Heath, *A History of Greek Mathematics*, Oxford, 1921, vol. I, p. 162.

tion of the five regular solids. At any rate, Euclid begins by constructing an equilateral triangle, and ends by constructing a dodecahedron.

With each of these polyhedra we may associate three concentric spheres : one (the " circum-sphere ") through all the vertices, one touching all the edges, and one (the " in-sphere ") touching all the faces. Consider the second of these spheres. If we replace each edge by a perpendicular line touching this sphere at the same point, the edges at a vertex

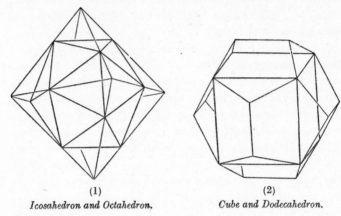

(1)

Icosahedron and Octahedron.

(2)

Cube and Dodecahedron.

lead to the sides of a polygon. Such polygons are the V faces of another " reciprocal " polyhedron, which has F vertices. The reciprocal of n^m is m^n, and *vice versa*. Thus the cube and octahedron are reciprocal, and so are the dodecahedron and icosahedron. The tetrahedron is self-reciprocal, or rather reciprocal to another tetrahedron. The diagonals of the faces of a cube are the edges of two reciprocal tetrahedra. (See Plate II, figure 27, facing page 134.)

Mystically minded Greeks associated the regular polyhedra with the four Elements and the Universe. Kepler * justified the correspondence as follows. Of the five solids, the tetrahedron has the smallest volume for its surface, the icosahedron

* *Opera Omnia*, Frankfort, 1864, vol. v, p. 121.

the largest; these therefore exhibit the qualities of dryness and wetness, respectively, and correspond to Fire and Water. The cube, standing firmly on its base, corresponds to the stable Earth; but the octahedron, which rotates freely when held by two opposite corners, corresponds to the mobile Air. Finally, the dodecahedron corresponds to the Universe, because the zodiac has twelve signs. He illustrated this correspondence by drawing a bonfire on his tetrahedron, a lobster and fishes on his icosahedron, a tree, a carrot, and gardening tools on his cube, birds and clouds on his octahedron, and the sun, moon, and stars on his dodecahedron.

Kepler also associated these five polyhedra with the spaces between the orbits of the six planets then known.* He imagined a set of six spheres, with the sun for centre, each (approximately) containing the orbit of a planet. Every two consecutive spheres were the in- and circum-spheres of a regular polyhedron. In this sense he put the octahedron between Mercury and Venus, the icosahedron between Venus and the Earth, the dodecahedron between the Earth and Mars, the tetrahedron between Mars and Jupiter, and the cube between Jupiter and Saturn. The approximations are not very close; moreover, this correspondence involves an essential ambiguity. The ratio of circum-radius R to in-radius r is exactly the same for the cube as for the octa-hedron, and for the dodecahedron as for the icosahedron. In fact, if the reciprocating sphere has radius ρ, the reciprocal of a given polyhedron has circum-radius ρ^2/r and in-radius ρ^2/R. Thus the relative size of two reciprocal polyhedra may be adjusted so as to make them have the same circum-sphere and the same in-sphere. (In general, their corresponding edges will no longer intersect.)

If two reciprocal regular solids of the same in-radius (and therefore the same circum-radius) stand side by side on a horizontal plane (such as a table top), the distribution of vertices in horizontal planes is the same for both—*i.e.* the

* *Op. cit.*, p. 276.

planes are the same, and the numbers of vertices in each plane are proportional. This fact was noticed by Pappus,* but has only recently been adequately explained, although its various extensions indicated that it was no mere accident. One of these extensions is to the Kepler-Poinsot polyhedra, which will be described later. Another is to tessellations of a plane. Consider the tessellation 6^3 (*i.e.* hexagons, three around each vertex). By picking out alternate vertices of each hexagon in a consistent manner, we derive the triangular tessellation 3^6 (which, in a different position, is the reciprocal tessellation). We then find that every circle concentric with a face of the 6^3 contains twice as many vertices of the 6^3 as of the 3^6. (This, however, is obvious, since the omitted vertices of the 6^3 belong to another 3^6, exactly like the first.)

The fact that the vertices of a hexagonal tessellation belong also to two triangular tessellations is analogous to the more familiar fact that the vertices of a cube belong also to two regular tetrahedra. These two tetrahedra may be said to form a *compound*—Kepler's *stella octangula*; their eight faces lie in the facial planes of an octahedron. There is also a compound of *five tetrahedra* having the vertices of a dodeca- hedron and the facial planes of an icosahedron; this occurs in two enantiomorphous varieties. By putting the two varieties together, so as to have the same twenty vertices, we obtain a compound of *ten tetrahedra*, oppositely situated pairs of which can be replaced by *five cubes* (having the twenty vertices of the dodecahedron, each taken twice). It is quite easy to visualize one such cube in a given dodecahedron (as in the second drawing on page 132); the whole set of five makes a very pretty model. Finally, by reciprocating the five cubes we obtain a compound of *five octahedra* having the facial planes of an icosahedron, each taken twice. This icosahedron is inscribed in each one of the octahedra as in the first drawing on page 132 (see Plate II, figures 27, 33, 35, 36, 37).

* T. Heath, *A History of Greek Mathematics*, vol. II, pp. 368—369.

PLATE II

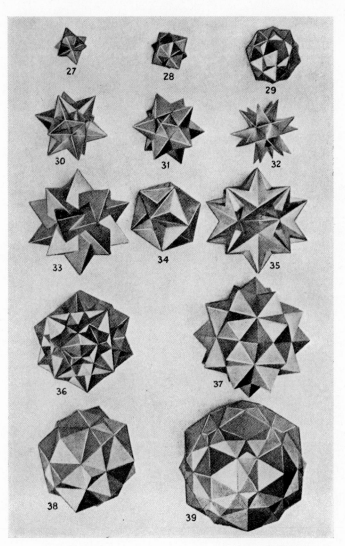

Among the edges of a regular polyhedron, we easily pick out a skew polygon or zig-zag, in which the first and second edges are sides of one face, the second and third are sides of another face, and so on. This zig-zag is known as a *Petrie polygon*, and has many applications. Each finite polyhedron can be orthogonally projected on to a plane in such a way that one Petrie polygon becomes a regular polygon with the rest of the projection inside it. It can be shown in various simple ways that the Petrie polygon of n^m has h sides, where

$$\cos^2(\pi/h) = \cos^2(\pi/m) + \cos^2(\pi/n).$$

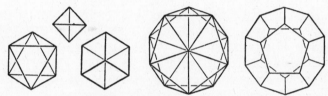

The Platonic Solids and their Petrie Polygons.

The h sides of the Petrie polygon of n^m are crossed by h edges of the reciprocal polyhedron m^n; these form a Petrie polygon for m^n.

The regular polyhedra are symmetrical in many different ways. There is an *axis* of symmetry through the centre of every face, through the mid-point of every edge, and through every vertex: $E + 1$ axes altogether. There are also $3h/2$ *planes* of symmetry.

THE ARCHIMEDEAN SOLIDS

A polyhedron is said to be *uniform* if it has regular faces and admits symmetries which will transform a given vertex into every other vertex in turn. The Platonic polyhedra are uniform; so are the right regular prisms and antiprisms, of suitable height—namely, when their lateral faces are squares and equilateral triangles, respectively. Such a polyhedron may be denoted by a symbol giving the numbers of sides of the faces around one vertex (in their proper cyclic order); thus the n-gonal prism and antiprism are $4^2 . n$ and $3^3 . n$. It is quite easy to prove* that, apart from these, there are just thirteen (finite, convex) uniform polyhedra :

$$3 . 6^2, \quad 4 . 6^2, \quad 3 . 8^2, \quad 5 . 6^2, \quad 3 . 10^2, \quad 4 . 6 . 8, \quad 4 . 6 . 10,$$
$$(3 . 4)^2, \quad (3 . 5)^2, \quad 3 . 4^3, \quad 3 . 4 . 5 . 4, \quad 3^4 . 4, \quad 3^4 . 5.$$

These are the *Archimedean solids*.

Let σ denote the sum of the face-angles at a vertex. (This must be less than 2π in order to make a solid angle.) Then the number of vertices is given by the formula † $(2\pi - \sigma)V = 4\pi$. For instance, $3^4 . 5$ has 60 vertices, since $\sigma = (\frac{4}{3} + \frac{3}{5})\pi$.

If we regard the *stella octangula* as consisting of two interpenetrating solid tetrahedra, we may say that their common part is an octahedron. Also, as we have already observed, their edges are diagonals of the faces of a cube. Analogously, the common part of a cube and an octahedron, in the properly reciprocal position (with corresponding edges perpendicularly bisecting each other), is the *cuboctahedron*, $(3 . 4)^2$. Each pair of corresponding edges (of the cube and octahedron) are the diagonals of a rhomb, and the twelve such rhombs are the faces of a "semi-regular" polyhedron known as the *rhombic dodecahedron*. (The latter is not uniform, but "isohedral." See the first drawing on page 150.) After suitable magnification, the edges of the cuboctahedron intersect those of the rhombic dodecahedron (at right angles); in fact, these two polyhedra are reciprocal, just as the octahedron and cube are reciprocal. The icosahedron and dodecahedron lead similarly to the *icosidodecahedron* $(3 . 5)^2$, and to its reciprocal, the *triacontahedron*. (See Plate II, figures 28, 29, and Plate I, figures 12, 10, 20, 18. Cf. the tessellations drawn on page 107.) The compound of five cubes has the 30 facial planes of a triacontahedron. Reciprocally, the compound of five octahedra has the 30 vertices of an icosidodecahedron.

The faces of the icosidodecahedron consist of 20 triangles

---

* See, for instance, L. Lines, *Solid Geometry*, London, 1935, p. 165.

† E. Steinitz and H. Rademacher, *Vorlesungen über die Theorie der Polyeder*, Berlin, 1934, p. 11.

and 12 pentagons (corresponding to the faces of the two
parent regulars). Its 60 edges are perpendicularly bisected
by those of the reciprocal triacontahedron (although the latter
edges are not bisected by the former : see Plate II, figure 39).
The 60 points where these pairs of edges cross one another are
the vertices of a polyhedron whose faces consist of 20 triangles,
12 pentagons, and 30 rectangles.   By slightly displacing these
points (towards the mid-points of the edges of the triacontahedron), the rectangles can be distorted into squares, and we
have another Archimedean solid, the *rhombicosidodecahedron*,
3 . 4 . 5 . 4.   (Plate I, figure 23.   Cf. the tessellation 3 . 4 . 6 . 4.)

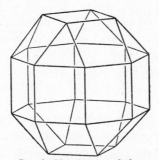

Pseudo-Rhombicuboctahedron.

An analogous construction leads to the *rhombicuboctahedron**
3 . 4³, whose faces consist of 8 triangles and 6 + 12 squares.
(See Plate II, figure 38, and Plate I, figure 13.)   In attempting
to make a model of this polyhedron, J. C. P. Miller † accidentally discovered a " pseudo-rhombicuboctahedron," bounded
likewise by 8 triangles and 18 squares, and isogonal in the
loose or " local " sense (each vertex being surrounded by one
triangle and three squares), but not in the strict sense (which
implies that the appearance of the solid as a whole must
remain the same when viewed from the direction of each
vertex in turn).

     * *I.e.,* "rhombi-cub-octahedron "; but the other is "rhomb-icosi-
dodecahedron."
     † *Philosophical Transactions of the Royal Society,* 1930, series A, vol.
ccxxix, p. 336.

On cutting off the corners of a cube, by planes parallel to the faces of the reciprocal octahedron, we leave small triangles, and reduce the square faces to octagons. For suitable positions of the cutting planes these octagons will be regular, and we have another Archimedean solid, the *truncated cube*, $3 . 8^2$. (Cf. the tessellations $4 . 8^2$ and $3 . 12^2$.) Each of the five Platonic solids has its truncated variety ; * so have the cuboctahedron and the icosidodecahedron, but in these last cases ($4 . 6 . 8$ and $4 . 6 . 10$) a distortion is again required, to convert rectangles into squares.† (Cf. the tessellation $4 . 6 . 12$.)

All the Archimedean solids so far discussed are reflexible (by reflection in the plane that perpendicularly bisects any edge). The remaining two, however, are not reflexible : the *snub cube* $3^4 . 4$, and the *snub dodecahedron* $3^4 . 5$ (Plate I, figures 17 and 21). Let us draw one diagonal in each of the 30 squares of the rhombicosidodecahedron, choosing between the two possible diagonals in such a way that just one of these new lines shall pass through each of the 60 vertices. (The choice in the first square determines that in all the rest.) Each square has now been divided into two right-angled isosceles triangles ; by distorting these into equilateral triangles we obtain the snub dodecahedron.‡ The snub cube is similarly derivable from the rhombicuboctahedron, provided we remember to operate only on the 12 squares that correspond to the edges of the cube (and not on the 6 squares that correspond to its faces). The tessellation $3^4 . 6$ may be regarded as a " snub 6^3," and $3^2 . 4 . 3 . 4$ as a " snub 4^4." Moreover, the " snub tetrahedron " is the icosahedron 3^5, as derived from the cuboctahedron (or " rhombi-tetra-tetrahedron ").

---

* The " truncated n^m " is $m . (2n)^2$. See Plate I, figures 11, 16, 15, 22, 25.

† On account of this distortion, the truncated cuboctahedron ($4 . 6 . 8$) is sometimes called the " great rhombicuboctahedron," and then $3 . 4^3$ is called the *small* rhombicuboctahedron ; similarly for the truncated icosidodecahedron and rhombicosidodecahedron.

‡ This name is unfortunate, since the figure is related to the icosahedron just as closely as to the dodecahedron. " Snub icosidodecahedron " would be far better.

The snub cube and the snub dodecahedron both occur in two enantiomorphous varieties. Their metrical properties involve the solution of cubic equations, whereas those of the reflexible Archimedeans (and of the regulars) involve nothing worse than square roots; in other words, the reflexibles are capable of Euclidean construction, but the two proper snubs are not.

MRS. STOTT'S CONSTRUCTION

The above description of the Archimedean solids is essentially Kepler's. A far more elegant construction for the reflexible

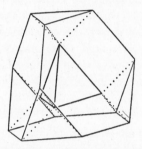

(1) *Tetrahedron and Truncated Tetrahedron.*

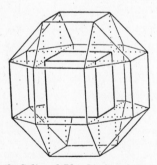

(2) *Cube and Rhombicuboctahedron.*   (3) *Truncated Cube and Cuboctahedron.*

figures has been devised by Alicia Boole Stott.* Her method is free from any employment of distortion, and the final edge-length is the same as that of the regular solid

* *Verhandelingen der Koninklijke Akademie van Wetenschappen,* Amsterdam, 1910, vol. XI, No. 1.

from which we start.   In the process called *expansion*, certain sets of elements (viz., edges or faces) are moved directly away from the centre, retaining their size and orientation, until the consequent interstices can be filled with new regular faces. The reverse process is called *contraction*.   By expanding any regular solid according to its edges, we derive the " truncated " variety.   By expanding the cube (or the octahedron) according to its faces, we derive the rhombicuboctahedron, $3 . 4^3$.   By expanding this according to its 12 squares which correspond to the edges of the cube, or by expanding the truncated cube according to its octagons, we derive the truncated cuboctahedron, $4 . 6 . 8$.   By contracting the truncated cube according to its triangles, we derive the cuboctahedron.   And so on. Mrs. Stott has represented these processes by a compact symbolism, and extended them to space of more than three dimensions, where they are extraordinarily fruitful.

EQUILATERAL ZONOHEDRA

The solids that I am about to describe were first investigated by E. von Fedorow.*   Their interest has lately been enhanced by P. S. Donchian's observation that they may be regarded as three-dimensional projections of n-dimensional *hyper-cubes* (or *measure-polytopes*, or *regular orthotopes* †).   Their edges are all equal, and their faces are generally rhombs, but sometimes higher " parallel-sided $2m$-gons "—*i.e.* equilateral $2m$-gons whose opposite sides are parallel.   The subject begins with the following theorem on polygonal dissection.

Every parallel-sided $2m$-gon (and, in particular, every

* *Zeitschrift für Krystallographie und Mineralogie*, 1893, vol. XXI, p. 689; *Russisch-kaiserliche Mineralogische Gesellschaft Verhandlungen*, 1885, vol. XXI, Abschnitt IV. (The latter periodical is to be found, under the title " Mineralogicheskoe obshchestvo, Leningrad," in the American Museum of Natural History, New York.)

† L. Schläfli, *Quarterly Journal of Mathematics*, 1860, vol. III, p. 66 : " (4, 3, 3, . . ., 3)."   C. H. Hinton, *The Fourth Dimension*, London, 1906; P. H. Schoute, *Mehrdimensionale Geometrie*, Leipzig, 1905, vol. II, pp. 243—246; D. M. Y. Sommerville, *An Introduction to the Geometry of* n *Dimensions*, London, 1929, pp. 49, 171, 182, 190.

regular $2m$-gon) can be dissected * into $\frac{1}{2}m(m-1)$ rhombs of the same length of side. This is easily proved by induction, since every parallel-sided $2(m+1)$-gon can be derived from a parallel-sided $2m$-gon by adding a "ribbon" of m rhombs. In fact, the pairs of parallel sides of such a $2m$-gon can take any m different directions, and there is a component rhomb for every pair of these directions; hence the number $\frac{1}{2}m(m-1)$. For two perpendicular directions, the rhomb is a square.

Consider now any sheaf of n lines through one point of space,† and suppose first that no three of the lines are coplanar. Then there is a polyhedron whose faces consist of $n(n-1)$

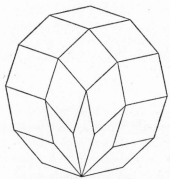

Fifteen Rhombs in a Dodecagon.

rhombs, and whose edges, in sets of $2(n-1)$, are parallel to the n given lines. In fact, for every pair of the n lines, there is a pair of opposite faces whose sides lie in those directions. To construct this *equilateral zonohedron*, imagine a plane through any one of the n lines, gradually rotating through a complete turn. Each time that this plane passes through one of the other $n-1$ lines, take a rhomb whose edges are parallel to the two lines, and juxtapose it to the rhomb previously found (without changing its orientation). This process leads eventually to a closed ribbon of $2(n-1)$ rhombs. By fixing our attention on another of the n lines, we obtain another

* In how many ways?   † This construction is due to P. S. Donchian.

such ribbon, having two parallel faces in common with the first. When a sufficient number of these ribbons (or *zones*) have been added, the polyhedron is complete.

If m of the n lines are coplanar, we have a pair of opposite parallel-sided $2m$-gons, to replace $\frac{1}{2}m(m-1)$ pairs of opposite rhombs. If these m lines are symmetrically disposed, the $2m$-gons will be regular.

In this manner, three perpendicular lines lead to a cube, and three lines of general direction to a *rhombohedron* * (or rhombic prism). More generally, m coplanar lines and one other line lead to a parallel-sided $2m$-gonal prism (a *right* prism if the " other " line is perpendicular to the plane of the first m).

The four " diameters " of the cube (joining pairs of opposite vertices) lead to the rhombic dodecahedron, the six diameters of the icosahedron lead to the triacontahedron, and the ten diameters of the (pentagonal) dodecahedron lead to an *enneacontahedron* † whose faces are 30 rhombs of one kind and 60 of another. The six diameters of the cuboctahedron lead to the truncated octahedron, whose faces are 6 squares and 8 hexagons (the equivalent of 8×3 rhombs), and the fifteen diameters of the icosidodecahedron lead to the truncated icosidodecahedron, whose faces are 30 squares, 20 hexagons ($= 20 \times 3$ rhombs) and 12 decagons ($= 12 \times 10$ rhombs). As a final example, the nine diameters of the octahedron and cuboctahedron (taken together in corresponding positions) ‡ lead to the truncated cuboctahedron, whose faces are 12 squares, 8 hexagons ($= 24$ rhombs) and 6 octagons ($= 36$ rhombs). (See Plate I, figures 10, 18, 24, 16, 26, 19.)

As in these examples, so in general, the solid has the same type of symmetry as the given sheaf of lines. A rhombic

---

* In using this term, I do not mean to imply that the six rhombic faces are all alike.

† This somewhat resembles a figure described by A. Sharp, *Geometry Improv'd*, p. 87.

‡ *I.e.*, perpendiculars to the nine planes of symmetry of the cube (or of the octahedron).

$n(n-1)$-hedron having the symmetry of a right regular prism occurs for every value of n, being given by a sheaf of n lines symmetrically disposed around a cone.* The faces are all alike when n is 3 ; they can be all alike when n is 4 or 5, if the lines are suitably chosen, viz., if the angle between alternate lines is supplementary to the angle between consecutive lines. Then $n = 4$ gives the rhombic dodecahedron; $n = 5$ gives a *rhombic icosahedron* † (Plate I, figure 14) which can be derived from the triacontahedron by removing any one of the zones and bringing together the two pieces into which the remainder of the surface is thereby divided.

Fedorow's general zonohedron can be derived from the equilateral zonohedron by lengthening or shortening all the edges that lie in each particular direction. Thus rhombic faces become parallelograms, and " parallel-sided $2m$-gons " cease to be equilateral. When each higher face is replaced by its proper number of parallelograms,‡ we have $F = n(n-1)$, $E = 2F$, and $V = F + 2$. The following theorem is irresistibly suggested, although a proof is still lacking. *If all the faces of a convex polyhedron are parallelograms, their number is of the form $n(n-1)$.*

One final remark on this subject : there is a three-dimensional analogue for the theorem that a parallel-sided $2m$-gon can be dissected into $\frac{1}{2}m(m-1)$ parallelograms. The zonohedron can be dissected into $\frac{1}{6}n(n-1)(n-2)$ parallelepipeds (viz., one for every three of the n directions).

THE KEPLER–POINSOT POLYHEDRA

By producing the sides of a regular pentagon till they meet again, we derive the star-pentagon or pentacle or *pentagram*, which has long been used as a mystic symbol. We may regard the pentagram as a generalized polygon, having five sides

---

* This family of polyhedra has been investigated by C. H. H. Franklin, *Mathematical Gazette*, 1937, vol. XXI, p. 363.

† Fedorow, *loc. cit.* (" Isozonoëder ").

‡ Fedorow, *loc. cit.* (Satz 27).

which enclose the centre twice. Each side subtends an angle $\frac{4}{5}\pi$ at the centre, whereas each side of an ordinary n-gon subtends an angle $2\pi/n$. Thus the pentagram behaves as if it were an n-gon with $n = \frac{5}{2}$. Analogously, any rational number n (> 2) leads to a polygon, the numerator giving the number of sides, and the denominator the " density " (or " species ").

This process of " stellation " may also be applied in space. The stellated faces of the regular dodecahedron meet by fives at twelve new vertices, forming the *small stellated dodecahedron* $(\frac{5}{2})^5$. These new vertices belong also to an icosahedron. By inserting the edges of this icosahedron, but keeping the original twelve facial planes, we obtain a polyhedron whose faces are twelve ordinary pentagons, while the section near a vertex is a

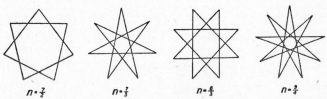

$n \cdot \frac{7}{2}$　　　　$n \cdot \frac{7}{3}$　　　　$n \cdot \frac{8}{3}$　　　　$n \cdot \frac{9}{4}$

pentagram; this is the *great dodecahedron*,* $5^{5/2}$. It is reciprocal to $(\frac{5}{2})^5$, as its symbol implies. By stellating the faces of $5^{5/2}$, we derive the *great stellated dodecahedron*, $(\frac{5}{2})^3$, which has the twenty vertices of an ordinary dodecahedron. Its reciprocal, the *great icosahedron* † $3^{5/2}$, has twenty triangular faces, and its vertices are those of an ordinary icosahedron. (See Plate II, figures 31, 34, 32, 30.)

Thus we increase the number of finite regular polyhedra from five to nine. The easiest way to see that these exhaust all the possibilities ‡ is by observing that the " Petrie polygon " of n^m is still characterized by the number h, where

$$\cos^2 (\pi/h) = \cos^2 (\pi/m) + \cos^2 (\pi/n),$$

---

* The *Encyclopaedia Britannica* (XIVth edition, article " Solids ") unhappily calls this the " small stellated dodecahedron," and *vice versa*. (Cf. the XIth edition, article " Polyhedron.")

† Good drawings of these figures are given by Lucas (in his *Récréations Mathématiques*), vol. II, pp. 206—208, 224.

‡ This was first proved (another way) by Cauchy, *Journal de l'École Polytechnique*, 1813, vol. IX, pp. 68—86.

even when m and n are not integers.   Writing this equation in the symmetrical form

$$\cos^2 (\pi/m) + \cos^2 (\pi/n) + \cos^2 (\pi/k) = 1$$

(where $1/k + 1/h = \frac{1}{2}$), we find its rational solutions to be the three permutations of 3, 3, 4, and the six permutations of 3, 5, $\frac{5}{2}$, making nine in all, as required.

The polyhedra $(\frac{5}{2})^5$ and $5^{5/2}$ fail to satisfy Euler's Theorem, $V - E + F = 2$, which holds for all ordinary polyhedra. The reason for this failure (which apparently induced Schläfli * to deny the existence of these two figures) will appear in Chapter VIII.   However, all the nine finite regular polyhedra satisfy the following extended theorem, due to Cayley :

$$d_V V - E + d_F F = 2D,$$

where d_F is the " density " of a face (viz., 1 for an ordinary polygon, 2 for a pentagram), d_V is the density of a vertex (or rather, of the section near a vertex), and D is the density of the whole polyhedron (*i.e.* the number of times the faces enclose the centre).

n^m	V	E	F	D	Name	Discoverer
$(\frac{5}{2})^5$	12	30	12	3	Small stellated dodecahedron	Kepler (1619)
$(\frac{5}{2})^3$	20	30	12	7	Great stellated dodecahedron	,,
$5^{5/2}$	12	30	12	3	Great dodecahedron	Poinsot (1809)
$3^{5/2}$	12	30	20	7	Great icosahedron	,,

" Archimedean " star polyhedra have been investigated,[†] but are beyond the scope of this book.

THE 59 ICOSAHEDRA

Imagine a large block of wood with a small tetrahedron or cube (somehow) drawn in the middle.   If we make saw-cuts

* *Quarterly Journal of Mathematics*, 1860, vol. III, pp. 66, 67. He defined " $(\frac{5}{2}, 3)$, $(3, \frac{5}{2})$," but not " $(\frac{5}{2}, 5)$, $(5, \frac{5}{2})$."

† Badoureau, *Journal de l'École Polytechnique*, 1881, vol. XXX, pp. 47— 172.

along all the facial planes of the small solid, and throw away all the pieces that extend to the surface of the block, nothing remains but the small solid itself.   But if, instead of a tetrahedron or cube, we start with an octahedron, we shall be left with nine pieces : the octahedron itself, and a tetrahedron on each face, converting it into a *stella octangula* which has the appearance of two interpenetrating tetrahedra (the regular compound mentioned above).   Similarly, a dodecahedron leads to $1 + 12 + 30 + 20$ pieces : the dodecahedron itself, twelve pentagonal pyramids which convert this into the small stellated dodecahedron, thirty wedge-shaped tetrahedra which convert the latter into the great dodecahedron, and twenty triangular double-pyramids which convert this last into the great stellated dodecahedron.

Finally, the icosahedron * leads to $1 + 20 + 30 + 60 + 20 + 60 + 120 + 12 + 30 + 60 + 60$ pieces, which can be put together to form 32 different reflexible solids, all having the full icosahedral symmetry, and 27 pairs of enantiomorphous solids, having only the symmetry of rotation.   The former set of solids includes the original icosahedron, the compound of five octahedra (made of the first $1 + 20 + 30$ pieces), the compound of ten tetrahedra (made of the first $1 + 20 + 30 + 60 + 20 + 60 + 120$ pieces), and the great icosahedron (made of all save the last 60 pieces).   The latter set includes the compound of five tetrahedra, and a number of more complicated figures having the same attractively " twisted " appearance.†

SOLID TESSELLATIONS

Just as there are many symmetrical ways of filling a plane with regular polygons, so there are many symmetrical ways of

* A. H. Wheeler, *Proceedings of the International Mathematical Congress, Toronto*, 1924, vol. I, pp. 701—708. M. Brückner, *Vielecke und Vielflache*, Leipzig, 1900 (Plate VIII, Nos 2, 26; Plate IX, Nos. 3, 6, 11, 17, 20; Plate X, No. 3; Plate XI, Nos. 14, 24).

† For J. F. Petrie's exquisite drawings of all these figures, see " The 59 Icosahedra," *University of Toronto Studies* (Mathematical Series), No. 6, 1938.

filling space with regular and Archimedean solids. For the
sake of brevity, let us limit our discussion to those ways in
which all the edges (as well as all the vertices) are surrounded
alike. Of such "solid tessellations" there are just five,* an
edge being surrounded by (i) four cubes, or (ii) two tetrahedra
and two octahedra, arranged alternately, or (iii) a tetrahedron
and three truncated tetrahedra, or (iv) three truncated
octahedra, or (v) an octahedron and two cuboctahedra. Let

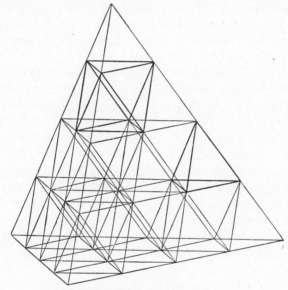

The Solid Tessellation [3⁴].

us denote these by the symbols [4⁴], [3⁴], [3² . 6²], [4 . 6²],
[3² . 4], which indicate the polygons (interfaces) that meet at
an edge.

The "regular" space-filling [4⁴] is familiar. It is "self-
reciprocal" in the sense that the centres of all the cubes are
the vertices of an identical space-filling. Its alternate vertices
give the space-filling [3⁴], one tetrahedron being inscribed in

* A. Andreini, *Memorie della Società italiana delle Scienze*, 1905, series 2,
vol. xiv, pp. 75—129, figs. 12, 15, 14, 18, 33.

each cube, and one octahedron surrounding each omitted vertex. This has a particularly high degree of regularity (although its solids are of two kinds, unlike those of [4⁴]) ; for, not merely the vertices and edges, but also the triangular interfaces, are all surrounded alike ; in fact, each triangle belongs to one solid of either kind.   If we join the centres of adjacent solids, by lines perpendicular to the interfaces, and by planes perpendicular to the edges, we obtain the " reciprocal " space-filling, say [3⁴]′ ; this consists of rhombic dodecahedra, of which four surround some vertices (originally centres of tetrahedra), while six surround others (originally centres of octahedra).

The space-filling [3² . 6²] can be derived from [3⁴] by making each of a certain set of tetrahedra of the latter adhere to its four adjacent octahedra and to six other tetrahedra which connect these in pairs, so as to form a truncated tetrahedron.* Thus [3² . 6²] has half the vertices of [3⁴], which in turn has half the vertices of [4⁴].

The space-filling of truncated octahedra, [4 . 6²], is reciprocal to a space-filling of " isosceles " tetrahedra (or tetragonal bisphenoids) whose vertices belong to two reciprocal [4⁴]'s (the " body-centred cubic lattice " of crystallography). The vertices of [3² . 4] are the mid-points of the edges (or the centres of the squares) of [4⁴].

BALL-PILING OR CLOSE-PACKING

A large box can be filled with a number of small equal spheres arranged in horizontal layers, one on top of another, in various ways, of which I will describe three.   It might be filled so that each sphere rests on the top of the sphere immediately below it in the next layer, touches each of four adjacent spheres in the same layer, and touches one sphere in the layer above it ; thus each sphere is in contact with six others.   Or we might slightly

---

* Analogously, any of the plane tessellations 6³, (3 . 6)², 3⁴ . 6 may be derived from 3⁶ by making certain sets of six triangles coalesce to form hexagons.

spread out the spheres of each layer, so as to be not quite in contact, and let each sphere rest on four in the layer below and help to support four in the layer above, the " spreading out " being adjusted so that the points of contact are at the vertices of a cube. We might also fill the box with spheres arranged so that each of them is in contact with four spheres in the next lower layer, with four in the same layer, and with four in the next higher layer. This last arrangement is known as *normal piling* or *spherical close-packing*; it gives the greatest number of spheres with which the box can be filled. (Although it is impossible for one sphere to touch more than twelve others of the same size, we shall see later that there are many different ways of packing equal spheres so that each touches exactly twelve others.)

These three arrangements may be described as follows. In the first, the centres of the spheres are at the vertices of the space-filling $[4^4]$, and the spheres themselves are inscribed in the cubes of the reciprocal $[4^4]$. In the second, the spheres are inscribed in the truncated octahedra of $[4 . 6^2]$ (touching the hexagons, but just missing the squares). In the third, the spheres are inscribed in the rhombic dodecahedra of $[3^4]'$, and their centres are at the vertices of $[3^4]$.

Now, the vertices of $[3^4]$ form triangular tessellations 3^6 in a series of parallel planes.

$$
\begin{array}{cccccccc}
A & & A & & A & & A \\
 & B & & B & & B & \\
C & & C & & C & & C \\
 & A & & A & & A & \\
B & & B & & B & & B \\
 & C & & C & & C & \\
A & & A & & A & & A \\
 & B & & B & & B & \\
C & & C & & C & & C
\end{array}
$$

Our figure shows a "plan" of this arrangement of points, projected orthogonally on one of the planes, which we take to be horizontal. The points A are projected from one plane, the points B from the next, C from the next, A again from the next, and so on, in cyclic order. Now imagine solid spheres centred at all these points. The points A give a layer of close-packed spheres, each touching six others. The points B represent another such layer, resting on the first; each sphere of either layer touches three of the other. The points C represent a third layer, resting on the second; but an equally "economical" piling of spheres is obtained if the centres of the third layer lie above the points A again, instead of lying above the points C. And so, at every stage, the new layer may or may not lie vertically above the last but one.

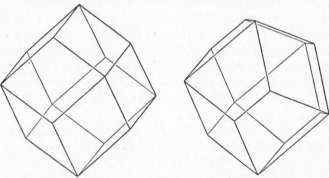

(1) *Rhombic Dodecahedron.*   (2) *Trapezo-Rhombic Dodecahedron.*

The arrangement $ABCABC\ldots$ represents spherical close-packing; on the other hand, the arrangement $ABABAB\ldots$ is known as *hexagonal* close-packing. If a large number of plastic spheres, made of bread or putty, are shaken and then squeezed together, those near the middle tend to form rhombic dodecahedra, showing that they were shaken into spherical close-packing. If we deliberately arrange them in hexagonal close-packing before squeezing, the form of each will be an irregular solid bounded by six rhombs and six trapezia.*

* Cf. Steinhaus, *Mathematical Snapshots*, New York, 1938, p. 88.

We also find an approximation to normal piling in a mass of soap-bubbles; the size being uniform, each bubble takes the form of a rhombic dodecahedron.

The two aspects of normal piling are well illustrated by the geometrical interpretation of tetrahedral and pyramidal numbers (see page 59). We know that $\frac{1}{6}n(n+1)(n+2)$ cannon-balls can be piled in the form of a tetrahedron, and that $\frac{1}{6}n(n+1)(2n+1)$ can be piled in the form of a square pyramid; in *both* cases the piling is " normal."

If you stand on wet sand, near the sea-shore, it is very noticeable that the sand gets comparatively dry around your feet, whereas the footprints that you leave contain free water. The following explanation is due, I believe, to Osborne Reynolds. The grains of sand, rolled into approximately spherical shape by the motion of the sea, have been deposited in something like normal piling. The pressure of your feet disturbs this piling, increasing the interstices between the grains. Water is sucked in from round about, to fill up these enlarged interstices. When you remove your feet, the normal piling is partially restored, and the water is left above.

Regular Sponges

The definition of regularity on page 130 depends on two symmetries, which, in every case so far discussed, are *rotations*. By allowing the number of vertices, edges and faces to be infinite, this definition includes the plane tessellations 3^6, 6^3, 4^4. It would be absurd to allow each face to have infinitely many sides, or to allow infinitely many faces to surround one vertex; therefore the special symmetries must be periodic. However, they need not be rotations; they may be rotary reflections. (A rotary reflection is 'the combination of a rotation and a reflection, which may always be chosen so that the axis of the rotation is perpendicular to the reflecting plane.) Such an operation interchanges the " inside " and " outside " of the polyhedron; consequently the inside and outside are identical, and the polyhedron (dividing space into two equal parts) must be infinite. The dihedral angles

at the edges of a given face are alternately positive and negative, and the edges at a vertex lie alternately on the two sides
of a certain plane. This allows the sum of the face-angles
at a vertex to exceed 2π.

It can be proved that the polyhedra n^m of this type are given
by the integral solutions of the equation

$$2 \sin (\pi/m) \sin (\pi/n) = \cos (\pi/k),$$

namely 6^6 ($k = 3$), 6^4 and 4^6 ($k = 4$), 6^3 and 3^6 ($k = 6$), and
4^4 ($k = \infty$). The three plane tessellations occur because a
plane rotation may be regarded indifferently as a rotation in
space or as a rotary reflection. The three new figures are
" sponges " with k-gonal holes.*

The faces of 6^6 are the hexagons of the solid tessellation
$[3^2 . 6^2]$; those of 6^4 are the hexagons of $[4 . 6^2]$; and those of
4^6 are half the squares of $[4^4]$. The remaining interfaces of
the solid tessellations appear as holes. The sponges 6^4 and
4^6 (discovered by J. F. Petrie in 1926) are *reciprocal*, in the
sense that the vertices of each are the centres of the faces of
the other; † 6^6 is self-reciprocal, or rather, reciprocal to another
equal 6^6.

* For photographs of models, see Coxeter, *Proceedings of the London
Mathematical Society*, 1937, series 2, vol. XLIII, p. 34, where the three sponges
are denoted by {6,6 | 3}, {6,4 | 4}, {4,6 | 4}.

† Plane tessellations can be reciprocal in this sense, but finite polyhedra
cannot. The centres of the faces of an octahedron are the vertices of a
cube, while the vertices of the octahedron are the centres of the faces of
another (larger) cube.

To make a model of 6^6, cut out sets of four hexagons (of thin cardboard), stick each set together in the form of the hexagonal faces of a truncated tetrahedron (3 . 6^2), and then stick the sets together, hexagon on hexagon, taking care that no edge shall belong to more than two faces. (In the finished model, the faces are double, which makes for greater strength besides facilitating the construction.) Similarly, to make 6^4, use sets of eight hexagons, forming the hexagonal faces of truncated octahedra (4 . 6^2). Finally, to make 4^6, use rings of four squares. This last model, however, is not rigid; it can gradually collapse, the square holes becoming rhombic. (In fact, I once received, by post, an extensive model, flat in an envelope).

ROTATING RINGS OF TETRAHEDRA

J. M. Andreas and R. M. Stalker have independently discovered a family of non-rigid finite polyhedra having $2n$ vertices, $6n$ edges (of which $2n$ coincide in pairs) and $4n$

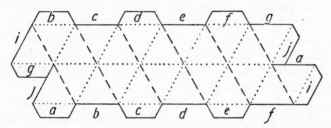

triangular faces, for $n = 6$ or 8 or any greater integer. The faces are those of n tetrahedra, joined together in cyclic order at a certain pair of opposite edges of each, so as to form a kind of ring. When $n = 6$, the range of mobility is quite small, but when $n = 8$, the ring can turn round indefinitely, like a smoke-ring. When n is even, the figure tends to take up a symmetrical position; it is particularly pretty when $n = 10$.*

* One of the " Stephanoids " described by M. Brückner in his *Vielecke und Vielflache*, p. 216 (and Plate VIII, No. 4) consists of a ring of ten irregular tetrahedra.

When n is odd, the entire lack of symmetry seems to make the motion still more fascinating. When $n \geqslant 22$, the ring can occur in a knotted form.

A model of any such ring may be made from a single sheet of paper. For the case when $n = 6$, copy the above diagram, cut it out, bend the paper along the inner lines, upwards or downwards according as these lines are broken or dotted, and stick the flaps in the manner indicated by the lettering. The ends have to be joined somewhat differently when n is a multiple of 4 (see figure xxxiv, page 216). When n is odd, either method of joining can be used at will.

Since there are two types of edge, such a polyhedron is not regular, and no symmetry is lost by making the triangles isosceles instead of equilateral. If the doubled edges are sufficiently short compared to the others, the ring with $n = 6$ * can be made to turn completely, like the rings with $n \geqslant 8$.

The Kaleidoscope †

The ordinary kaleidoscope consists essentially of two plane mirrors, inclined at $\pi/3$ or $\pi/4$, and an object (or set of objects) placed in the angle between them so as to be reflected in both. The result is that the object is seen 6 or 8 times (according to the angle), in an attractively symmetrical arrangement. By making a hinge to connect two (unframed) mirrors, the angle between them can be varied at will, and it is clear that an angle π/n gives $2n$ images (including the object itself). As a limiting case, we have two parallel mirrors and a theoretically infinite number of images (restricted in practice only by the brightness of the illumination and the quality of the mirrors). If the object is a point on the bisector of the angle between the mirrors, the images are the vertices of a regular $2n$-gon.

* Such a ring (of six tetragonal bisphenoids) has been on sale in the United States as a child's toy, with letters of the alphabet on its 24 faces. (Patent No. 1,997,022, issued in 1935.) Michael Goldberg has remarked that a ring of such elongated tetrahedra is also possible with $n = 7$.

† E. Hess, *Neues Jahrbuch für Mineralogie, Geologie und Palaeontologie*, 1889, vol. I, pp. 54—65.

If the object is a point on one of the mirrors, the images coincide in pairs at the vertices of a regular n-gon. The point may be represented in practice by a candle, or by a little ball of plastic clay or putty.

Regarding the two mirrors as being vertical, let us introduce a third vertical mirror in such a way that each pair of the three mirrors makes an angle of the form π/n. In other words, any horizontal section is to be a triangle of angles π/l, π/m, π/n, where l, m, n are integers. The solutions of the consequent equation

$$\frac{1}{l} + \frac{1}{m} + \frac{1}{n} = 1$$

are $3, 3, 3$; $2, 3, 6$; $2, 4, 4$. In each case the number of images is infinite. By varying the position of a point-object in the triangle, we obtain the vertices of certain isogonal tessellations.* In particular, if the point is taken at a vertex of the triangle, or where an angle-bisector meets the opposite side, or at the in-centre (where all three angle-bisectors concur), then the tiles of the tessellation are regular polygons. In the notation of page 107, the results of putting the point in these various positions are as indicated in the following diagrams.

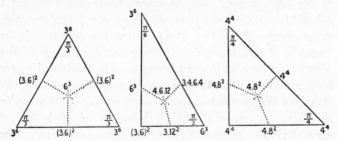

The network of triangles, which the mirrors appear to create, may be coloured alternately white and black. By taking a suitable point within every triangle of one colour

* Placing a lighted candle between three (unframed) mirrors, the reader will see an extraordinarily pretty effect.

(but ignoring the corresponding point within every triangle of the other colour), we obtain the vertices of 3^6 (again), $3^4 \cdot 6$, and $3^2 \cdot 4 \cdot 3 \cdot 4$, respectively. (The remaining uniform tessellation, $3^3 \cdot 4^2$, is not derivable by any such method.) The above diagrams reveal many relationships between the various tessellations: that the vertices of 3^6 occur among the vertices of 6^3, that the vertices of 6^3 trisect the edges of (another) 3^6, that the vertices of one 4^4 bisect the edges of another, and so on.

If the third mirror is placed horizontally instead of vertically —*i.e.* if the two hinged mirrors stand upon it—the number of images is no longer infinite; in fact, it is $4n$, where π/n is the angle between the two vertical mirrors. For a point on one of the vertical mirrors, the images coincide in pairs at the vertices of an n-gonal prism. Two of the three dihedral angles between pairs of the three mirrors are now right angles. A natural generalization is the case where these three angles are π/l, π/m, π/n.

Since, for any reflection in a plane mirror, object and image are equidistant from the plane, we easily see that all the images of a point in this generalized kaleidoscope lie on a sphere, whose centre is the point of intersection of the planes of the three mirrors. On the sphere, these planes cut out a spherical triangle, of angles π/l, π/m, π/n. The resulting image-planes divide the whole sphere into a network (or "map") of such triangles, each containing one image of any object placed within the first triangle. The number of images is therefore equal to the number of such triangles that will suffice to fill the whole spherical surface. Taking the radius as unity, the area of the whole sphere is 4π, while that of each triangle is $(\pi/l) + (\pi/m) + (\pi/n) - \pi$. Hence the required number is

$$4/\left(\frac{1}{l} + \frac{1}{m} + \frac{1}{n} - 1\right).$$

Since this must be positive, the numbers l, m, n have to be chosen so as to satisfy

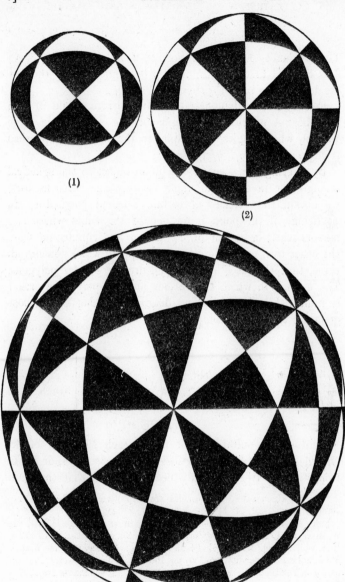

(1)

(2)

(3)

$$\frac{1}{l} + \frac{1}{m} + \frac{1}{n} > 1.$$

This inequality has the solutions 2, 2, n; 2, 3, 3; 2, 3, 4; 2, 3, 5. The first case has already been mentioned; the rest are depicted on page 157 (by J. F. Petrie).

For a practical demonstration, the mirrors should in each case be cut as circular sectors (of the same fairly large radius), whose angles * are equal to the sides of a spherical triangle of angles π/l, π/m, π/n.

By varying the position of a point-object in the spherical triangle (or in the solid angle between the three mirrors) we obtain the vertices of certain isogonal polyhedra. In particular, if the point is on one of the edges where two mirrors meet, or on one of the mirrors and equidistant from the other two, or at the centre of a sphere which touches all three, then the faces of the polyhedra are regular polygons. The manner in which the various uniform polyhedra arise † is indicated in the following diagrams, analogous to those given for tessellations on page 155.

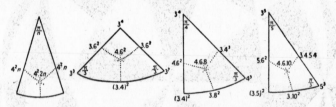

By taking a suitable point within each white (or black) triangle,‡ we obtain the vertices of $3^3 . n$, 3^5, $3^4 . 4$, or $3^4 . 5$, respectively. It has already been remarked that the snub

* In the three cases, these angles are respectively: 54° 44′, 54° 44′, 70° 32′; 35° 16′, 45°, 54° 44′; 20° 54′, 31° 43′, 37° 23′.

† See Möbius, *Gesammelte Werke*, 1861, vol. II, p. 656, figs. 47, 51, 54; W. A. Wythoff, *Proceedings of the Royal Academy of Sciences, Amsterdam*, 1918, vol. XX, pp. 966—970; G. de B. Robinson, *Journal of the London Mathematical Society*, 1931, vol. VI, pp. 70—75; H. S. M. Coxeter, *Proceedings of the London Mathematical Society*, 1935, series 2, vol. XXXVIII, pp. 327—339.

‡ Möbius, *loc. cit.*, figs. 46, 49, 53.

cube $3^4 \cdot 4$ exists in two enantiomorphous forms; the vertices of one form lie in the white triangles, those of the other in the black. The same thing happens in the case of the snub dodecahedron, $3^4 \cdot 5$.

By introducing a fourth mirror, we obtain solid tessellations. Tetrahedra of three different shapes can be formed by four planes inclined at angles that are submultiples of π. These three shapes can conveniently be cut out from a rectangular block of dimensions $1 \times \sqrt{2} \times \sqrt{2}$. Suppose $ABCD$ to be a horizontal square of side $\sqrt{2}$, at height 1 above an equal square $A'B'C'D'$. After cutting off the alternate corners A', B, C', D, by planes through sets of three other vertices, we are left with the tetragonal bisphenoid $AB'CD'$, which is

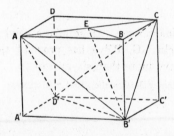

one of the required shapes. Another is any one of the corner pieces that were cut off, such as $ABCB'$. (Two such pieces can be fitted together to make a shape just like $AB'CD'$.) The third is obtained by cutting $ABCB'$ in half along its plane of symmetry, which is the plane $BB'E$, where E is the mid-point of AC. One half is $AEBB'$. Note that the edges AE, EB, BB' are three equal lines in three perpendicular directions.

A point-object in such a tetrahedron will give rise to the vertices of a solid tessellation in various ways,* some of which are indicated in the following diagrams (which show $AB'CD'$, $ABCB'$, $AEBB'$, in the same orientation as before).

Five mirrors can be arranged in the form of certain triangular

---

* Andreini, *loc. cit.* (p. 147 above), figs. 17—24 bis.

prisms; these lead to solid tessellations of prisms. Six can
be arranged rectangularly in three pairs of parallels, as when
we have a mirror in the ceiling and floor as well as all four

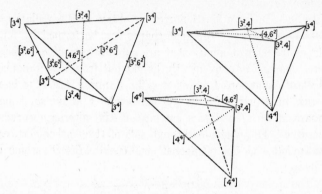

walls of an ordinary room; these give a solid tessellation of
rectangular blocks. G. Pólya has proved * that a kaleidoscope cannot have more than six mirrors.

* *Annals of Mathematics*, 1934, vol. xxxv, p. 594.

CHAPTER VI

CHESS-BOARD RECREATIONS

A CHESS-BOARD and chess-men lend themselves to recreations, many of which are geometrical. The problems are, however, of a distinct type, and sufficiently numerous to deserve a chapter to themselves. A few problems which might be included in this chapter have been already considered in Chapter IV.

The ordinary chess-board consists of 64 small squares, known as cells, arranged as shown below in 8 rows and 8 columns. Usually the cells are coloured alternately white and black, or white and red. The cells may be defined by the numbers 11, 12, etc., where the first digit denotes the number of the column,

18	28	38	48	58	68	78	88
17	27	37	47	57	67	77	87
16	26	36	46	56	66	76	86
15	25	35	45	55	65	75	85
14	24	34	44	54	64	74	84
13	23	33	43	53	63	73	83
12	22	32	42	52	62	72	82
11	21	31	41	51	61	71	81

and the second digit the number of the row—the two digits representing respectively the abscissa and ordinate of the midpoints of the cells. I use this notation in the following pages. A generalized board consists of n^2 cells arranged in n rows and n columns. Most of the problems which I shall describe can be extended to meet the case of a board of n^2 cells.

M

The usual chess-pieces are Kings, Queens, Bishops, Knights, and Rooks or Castles; there are also Pawns. I assume that the moves of these pieces are known to the reader.

With the game itself and with chess problems of the usual type I do not concern myself. Particular positions of the pieces may be subject to mathematical analysis, but in general the moves open to a player are so numerous as to make it impossible to see far ahead. Probably this is obvious, but it may emphasize how impossible it is to discuss the theory of the game effectively if I add that it has been shown that there may be as many as 197299 ways of playing the first four moves, and 71782 different positions at the end of the first four moves (two on each side), of which 16556 arise when the players move pawns only.*

RELATIVE VALUE OF PIECES

The first question to which I will address myself is the determination of the relative values of the different chess-pieces.†

If a piece is placed on a cell, the number of cells it commands depends in general on its position. We may estimate the value of the piece by the average number of cells which it commands when placed in succession on every cell of the board. This is equivalent to saying that the value of a piece may be estimated by the chance that if it and a king are put at random on the board, the king will be in check : if no other restriction is imposed, this is called a simple check. On whatever cell the piece is originally placed there will remain 63 other cells on which the king may be placed. It is equally probable that it may be put on any one of them. Hence the chance that it will be in check is 1/63 of the average number of cells commanded by the piece.

* *L'Intermédiaire des Mathématiciens*, Paris, December, 1903, vol. x, pp. 305—308 : also *Royal Engineers Journal*, London, August—November, 1889; or *British Association Transactions*, 1890, p. 745.

† H. M. Taylor, *Philosophical Magazine*, March, 1876, series 5, vol. i, pp. 221—229.

A rook put on any cell commands 14 other cells. Wherever the rook is placed there will remain 63 cells on which the king may be placed, and on which it is equally likely that it will be placed. Hence the chance of a simple check is 14/63, that is, 2/9. Similarly, on a board of n^2 cells the chance is $2(n - 1)/(n^2 - 1)$—that is, $2/(n + 1)$.

A knight, when placed on any of the 4 corner cells like 11, commands 2 cells. When placed on any of the 8 cells like 12 and 21, it commands 3 cells. When placed on any of the 4 cells like 22 or any of the 16 boundary cells like 13, 14, 15, 16, it commands 4 cells. When placed on any of the 16 cells like 23, 24, 25, 26, it commands 6 cells. And when placed on any of the remaining 16 middle cells, it commands 8 cells. Hence the average number of cells commanded by a knight put on a chess-board is $(4\times2+8\times3+20\times4+16\times6+16\times8)/64$—that is, 336/64. Accordingly, if a king and a knight are put on the board, the chance that the king will be in simple check is $336/(64 \times 63)$—that is, 1/12. Similarly, on a board of n^2 cells the chance is $8(n - 2)/n^2(n + 1)$.

A bishop when placed on any of the ring of 28 boundary cells commands 7 cells. When placed on any ring of the 20 cells next to the boundary cells, it commands 9 cells. When placed on any of the 12 cells forming the next ring, it commands 11 cells. When placed on the 4 middle cells, it commands 13 cells. Hence, if a king and a bishop are put on the board, the chance that the king will be in simple check is $(28\times7+20\times9+12\times11+4\times13)/(64\times63)$—that is, 5/36. Similarly, on a board of n^2 cells, when n is even, the chance is $2(2n - 1)/3n(n + 1)$. When n is odd, the analysis is longer, owing to the fact that in this case the number of white cells on the board differs from the number of black cells. I do not give the work, which presents no special difficulty.

A queen when placed on any cell of a board commands all the cells which a bishop and a rook when placed on that cell would do. Hence, if a king and a queen are put on the board, the chance that the king will be in simple check is $2/9+5/36$—

that is, 13/36. Similarly, on a board of n^2 cells, when n is even, the chance is $2(5n - 1)/3n(n + 1)$.

On the above assumptions the relative values of the rook, knight, bishop, and queen are 8, 3, 5, 13. According to Staunton's *Chess-Player's Handbook*, the actual values, estimated empirically, are in the ratio of 548, 305, 350, 994; according to Von Bilguer, the ratios are 540, 350, 360, 1000— the value of a pawn being taken as 100.

There is considerable discrepancy between the above results as given by theory and practice. It has been, however, suggested that a better test of the value of a piece would be the chance that when it and a king were put at random on the board, it would check the king without giving the king the opportunity of taking it. This is called a safe check, as distinguished from a simple check.

Applying the same method as above, the chances of a safe check work out as follows. For a rook the chance of a safe check is $(4 \times 12 + 24 \times 11 + 36 \times 10)/(64 \times 63)$—that is, 1/6—or on a board of n^2 cells is $2(n - 2)/n(n + 1)$. For a knight all checks are safe, and therefore the chance of a safe check is 1/12; or on a board of n^2 cells is $8(n - 2)/n^2(n + 1)$. For a bishop the chance of a safe check is $364/(64 \times 63)$—that is, 13/144—or on a board of n^2 cells, when n is even, is $2(n-2)(2n-3)/3n^2(n+1)$. For a queen the chance of a safe check is $1036/(64 \times 63)$—that is, $37/144$—or on a board of n^2 cells, is $2(n-2)(5n-3)/3n^2(n+1)$, when n is even.

On this view the relative values of the rook, knight, bishop, and queen are 24, 12, 13, 37 ; while, according to Staunton, experience shows that they are approximately 22, 12, 14, 40, and according to Von Bilguer, 18, 12, 12, 33.

The same method can be applied to compare the values of combinations of pieces. For instance, the value of two bishops (one restricted to white cells and the other to black cells) and two rooks, estimated by the chance of a simple check, are respectively 35/124 and 37/93. Hence on this view a queen in general should be more valuable than two bishops, but less valuable than two rooks. This agrees with experience.

An analogous problem consists in finding the chance that two kings, put at random on the board, will not occupy adjoining cells—that is, that neither would (were such a move possible) check the other. The chance is 43/48, and therefore the chance that they will occupy adjoining cells is 5/48. If three kings are put on the board, the chance that no two of them occupy adjoining cells is 1061/1488. The corresponding chances * for a board of n^2 cells are $(n - 1)(n - 2)(n^2 + 3n - 2)/n^2(n^2 - 1)$ and $(n - 1)(n - 2)(n^4 + 3n^3 - 20n^2 - 30n + 132)/n^2(n^2 - 1)(n^2 - 2)$.

THE EIGHT QUEENS PROBLEM †

One of the classical problems connected with a chess-board is the determination of the number of ways in which eight queens can be placed on a chess-board—or, more generally, in which n queens can be placed on a board of n^2 cells—so that no queen can take any other. This was proposed originally by Franz Nauck in 1850.

In 1874 Dr. S. Günther ‡ suggested a method of solution by means of determinants. For, if each symbol represents the corresponding cell of the board, the possible solutions for a board of n^2 cells are given by those terms, if any, of the determinant

$$
\begin{vmatrix}
a_1 & b_2 & c_3 & d_4 & \cdots \\
\beta_2 & a_3 & b_4 & c_5 & \cdots \\
\gamma_3 & \beta_4 & a_5 & b_6 & \cdots \\
\delta_4 & \gamma_5 & \beta_6 & a_7 & \cdots \\
\cdots & \cdots & \cdots & \cdots \\
\cdots & \cdots & a_{2n-3} & b_{2n-2} \\
\cdots & \cdots & \beta_{2n-2} & a_{2n-1}
\end{vmatrix}
$$

in which no letter and no suffix appears more than once.

* *L'Intermédiaire des Mathématiciens*, Paris, 1897, vol. IV, p. 6, and 1901, vol. VIII, p. 140.

† On the history of this problem see W. Ahrens, *Mathematische Unterhaltungen und Spiele*, Leipzig, 1901, chap. IX. For later developments, see Kraïtchik, *La Mathématique des Jeux*, Brussels, 1930, pp. 300—356.

‡ Grunert's *Archiv der Mathematik und Physik*, 1874, vol. LVI, pp. 281—292.

The reason is obvious. Every term in a determinant contains one, and only one, element out of every row and out of every column : hence any term will indicate a position on the board in which the queens cannot take one another by moves rook-wise. Again, in the above determinant the letters and suffixes are so arranged that all the same letters and all the same suffixes lie along bishop's paths : hence, if we retain only those terms in each of which all the letters and all the suffixes are different, they will denote positions in which the queens cannot take one another by moves bishop-wise. It is clear that the signs of the terms are immaterial.

In the case of an ordinary chess-board the determinant is of the 8th order, and therefore contains 8!—that is, 40320 terms—so that it would be out of the question to use this method for the usual chess-board of 64 cells or for a board of larger size unless some way of picking out the required terms could be discovered.

A way of effecting this was suggested by Dr. J. W. L. Glaisher [*] in 1874, and so far as I am aware the theory remains as he left it. He showed that if all the solutions of n queens on a board of n^2 cells were known, then all the solutions of a certain type for $n + 1$ queens on a board of $(n + 1)^2$ cells could be deduced, and that all the other solutions of $n + 1$ queens on a board of $(n + 1)^2$ cells could be obtained without difficulty. The method will be sufficiently illustrated by one instance of its application.

It is easily seen that there are no solutions when $n = 2$ or $n = 3$. If $n = 4$ there are two terms in the determinant which give solutions—namely, $b_2 c_5 \gamma_3 \beta_6$ and $c_3 \beta_2 b_6 \gamma_5$. To find the solutions when $n = 5$, Glaisher proceeded thus. In this case, Günther's determinant is

$$\begin{vmatrix} a_1 & b_2 & c_3 & d_4 & e_5 \\ \beta_2 & a_3 & b_4 & c_5 & d_6 \\ \gamma_3 & \beta_4 & a_5 & b_6 & c_7 \\ \delta_4 & \gamma_5 & \beta_6 & a_7 & b_8 \\ \epsilon_5 & \delta_6 & \gamma_7 & \beta_8 & a_9 \end{vmatrix}$$

[*] *Philosophical Magazine*, London, December, 1874, series 4, vol. XLVIII, pp. 457—467.

To obtain those solutions (if any) which involve a_9, it is sufficient to append a_9 to such of the solutions for a board of 16
cells as do not involve a. As neither of those given above
involves an a, we thus get two solutions—namely, $b_2c_5\gamma_3\beta_6a_9$
and $c_3\beta_2b_6\gamma_5a_9$. The solutions which involve a_1, e_5 and ϵ_5
can be written down by symmetry. The eight solutions thus
obtained are all distinct; we may call them of the first type.

The above are the only solutions which can involve elements
in the corner squares of the determinant. Hence the remaining
solutions are obtainable from the determinant

$$\begin{vmatrix} 0 & b_2 & c_3 & d_4 & 0 \\ \beta_2 & a_3 & b_4 & c_5 & d_6 \\ \gamma_3 & \beta_4 & a_5 & b_6 & c_7 \\ \delta_4 & \gamma_5 & \beta_6 & a_7 & b_8 \\ 0 & \delta_6 & \gamma_7 & \beta_8 & 0 \end{vmatrix}$$

If, in this, we take the minor of b_2 and in it replace by zero
every term involving the letter b or the suffix 2, we shall get
all solutions involving b_2. But in this case the minor at once
reduces to $d_6a_5\delta_4\beta_8$. We thus get one solution—namely,
$b_2d_6a_5\delta_4\beta_8$. The solutions which involve β_2, δ_4, δ_6, β_8, b_8, d_6,
and d_4 can be obtained by symmetry. Of these eight solutions
it is easily seen that only two are distinct: these may be
called solutions of the second type.

Similarly, the remaining solutions must be obtained from
the determinant

$$\begin{vmatrix} 0 & 0 & c_3 & 0 & 0 \\ 0 & a_3 & b_4 & c_5 & 0 \\ \gamma_3 & \beta_4 & a_5 & b_6 & c_7 \\ 0 & \gamma_5 & \beta_6 & a_7 & 0 \\ 0 & 0 & \gamma_7 & 0 & 0 \end{vmatrix}$$

If, in this, we take the minor of c_3, and in it replace by zero
every term involving the letter c or the suffix 3, we shall get
all the solutions which involve c_3. But in this case the minor
vanishes. Hence there is no solution involving c_3, and therefore
by symmetry no solutions which involve γ_3, γ_7, or c_7. Had
there been any solutions involving the third element in the first

or last row or column of the determinant, we should have described them as of the third type.

Thus in all there are ten, and only ten, solutions—namely, eight of the first type, two of the second type, and none of the third type.

Similarly, if $n = 6$, we obtain no solutions of the first type, four solutions of the second type, and no solutions of the third type—that is, four solutions in all. If $n = 7$, we obtain sixteen solutions of the first type, twenty-four solutions of the second type, no solutions of the third type, and no solutions of the fourth type—that is, forty solutions in all. If $n = 8$, we obtain sixteen solutions of the first type, fifty-six solutions of the second type, and twenty solutions of the third type—that is, ninety-two solutions in all.

It will be noticed that all the solutions of one type are not always distinct. In general, from any solution seven others can be obtained at once. Of these eight solutions, four consist of the initial or fundamental solution and the three similar ones obtained by turning the board through one, two, or three right angles; the other four are the reflections of these in a mirror: but in any particular case it may happen that the reflections reproduce the originals, or that a rotation through one or two right angles makes no difference. Thus on boards of 4^2, 5^2, 6^2, 7^2, 8^2, 9^2, 10^2, 11^2, 12^2 cells there are respectively 1. 2, 1, 6, 12, 46, 92, 341, 1784 fundamental solutions; while altogether there are respectively 2, 10, 4, 40, 92, 352, 724, 2680, 14200 solutions.

The following collection of fundamental solutions may interest the reader. Each position on the board of the queens is indicated by a number, but as necessarily one queen is on each column, I can use a simpler notation than that explained on page 161. In this case the first digit represents the number of the cell occupied by the queen in the first column reckoned from one end of the column, the second digit the number in the second column, and so on. Thus on a board of 4^2 cells the solution 3142 means that one queen is on the 3rd square of the first column, one on the 1st square of the second column, one on the 4th square of the third column, and one on the 2nd square of the fourth column. If a fundamental solution gives rise to only four solutions, the number which indicates it is placed in curved brackets, ( ); if it gives rise to only two solutions, the number which indicates it is placed in square brackets, [ ]; the other fundamental solutions give rise to eight solutions each.

On a board of 4^2 cells there is 1 fundamental solution—namely, [3142].

On a board of 5^2 cells there are 2 fundamental solutions—namely, 14253, [25314]. It may be noted that the cyclic solutions 14253, 25314, 31425, 42531, 53142 give five superposable arrangements by which five white queens, five black queens, five red queens, five yellow queens, and five blue queens can be put simultaneously on the board so that no queen can be taken by any other queen of the same colour.

On a board of 6^2 cells there is 1 fundamental solution—namely, (246135). The four solutions are superposable. The puzzle for this case was sold in the streets of London for a penny, a small wooden board being ruled in the manner shown in the diagram and having holes drilled in it at the points marked by dots. The object is to put six pins into the holes so that no two are connected by a straight line.

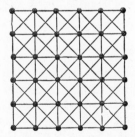

On a board of 7^2 cells there are 6 fundamental solutions: namely, 1357246, 3572461, (5724613), 4613572, 3162574, (2574136). It may be noted that the solution 1357246 gives by cyclic permutations seven superposable arrangements.

On a board of 8^2 cells, the fourth cell from some corner is always occupied. There are 12 fundamental solutions: namely, 41582736, 41586372, 42586137, 42736815, 42736851, 42751863, 42857136, 42861357, 46152837, (46827135), 47526138, 48157263. The arrangement in this order is due to J. M. Andreas. The 7th solution is the only one in which no three queens are in a straight line. It is impossible * to find eight superposable solutions; but we can in five typical ways pick out six solutions which can be superposed, and to some of these it is possible to add 2 sets of 7 queens, thus filling 62 out of the 64 cells with 6 sets of 8 queens and 2 sets of 7 queens, no one of which can take another of the same set. Here is such a solution: 16837425, 27368514, 35714286, 41586372, 52473861, 68241753, 73625140, 04152637. Similar superposition problems can be framed for boards of other sizes.

For any reader who wishes to go further, I may add that it has been shown that on a board of n^2 cells, there are 46 fundamental solutions when $n = 9$, there are 92 when $n = 10$, there are 341 when $n = 11$, there are 1766 when $n = 12$, and there are 1346 when $n = 13$.

On any board empirical solutions may be found with but little difficulty, and Mr. Derrington has constructed the following table of solutions:

2.4.1.3	for a board of	4^2 cells
2.4.1.3.5	,, ,,	5^2 ,,
2.4.6.1.3.5	,, ,,	6^2 ,,
2.4.6.1.3.5.7	,, ,,	7^2 ,,
2.4.6.8.3.1.7.5	,, ,,	8^2 ,,
2.4.1.7.9.6.3.5.8	,, ,,	9^2 ,,
2.4.6.8.10.1.3.5.7.9	,, ,,	10^2 ,,
2.4.6.8.10.1.3.5.7.9.11	,, ,,	11^2 ,,
2.4.6.8.10.12.1.3.5.7.9.11	,, ,,	12^2 ,,
2.4.6.8.10.12.1.3.5.7.9.11.13	,, ,,	13^2 ,,
9.7.5.3.1.13.11.6.4.2.14.12.10.8	,, ,,	14^2 ,,
15.9.7.5.3.1.13.11.6.4.2.14.12.10.8	,, ,,	15^2 ,,
2.4.6.8.10.12.14.16.1.3.5.7.9.11.13.15	,, ,,	16^2 ,,
2.4.6.8.10.12.14.16.1.3.5.7.9.11.13.15.17	,, ,,	17^2 ,,
2.4.6.8.10.12.14.16.18.1.3.5.7.9.11.13.15.17	,,	,,	18^2 ,,
2.4.6.8.10.12.14.16.18.1.3.5.7.9.11.13.15.17.19	,,	,,	19^2 ,,
12.10.8.6.4.2.20.18.16.14.9.7.5.3.1.19.17.15.13.11	,,	20^2 ,,
21.12.10.8.6.4.2.20.18.16.14.9.7.5.3.1.19.17.15.13.11,,		21^2 ,,

* See Thorold Gosset, *The Messenger of Mathematics*, Cambridge, July, 1914, vol. XLIV, p. 48.

and so on. The rule is obvious except when n is of the form $6m + 2$ or $6m + 3$.

MAXIMUM PIECES PROBLEM

The Eight Queens Problem suggests the somewhat analogous question of finding the maximum number of kings—or more generally of pieces of one type—which can be put on a board so that no one can take any other, and the number of solutions possible in each case.

In the case of kings the number is 16; for instance, one solution is when they are put on the cells 11, 13, 15, 17, 31, 33, 35, 37, 51, 53, 55, 57, 71, 73, 75, 77. For queens, it is obvious that the problem is covered by the analysis already given, and the number is 8. For bishops the number is 14, the pieces being put on the boundary cells; for instance, one solution is when they are put on the cells 11, 12, 13, 14, 15, 16, 17, 81, 82, 83, 84, 85, 86, 87; there are 256 solutions. For knights the number is 32; for instance, they can be put on all the white or on all the black cells, and there are 2 fundamental solutions. For rooks it is obvious that the number is 8, and there are in all 8! solutions.

MINIMUM PIECES PROBLEM

Another problem of a somewhat similar character is the determination of the minimum number of kings—or more generally of pieces of one type—which can be put on a board so as to command or occupy all the cells.

For kings the number is 9; for instance, they can be put on the cells 11, 14, 17, 41, 44, 47, 71, 74, 77. For queens the number is 5; for instance, they can be put on the cells 18, 35, 41, 76, 82. For bishops the number is 8; for instance, they can be put on the cells 41, 42, 43, 44, 45, 46, 47, 48. For knights the number is 12; for instance, they can be put on the cells 26, 32, 33, 35, 36, 43, 56, 63, 64, 66, 67, and 73—constituting four triplets arranged symmetrically. For rooks the number is 8, and the solutions are obvious.

For queens the problem has been also discussed for a board of n^2 cells where n has various values.* One queen can be placed so as to command all the cells when $n = 2$ or 3, and there is only 1 fundamental solution. Two queens are required when $n = 4$; and there are 3 fundamental solutions—namely, when they are placed on the cells 11 and 33, or on the cells 12 and 42, or on the cells 22, 23 : these give 12 solutions in all. Three queens are required when $n = 5$; and there are 37 fundamental solutions, giving 186 solutions in all. Three queens are also required when $n = 6$, but there is only 1 fundamental solution—namely, when they are put on the cells 11, 35, and 53, giving 4 solutions in all. Four queens are required when $n = 7$; one solution is when they are put on the cells 12, 26, 41, 55.

Jaenisch proposed also the problem of the determination of the minimum number of queens which can be placed on a board of n^2 cells so as to command all the unoccupied cells, subject to the restriction that no queen shall attack the cell occupied by any other queen. In this case three queens are required when $n = 4$—for instance, they can be put on the cells 11, 23, 42; and there are 2 fundamental solutions, giving 16 solutions in all. Three queens are required when $n = 5$—for instance, they can be put on the cells 11, 24, 43, or on the cells 11, 34, 53; and there are 2 fundamental solutions in all. Four queens are required when $n = 6$—for instance, when they are put on the cells 13, 36, 41, 64; and there are 17 fundamental solutions. Four queens are required when $n = 7$, and there is only 1 fundamental solution—namely, that already mentioned, when they are put on the cells 12, 26, 41, 55, which gives 8 solutions in all. Five queens are required when $n = 8$, and there are no less than 91 fundamental solutions—for instance, one is when they are put on the cells 11, 23, 37, 62, 76.

I leave to any of my readers who may be interested in such

---

* C. F. de Jaenisch, *Applications de l'Analyse Mathématique au Jeu des Échecs*, Petrograd, 1862, Appendix, pp. 244 *et seq.*; see also *L'Intermédiaire des Mathématiciens*, Paris, 1901, vol. VIII, p. 88.

questions the discussion of the corresponding problems for the
other pieces,* and of the number of possible solutions in each
case.

A problem of the same nature would be the determination
of the minimum number of queens (or other pieces) which
can be placed on a board so as to protect one another and
command all the unoccupied cells. For queens the number
is 5; for instance, they can be put on the cells 24, 34, 44,
54 and 84. For bishops the number is 10; for instance, they
can be put on the cells 24, 25, 34, 35, 44, 45, 64, 65, 74, and 75.
For knights the number is 14; for instance, they can be put on
the cells 32, 33, 36, 37, 43, 44, 45, 46, 63, 64, 65, 66, 73, and 76 :
the solution is semi-symmetrical. For rooks the number is 8,
and a solution is obvious. I leave to any who are interested
in the subject the determination of the number of solutions in
each case.

In connection with this class of problems, I may mention
two other questions, to which Captain Turton first called my
attention, of a somewhat analogous character.

The first of these is to place eight queens on a chess-board
so as to command the fewest possible squares. Thus, if queens
are placed on cells 21, 22, 62, 71, 73, 77, 82, 87, eleven cells on
the board will not be in check; the same number can be
obtained by other arrangements. Is it possible to place the
eight queens so as to leave more than eleven cells out of check ?
I have never succeeded in doing so, nor in showing that it is
impossible to do it.

The other problem is to place m queens (m being less than
5) on a chess-board so as to command as many cells as possible.
For instance, four queens can be placed in several ways on the
board so as to command 58 cells besides those on which the
queens stand, thus leaving only 2 cells which are not com-

* The problem for knights was discussed in *L'Intermédiaire des Mathématiciens*, Paris, 1896, vol. III, p. 58; 1897, vol. IV, pp. 15—17, 254; 1898,
vol. V, pp. 87, 230—231.

manded; for instance, queens may be placed on the cells 35, 41, 76, and 82. Analogous problems with other pieces will suggest themselves.

There are endless similar questions in which combinations of pieces are involved. For instance, if queens are put on the cells 35, 41, 76, and 82, they command or occupy all but two cells, and these two cells may be commanded or occupied by a queen, a king, a rook, a bishop, or a pawn. If queens are put on the cells 22, 35, 43, and 54, they command or occupy all but three cells, and two of these three cells may be commanded by a knight which occupies the third of them.

RE-ENTRANT PATHS ON A CHESS-BOARD

Another problem connected with the chess-board consists in moving a piece in such a manner that it shall move successively on to every possible cell once, and only once.

Knight's Re-entrant Path. I begin by discussing the classical problem of a knight's tour. The literature * on this subject is so extensive that I make no attempt to give a full account of the various methods for solving the problem, and I shall content myself by putting together a few notes on some of the solutions I have come across, particularly on those due to De Moivre, Euler, Vandermonde, Warnsdorff, and Roget.

On a board containing an even number of cells the path may or may not be re-entrant, but on a board containing an odd number of cells it cannot be re-entrant. For, if a knight begins on a white cell, its first move must take it to a black cell, the next to a white cell, and so on. Hence, if its path passes through all the cells, then on a board of an odd number

---

* For a bibliography see A. van der Linde, *Geschichte und Literatur des Schachspiels*, Berlin, 1874, vol. II, pp. 101—111. On the problem and its history see a memoir by P. Volpicelli in *Atti della Reale Accademia de Lincei*, Rome, 1872, vol. XXV, pp. 87—162: also *Applications de l'Analyse Mathématique au Jeu des Échecs*, by C. F. de Jaenisch, 3 vols., Petrograd 1862-3; and General Parmentier, *Association Française pour l'Avancemen des Sciences*, 1891, 1892, 1894.

of cells the last move must leave it on a cell of the same colour as that on which it started, and therefore these cells cannot be connected by one move.

The earliest solutions of which I have any knowledge are those given at the beginning of the eighteenth century by De Montmort and De Moivre.* They apply to the ordinary chess-board of 64 cells, and depend on dividing (mentally) the board into an inner square containing sixteen cells surrounded by an outer ring of cells two deep. If initially the knight is placed on a cell in the outer ring, it moves round that ring always in the same direction so as to fill it up completely—going into

34	49	22	11	36	39	24	1
21	10	35	50	23	12	37	40
48	33	62	57	38	25	2	13
9	20	51	54	63	60	41	26
32	47	58	61	56	53	14	3
19	8	55	52	59	64	27	42
46	31	6	17	44	29	4	15
7	18	45	30	5	16	43	28

30	21	6	15	28	19
7	16	29	20	5	14
22	31	8	35	18	27
9	36	17	26	13	4
32	23	2	11	34	25
1	10	33	24	3	12

De Moivre's Solution.   *Euler's Thirty-six Cell Solution.*

the inner square only when absolutely necessary. When the outer ring is filled up, the order of the moves required for filling the remaining cells presents but little difficulty. If initially the knight is placed on the inner square, the process must be reversed. The method can be applied to square and rectangular boards of all sizes. It is illustrated sufficiently by De Moivre's solution, which is given above, where the numbers indicate the order in which the cells are occupied successively. I place by its side a somewhat similar re-entrant solution, due to Euler, for a board of 36 cells. If a chess-board is used it

* They were sent by their authors to Brook Taylor who seems to have previously suggested the problem. I do not know where they were first published; they were quoted by Ozanam and Montucla, see Ozanam, 1803 edition, vol. I, p. 178; 1840 edition, p. 80.

is convenient to place a counter on each cell as the knight leaves it.

The earliest serious attempt to deal with the subject by mathematical analysis was made by Euler * in 1759 : it was due to a suggestion made by L. Bertrand of Geneva, who subsequently (in 1778) issued an account of it. This method is applicable to boards of any shape and size, but in general the solutions to which it leads are not symmetrical, and their mutual connection is not apparent.

Euler commenced by moving the knight at random over the board until it has no move open to it. With care this will leave only a few cells not traversed : denote them by $a, b, \ldots.$ His method consists in establishing certain rules by which these vacant cells can be interpolated into various parts of the circuit, and by which the circuit can be made re-entrant.

The following example, mentioned by Legendre as one of exceptional difficulty, illustrates the method. Suppose that

55	58	29	40	27	44	19	22
60	39	56	43	30	21	26	45
57	54	59	28	41	18	23	20
38	51	42	31	8	25	46	17
53	32	37	a	47	16	9	24
50	3	52	33	36	7	12	15
1	34	5	48	b	14	c	10
4	49	2	35	6	11	d	13

22	25	50	39	52	35	60	57
27	40	23	36	49	58	53	34
24	21	26	51	38	61	56	59
41	28	37	48	3	54	33	62
20	47	42	13	32	63	4	55
29	16	19	46	43	2	7	10
18	45	14	31	12	9	64	5
15	30	17	44	1	6	11	8

Figure i.   Figure ii.
Example of Euler's Method.

we have formed the route given in figure i above—namely, 1, 2, 3, . . . , 59, 60; and that there are four cells left untraversed namely, $a, b, c, d.$

We begin by making the path 1 to 60 re-entrant. The

* *Mémoires de Berlin* for 1759, Berlin, 1766, pp. 310—337; or *Commentationes Arithmeticae Collectae*, Petrograd, 1849, vol. I, pp. 337—355.

cell 1 commands a cell p, where p is 32, 52, or 2. The cell 60 commands a cell q, where q is 29, 59, or 51. Then, if any of these values of p and q differ by unity, we can make the route re-entrant. This is the case here if $p = 52$, $q = 51$. Thus the cells 1, 2, 3, ..., 51; 60, 59, ..., 52 form a re-entrant route of 60 moves. Hence, if we replace the numbers 60, 59, ..., 52 by 52, 53, ..., 60, the steps will be numbered consecutively. I recommend the reader who wishes to follow the subsequent details of Euler's argument to construct this square on a piece of paper before proceeding further.

Next, we proceed to add the cells a, b, d to this route. In the new diagram of 60 cells formed as above the cell a commands the cells there numbered 51, 53, 41, 25, 7, 5, and 3. It is indifferent which of these we select: suppose we take 51. Then we must make 51 the last cell of the route of 60 cells, so that we can continue with a, b, d. Hence, if the reader will add 9 to every number on the diagram he has constructed, and then replace 61, 62, ..., 69 by 1, 2, ..., 9, he will have a route which starts from the cell occupied originally by 60, the 60th move is on to the cell occupied originally by 51, and the 61st, 62nd, 63rd moves will be on the cells a, b, d respectively.

It remains to introduce the cell c. Since c commands the cell now numbered 25, and 63 commands the cell now numbered 24, this can be effected in the same way as the first route was made re-entrant. In fact, the cells numbered 1, 2, ..., 24; 63, 62, ..., 25, c form a knight's path. Hence we must replace 63, 62, ..., 25 by the numbers 25, 26, ..., 63, and then we can fill up c with 64. We have now a route which covers the whole board.

Lastly, it remains to make this route re-entrant. First, we must get the cells 1 and 64 near one another. This can be effected thus. Take one of the cells commanded by 1, such as 28, then 28 commands 1 and 27. Hence the cells 64, 63, ..., 28; 1, 2, ..., 27 form a route; and this will be represented in the diagram if we replace the cells numbered 1, 2, ..., 27 by 27, 26, ..., 1.

The cell now occupied by 1 commands the cells 26, 38, 54, 12, 2, 14, 16, 28; and the cell occupied by 64 commands the cells 13, 43, 63, 55. The cells 13 and 14 are consecutive, and therefore the cells 64, 63, . . . , 14; 1, 2, . . . , 13 form a route. Hence we must replace the numbers 1, 2, . . . , 13 by 13, 12, . . . , 1, and we obtain a re-entrant route covering the whole board, which is represented in the second of the diagrams given on page 176. Euler showed how seven other re-entrant routes can be deduced from any given re-entrant route.

It is not difficult to apply the method so as to form a route which begins on one given cell and ends on any other given cell.

58	43	60	37	52	41	62	35
49	46	57	42	61	36	53	40
44	59	48	51	38	55	34	63
47	50	45	56	33	64	39	54
22	7	32	1	24	13	18	15
31	2	23	6	19	16	27	12
8	21	4	29	10	25	14	17
3	30	9	20	5	28	11	26

50	45	62	41	60	39	54	35
63	42	51	48	53	36	57	38
46	49	44	61	40	59	34	55
43	64	47	52	33	56	37	58
26	5	24	1	20	15	32	11
23	2	27	8	29	12	17	14
6	25	4	21	16	19	10	31
3	22	7	28	9	30	13	18

Euler's Half-board Solution.   *Roget's Half-board Solution.*

Euler next investigated how his method could be modified so as to allow of the imposition of additional restrictions.

An interesting example of this kind is where the first 32 moves are confined to one-half of the board. One solution of this is delineated above. The order of the first 32 moves can be determined by Euler's method. It is obvious that, if to the number of each such move we add 32, we shall have a corresponding set of moves from 33 to 64 which would cover the other half of the board; but in general the cell numbered 33 will not be a knight's move from that numbered 32, nor will 64 be a knight's move from 1.

Euler, however, proceeded to show how the first 32 moves

might be determined so that, if the half of the board containing the corresponding moves from 33 to 64 was twisted through two right angles, the two routes would become united and re-entrant. If x and y are the numbers of a cell reckoned from two consecutive sides of the board, we may call the cell whose distances are respectively x and y from the opposite sides a complementary cell. Thus the cells (x, y) and $(9 - x, 9 - y)$ are complementary, where x and y denote respectively the column and row occupied by the cell. Then in Euler's solution the numbers in complementary cells differ by 32 : for instance, the cell $(3, 7)$ is complementary to the cell $(6, 2)$, the one is occupied by 57, the other by 25.

Roget's method, which is described later, can be also applied to give half-board solutions. The result is indicated above. The close of Euler's memoir is devoted to showing how the method could be applied to crosses and other rectangular figures. I may note in particular his elegant re-entrant symmetrical solution for a square of 100 cells.

The next attempt of any special interest is due to Vandermonde,* who reduced the problem to arithmetic. His idea was to cover the board by two or more independent routes taken at random, and then to connect the routes. He defined the position of a cell by a fraction x/y, whose numerator x is the number of the cell from one side of the board, and whose denominator y is its number from the adjacent side of the board; this is equivalent to saying that x and y are the co-ordinates of a cell. In a series of fractions denoting a knight's path, the differences between the numerators of two consecutive fractions can be only one or two, while the corresponding differences between their denominators must be two or one respectively. Also x and y cannot be less than 1 or greater than 8. The notation is convenient, but Vandermonde applied it merely to obtain a particular solution of the problem for a board of 64 cells : the method by which he effected this is analogous to that established by Euler,

* *L'Histoire de l'Académie des Sciences* for 1771, Paris, 1774, pp. 566—574.

but it is applicable only to squares of an even order. The route that he arrives at is defined in his notation by the following fractions : 5/5, 4/3, 2/4, 4/5, 5/3, 7/4, 8/2, 6/1, 7/3, 8/1, 6/2, 8/3, 7/1, 5/2, 6/4, 8/5, 7/7, 5/8, 6/6, 5/4, 4/6, 2/5, 1/7, 3/8, 2/6, 1/8, 3/7, 1/6, 2/8, 4/7, 3/5, 1/4, 2/2, 4/1, 3/3, 1/2, 3/1, 2/3, 1/1, 3/2, 1/3, 2/1, 4/2, 3/4, 1/5, 2/7, 4/8, 3/6, 4/4, 5/6, 7/5, 8/7, 6/8, 7/6, 8/8, 6/7, 8/6, 7/8, 5/7, 6/5, 8/4, 7/2, 5/1, 6/3.

The path is re-entrant, but unsymmetrical. Had he transferred the first three fractions to the end of this series, he would have obtained two symmetrical circuits of thirty-two moves joined unsymmetrically and might have been enabled to advance further in the problem. Vandermonde also considered the case of a route in a cube.

In 1773 Collini * proposed the exclusive use of symmetrical routes arranged without reference to the initial cell, but connected in such a manner as to permit of our starting from it. This is the foundation of the modern manner of attacking the problem. The method was re-invented in 1825 by Pratt,† and in 1840 by Roget, and has been subsequently employed by various writers. Neither Collini nor Pratt showed skill in using this method. The rule given by Roget is described later.

One of the most ingenious of the solutions of the knight's path is that given in 1823 by Warnsdorff.‡ His rule is that the knight must be always moved to one of the cells from which it will command the fewest squares not already traversed. The solution is not symmetrical and not re-entrant ; moreover, it is difficult to trace practically. The rule has not been proved to be true, but no exception to it is known : apparently it applies also to all rectangular boards which can be covered completely by a knight. It is somewhat curious that in most

* *Solution du Problème du Cavalier au Jeu des Échecs*, Mannheim, 1773.

† *Studies of Chess*, sixth edition, London, 1825.

‡ H. C. Warnsdorff, *Des Rösselsprunges einfachste und allgemeinste Lösung*, Schmalkalden, 1823 : see also Jaenisch, vol. II, pp. 56—61, 273—289.

cases a single false step, except in the last three or four moves, will not affect the result.

Warnsdorff added that when, by the rule, two or more cells are open to the knight, it may be moved to either or any of them indifferently. This is not so, and with great ingenuity two or three cases of failure have been constructed, but it would require exceptionally bad luck to happen accidentally on such a route.

The above methods have been applied to boards of various shapes, especially to boards in the form of rectangles, crosses, and circles.*

All the more recent investigations impose additional restrictions : such as to require that the route shall be re-entrant, or more generally that it shall begin and terminate on given cells.

The simplest solution with which I am acquainted is due to De Lavernède, but is more generally associated with the name of Roget, whose paper in 1840 attracted general notice to it.†
It divides the whole route into four circuits, which can be combined so as to enable us to begin on any cell and terminate on any other cell of a different colour. Hence, if we like to select this last cell at a knight's move from the initial cell, we obtain a re-entrant route. On the other hand, the rule is applicable only to square boards containing $(4n)^2$ cells : for example, it could not be used on the board of the French *jeu des dames*, which contains 100 cells.

Roget began by dividing the board of 64 cells into four quarters. Each quarter contains 16 cells, and these 16 cells can be arranged in 4 groups, each group consisting of 4 cells which form a closed knight's path. All the cells in each such path are denoted by the same letter *l*, *e*, *a*, or *p*, as the case

* See, *e.g.*, T. Ciccolini's work *Del Cavallo degli Scacchi*, Paris, 1836.

† J. E. T. de Lavernède, *Mémoires de l'Académie Royale du Gard*, Nimes, 1839, pp. 151—179. P. M. Roget, *Philosophical Magazine*, April, 1840, series 3, vol. XVI, pp. 305—309; see also the *Quarterly Journal of Mathematics* for 1877, vol. XIV, pp. 354—359; and the *Leisure Hour*, Sept. 13, 1873, pp. 587—590, and Dec. 20, 1873, pp. 813—815.

may be. The path of 4 cells indicated by the consonants l and the path indicated by the consonants p are diamond-shaped : the paths indicated respectively by the vowels e and a are square-shaped, as may be seen by looking at one of the four quarters in figure i below.

Now, all the 16 cells on a complete chess-board which are marked with the same letter can be combined into one circuit, and wherever the circuit begins we can make it end on any other cell in the circuit, provided it is of a different colour from the initial cell. If it is indifferent on what cell the circuit terminates, we may make the circuit re-entrant, and

l	e	a	p	l	e	a	p
a	p	l	e	a	p	l	e
e	l	p	a	e	l	p	a
p	a	e	l	p	a	e	l
l	e	a	p	l	e	a	p
a	p	l	e	a	p	l	e
e	l	p	a	e	l	p	a
p	a	e	l	p	a	e	l

34	51	32	15	38	53	18	3
31	14	35	52	17	2	39	54
50	33	16	29	56	37	4	19
13	30	49	36	1	20	55	40
48	63	28	9	44	57	22	5
27	12	45	64	21	8	41	58
62	47	10	25	60	43	6	23
11	26	61	46	7	24	59	42

Roget's Solution (i).   Roget's Solution (ii).

in this case we can make the direction of motion round each group (of 4 cells) the same. For example, all the cells marked p can be arranged in the circuit indicated by the successive numbers 1 to 16 in figure ii above. Similarly all the cells marked a can be combined into the circuit indicated by the numbers 17 to 32; all the l cells into the circuit 33 to 48; and all the e cells into the circuit 49 to 64. Each of the circuits indicated above is symmetrical and re-entrant. The consonant and the vowel circuits are said to be of opposite kinds.

The general problem will be solved if we can combine the four circuits into a route which will start from any given cell, and terminate on the 64th move on any other given cell of a different colour. To effect this Roget gave the two following rules.

First. If the initial cell and the final cell are denoted the one by a consonant and the other by a vowel, take alternately circuits indicated by consonants and vowels, beginning with the circuit of 16 cells indicated by the letter of the initial cell and concluding with the circuit indicated by the letter of the final cell.

Second. If the initial cell and the final cell are denoted both by consonants or both by vowels, first select a cell, Y, in the same circuit as the final cell, Z, and one move from it; next select a cell, X, belonging to one of the opposite circuits and one move from Y. This is always possible. Then, leaving out the cells Z and Y, it always will be possible, by the rule already given, to travel from the initial cell to the cell X in 62 moves, and thence to move to the final cell on the 64th move.

In both cases, however, it must be noticed that the cells in each of the first three circuits will have to be taken in such an order that the circuit does not terminate on a corner, and it may be desirable also that it should not terminate on any of the border cells. This will necessitate some caution. As far as is consistent with these restrictions, it is convenient to make these circuits re-entrant, and to take them and every group in them in the same direction of rotation.

As an example, suppose that we are to begin on the cell numbered 1 in figure ii above, which is one of those in a p circuit, and to terminate on the cell numbered 64, which is one of those in an e circuit. This falls under the first rule : hence first we take the 16 cells marked p, next the 16 cells marked a, then the 16 cells marked l, and lastly the 16 cells marked e. One way of effecting this is shown in the diagram. Since the cell 64 is a knight's move from the initial cell, the route is re-entrant. Also each of the four circuits in the diagram is symmetrical, re-entrant, and taken in the same direction, and the only point where there is any apparent breach in the uniformity of the movement is in the passage from the cell numbered 32 to that numbered 33.

A rule for re-entrant routes, similar to that of Roget, has been given by various subsequent writers, especially by De Polignac * and by Laquière,† who have stated it at much greater length. Neither of these authors seems to have been aware of Roget's theorems. De Polignac, like Roget, illustrates the rule by assigning letters to the various squares in the way explained above, and asserts that a similar rule is applicable to all even squares.

Roget's method can be also applied to two half-boards, as indicated in the figure given above on page 178.

The method which Jaenisch gives as the most fundamental is not very different from that of Roget. It leads to eight forms, similar to that in the diagram printed below, in which the sum of the numbers in every column and every row is 260; but, although symmetrical, it is not, in my opinion, so easy to reproduce as that given by Roget. Other solutions, notably those by Moon and by Wenzelides, were given in former editions of this work. The two re-entrant routes printed below,

63	22	15	40	1	42	59	18
14	39	64	21	60	17	2	43
37	62	23	16	41	4	19	58
24	13	38	61	20	57	44	3
11	36	25	52	29	46	5	56
26	51	12	33	8	55	30	45
35	10	49	28	53	32	47	6
50	27	34	9	48	7	54	31

15	20	17	36	13	64	61	34
18	37	14	21	60	35	12	63
25	16	19	44	5	62	33	56
38	45	26	59	22	55	4	11
27	24	39	6	43	10	57	54
40	49	46	23	58	3	32	9
47	28	51	42	7	30	53	2
50	41	48	29	52	1	8	31

Jaenisch's Solution.   *Two Half-board Solutions.*

* *Comptes Rendus*, April, 1861; and *Bulletin de la Société Mathématique de France*, 1881, vol. IX, pp. 17—24.

† *Bulletin de la Société Mathématique de France*, 1880, vol. VIII, pp. 82—102, 132—158.

each covering 32 cells, and together covering the board, are remarkable as constituting a magic square.*

It is as yet impossible to say how many solutions of the problem exist. Legendre † mentioned the question, but Minding ‡ was the earliest writer to attempt to answer it. More recent investigations have shown that on the one hand the number of possible routes is less § than the number of combinations of 168 things taken 63 at a time, and on the other hand is greater than 122,802512—since this latter number is the number of re-entrant paths of a particular type.∥

Analogous Problems. Similar problems can be constructed in which it is required to determine routes by which a piece moving according to certain laws (*e.g.* a chess-piece such as a king, etc.) can travel from a given cell over a board so as to occupy successively all the cells, or certain specified cells, once, and only once, and terminate its route in a given cell. Euler's method can be applied to find routes of this kind : for instance, he applied it to find a re-entrant route by which a piece that moved two cells forward like a castle and then one cell like a bishop would occupy in succession all the black cells on the board.

King's Re-entrant Path.¶ As one example here is a re-entrant tour of a king which moves successively to every cell of the board. I give it because the numbers indicating the cells successively occupied form a magic square. Of course, this also gives a solution of a re-entrant route of a queen covering the board.

---

* See A. Rilly, *Le Problème du Cavalier des Échecs*, Troyes, 1905.

† *Théorie des Nombres*, Paris, 2nd edition, 1830, vol. II, p. 165.

‡ *Cambridge and Dublin Mathematical Journal*, 1852, vol. VII, pp. 147—156; and *Crelle's Journal*, 1853, vol. XLIV, pp. 73—82.

§ Jaenisch, vol. II, p. 268.

∥ Kraïtchik, pp. 360, 402.

¶ Cf. I. Ghersi, *Matematica dilettevole e curiosa*, Milan, 1921, p. 320 (fig. 261).

61	62	63	64	1	2	3	4
60	11	58	57	8	7	54	5
12	59	10	9	56	55	6	53
13	14	15	16	49	50	51	52
20	19	18	17	48	47	46	45
21	38	23	24	41	42	27	44
37	22	39	40	25	26	43	28
36	35	34	33	32	31	30	29

King's Magic Tour on a Chess-board.

Rook's Re-entrant Path. There is no difficulty in constructing re-entrant tours for a rook which moves successively to every cell of the board. For instance, if the rook starts from the cell 11, it can move successively to the cells 18, 88, 81, 71, 77, 67, 61, 51, 57, 47, 41, 31, 37, 27, 21, and so back to 11 : this is a symmetrical route. Of course, this also gives a solution of a re-entrant route for a king or a queen covering the board. If we start from any of the cells mentioned above, the rook takes sixteen moves. If we start from any cell in the middle of one of these moves, it will take seventeen moves to cover this route, but I believe that in most cases wherever the initial cell be chosen, sixteen moves will suffice, though in general the route will not be symmetrical. On a board of n^2 cells it is possible to find a route by which a rook can move successively from its initial cell to every other cell once, and only once. Moreover,* starting on any cell, its path can be made to terminate, if n be even, on any other cell of a different colour, and if n be odd, on any other cell of the same colour.

Bishop's Re-entrant Path. As yet another instance, a bishop can traverse all the cells of one colour on the board in seventeen moves if the initial cell is properly chosen ; † for instance,

---

* *L'Intermédiaire des Mathématiciens,* Paris, 1901, vol. VIII, pp. 153—154.
† H. E. Dudeney, *The Tribune,* Dec. 3, 1906.

starting from the cell 11, it may move successively to the cells
55, 82, 71, 17, 28, 46, 13, 31, 86, 68, 57, 48, 15, 51, 84, 66, 88.
One more move will bring it back to the initial cell. From
the nature of the case, it must traverse some cells more than
once.

MISCELLANEOUS PROBLEMS

We may construct numerous such problems concerning
the determination of routes which cover the whole or part of
the board subject to certain conditions. I append a few others
which may tax the ingenuity of those not accustomed to such
problems.

Routes on a Chess-board. One of the simplest is the
determination of the path taken by a rook, placed in the cell
11, which moves, one cell at a time, to the cell 88, so that in
the course of its path it enters every cell once, and only once.
This can be done, though I have seen good mathematicians
puzzled to effect it. A hasty reader is apt to misunderstand
the conditions of the problem.

Another simple problem of this kind is to move a queen from
the cell 33 to the cell 66 in fifteen moves, entering every cell once
and only once, and never crossing its own track or entering a
cell more than once.*

A somewhat similar, but more difficult, question is the
determination of the greatest distance which can be travelled
by a queen starting from its own square in five consecutive
moves, subject to the condition that it never crosses its own
track or enters a cell more than once.† In calculating the
distance, it may be assumed that the paths go through the
centres of the cells. If the length of the side of a cell is 1
inch, the distance exceeds 33·97 inches.

Another familiar problem can be enunciated as follows.
Construct a rectangular board of mn cells by ruling $m + 1$
vertical lines and $n + 1$ horizontal lines. It is required to
know how many routes can be taken from the top left-hand

* H. E. Dudeney, *The Tribune*, Oct. 3, 1906.   † *Ibid.*, Oct. 2, 1906.

corner to the bottom right-hand corner, the motion being along the ruled lines and its direction being always either vertically downwards or horizontally from left to right. The answer is the number of permutations of $m + n$ things, of which m are alike of one kind and n are alike of another kind : this is equal to $(m + n)!/m!n!$. Thus on a square board containing 16 cells (*i.e.* one-quarter of a chess-board), where $m = n = 4$, there are 70 such routes; while on a common chess-board, where $m = n = 8$, there are no less than 12870 such routes. A rook, moving according to the same law, can travel from the top left-hand cell to the bottom right-hand cell in $(m + n - 2)!/(m - 1)!(n - 1)!$ ways. Similar theorems can be enunciated for a parallelepiped.

Another question of this kind is the determination of the number of closed routes through mn points arranged in m rows and n columns, following the lines of the quadrilateral network, and passing once and only once through each point.[*]

Guarini's Problem. One of the oldest European problems connected with the chess-board is the following, which was propounded in 1512. It was quoted by Lucas in 1894, but I believe has not been published otherwise than in his works and the earlier editions of this book. On a board of nine cells, such as that drawn below, the two white knights are placed on the

a	C	d
D		B
b	A	c

two top corner cells (a, d), and the two black knights on the two bottom corner cells (b, c) : the other cells are left vacant. It is required to move the knights so that the white knights shall occupy the cells b and c, while the black shall occupy the cells a and d. The solution is obvious.

* See C. F. Sainte-Marie in *L'Intermédiaire des Mathématiciens*, Paris, vol. XI, March, 1904, pp. 86—88.

Queens' Problem. Another problem consists in placing sixteen queens on a board so that no three are in a straight line.* One solution is to place them on the cells 15, 16, 25, 26, 31, 32, 41, 42, 57, 58, 67, 68, 73, 74, 83, 84. It is, of course, assumed that each queen is placed on the middle of its cell.

LATIN SQUARES

Another problem of the chess-board type is the determination of the number x_n of Latin squares of any assigned order n : a Latin square of the nth order being defined as a square of n^2 cells (in n rows and n columns) in which n^2 letters consisting

2	0	1
1	2	0
0	1	2

$(1, 1)_3$

2	1	0
1	0	2
0	2	1

$(2, 1)_3$

1	2	3	0
2	3	0	1
3	0	1	2
0	1	2	3

$(1, 3)_4$

4	1	3	0	2
3	0	2	4	1
2	4	1	3	0
1	3	0	2	4
0	2	4	1	3

$(2, 1)_5$

of n " a's," n " b's," ..., are arranged in the cells so that the n letters in each row and each column are different. The general theory is difficult,† but it may amuse my readers to verify that $x_n = n! \ (n-1)! \ R_n$, where R_n is an integer, the first few values being $R_2 = R_3 = 1, R_4 = 4, R_5 = 56, R_6 = 9408$. H. W. Norton has conjectured that $R_7 = 16,927968$.

Latin squares of a special type may be constructed as *tables*

* H. E. Dudeney, *The Tribune*, November 7, 1906.

† See Fisher and Yates, *Proceedings of the Cambridge Philosophical Society*, 1934, vol. xxx, pp. 492–507; Norton, *Annals of Eugenics*, 1939, vol. ix, pp. 269–307.

of addition in the finite arithmetic modulo n (cf. page 109). The bottom row contains the numbers 0, α, 2α, ..., $(n-1)\alpha$, and the left-hand column contains 0, β, 2β, ..., $(n-1)\beta$. In every other cell we place the sum of the numbers which thus define its column and row. The resulting square may be denoted by $(\alpha, \beta)_n$.

Clearly α and β must be prime to n. If also $\alpha + \beta$ and $\alpha - \beta$ are prime to n (as in the last of the above examples), we have a " diagonal " Latin square : the n numbers in each diagonal (as well as those in each row and column) are all different.

Magic Card Square. * By superposing two properly related Latin squares of the fourth order, we can solve the familiar problem of placing the sixteen court cards (taken out of a pack) in the form of a square so that no row, no column, and neither of the diagonals shall contain more than one card of each suit and one card of each rank. There are 72 fundamental solutions, each of which by reflections and reversals produces 7 others.

Euler's Officers Problem.† A similar problem, proposed by Euler in 1779, consists in arranging, if it be possible, thirty-six officers taken from six regiments—the officers being in six groups, each consisting of six officers of equal rank, one drawn from each regiment ; say officers of rank, a, b, c, d, e, f, drawn from the 1st, 2nd, 3rd, 4th, 5th, and 6th regiments—in a solid square formation of six by six, so that each row and each file shall contain one and only one officer of each rank and one and only one officer from each regiment. The problem is insoluble.

Eulerian Squares. This suggests the general problem of superposing two Latin squares of the nth order in such a way

---

* Ozanam, 1723 edition, vol. IV, p. 434.

† Euler's *Commentationes Arithmeticae*, Petrograd, 1849, vol. II, pp. 302—361. See also a paper by G. Tarry in the *Comptes rendus* of the French Association for the Advancement of Science, Paris, 1900, vol. II, pp. 170—203 ; and various notes in *L'Intermédiaire des Mathématiciens*, Paris, vol. III, 1896, pp. 17, 90 ; vol. V, 1898, pp. 83, 176, 252 ; vol. VI, 1899, p. 251 ; vol. VII, 1900, pp. 14, 311.

that the n^2 " marks," each consisting of two digits, shall be all different.   Such arrangements are termed Eulerian Squares. So far as I know, the problem is insoluble when n is singly-even. But it is easily solved in every other case.

22	01	10
11	20	02
00	12	21

34	41	03	10	22
13	20	32	44	01
42	04	11	23	30
21	33	40	02	14
00	12	24	31	43

12	03	30	21
31	20	13	02
23	32	01	10
00	11	22	33

The two Latin squares $(\alpha, \beta)_n$ and $(\alpha', \beta')_n$ can be superposed to form an Eulerian square, say * $(\alpha'\alpha, \beta'\beta)_n$, whenever the determinant $\alpha\beta' - \alpha'\beta$ is prime to n. Since also α, β, α', β' must be prime to n, this method applies only when n is odd. The Eulerian square $(\alpha'\alpha, \beta'\beta)_n$, is " diagonal " if $\alpha \pm \beta$ and $\alpha' \pm \beta'$ are prime to n.   The squares $(12, 11)_3$ and $(12, 21)_5$ are drawn above, along with a diagonal Eulerian square of order 4, which solves the problem of the Magic Card Square.† There is an Eulerian square $(12, 11)_n$ for every odd value of n; and a diagonal Eulerian square $(12, 21)_n$ for every odd value not divisible by 3.   There is no diagonal Eulerian square of

* This square may be regarded as a table of addition in a Galois arithmetic (page 73), the bottom row containing the multiples of $a'a$, and the left-hand column the multiples of $\beta'\beta$. See E. Cazalas, *Sphinx*, 1936, pp. 134, 135.

† If the two Latin squares of which this Eulerian square is composed are written out in the binary scale, they are formally identical with tables of addition in the Galois arithmetic with moduli 2 and 111. In both cases the bottom row contains the four marks of the arithmetic in their "natural" order : 0, 1, 10, 11. The left-hand column contains these same marks in a different order, derivable from the " natural " order by multiplying through-out by the mark 10 or 11, respectively. Extending the $(a, \beta)_n$ notation, we might call these Latin squares $(1, 10)_{2^2}$ and $(1, 11)_{2^2}$. Such a construction leads to a Latin square $(a, \beta)_{p^m}$, whenever p is prime and $a\beta \neq 0$. This is a *diagonal* square if also $(a - \beta)(a + \beta) \neq 0$. Finally, two Latin squares $(a, \beta)_{p^m}$, $(a', \beta')_{p^m}$ make an Eulerian square whenever $a\beta' - a'\beta \neq 0$.

order 3; for one of order 9 see figure xxix of the next chapter (page 213); it is also possible to construct one of order 27.*

Given Eulerian squares of orders m and n, we can easily construct one of order mn. Since Eulerian squares of every odd order are known, and also one of order 4 and one of order 8 (see figure xxviii of the next chapter), it follows that such squares can be constructed for every doubly-even order. Moreover, since the special squares of orders 4, 8, 9, and 27 are diagonal, diagonal Eulerian squares can be constructed for every odd or doubly-even order, except, possibly, when the order is divisible by 3, but not by 9.

Generalized Eulerian Squares. These notions may be generalized in two different directions. First, we may super-pose more than two Latin squares, so as to obtain a square of n^2 "marks" each consisting of k (> 2) digits. For instance, the Latin squares $(\alpha, \beta)_n, (\alpha', \beta')_n, (\alpha'', \beta'')_n$ lead to a three-digit Eulerian square $(\alpha''\alpha'\alpha, \beta''\beta'\beta)_n$ whenever one (at least) of the determinants $\alpha\beta' - \alpha'\beta, \alpha\beta'' - \alpha''\beta, \alpha'\beta'' - \alpha''\beta'$ is prime to n.

Secondly, we may use Latin cubes instead of Latin squares, a Latin cube of the nth order being defined as a cube of n^3 cells (in n rows, n columns, and n files) in which n^3 letters (or numbers) consisting of n^2 a's, n^2 b's, ..., are arranged in the cells so that the n letters in each row, each column, and each file, are different. In particular, a three-dimensional table of addition (mod n) provides a Latin cube $(\alpha, \beta, \gamma)_n$. Three such cubes can be superposed so as to form the Eulerian Cube $(\alpha''\alpha'\alpha, \beta''\beta'\beta, \gamma''\gamma'\gamma)_n$ provided the determinant

$$\begin{vmatrix} \alpha & \beta & \gamma \\ \alpha' & \beta' & \gamma' \\ \alpha'' & \beta'' & \gamma'' \end{vmatrix}$$

is prime to n. (It is necessary to superpose at least three Latin cubes, in order to make the n^3 "marks" all different.)

---

* In the notation of the preceding footnote, a diagonal Eulerian square of order 27 can be derived from the Latin squares $(1, 10)_{3^3}$, $(1, 11)_{3^3}$, which are constructed as tables of addition in the Galois arithmetic with moduli 3 and 1021.

CHAPTER VII

MAGIC SQUARES

A *Magic Square* consists of a number of integers arranged in the form of a square, so that the sum of the numbers in every row, in every column, and in each diagonal is the same. If the integers are the consecutive numbers from 1 to n^2, the square is said to be of the nth order, and it is easily seen that in this case the sum of the numbers in every row, column, and diagonal is equal to $\frac{1}{2}n(n^2 + 1)$. Unless otherwise stated, I confine my account to such magic squares—that is, to squares formed with consecutive integers from 1 upwards. The same rules cover similar problems with n^2 numbers in arithmetical progression.

Thus the first 16 integers, arranged in either of the forms in figures i and ii below, represent magic squares of the fourth

16	3	2	13
5	10	11	8
9	6	7	12
4	15	14	1

Figure i. $n = 4$.

15	10	3	6
4	5	16	9
14	11	2	7
1	8	13	12

Figure ii. $n = 4$.

order, the sum of the numbers in each row, column, and diagonal being 34. Similarly, figure iii on page 195 and figure xvi on page 206 represent magic squares of the fifth order; figure vi on page 197 represents a magic square of the sixth order; figure xiv on page 201 and figure xvii on page 206 represent magic squares of the seventh order; figures xiii, xx, xxviii, xxxix represent magic squares of the eighth order;

figures xxii, xxix represent magic squares of the ninth order; and figure ix represents a magic square of the tenth order.

The formation of these squares is an old amusement, and in times when mystical ideas were associated with particular numbers it was natural that such arrangements should be studied. Magic squares were constructed in China before the Christian era : their introduction into Europe appears to have been due to Moschopulus, who lived at Constantinople in the early part of the fifteenth century. The famous Cornelius Agrippa (1486—1535) constructed magic squares of the orders 3, 4, 5, 6, 7, 8, 9, which were associated by him with the seven astrological " planets " : namely, Saturn, Jupiter, Mars, the Sun, Venus, Mercury, and the Moon. A magic square engraved on a silver plate was sometimes prescribed as a charm against the plague, and one—namely, that represented in figure i on the previous page—is drawn in the picture of Melancholy, painted in 1514 by Albert Dürer, the numbers in the middle cells of the bottom row giving the date of the work. The mathematical theory of the construction of these squares was taken up in France in the seventeenth century, and later has been a favourite subject with writers in many countries.*

It is convenient to use the following terms. The spaces or small squares occupied by the numbers are called *cells*. It is customary to call the rows first, second, etc., reckoning from the top, and the columns first, second, etc., reckoning from the left. The hth and $(n + 1 - h)$th rows (or columns) are said to be *complementary*. The kth cell in the hth row is said to be *skewly related* to the $(n + 1 - k)$th cell in the $(n + 1 - h)$th row. Skewly related cells are situated symmetrically to the centre of the square.

Magic squares of any order higher than two can be constructed at sight. The rule to be used varies according as the

* For a sketch of the history of the subject and its bibliography see S. Günther's *Geschichte der mathematischen Wissenschaften*, Leipzig, 1876, chapter IV; W. Ahrens, *Mathematische Unterhaltungen und Spiele*, Leipzig, 1901, chapter XII; and W. S. Andrews, *Magic Squares and Cubes*, Chicago, 1917.

order n is odd—that is, of the form $2m + 1$; or singly-even—
that is, of the form $2(2m + 1)$; or doubly-even—that is, of the
form $4m$. In each case, I now give the simplest rule with
which I am acquainted.

MAGIC SQUARES OF AN ODD ORDER

A magic square of the nth order, where $n = 2m + 1$, can
be constructed by the following rule due to De la Loubère.*
First, the number 1 is placed in the middle cell of the top row.
The successive numbers are then placed in their natural order
in a diagonal line which slopes upwards to the right, except
that (i) when the top row is reached, the next number is
written in the bottom row as if it came immediately above the
top row; (ii) when the right-hand column is reached, the next

17	24	1	8	15
23	5	7	14	16
4	6	13	20	22
10	12	19	21	3
11	18	25	2	9

Figure iii. $n = 5$.

31	43	00	12	24
42	04	11	23	30
03	10	22	34	41
14	21	33	40	02
20	32	44	01	13

Figure iv. $n = 5$.

number is written in the left-hand column, as if it immediately
succeeded the right-hand column; and (iii) when a cell which
has been filled up already or when the top right-hand square
is reached, the path of the series drops to the row vertically
below it and then continues to mount again. Probably a
glance at the diagram in figure iii, showing the construction by
this rule of a square of the fifth order, will make the rule clear.

The reason why such a square is magic can be best explained
by taking a particular case, for instance $n = 5$, and expressing
all the numbers in the scale of notation whose radix is 5 (or n,

---

* S. De la Loubère, *Du Royaume de Siam* (Eng. Trans.), London, 1693,
vol. II, pp. 227—247. De la Loubère was the envoy of Louis XIV to Siam
in 1687—1688, and there learnt this method.

if the magic square is of order n). To simplify the discussion, let us at the same time diminish each number by unity; this clearly makes no difference to the magic properties. The resulting square (figure iv) may be regarded as an Eulerian square.* Since every row and every column contains one of each of the 5 possible unit digits and one of each of the radix digits, the magic property of the rows and columns is automatically assured; so is that of the leading diagonal. The other diagonal suffers from a repetition of the radix digit 2 (in general, m), but it still has the correct sum. Moreover, every number from 0 to $n^2 - 1$ occurs once and only once.

The reader can easily apply this rule to construct a magic square of the third order. Such a square, called the *lo-shu*,† is attributed to the Chinese Emperor Yu, about 2200 B.C., and is still used as a charm by various Oriental peoples. Even in the West it is generally to be seen on the deck of any large passenger ship, for scoring in such games as " shuffleboard."

MAGIC SQUARES OF A SINGLY-EVEN ORDER

A magic square of the nth order, where $n = 2(2m + 1)$, can be constructed by the following rule due to Ralph Strachey.‡ Divide the square into four equal quarters A, B, C, D. Construct in A, by De la Loubère's method, a magic square with

the numbers 1 to u^2 where $u = n/2$. Construct by the same rule, in B, C, D, similar magic squares with the numbers

---

* See page 191. The Eulerian square that underlies De la Loubère's rule is derivable from $(12, 11)_n$, by reversing the order of the rows, and cyclically permuting the columns.

† D. E. Smith, *History of Mathematics*, Boston, 1925, vol. II, p, 591.

‡ Communicated to me in a letter, August 1918.

$u^2 + 1$ to $2u^2$, $2u^2 + 1$ to $3u^2$, and $3u^2 + 1$ to $4u^2$. Clearly the resulting composite square is magic in columns. In the middle row of A take the m cells next but one to the left-hand side, in each of the other rows take the m cells nearest to the left-hand side, and interchange the numbers in these cells with the numbers in the corresponding cells in D. Next interchange the numbers in the cells in each of the $m - 1$ columns

8	1	6	26	19	24
3	5	7	21	23	25
4	9	2	22	27	20
35	28	33	17	10	15
30	32	34	12	14	16
31	36	29	13	18	11

Figure v. *Initial Quarter-Squares.*

35	1	6	26	19	24
3	32	7	21	23	25
31	9	2	22	27	20
8	28	33	17	10	15
30	5	34	12	14	16
4	36	29	13	18	11

Figure vi. *Final Square, $n = 6$.*

27+8	0+1	0+6	18+8	18+1	18+6
0+3	27+5	0+7	18+3	18+5	18+7
27+4	0+9	0+2	18+4	18+9	18+2
0+8	27+1	27+6	9+8	9+1	9+6
27+3	0+5	27+7	9+3	9+5	9+7
0+4	27+9	27+2	9+4	9+9	9+2

Figure vii. *Final Square, $n = 6$.*

next to the right-hand side of C with the numbers in the corresponding cells in B. Of course, the resulting square remains magic in columns. It will also now be magic in rows and diagonals, since the construction is equivalent to writing in each of the quarters A, B, C, D, equal magic squares of the order u made with the numbers 1 to u^2, and then superposing on them a magic square of the nth order made with the four radix numbers 0, u^2, $2u^2$, $3u^2$, each repeated u^2 times. The

component squares being magic, the square resulting from
their superposition must be magic, and they are so formed

17	24	1	8	15	67	74	51	58	65
32	5	7	14	16	73	55	57	64	6
4	6	13	20	22	54	56	63	70	72
0	12	19	21	3	60	62	69	71	53
11	18	25	2	9	61	68	75	52	59
92	99	76	83	90	42	49	26	33	40
98	80	82	89	91	48	30	32	39	41
79	81	88	95	97	29	31	38	45	47
85	87	94	96	78	35	37	44	46	28
86	93	100	77	84	36	43	50	27	34

Figure viii.   *Initial Quarter-Squares, n* = 10.

92	99	1	8	15	67	74	51	58	40
98	80	7	14	16	73	55	57	64	41
4	81	88	20	22	54	56	63	70	47
85	87	19	21	3	60	62	69	71	28
86	93	25	2	9	61	68	75	52	34
17	24	76	83	90	42	49	26	33	65
23	5	82	89	91	48	30	32	39	66
79	6	13	95	97	29	31	38	45	72
10	12	94	96	78	35	37	44	46	53
11	18	100	77	84	36	43	50	27	59

Figure ix.   *Final Square, n* = 10.

that their superposition ensures that every number from 1 to
n^2 appears once and only once in the resulting square.

Figures v and vi show the application of the rule to the
construction of a magic square of the sixth order. In figure v,

those numbers in the cells in the initial quarter-square A which are to be interchanged vertically with the numbers in the corresponding cells in D are underlined; figure vi represents the final square obtained; and figure vii shows how these interchanges serve to bring the radix numbers to a position which makes the square magic.

Since this construction is novel, I add figures to show the application of the rule to the formation of a square of the tenth order: in figure viii those numbers in the quarter-squares A and C which have to be interchanged vertically with the numbers in the corresponding cells in D and B are underlined, while figure ix represents the final magic square of the tenth order thus obtained.

MAGIC SQUARES OF A DOUBLY-EVEN ORDER

A magic square of the fourth order (figure xi), scarcely different from Dürer's (figure i), can be constructed by writing the numbers from 1 to 16 in their natural order in rows of

Figure x.

Figure xi. $n = 4$.

Figure xii.

Figure xiii. $n = 8$.

four, and then replacing the numbers in the *diagonal* cells by their complements. The same rule * applies to a magic square of any doubly-even order, if we change the numbers in those cells which are crossed by the diagonals of every component block of 4^2 cells. Figures xii and xiii show the case when $n = 8$.

BORDERED SQUARES

One other general method, due to Frénicle, of constructing magic squares of any order should be mentioned. By this method, to form a magic square of the nth order we first construct one of the $(n - 2)$th order, add to every number in it an integer, and then surround it with a border of the remaining numbers in such a way as to make the resulting square magic. In this manner from the magic square of the 3rd order we can build up successively squares of the orders 5, 7, 9, etc.—that is, every odd magic square. Similarly from a magic square of the 4th order we can build up successively all higher even magic squares.

The method of construction will be clear if I explain how the square in figure xiv, where $n = 7$, is built up. First the inner magic square of the $(n - 2)$th order is formed by any rule we like to choose : the sum of the numbers in each line being $(n - 2)\{(n - 2)^2 + 1\}/2$. To every number in it, $2n - 2$ is added : thus the sum of the numbers in each row, column, and diagonal is now $(n - 2)\{n^2 + 1\}/2$. The numbers not used are $1, 2, \ldots, 2n - 2$, and their complements, $n^2, n^2 - 1, \ldots, n^2 - 2n + 3$. These reserved numbers are placed in the $4(n - 1)$ border cells so that complementary numbers occur at the end of each row, column, and diagonal of the inner square : this makes the sum of the numbers in each of these latter lines equal to $n(n^2 + 1)/2$. It only remains to make the sum of the numbers in each of the border lines also have this value : such an arrangement is easily

* Kraïtchik, p. 176. R. V. Heath has devised a similar rule for constructing a Magic Cube.

made by trial and error. With a little patience a magic square of any order can be thus built up, border upon border, and, of course, it will have the property that, if each border is successively stripped off, the remaining square will still be magic. This is a method of construction much favoured by self-taught mathematicians.

Definite rules for arranging the numbers in the border cells have been indicated,* though usually not in a precise form. Recently, Mr. J. Travers † has proposed a simple rule for constructing an odd square, where $n = 2m + 1$. Rather

46	1	2	3	42	41	40
45	35	13	14	32	31	5
44	34	28	21	26	16	6
7	17	23	25	27	33	43
12	20	24	29	22	30	38
11	19	37	36	18	15	39
10	49	48	47	8	9	4

	1	2	3			
		13	14			5
			21		16	6
7	17	23	25			
12	20	24		22		
11	19			18	15	
10				8	9	4

Figure xiv. A Bordered Square,   Figure xv.
$n = 7$.

than describe it in words, I illustrate its application to the above example (which is in fact a multiple bordered square). Figure xv indicates the proper positions for the numbers 1, 2, ..., m; $m + 1$; $m + 2$, ..., $2m$; $2m + 1$; $2m + 2$, ..., $3m$; $3m + 1$, ..., $4m$. The complementary numbers are easily inserted afterwards. It may interest my readers to see if they can evolve a similar simple rule for the formation of bordered even squares.‡

* For instance, see *Japanese Mathematics* by D. E. Smith and Y. Mikami, Chicago, 1914, pp. 116—120 : in this work, in the diagram on p. 120, the numbers 8 and 29 should be interchanged.

† *Education Outlook*, 1936. For another good rule, see R. V. Heath, *Scripta Mathematica*, 1936, vol. IV, p. 67.

‡ A somewhat more complicated rule for even squares has been given by J. Travers, *Engineering Gazette*, Aug. 13, 1938, p. 6.

NUMBER OF SQUARES OF A GIVEN ORDER

One unsolved problem in the theory is the determination of the number of magic squares of the fifth (or any higher) order. There is, in effect, only one magic square of the third order, though by reflections and rotations it can be presented in 8 forms. There are 880 magic squares of the fourth order, but by reflections and rotations these can be presented in 7040 forms. The problem of the number of magic squares of the fifth order is incompletely solved. From the square given in figure iv (page 195) formed by De la Loubère's method, we can get 720 distinct squares; for we can permute the unit digits 0, 1, 2, 3, 4 in 5! ways, and the radix digits 0, 1, 3, 4 in 4! ways. We thus obtain 2880 magic squares of the fifth order, though only 720 of them are distinct. Bachet gave a somewhat similar construction,* in which he began by placing 1 in the cell immediately above the middle cell; his method gives another 720 distinct magic squares of the fifth order. There are, however, numerous other rules for constructing odd magic squares, and De la Hire showed that by methods known in his day, and apart from mere reflections and rotations, there were 57600 magic squares of the fifth order which could be formed by the methods he enumerated, and taking account of other methods, it is now known that the total number of magic squares of the fifth order considerably exceeds thirteen million.

SYMMETRICAL AND PANDIAGONAL SQUARES

With the exception of determining the number of squares of a given order, we may fairly say that the theory of the construction of magic squares, as defined above, has been sufficiently worked out. Accordingly, attention has of late been chiefly directed to the construction of squares which, in addition to being magic, satisfy other conditions. It has been suggested that we might impose on the construction of

* See Kraïtchik, p. 128.

a square of order n the condition that the sum of any two numbers in cells skewly related to one another shall be constant and equal to $n^2 + 1$. Such squares are called *Symmetrical* (or *Associated*). Dürer's square (figure i) is symmetrical; so are all De la Loubère's squares (such as figure iii), and all squares of doubly-even order that are constructed by the rule described above (such as figures xi and xiii). There are no symmetrical magic squares of singly-even order.*

One of the earliest additional conditions to be suggested was that the square should be magic along the broken diagonals as well as along the two ordinary diagonals.† Such squares are called *Pandiagonal*. They are also known as nasik, perfect, and diabolic squares.

A magic pandiagonal square of the fourth order ‡ was inscribed at Khajuraho, India, as long ago as the eleventh or twelfth century. A slightly different square of the same kind is represented in figure ii on page 193. In it the sum of the numbers in each row, column, and in the two diagonals is 34, as also is the sum of the numbers in the six broken diagonals formed by the numbers 15, 9, 2, 8, the numbers 10, 4, 7, 13, the numbers 3, 5, 14, 12, the numbers 6, 4, 11, 13, the numbers 3, 9, 14, 8, and the numbers 10, 16, 7, 1.

It follows from the definition that if a pandiagonal square be cut into two pieces along a line between any two rows or any two columns, and the two pieces be interchanged, the new square so formed will be also pandiagonally magic. Hence it is obvious that by one vertical and one horizontal transposition

---

* C. Planck, *The Monist*, Chicago, 1919, vol. xxix, p. 308.

† Squares of this type were mentioned by P. De la Hire, J. Sauveur, and Euler. Attention was again called to them by A. H. Frost in the *Quarterly Journal of Mathematics*, London, 1878, vol. xv, pp. 34—49, and subsequently their properties have been discussed by several writers. Besides Frost's papers I have made considerable use of a paper by E. McClintock in the *American Journal of Mathematics*, vol. xix, 1897, pp. 99—120.

‡ D. E. Smith, *History of Mathematics*, Boston, 1925, vol. ii, p. 594. For the general theory of such squares, see J. B. Rosser and R. J. Walker, *Bulletin of the American Mathematical Society*, 1938, vol. xliv, pp. 416—420.

of this kind any number can be made to occupy any specified cell.

I have already remarked that there is essentially only one magic square of the third order; this is not pandiagonal, so the order of a pandiagonal square must exceed three. Moreover, there are no pandiagonal squares of singly-even order.* Pandiagonal squares of odd order, not divisible by 3, can be constructed by a rule somewhat analogous to De la Loubère's; and new rules have been devised to cover the cases where the order is divisible by 3 or 4.

Of the 880 magic squares of the fourth order, 48 are pandiagonal. Rosser and Walker have shown that there are exactly 3600 pandiagonal squares of the fifth order, more than 38 million of the seventh order, and more than $6\frac{1}{2}$ billion † of the eighth order.

Generalization of De la Loubère's Rule.   It is convenient to name the n^2 cells by pairs of co-ordinates in such a way that the cells of the bottom row (from left to right) are $(0, 0)$, $(1, 0)$, ..., $(n - 1, 0)$, while those of the left-hand column (from bottom to top) are $(0, 0)$, $(0, 1)$, ..., $(0, n - 1)$. It follows that the cell (x, y) lies in the $(n - y)$th row and in the $(x + 1)$th column. The conventions (i) and (ii) on page 195 are equivalent to reducing the co-ordinates modulo n, so that the cells $(n + x, y)$ and $(x, n + y)$ are identified with (x, y).

In De la Loubère's method, the step from 1 to 2 increases both co-ordinates by unity—*i.e.* it is made by the " vector " $(1, 1)$. Similarly, the " cross-step " from n to $n + 1$ is made by the vector $(0, -1)$. This method may evidently be generalized by taking other vectors : say (a, b) for the step from ξ to $\xi + 1$ $(\xi = 1, 2, ..., n - 1)$, and $(a + a', b + b')$ for the cross-step from $\xi'n$ to $\xi'n + 1$ $(\xi' = 1, 2, ..., n - 1)$. Consequently the step from 1 to $n + 1$ is $(n - 1)(a, b) + (a + a', b + b') \equiv (a', b') \pmod{n}$; the step from 1 to $\xi'n + 1$ is $(a'\xi', b'\xi')$; and the step from 1 to $\xi'n + \xi + 1$ is $(a\xi + a'\xi', b\xi + b'\xi')$.

* C. Planck, *loc. cit.*   † For American readers, $6\frac{1}{2}$ *trillion.*

Let (i, j) be the cell occupied by the number 1. The position of any other number s can be deduced by expressing $s - 1$ (as $\xi'\xi$) in the scale of n—i.e. by expressing s in the form $\xi'n + \xi + 1$, where ξ' and ξ are integers less than n (and positive or zero).

Applying the vector $(a\xi + a'\xi', b\xi + b'\xi')$, the required position is found to be $(i + a\xi + a'\xi', j + b\xi + b'\xi')$. Any other number—say $s + X'n + X$—must have a different position; therefore the congruences

$$aX + a'X' \equiv 0, \quad bX + b'X' \equiv 0 \pmod{n}$$

must imply $X \equiv X' \equiv 0$. The condition for this is that $ab' - a'b$ shall be prime to n. (In De la Loubère's case $ab' - a'b = -1$.)

If also a, b, a', b' are prime to n (and therefore not zero), the square will be magic as far as rows and columns are concerned. For, the numbers in a column are given by the n solutions of a congruence of the form $a\xi + a'\xi' \equiv c$, and these involve all the possible values, $0, 1, \ldots, n - 1$ for both ξ and ξ' (in some combination); similarly for the numbers in a row. Since a, b, a', b' and $ab' - a'b$ are all prime to n, n must be odd. For, if n were even, a, b, a', b' would have to be odd, and then $ab' - a'b$ would be even. Accordingly we may write $n = 2m + 1$.

Finally, let us choose i and j so as to put the middle number (for which $\xi = \xi' = m$) into the middle cell (m, m). This requires

$$i \equiv (1 - a - a')m, \quad j \equiv (1 - b - b')m.$$

(In De la Loubère's case, $i = m, j = 2m$; hence the position of 1 in the middle of the top row.) It now follows that the square is symmetrical—i.e. that the numbers in the skewly related cells (x, y) and $(2m - x, 2m - y)$ are complementary. This ensures the magic property for the diagonals.

It is convenient to denote this magic square by the symbol $\begin{pmatrix} a & a' \\ b & b' \end{pmatrix}_n$. Thus De la Loubère's square is $\begin{pmatrix} 1 & -1 \\ 1 & -2 \end{pmatrix}_n$, and

Bachet's is $\begin{pmatrix} 1 & -1 \\ 1 & 1 \end{pmatrix}_n$. What we have proved is that such a square can be constructed whenever a, b, a', b' and $ab' - a'b$ are all prime to n.

If also $a + b$, $a - b$, $a' + b'$, $a' - b'$ are prime to n, the square will be *pandiagonal*. For, the numbers in a generalized diagonal are given by the n solutions of a congruence of the form $(a \pm b)\xi + (a' \pm b')\xi' = c$. It is impossible to satisfy all these conditions when n is a multiple of 3; in such cases, therefore, the method has to be modified.

When the conditions are all satisfied, the values of i and j

(*Pandiagonal Squares.*)

7	20	3	11	24
13	21	9	17	5
19	2	15	23	6
25	8	16	4	12
1	14	22	10	18

Figure xvi. $n = 5$.

26	21	9	4	48	36	31
44	39	34	22	17	12	7
20	8	3	47	42	30	25
38	33	28	16	11	6	43
14	2	46	41	29	24	19
32	27	15	10	5	49	37
1	45	40	35	23	18	13

Figure xvii. $n = 7$.

obtained above render the square symmetrical as well as pandiagonal; but, of course, the square will still be pandiagonal if the position of the number 1 is chosen arbitrarily. For instance, n being prime to 6, the conditions are all satisfied by $\begin{pmatrix} 1 & -1 \\ 2 & -3 \end{pmatrix}_n$. Thus, to form a pandiagonal square of the fifth order (figure xvi) we may put 1 in any cell; proceed by four successive steps, like a knight's move, of one cell to the right, and two cells up, writing consecutively numbers 2, 3, 4, 5 in each cell, until we come to a cell already occupied; then take one step, like a rook's move, one cell down; and so on until the square is filled. Again, in the square $\begin{pmatrix} 1 & 1 \\ 2 & -3 \end{pmatrix}_n$ the successive numbers can be written in with a knight's move at *every* step, as in figure xvii; but, since $ab' - a'b = -5$, this formation is impossible when n is 5 or a multiple of 5.

Arnoux's Method.[*] If the numbers in figures xvi and xvii are all diminished by 1 and expressed in the scale of $n (= 5$ or $7)$, the results are immediately recognizable as the Eulerian squares $(23, 44)_5$ and $(62, 43)_7$. Conversely, it is obvious that any diagonal Eulerian square, composed of the marks 00, 01, ..., $(n-1)(n-1)$, becomes a magic square when its marks are interpreted as numbers in the scale of n.

Moreover, any Eulerian square of the form $(\alpha'\alpha, \beta'\beta)_n$ (even if not *diagonally* Eulerian) becomes a magic square when its rows and columns are cyclically permuted in such a way as to put the middle number mm into the middle cell (m, m); for, this permutation makes the square symmetrical— *i.e.* it puts complementary numbers into the cells $(m + x, m + y)$ and $(m - x, m - y)$. In fact, the number in the cell $(m + x, m + y)$ has digits congruent to $m + \alpha'x + \beta'y$, $m + \alpha x + \beta y \pmod{n}$. (In order to make the numbers run from 1 to n^2, instead of 0 to $n^2 - 1$, we merely have to add 1 throughout.)

On the other hand, the above generalization of De la Loubère's rule puts the number $(m + \xi')n + (m + \xi) + 1$ into the cell $(m + a\xi + a'\xi', m + b\xi + b'\xi')$. The two methods lead to the same square if the congruences

$$x \equiv a\xi + a'\xi', y \equiv b\xi + b'\xi', \xi \equiv \alpha x + \beta y, \xi' \equiv \alpha'x + \beta'y \pmod{n}$$

are consistent—*i.e.* if

$$a\alpha + a'\alpha' \equiv b\beta + b'\beta' \equiv 1 \text{ and } a\beta + a'\beta' \equiv b\alpha + b'\alpha' \equiv 0.$$

Under these circumstances, $\begin{pmatrix} a & a' \\ b & b' \end{pmatrix}$ and $\begin{pmatrix} \alpha & \beta \\ \alpha' & \beta' \end{pmatrix}$ are called "inverse matrices," since, on multiplying them together by the usual rule for determinants, the result is $\begin{pmatrix} 1 & 0 \\ 0 & 1 \end{pmatrix} \pmod{n}$. In fact, the two methods correspond to the two aspects of a

---

[*] G. Arnoux, *Arithmétique graphique. Les espaces arithmétiques hyper-magiques*, Paris, 1894, p. 51. Cf. Kraïtchik, pp. 130—146.

transformation of co-ordinates.* Clearly, the statement that a, b, a', b' and $ab' - a'b$ are prime to n is equivalent to the statement that α, β, α', β' and $\alpha\beta' - \alpha'\beta$ are prime to n.

When n is prime to 6, we can choose α, β, α', β' so as to make $\alpha \pm \beta$, $\alpha' \pm \beta'$ (as well as α, β, α', β', $\alpha\beta' - \alpha'\beta$) all prime to n. Then the square $(\alpha'\alpha, \beta'\beta)_n$ is not merely diagonal, but *pandiagonal*. (There is no need to permute the rows or columns, unless the extra quality of symmetry is desired.) The simplest example, from this point of view, is $(12, 21)_n$. (See page 191.)

Margossian's Method.† I next describe an extension of Arnoux's method which enables us to construct a pandiagonal square whose order is a multiple of 4 or an odd multiple of 3 (but not 3 itself, of course).

23	31	03	11
02	10	22	30
21	33	01	13
00	12	20	32

Figure xviii.

32	21	02	11
03	10	33	20
31	22	01	12
00	13	30	23

Figure xix.

Figure xviii shows the square $(12, 21)_4$ (which is not properly Eulerian, since 2 divides 4). Though not magic as it stands, this square becomes magic, in fact pandiagonal, when every digit 2 is replaced by 3, and *vice versa*, as in figure xix. Figure ii shows the same square in the ordinary notation.

More generally, α being any even ‡ number, the square $(1\alpha, \alpha1)_{2\alpha}$ becomes pandiagonally magic when the digits α, $\alpha + 1$, ..., $2\alpha - 1$ are replaced by $2\alpha - 1$, $2\alpha - 2$, ..., α. The unit digits in a row consist of two particular digits, each

* O. Veblen, " On Magic Squares," *Messenger of Mathematics*, 1908, vol. xxxvii, pp. 116—118.

† Kraïtchik, pp. 148—152.

‡ This would fail if α were odd, since then the numbers in the square would not be all distinct. In fact, $\alpha\beta' - \alpha'\beta$ ($= \alpha^2 - 1$) would not be prime to n ($= 2\alpha$).

repeated α times; Margossian's substitution makes these two digits have the uniform sum $2\alpha - 1$; similarly for the radix digits in a column. A square formed by this rule (with $\alpha = 4$) is shown in figure xx.

74	63	54	43	04	13	24	33
05	12	25	32	75	62	55	42
76	61	56	41	06	11	26	31
07	10	27	30	77	60	57	40
73	64	53	44	03	14	23	34
02	15	22	35	72	65	52	45
71	66	51	46	01	16	21	36
00	17	20	37	70	67	50	47

Figure xx.   *A Pandiagonal Square,* $n = 8$ (*in the scale of* 8).

35	48	52	65	78	82	05	18	22
04	17	21	34	47	51	64	77	81
63	76	80	03	16	20	33	46	50
32	45	58	62	75	88	02	15	28
01	14	27	31	44	57	61	74	87
60	73	86	00	13	26	30	43	56
38	42	55	68	72	85	08	12	25
07	11	24	37	41	54	67	71	84
66	70	83	06	10	23	36	40	53

Figure xxi.

Similarly, a square of the form $(13, 31)_{3m}$, where m is odd, becomes pandiagonally magic when the digits, 0, 1, ..., $3m - 1$ are so permuted that, if they are written in their new order in m rows of three, the sum of the columns is uniform. For this purpose, $\frac{1}{2}(m - 1)$ of the m triads 0, 1, 2; 3, 4, 5;

... can be left unchanged if two of the rest are cyclically permuted (opposite ways) and the remaining $\frac{1}{2}(m-3)$ are reversed. Thus, for a square of the fifteenth order, the digits 0, 1, 2, 3, 4, 5 can be left unchanged if the rest are replaced by 7, 8, 6; 11, 9, 10; 14, 13, 12. In the special case when $m = 3$, *i.e.* for a square of the ninth order, we may cyclically permute the rows and columns of $(13, 31)_9$ so as to put 44 into the middle cell (figure xxi) and then replace the digits 0, 1, 2, 3, 4, 5, 6, 7, 8 by 1, 2, 0, 3, 4, 5, 8, 6, 7; the resulting square (figure xxii) is not merely pandiagonal * but also symmetrical.

35	47	50	85	67	70	15	27	00
14	26	02	34	46	52	84	66	72
83	68	71	13	28	01	33	48	51
30	45	57	80	65	77	10	25	07
12	24	06	32	44	56	82	64	76
81	63	78	11	23	08	31	43	58
37	40	55	87	60	75	17	20	05
16	22	04	36	42	54	86	62	74
88	61	73	18	21	03	38	41	53

Figure xxii.   *A Pandiagonal Symmetrical Square, n = 9*
(in the scale of 9).

MAGIC SQUARES OF NON-CONSECUTIVE NUMBERS

Although it is impossible to make a pandiagonal or symmetrical magic square of singly-even order, using *consecutive* numbers, C. Planck † has devised a method for making such squares with numbers that are *almost* consecutive. For a square of singly-even order n, he uses the numbers from 1 to $n^2 + 3$, omitting the "middle number" $\frac{1}{2}n^2 + 2$ and any two other even numbers whose sum is $n^2 + 4$. In particular, he

---

* Arnoux, *loc. cit.*, pp. 152—154.
† *The Monist* (Chicago), 1919, vol. xxix, pp. 307—316.

might simply omit the multiples of $\frac{1}{4}n^2 + 1$. The sum of the numbers in a row, column or diagonal is $\frac{1}{2}n(n^2 + 4)$. Moreover, for the pandiagonal square, the sum of the numbers in any component square of $(\frac{1}{2}n)^2$ cells is $\frac{1}{8}n^2(n^2 + 4)$.

28	1	26	36	8	21
3	35	7	27	23	25
34	24	22	2	29	9
4	32	19	12	39	14
13	17	15	37	5	33
38	11	31	6	16	18

Figure xxiii. *A Pandiagonal Square, n = 6.*

28	1	26	21	8	36
3	35	7	25	23	27
34	24	22	9	29	2
38	11	31	18	16	6
13	17	15	33	5	37
4	32	19	14	39	12

Figure xxiv. *A Symmetrical Square, n = 6.*

Figures xxiii and xxiv show the case when $n = 6$, omitting the multiples of 10.

Another problem involving non-consecutive numbers is that of constructing a magic square of *primes*. The first of the following examples is due to H. E. Dudeney, the second (figure xxvi) to E. Bergholt and C. D. Shuldham. Such squares, of orders 5, 6, ..., 12, have been constructed by H. A. Sayles and J. N. Muncey.* Muncey's square of the twelfth order is especially remarkable in that the 144 primes involved are the *first* 144 odd primes—namely 1, 3, 5, 7, 11, ..., 827. (It has been proved that the *first* n^2 odd primes cannot be used when $n < 12$.)

67	1	43
13	37	61
31	73	7

Figure xxv.

3	71	5	23
53	11	37	1
17	13	41	31
29	7	19	47

Figure xxvi.

Figure xxvii shows Bergholt's general form for any magic

* *The Monist*, 1913, vol. XXIII, pp. 623—630.

square of the fourth order * (pandiagonal if $a = b = d - c = \frac{1}{2}(A - B - C + D)$), symmetrical if $a + c = d = b - c$ and $A + C = B + D$; therefore never both pandiagonal and

$A - a$	$C + a + c$	$B + b - c$	$D - b$
$D + a - d$	B	C	$A - a + d$
$C - b + d$	A	D	$B + b - d$
$B + b$	$D - a - c$	$A - b + c$	$C + a$

Figure xxvii.

symmetrical, since then we should have $A - a = B$). Figure xxvi is obtained by taking $A = 13$, $B = 11$, $C = 37$, $D = 41$, $a = 10$, $b = 18$, $c = 24$, $d = -2$.

Doubly-Magic Squares

For certain values of n (not less than 8) it is possible to construct a magic square of the nth order in such a way that if the number in each cell is replaced by its square the resulting square shall also be magic.†

17	50	43	04	32	75	66	21
31	76	65	22	14	53	40	07
00	47	54	13	25	62	71	36
26	61	72	35	03	44	57	10
45	02	11	56	60	27	34	73
63	24	37	70	46	01	12	55
52	15	06	41	77	30	23	64
74	33	20	67	51	16	05	42

Figure xxviii.   A Doubly-Magic Pandiagonal Square, $n = 8$
(in the scale of 8).

---

* *Nature*, 1910, vol. LXXXIII, p. 368. See also J. Chernick, *American Mathematical Monthly*, 1938, vol. XLV, pp. 172—175.

† See M. Coccoz in *L'Illustration*, May 29, 1897. The subject has been studied by Messrs. G. Tarry, B. Portier, M. Coccoz, A. Rilly, E. Barbette and W. S. Andrews. More than 200 such squares have been given by Rilly in his *Études sur les Triangles et les Carrés Magiques aux deux premiers degrés*, Troyes, 1901.

Here are two examples. Figure xxviii represents a pan-diagonal magic square of the eighth order, due to M. H. Schots.* The numbers are expressed in the scale of 8 in order to exhibit the underlying Eulerian square. After adding 1 throughout, the sum of the numbers in each line is equal to 260, and the sum of their squares is equal to 11180. Figure xxix represents R. V. Heath's doubly-magic square of the ninth order, written in the scale of 9.

76	82	64	15	27	00	41	53	38
11	23	08	46	52	34	75	87	60
45	57	30	71	83	68	16	22	04
62	74	86	07	10	25	33	48	51
03	18	21	32	44	56	67	70	85
37	40	55	63	78	81	02	14	26
84	66	72	20	05	17	58	31	43
28	01	13	54	36	42	80	65	77
50	35	47	88	61	73	24	06	12

Figure xxix. A Doubly-Magic Symmetrical Square, $n = 9$
(in the scale of 9).

Trebly-Magic Squares. The construction of squares which shall be magic for the original numbers, for their squares, and for their cubes has also been studied. I know of no square of this kind which is of a lower order than 64, and the construction of a square of that order is not a " recreation."

Other Magic Problems

Other problems, closely related to magic squares, will suggest themselves; the following will serve as specimens.

Magic Domino Squares. An ordinary set of dominoes, ranging from double zero to double six, contains 28 dominoes.

---

* *Bulletin de la classe des Sciences de l'Académie Royale de Belgique*, 1931, pp. 339—361. Cf. *Sphinx*, 1931, p. 137. It should be observed that this is *not* a pandiagonal *Eulerian* square, since the broken diagonals contain repeated digits (although they have the proper sum).

Each domino is a rectangle formed by fixing two small square blocks together side by side: of these 56 blocks, eight are blank, on each of eight of them is one pip, on each of another eight of them are two pips, and so on. It is required to arrange the dominoes so that the 56 blocks form a square of 7 by 7 bordered by one line of 7 blank squares, and so that the sum of the pips in each row, column, and diagonal of the square is equal to 24. A solution * is given below.

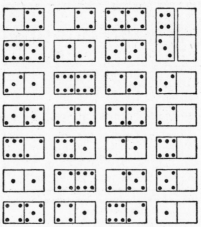

Figure xxx.   *Magic Domino Square.*

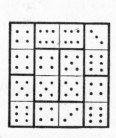
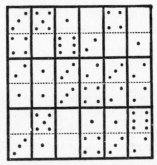

Figure xxxi.   *Magic Domino Squares.*

---

* See *L'Illustration*, July 10, 1897.

If we select certain dominoes out of the set and reject the others we can use them to make various magic puzzles. As instance, I give in figure xxxi two examples of magic squares of this kind due respectively to Escott and Dudeney.

Cubic and Octahedral Dice. The faces of a cube can obviously be numbered from 1 to 6 in such a way that the pairs of opposite faces sum to 7. A cube so marked is called a die. Dice are used in pairs, but no attention seems to have been paid to specifying whether a pair should be identical or enantiomorphous.

Another kind of die might be made by numbering the faces of a polyhedron from 1 to F in such a way that the faces around a vertex give a constant sum. If there are m faces around each vertex, the constant sum must be equal to $\frac{1}{2}m(F + 1)$; hence either m is even or F is odd. Every regular polyhedron has an even number of faces, so the only one which could be made into this kind of die is the octahedron (for which $m = 4$ and $F = 8$). The faces of the octahedron can be numbered (so that those around each vertex sum to 18) in three essentially distinct ways, each of which occurs in two enantiomorphous forms. Pairs of opposite faces have a constant difference, 1 or 2 or 4.

Figure xxxii.   *Octahedral Dice.**

Interlocked Hexagons. The problem of numbering the faces of the Rotating Ring of n tetrahedra (page 153), so that the faces around each vertex sum to $3(4n + 1)$, appears to be insoluble. But R. V. Heath has elegantly solved the corre-

* The third of these is due to J. M. Andreas.

sponding problem for the network of $36n$ triangles obtained by dividing each face of the Ring into nine. Such a network of triangles may be regarded as a symmetrical "map" on a torus (page 234), even when $n < 6$. (When $n \geqslant 6$, the map can be drawn on the rotating ring in nine distinct ways.) Figure xxxiii shows the simplest case ($n = 2$), but a similar method * applies in every case. The six triangles around any

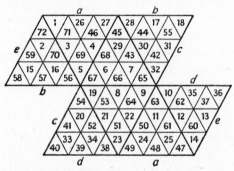

Figure xxxiii. *Interlocked Hexagons on a Torus.*

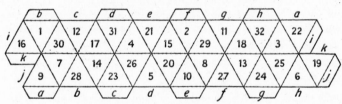

Figure xxxiv. *A Magic Rotating Ring.*

vertex sum to $3(36n + 1)$; so do the six triangles adjacent to these (which form a kind of star). Heath has succeeded in covering many other surfaces with such interlocked hexagons.

Figure xxxiv shows Heath's special arrangement of the numbers from 1 to 32 on the ring of eight tetrahedra, which is

* The method is precisely the same for all singly-even values of n. When n is odd or doubly-even, the ends have to be joined as in figure xxxiv. In the latter case, the regular arrangement of numbers has to be broken after $9n$ and $27n$.

magic in a quite different sense. The four faces of each tetrahedron sum to 66; "corresponding" faces, one from each tetrahedron, sum to 132 (for instance, $9 + 7 + 17 + 31 + 10 + 8 + 18 + 32 = 132$), and so do eight sets of eight faces which wind helically around the ring (for instance, $1 + 12 + 31 + 21 + 2 + 11 + 32 + 22 = 132$).

MAGIC CUBES

A *Magic Cube* of the nth order consists of the consecutive numbers from 1 to n^3, arranged in the form of a cube, so that the sum of the numbers in every row, every column, every file, and in each of the four diagonals (or "diameters"), is the same—namely, $\frac{1}{2}n(n^3 + 1)$. This sum occurs in $3n^2 + 4$ ways. I do not know of any rule for constructing magic cubes of singly-even order. But such cubes of any odd or doubly-even order can be constructed by a natural extension of the methods already used for squares.

As in the two-dimensional case (page 204), we proceed from cell to cell by steps, only now the vectors that make the steps are three-dimensional. In fact, we define the step (a, b, c) as taking us a cells "east," b cells "north," and c cells "up." As before, all the movements are taken cyclically, so that the numbers a, b, c may at any stage be reduced modulo n. We can make the same step $n - 1$ times before coming to an occupied cell. Then we make one cross-step $(a + a', b + b', c + c')$, follow this by $n - 1$ more steps (a, b, c), and so on. There will be no difficulty until we try to write the number $n^2 + 1$. At that stage the cross-step has to be altered, say to $(a + a' + a'', b + b' + b'', c + c' + c'')$, and this new kind of cross-step has to be used again after each multiple of n^2 has been reached. If a'', b'', c'' are suitably chosen, the whole cube can now be filled up. In fact, the position of the number $\xi''n^2 + \xi'n + \xi + 1$ is derived from that of the number 1 by applying ξ steps (a, b, c), ξ' steps (a', b', c'), and ξ'' steps (a'', b'', c''). Thus, if 1 is in the cell whose co-ordinates are (i, j, k), then $\xi''n^2 + \xi'n + \xi + 1$ is in that whose co-ordinates are

$$(i + a\xi + a'\xi' + a''\xi'', \; j + b\xi + b'\xi' + b''\xi'',$$
$$k + c\xi + c'\xi' + c''\xi'').$$

In order that different numbers may always occupy different positions, the congruences

$$aX + a'X' + a''X'' \equiv 0, \; bX + b'X' + b''X'' \equiv 0,$$
$$cX + c'X' + c''X'' \equiv 0 \; (\mathrm{mod}\ n)$$

must imply $X \equiv X' \equiv X'' \equiv 0$. The condition for this is that the determinant

$$\begin{vmatrix} a & a' & a'' \\ b & b' & b'' \\ c & c' & c'' \end{vmatrix}$$

shall be prime to n. The magic property of the rows, columns and files is secured by making all the two-rowed minors of the determinant likewise prime to n. (This is impossible if n is even). The magic property of the diagonals is secured by adjusting i, j, k so as to place the middle number in the middle cell; the cube will then be *symmetrical*.

(*Bottom layer*)   (*Middle layer*)   (*Top layer*)

4	12	26	20	7	15	18	23	1
11	25	6	9	14	19	22	3	17
27	5	10	13	21	8	2	16	24

Figure xxxv.   *A Magic Cube, $n = 3$.*

It is convenient to denote this magic cube by the symbol

$$\begin{pmatrix} a & a' & a'' \\ b & b' & b'' \\ c & c' & c'' \end{pmatrix}_n$$

What we have proved is that such a cube can be constructed whenever the determinant and all its first minors are prime to n. Clearly, these conditions are satisfied, for any odd value of n, if

$$a = a' = b = b'' = c' = c'' = 1, \ a'' = b' = c = 0,$$

and $i = j = k = \frac{1}{2}(n + 1)$. In practice it is easiest to insert first the numbers $1, n^2 + 1, 2n^2 + 1, \ldots$, proceeding by steps $(0, 1, 1)$, then to insert the rest of the numbers $1, n + 1, 2n + 1, \ldots$, proceeding by steps $(1, 0, 1)$, and finally to fill in the remaining numbers, proceeding by steps $(1, 1, 0)$. Figure xxxv shows the three "horizontal" layers of the magic cube

$$\begin{pmatrix} 1 & 1 & 0 \\ 1 & 0 & 1 \\ 0 & 1 & 1 \end{pmatrix}_3$$

The reader may be interested to try the same rule with $n = 5$. The resulting cube is *pandiagonal*, having the magic property not merely in its four main diagonals, but in all the broken diagonals as well. In such a cube the magic sum occurs $(3 + 4)n^2$ times, instead of only $3n^2 + 4$.

It can be shown that the cube

$$\begin{pmatrix} a & b & 0 \\ b & 0 & a \\ 0 & a & b \end{pmatrix}_n$$

is pandiagonal whenever a, b, $a + b$ and $a^2 \pm ab \pm b^2$ (with all four distributions of sign) are prime to n. Thus $a = b = 1$ gives a solution whenever n is not divisible by 3 (nor by 2); $a = 2$, $b = 1$ gives another solution whenever n is divisible by none of 2, 3, 5, 7.

If a, b, $a \pm b$ and $a^2 + b^2$ are prime to n, the cube, without necessarily being pandiagonal itself, has pandiagonal squares for its n layers in each of the three principal directions, so that the magic sum occurs $(3 + 6)n^2$ times. For instance, $a = 2$, $b = 1$ gives a solution whenever n is prime to 30, and in particular when n is 7 or any larger prime. This cube will

itself be pandiagonal if n is prime to 210, and in particular
when $n = 11$ or any larger prime. The magic sum will then
occur $(3 + 4 + 6)n^2$ times. Rosser and Walker have shown
that a magic cube can be pandiagonal in this stricter sense
when $n = 8$ or any multiple of 8, and when $n = 9$ or any
larger odd number, but in no other cases.

010	102	221	201	020	112	122	211	000
101	220	012	022	111	200	210	002	121
222	011	100	110	202	021	001	120	212

Figure xxxvi.   An Eulerian Cube, $n = 3$.

Figure xxxvi shows the same cube as figure xxxv, but with
every number diminished by 1 and expressed in the scale of 3.
Apart from cyclic permutations of the layers, this is just the
Eulerian cube $(122, 212, 221)_3$; for, the row, column, and file
involving 000 contain the Galois multiples (mod 3) of the
marks 122, 212 and 221, and the whole cube constitutes a
table of Galois addition based on this row, column, and file.*

Since

$$\begin{pmatrix} 1 & 1 & 0 \\ 1 & 0 & 1 \\ 0 & 1 & 1 \end{pmatrix} \quad \text{and} \quad \begin{pmatrix} 2 & 2 & 1 \\ 2 & 1 & 2 \\ 1 & 2 & 2 \end{pmatrix}$$

are inverse matrices (mod 3), the two methods of construction
again correspond to the two aspects of a transformation of
co-ordinates.

232	310	032	110	013	131	213	331	230	312	030	112	011	133	211	333
020	102	220	302	201	323	001	123	022	100	222	300	203	321	003	121
212	330	012	130	033	111	233	311	210	332	010	132	031	113	231	313
000	122	200	322	221	303	021	103	002	120	202	320	223	301	023	101

Figure xxxvii. $n = 4$.

* Arnoux, loc. cit., p. 63.

Figure xxxvii shows the cube $(122, 212, 221)_4$ (which is not properly Eulerian, since 2 divides 4). This becomes magic, in fact pandiagonal, when every digit 2 is replaced by 3, and *vice versa*. The result, in the ordinary notation, is shown in figure xxxviii. In fact, Margossian's substitution (page 208) gives a pandiagonal cube $(1\alpha\alpha, \alpha1\alpha, \alpha\alpha1)_{2a}$ for every even value of α.

60	37	12	21	7	26	55	42	57	40	9	24	6	27	54	43
13	20	61	36	50	47	2	31	16	17	64	33	51	46	3	30
56	41	8	25	11	22	59	38	53	44	5	28	10	23	58	39
1	32	49	48	62	35	14	19	4	29	52	45	63	34	15	18

Figure xxxviii.   *A Pandiagonal Magic Cube, n = 4.*

(First layer)   (Second layer)

1	8	61	60	48	41	20	21
62	59	2	7	19	22	47	42
52	53	16	9	29	28	33	40
15	10	51	54	34	39	30	27
32	25	36	37	49	56	13	12
35	38	31	26	14	11	50	55
45	44	17	24	4	5	64	57
18	23	46	43	63	58	3	6

(Fourth layer)   (Third layer)

Figure xxxix.   *A Magic Square which is also a Pandiagonal Cube.*

Figure xxxix, by R. V. Heath, is remarkable as being both a magic square of the eighth order and a pandiagonal cube of the fourth order. As a magic square, it has the interesting property that *alternate* numbers in any row or column, or in either diagonal, sum to 130. As a pandiagonal cube, it excels figure xxxviii in that the four horizontal layers (which are the four quarters of the eighth-order square) are themselves magic squares.

CHAPTER VIII

MAP-COLOURING PROBLEMS

THIS chapter and the next are concerned with the branch of mathematics known as Topology or Analysis Situs, which differs from Geometry in having no connection with the idea of straightness, flatness, or measurement. Here every oval is equivalent to a circle, every spheroid to a sphere; in fact, no distinction is made between any two figures derivable from one another by the kind of transformations that are familiar as crumpling and stretching, without tearing or joining. (One's thoughts turn naturally to indiarubber.) But topology does distinguish between a solid sphere and a hollow sphere, and between either of these and a *torus* or anchor-ring. It also distinguishes between a simple closed curve and a knotted curve, provided these are definitely understood to lie in the same three-dimensional space; in four-dimensional space, any such knot could be untied without breaking the circuit.

THE FOUR-COLOUR THEOREM

I shall first mention a famous theorem which appears to be simple, and seems to be true, but has never yet been proved, although more complicated theorems of a similar type are fairly easy to prove. The theorem is that *not more than four colours are necessary in order to colour a map of a country (divided into districts) in such a way that no two contiguous districts shall be of the same colour*. By contiguous districts are meant districts having a common *line* as part of their boundaries—districts which touch only at points are not contiguous in this sense. The map is drawn on a simply-connected surface, such as a plane or a sphere. The number of districts is finite, and no district consists of two or more disconnected pieces.   The map may or may not fill up the whole surface.   (If the map is plane, and fills up the plane, one district at least must have an infinite area, since the number is finite.)   Of course, some maps can be coloured with fewer than four colours; thus a chess-board requires only two, a hexagonal tessellation three.

The problem was mentioned by A. F. Möbius * in his Lectures in 1840, but it was not until Francis Guthrie † com-

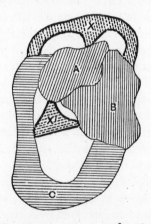

municated it to De Morgan about 1850 that attention was generally called to it : it is said that the fact had been familiar to practical map-makers for a long time previously.   Through De Morgan the proposition then became generally known ; and in 1878 Cayley ‡ recalled attention to it by stating that he could not obtain a rigorous proof of it.

Probably the following argument, though not a formal demonstration, will satisfy the reader that the result is true. Let A, B, C be three contiguous districts, and let X be any

* *Leipzig Transactions* (*Math.-phys. Classe*), 1885, vol. xxxvii, pp. 1—6.

† See *Proceedings of the Royal Society of Edinburgh,* July 19, 1880, vol. x, p. 728.

‡ *Proceedings of the London Mathematical Society,* 1878, vol. ix, p. 148, and *Proceedings of the Royal Geographical Society,* London, 1879, N.S., vol. i, pp. 259—261, where some of the difficulties are indicated.

other district contiguous with all of them.   Then X must lie
either wholly outside the external boundary of the area ABC or
wholly inside the internal boundary—that is, it must occupy a
position either like X or like X'.   In either case there is no
possible way of drawing another area Y which shall be contiguous with A, B, C, and X.   In other words, it is possible to
draw on a plane four areas which are contiguous, but it is not
possible to draw five such areas.   If A, B, C are not contiguous,
each with the other, or if X is not contiguous with A, B, and C,
it is not necessary to colour them all differently, and thus the
most unfavourable case is that already treated.   Moreover any
of the above areas may diminish to a point, and finally
disappear without affecting the argument.

That we may require at least four colours is obvious from the
above diagram, since in that case the areas A, B, C, and X
would have to be coloured differently.

A proof of the proposition involves difficulties of a high
order, which as yet have baffled all attempts to surmount them.
This is partly due to the fact that if, using only four colours, we
build up our map, district by district, and assign definite
colours to the districts as we insert them, we can always con-
trive the addition of two or three fresh districts which cannot
be coloured differently from those next to them, and which
accordingly upset our scheme of colouring.   But by starting
afresh, it would seem that we can always rearrange the
colours so as to allow of the addition of such extra districts.

The argument by which the truth of the proposition was
formerly supposed to be demonstrated was given by A. B.
Kempe * in 1879, but there is a flaw in it.

In 1880, Tait published a solution † depending on the

* He sent his first demonstration across the Atlantic to the *American
Journal of Mathematics*, 1879, vol. II, pp. 193—200; but subsequently he
communicated it in simplified forms to the London Mathematical Society,
Transactions, 1879, vol. X, pp. 229—231, and to *Nature*, Feb. 26, 1880,
vol. XXI, pp. 399—400.   The flaw in the argument was indicated in articles
by P. J. Heawood in the *Quarterly Journal of Mathematics*, London, 1890,
vol. XXIV, pp. 332—338; and 1897, vol. XXIX, pp. 270—285.

† *Proceedings of the Royal Society of Edinburgh*, July 19, 1880, vol. X,

theorem that if a closed network of lines joining an even number of points is such that three and only three lines meet at each point, then three colours are sufficient to colour the lines in such a way that no two lines meeting at a point are of the same colour; a closed network being supposed to exclude the case where the lines can be divided into two groups between which there is but one connecting line.

This theorem may be true, if we understand it with the limitation that the network is in one plane and that no line meets any other line except at one of the vertices, which is all

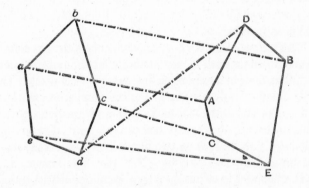

that we require for the map theorem; but it has not been proved. Without this limitation it is not correct. For instance, the accompanying figure, representing a closed network in three dimensions of 15 lines formed by the sides of two pentagons and the lines joining their corresponding angular points, cannot be coloured as described by Tait. If the figure is in three dimensions, the lines intersect only at the ten vertices of the network. If it is regarded as being in two dimensions, only the ten angular points of the pentagons are treated as vertices of the network, and any other point of intersection of the lines is not regarded as such a vertex. Expressed in

p. 729; *Philosophical Magazine*, January, 1884, series 5, vol. XVII, p. 41; and *Collected Scientific Papers*, Cambridge, vol. II, 1890, p. 93.

simple language the difficulty is this.   Petersen * has shown
that any network in which just three lines meet at each
point can be coloured with two colours, say red and green,
in such a way that at each point one red and two green
lines meet.   The green lines will form certain loops, and Tait
assumed that these loops can always be arranged so that each
contains an even number of lines.   This would enable us to
colour the lines of each loop alternately blue and yellow,
instead of all green.

Let us suppose that Tait's assumption, as applied to a
plane network, can in fact be justified.   His argument that
four colours will suffice for a map is divided into two parts
and is as follows.

First, suppose that the boundary lines of contiguous districts
form a closed network of lines joining an even number of points
such that three and only three lines meet at each point.   Then
if the number of districts is $n + 1$, the number of boundaries
will be $3n$, and there will be $2n$ points of junction; also by
Tait's theorem, the boundaries can be marked with three
colours β, γ, δ, so that no two like colours meet at a point of
junction.   Suppose this done.   Now take four colours, A, B,
C, D, wherewith to colour the map.   Paint one district with the
colour A; paint the district adjoining A and divided from it by
the line β with the colour B; the district adjoining A and
divided from it by the line γ with the colour C; the district
adjoining A and divided from it by the line δ with the colour
D.   Proceed in this way so that a line β always separates the
colours A and B, or the colours C and D; a line γ always
separates A and C, or D and B; and a line δ always separates
A and D, or B and C.   It is easy to see that, if we come to a
district bounded by districts already coloured, the rule for
crossing each of its boundaries will give the same colour; this

* See J. Petersen of Copenhagen, *L'Intermédiaire des Mathématiciens,*
vol. v, 1898, pp. 225—227; and vol. vi, 1899, pp. 36—38.   Also *Acta
Mathematica,* Stockholm, vol. xv, 1891, pp. 193—220.   The simplest non-
plane graph that *can* be given a Tait colouring has six vertices, say P,
Q, R, p, q, r, joined as follows : Pp, Qr, Rq ; Qq, Rp, Pr ; Rr, Pq, Qp.

also follows from the fact that, if we regard β, γ, δ as indicating certain operations, then an operation like δ may be represented as equivalent to the effect of the two other operations β and γ performed in succession in either order. Thus for such a map the problem is solved.

In the second case, suppose that at any point four or more boundaries meet, then at any such point introduce a small district as indicated below : this will reduce the problem to the first case. The small district thus introduced may be

coloured by the previous rule ; but after the rest of the map is coloured this **district will have** served its purpose, it may be then made to contract without limit to a mere point and will disappear leaving the boundaries as they were at first.

For a further discussion of the problem * it is desirable to develop the notion of reducing the map to a " standard " map, of simpler type than the original, and such that, if the reduced map can be coloured with four colours, so can the original. (*A fortiori*, if the reduced map can be coloured with five or more colours, so can the original.)

We suppose the map drawn on a sphere ; if it does not already cover the whole sphere, we regard " the rest of the world " as one more district. Secondly, we reduce to vertices of degree three, not as above (since that method increases the number of districts), but by observing that a higher vertex

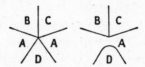

must involve a pair of non-contiguous districts, which can be given the same colour ; we then open out the vertex, and

---

* Heawood, *Quarterly Journal of Mathematics*, 1890, vol. XXIV, p. 333. This simplified account of Heawood's paper is due to L. A. Pars.

merge these two into one district. Thirdly, we get rid of districts having one, two or three sides. (We merely have to

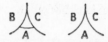

remove one side, and merge the district into an adjacent district.) Fourthly, we get rid of four-sided districts. (Of the four districts that surround such a district, at least one pair are non-contiguous; this pair can be merged with the four-sided district. If the map so formed can be coloured with four

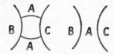

colours, so can the original; for, when we restore the four-sided district, only three colours at most surround it, and we have a colour to spare for it.) Fifthly, we get rid of ring-shaped districts, so that each district is bounded by a single continuous line, and no district encloses one or more others.

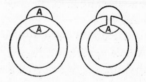

(A ring-shaped district may be broken by a corridor joining one district inside to one outside, and these two districts may be merged with the corridor.)

If we started with a fairly simple sort of map, the chances are that we have reduced the map away, so that we are left with a single district covering the sphere, and the theorem is proved for that particular map. At worst we shall be left with a "standard" map, in which no district has fewer than five sides.

Such a map may be regarded as a polyhedron, having F

faces (the districts), E edges (the lines separating pairs of
contiguous districts), and V vertices. Since each vertex
belongs to three districts, and each edge to two, we have

$$3V = 2E = aF,$$

where a is the average number of sides of a district. By
Euler's Theorem (which we shall prove later),

$$F - E + V = 2.$$

Eliminating V and E, we find that $a = 6 - 12/F$. Since
$a < 6$, there is at least one pentagon.

We can now prove by induction that a standard map, and
therefore any map, can be coloured with *six* colours. Consider a district having five sides, and merge it with one of the
contiguous districts by removing one side. If the new map
can be coloured with six colours, so can the original; for, when
we restore the five-sided district, only five colours are adjacent
to it, and we have a colour to spare for it. But we can reduce,
step by step, and the six-colour theorem is proved. (The
argument is rather subtler than it looks at first sight. For,
when we remove the side, the new map will not necessarily be
" standard," and we may have to reduce it by one of the above
processes before we can apply the same argument again. I
shall refer to this later as " the crude induction argument.")

By a subtler argument, likewise due to Heawood,* we can
show that *five* colours are always sufficient. Consider a five-
sided district, P. Of the districts Q, R, S, T, U which touch it,
there must be at least one non-contiguous pair—say Q and S.
Merge Q, P, S into a single district P' by deleting two sides of P.
If the resulting map can be coloured with five colours, so can
the original; for the districts P', R, T, U use up at most four
colours, and there is a colour left for P when we return to the
original map. Again we reduce, step by step, until the five-
colour theorem is proved.

But this is as far as we can go. The gap between the five
colours that are always sufficient and the four that are generally

* *Loc. cit.*, p. 337.

necessary has never been bridged, save for small values of F. Suppose the map has F_n n-sided regions ($n = 5, 6, 7, \ldots$). Then

$$
\begin{aligned}
F - E + V &= F - \tfrac{1}{6}aF \\
&= (F_5 + F_6 + F_7 + \ldots) - \tfrac{1}{6}(5F_5 + 6F_6 + 7F_7 + \ldots) \\
&= \tfrac{1}{6}(F_5 - F_7 - 2F_8 - \ldots),
\end{aligned}
$$

whence $\qquad F_5 - F_7 - 2F_8 - 3F_9 - \ldots = 12$

and $F_5 \geqslant 12$. Thus every standard map contains (at least) twelve pentagons. The simplest standard map is the dodecahedron. We can colour this with four colours. It follows that every map having not more than 12 districts can be coloured with four colours. In other words, any map that requires five colours must have at least 13 districts, including at least 12 pentagons.

These numbers have been improved by various investigators.[*] In 1922, P. Franklin showed that a map requiring five colours must have at least 26 districts. In 1924, A. Errera showed that such a map must include at least 13 pentagons. In 1926, C. N. Reynolds increased the number of districts to 28. In 1936, Franklin increased the number of districts to 32, and the number of pentagons to 15. Still more recently, C. E. Winn showed that such a map must contain at least two districts with more than six sides.

In his second paper [†] Heawood showed how the problem may be reduced to purely number-theoretical considerations. Consider again Tait's network of $3n$ lines joining pairs of $2n$ vertices (page 226). Through each vertex pass three lines, marked β, γ, δ. We may distribute the vertices into two classes—say "positive" and "negative"—according as the incident lines β, γ, δ occur in a counter-clockwise or clockwise sense. Then every district has a number of positive vertices, and a number of negative vertices, which differ by a multiple

---

[*] *Transactions of the American Mathematical Society*, 1922, vol. XLIV, pp. 225—236; *Annals of Mathematics*, 1927, series 2, vol. XXVIII, pp. 1—15; *Bulletin of the American Mathematical Society*, 1936, vol. XLII, p. 491; *American Journal of Mathematics*, 1937, vol. LIX, pp. 515—528.

[†] *Quarterly Journal of Mathematics*, 1897, vol. XXIX, pp. 277, 278.

of 3. For, in the succession of sides of a district, taken clock-wise, each positive vertex takes us one step onwards, and each negative vertex one step backwards, in the cyclic order β, γ, δ; and when we get round to the starting-point, the difference between the numbers of onward and backward steps must be a multiple of 3. Conversely, given such a distribution of the vertices into two classes, the lines can be consistently marked

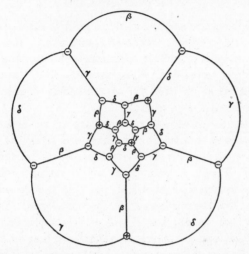

β, γ, δ, and then Tait's argument shows that the given map can be coloured with four colours.

The description of the vertices as positive or negative is equivalent to associating with them $2n$ variables x_1, x_2, ..., x_{2n}, having the values ± 1. The colouring problem thus reduces to the solution of a system of $n + 2$ $(= F)$ congruences of the form

$$x_a + x_b + \ldots \equiv 0 \pmod{3},$$

without any zeros. Each of the $2n$ $(= V)$ variables occurs in just three of the congruences. The question now is, whether every such system is soluble.

Considering "extended" congruences of the form

$$x_a + x_b + \ldots \equiv \rho \pmod{3},$$

where ρ may take any of the values 0, 1, 2, Heawood found *
that, as the number n increases, the number of "failures"
(*i.e.* of insoluble systems of congruences) diminishes rapidly.
But in a later paper he showed that failures (for the extended
congruences) always occur.

UNBOUNDED SURFACES

A surface is said to be *orientable* if a positive sense of rotation
can be assigned consistently at all points of it.† A surface in
ordinary space is orientable or unorientable according as it is
two-sided or one-sided. For instance, the "paradromic
rings" described on page 126 are orientable or unorientable
according as m is even or odd.

In order to investigate the topology of an unbounded ‡
surface (such as the surface of a sphere or a torus), we cover it
with a map—*i.e.* we divide it into F polygonal "districts" by
means of E arcs, joining (pairs of) V points. When the
surface is crumpled or stretched, the map is supposed to go
with it, so that the numbers F, E, V are unaltered. I proceed
to prove that the number $F - E + V$ is a property of the
surface itself, and not merely of a particular map—*i.e.* that if
a second map on the same surface has F' districts, E' lines and
V' points, then $F' - E' + V' = F - E + V$. For this
purpose let us superpose the two maps,§ allowing the lines of
each to break up the districts of the other, so as to make a third
map, having (say) f districts, e lines and v points. The v

* *Proceedings of the London Mathematical Society*, 1932, series 2, vol.
XXXIII, pp. 253—286.

† To be more precise, the positive sense of rotation may be defined at
any point by a "directrix," that is, a small circle with an arrow-head
marked on its circumference. A surface is *unorientable* if there can be
found on it a closed path such that the directrix is reversed when moved
around this path.

‡ *I.e.* without any periphery (or "rim," or "edge"). For an interesting
bounded surface, see Steinhaus, *Mathematical Snapshots*, New York, 1938,
p. 117.

§ This method of proof was suggested to me by Professor J. W. Alexander vertices of this third map consist of the $V + V'$ vertices of the other two,* together with the points where their lines cross.

Let us modify the first map by admitting these crossing-points as vertices, and consequently breaking up the lines on which they lie. Since E and V are equally increased, the value of $F - E + V$ is unchanged. The remaining lines and vertices of the third map may now be added in the form of successive " chains," each joining two given vertices and dividing a given district into two parts. Such a chain consists of (say) n new lines meeting consecutively at $n - 1$ new vertices ($n \geqslant 1$). Its insertion therefore increases F by 1, E by n, and V by $n - 1$, leaving $F - E + V$ unchanged. Continuing in this way until the third map is complete, we thus find that $f - e + v = F - E + V$. Similarly, $f - e + v = F' - E' + V'$. Hence $F' - E' + V' = F - E + V$, as required.

This incidentally proves Euler's Theorem (viz., that for a sphere, $F - E + V = 2$), since it shows that every map on a sphere has the same value for $F - E + V$ as a particular map, such as the tetrahedron (for which $F = V = 4$ and $E = 6$). The invariant $F - E + V$ is called the *characteristic* † of any surface. The value for a torus is zero, since two circles crossing at one point make a map for which $F = V = 1$ and $E = 2$. (More convincingly, two systems of r circles on a torus make a map for which $F = V = r^2$ and $E = 2r^2$.)

From any given surface, we can derive a topologically different surface by adding a " handle," which may be thought of as a bent prism connecting two separate n-gons of a map on the given surface. Such a prism has $2n$ vertices, all of which belong to the original map, $3n$ edges, of which all but n belong to the original map, and $n + 2$ faces, of which 2 (the bases) are

---

* There is no loss of generality in supposing these $V + V'$ points to be distinct, since a slight distortion would shift any vertex of either map.

† It " characterizes " the surface in the following sense. Two unbounded surfaces, both orientable or both unorientable, which have the same characteristic, are homeomorphic (or topologically equivalent). Some authors prefer to change the sign—*i.e.* to define the characteristic as $- V + E - F$.

the faces of contact, which are supposed to be removed. Hence the operation of adding the handle leaves V unchanged, increases E by n, and increases F by $n - 2$; altogether, it diminishes the characteristic by 2.

The most general (unbounded) orientable surface may be regarded as a sphere with p handles. The number p is called the *genus* of the surface. Thus the sphere is of genus zero; the torus, of genus one. The above argument shows that the characteristic is equal to $2 - 2p$. Thus every orientable surface has an even characteristic.

The characteristic of an unorientable surface may be either even or odd (but cannot be greater than 1). In ordinary space there is no unbounded unorientable surface that does not cut itself.

Dual Maps

Given any map (covering an unbounded surface), we can define a *dual* map (covering the same surface), each of whose vertices lies within a corresponding district of the first map, while each of its lines crosses a corresponding line of the first map. (For an example, see page 107.) Clearly, the vertices of the first map lie in separate districts of the second, and the relationship between the two maps is symmetrical. The dualizing process replaces the numbers F, E, V by V, E, F, respectively. The dual of a " standard " map has triangular districts throughout. Reciprocal polyhedra may be regarded as a special case of dual maps.

The great dodecahedron, $5^{5/2}$ (page 144), is a map of twelve pentagons on a surface of genus 4, since $F - E + V = 12 - 30 + 12 = 2 - 8$. This map being self-dual (or rather, dual to an identical map), the polyhedra $5^{5/2}$ and $(\frac{5}{2})^5$ are topologically equivalent (or " homeomorphic "). In the same sense, the polyhedra $3^{5/2}$ and $(\frac{5}{2})^3$ are equivalent to the ordinary icosahedron and dodecahedron, respectively.

The rotating ring of tetrahedra (page 153) provides a map of $4n$ triangles on a torus. The genus is 1, since $F - E + V = 4n - 6n + 2n = 0$.

THE SEVEN-COLOUR THEOREM

It is natural to ask how many colours are required for a map
on a torus, or on any other orientable surface.   Heawood * has
discussed this question, with the remarkable conclusion that for
these surfaces of higher genus the problem is capable of
complete solution.

Consider a map covering a torus, reduced so as to have all
vertices of degree three (and no ring-shaped districts).   As
before, $3V = 2E = aF$, where a is the average number of
sides of a district.   But now $F - E + V = 0$, whence $a = 6$;

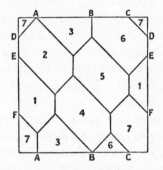

so there is a district having not more than six sides.   The
crude induction argument, which proves that every map on a
sphere can be coloured with six colours, suffices to prove that
every map on a torus can be coloured with seven.   But,
whereas in the spherical case the number six was soon seen to
be too large, in the present case the number seven is exactly
right; for we can construct a map consisting of seven hexagons each of which touches all the other six.   For such a map †
seven colours are clearly necessary; and, as we have just seen,

---

* *Quarterly Journal of Mathematics*, 1890, vol. XXIV, pp. 332—335.

† Drawn in this elegant form by A. E. Ingham. (The rectangle is rolled
into a cylinder or "tube" by bringing together the two sides *ABC*. This
is bent into a torus by bringing together the two ends *DEF*.) Andreas
has pointed out that the seven hexagons can easily be drawn on his Rotating
Ring (page 153), whose surface is very accessible to examination. Cf. D.
Hilbert and S. Cohn-Vossen, *Anschauliche Geometrie* (Berlin, 1932), p. 296.

seven colours are always sufficient. There is thus no gap waiting to be filled, and the problem is completely solved.

For the general surface of genus $p\ (\geqslant 1)$ the situation is similar. Since $F - E + V = 2 - 2p$, we have

$$a = 6 + 12(p - 1)/F.$$

Let F_0 denote $\frac{1}{2}(7 + \sqrt{48p + 1})$—*i.e.* the positive root of the equation (for F) $a + 1 = F$. When $F \leqslant F_0$, $[F_0]^*$ colours are certainly sufficient, since F are sufficient.

When $F > F_0$, $a + 1 < F_0$. Since a is the average number of sides, there is a district having not more than a sides. *A fortiori*, there is a district having not more than $[F_0] - 1$ sides. By merging such a district with one of its neighbours, we see that the given map (of F districts) can be coloured with $[F_0]$ colours *if* a certain map of $F - 1$ districts can be so coloured. If $F - 1 > F_0$, this argument can be repeated, until we reach a map of only $[F_0]$ districts. Hence, finally, $[\frac{1}{2}(7 + \sqrt{48p + 1})]$ colours always suffice.†

This formula gives the correct value (seven) when $p = 1$; and it is interesting to note that it gives the presumably correct value (four) when $p = 0$, although then, of course, the argument which led to it is quite inapplicable.

The fact that so many colours may be *necessary* can hardly be doubted, although it depends on the possibility of constructing certain special maps. If each district of a map touches every other district at least once, we must have $a \geqslant F - 1$, and therefore $F \leqslant F_0$. If such a map exists with $F = [F_0]$, then this number of colours will be necessary for its colouring. Suppose that there are $x\ (F - 1)$-sided and $F - x$ F-sided districts, where x remains to be determined. Then

$$x(F - 1) + (F - x)F = aF = 6F + 12(p - 1),$$

whence $x = F^2 - 6F - 12(p - 1)$. For instance, when $p = 2$, so that $F = [\frac{1}{2}(7 + \sqrt{97})] = 8$, we have $x = 4$, and the required map consists of four heptagons and four octagons.

---

* $[F_0]$ means the greatest integer not exceeding F_0.

† The *great dodecahedron* $(p = 4)$ does not need its full allowance of 10 colours, but can obviously be done with 6 by colouring opposite faces alike.

(In I. N. Kagno's drawing of this 8-colour map, districts 1, 3, 5, 7 are heptagons, while 2, 4, 6, 8 are octagons. The free edges are to be identified in pairs, according to the lettering.) When $48p + 1$ is a perfect square (*i.e.* when $p = 0, 1, 6, 11, 13, \ldots$), we have $x = F$, and the map consists solely of $(F - 1)$-gons (each touching all the rest).

Although these " standard " maps have not all been drawn, L. Heffter * has established the necessity of the full number of

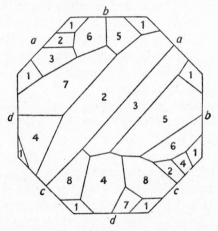

colours for every $p \leqslant 6$ (and for many higher values) by constructing special maps of F $(F - 1)$-sided districts, in which some vertices may belong to more than three districts. (When $1 \leqslant p \leqslant 6$, the full number of colours is given by the simple formula $F = p + 6$.)

The above proof, of the sufficiency of $[\frac{1}{2}(7 + \sqrt{49 - 24K})]$ colours for a surface of characteristic K $(= 2 - 2p)$, remains valid when the surface is unorientable. Heffter and Kagno † have established the necessity of the full number of colours in the special cases $K = 1, -1, -2, -4$. But Franklin ‡

* *Mathematische Annalen*, 1891, vol. XXXVIII, pp. 477—508.

† I. N. Kagno, *Journal of Mathematics and Physics*, 1935, vol. XIV, pp. 228—231.

‡ P. Franklin, *ibid.*, 1934, vol. XIII, pp. 363—369. (A particularly interesting paper.)

has obtained the remarkable theorem that *six* colours suffice when $K = 0$ (in the unorientable case). Thus Heawood's formula does not always give the best possible result.

COLOURING THE ICOSAHEDRON

The faces of a tetrahedron can be map-coloured with four given colours in two enantiomorphous ways, and those of a dodecahedron * in four ways, consisting of two enantiomorphous pairs. The faces of an octahedron or of a cube can be coloured with two or three colours, respectively, in just one way. It is therefore interesting to observe that the faces of an icosahedron can be coloured with three given colours in as many as 144 ways. This number seems to have been first obtained by J. M. Andreas.

It is easily found to be impossible to colour the icosahedron in such a way that no face is surrounded by three that are all coloured alike. In fact, there are always just two such faces. Let the three colours be white, black, and grey, and suppose that one black face is surrounded by three white faces. Between each pair of these there occur two further faces, which must be black and grey (since they are contiguous). Beyond these, again, occur two more faces, which may be grey and black, white and black, grey and white, or both white. Let these four possibilities be denoted by a, b, c, d, respectively, with or without a dash ($'$) according as the first-mentioned " black and grey " occur clockwise or counterclockwise when we go round the original black face. The colouring (of $1 + 3 + 6 + 6$ of the twenty faces) may now be represented by a symbol consisting of three of the letters a, b, c, d (repetitions allowed), with a certain distribution of dashes. The colouring is unaltered by cyclic permutation of the three letters, and it is natural to let the same symbol describe any new colouring that may result from permuting the colours. Thus, in the above definitions for a, b, c, d, *black* merely means the colour of the

---

* See the elegant self-unfolding model at the end of Steinhaus's *Mathematical Snapshots*.

special face, *white* the colour of the three surrounding faces, and *grey* the remaining colour.

Given any colouring, we can derive another by making the special face grey instead of black. This is equivalent to leaving it black, and interchanging black and grey everywhere else, which involves changing b into c, c into b, and adding or removing dashes. (Thus a^2b becomes a'^2c'.)

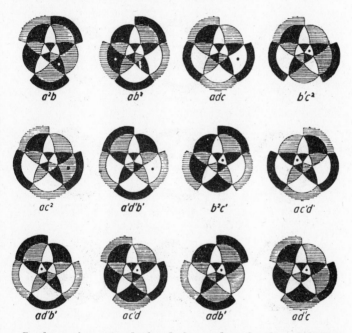

a^2b $\qquad$ ab^2 $\qquad$ adc $\qquad$ $b'c^2$

ac^2 $\qquad$ $a'd'b'$ $\qquad$ b^2c' $\qquad$ $ac'd'$

$ad'b'$ $\qquad$ $ac'd$ $\qquad$ adb' $\qquad$ $ad'c$

In the twelve cases depicted above, the colouring of the first sixteen faces unequivocally determines that of the remaining four. (The icosahedron has been projected radially on its circum-sphere, and then stereographically on a plane. One vertex has been projected to infinity. In each case, the special black face is the one just above the centre of the drawing.)

I have already remarked that there is always a second face surrounded by three that are all coloured alike. (In the drawings, this face is distinguished by a spot.) After a suitable permutation of the colours, this will be a black face surrounded by white faces, and then an alternative symbol can be assigned, to describe the colouring from this second point of view. This change of aspect leaves a^2b, ab^2, adc and $b'c^2$ unaltered, but interchanges ac^2 and $a'd'b'$, b^2c' and $ac'd'$, $ad'b'$ and $ac'd$, adb' and $ad'c$. Since neither of the two special

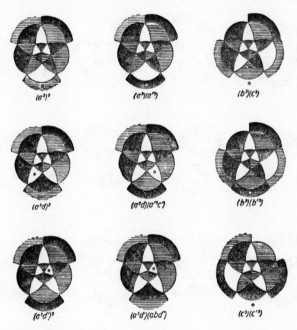

faces takes precedence over the other, it is desirable to combine the two symbols, and to describe the colouring types as $(a^2b)^2$, $(ab^2)^2$, $(adc)^2$, $(b'c^2)^2$, $(ac^2)(a'd'b')$, $(b^2c')(ac'd')$, $(ad'b')(ac'd)$, $(adb')(ad'c)$.

Each of these eight colouring types gives rise to another by reflection in a mirror. The new symbol is derived by inserting or removing dashes, and reversing the cyclic order of the letters in each triad. Thus $(b^2c')(ac'd')$ leads to the enantiomorph $(b'^2c)(a'dc)$.

In the nine cases given on page 240, the colouring of the first 16 faces does not determine that of the remaining four; but the ambiguity is removed by the use of double symbols.

In order to show that these and their enantiomorphs cover all possibilities, we merely have to make a list of all cyclic triads of letters which do not include any of the following consecutive pairs: aa', $a'a$, ab', ba', $a'c$, $c'a$, bb', $b'b$, cc', $c'c$, bc, $c'b'$, $b'c'$, cb, $b'd$, $d'b$, $b'd'$, db, cd, $d'c'$, cd', dc', d^2, dd', $d'd$, d'^2. For, each of these pairs leads to two adjacent faces having the same colours. For the same reason, the triads acb' and $a'bc'$ must also be ruled out. The remaining triads are just those which have been considered above.

The actual enumeration now proceeds as follows. Each of the 14 colourings $(a^3)^2$, $(a'^3)^2$, $(a^2b)^2$, $(a'^2b')^2$, $(ab^2)^2$, $(a'b'^2)^2$, $(a^2d)^2$, $(a'^2d')^2$, $(adc)^2$, $(a'c'd')^2$, $(a^2d')^2$, $(a'^2d)^2$, $(b'c^2)^2$, $(bc'^2)^2$ is unchanged by transposing a certain pair of colours; therefore these (by cyclic permutation of the colours) give rise to 42 solutions. In the case of $(b^3)(b'^3)$ or of $(c^3)(c'^3)$, transposition of a pair of colours is equivalent to reflection in a mirror; these give rise to 12 solutions. Finally, the 15 colourings $(a^3)(a'^3)$, $(b^3)(c^3)$, $(b'^3)(c'^3)$, $(a^2d)(a'^2c')$, $(a'^2d')(a^2c)$, $(ac^2)(a'd'b')$, $(a'c'^2)(abd)$, $(a^2d')(abd')$, $(a'^2d)(a'db')$, $(b^2c')(ac'd')$, $(b'^2c)(a'dc)$, $(ad'b')(ac'd)$, $(a'bd)(a'd'c)$, $(adb')(ad'c)$, $(a'bd')(a'c'd)$ admit all six permutations of the colours, and so give rise to 90 solutions, making the grand total $42 + 12 + 90 = 144$.

The six solutions $(a^3)(a'^3)$ are special, in that reflection leaves them entirely unaltered. We may call these six reflexible solutions, and describe the rest as 69 enantiomorphous pairs.

CHAPTER IX

UNICURSAL PROBLEMS

I PROPOSE to consider in this chapter some problems which arise out of the theory of unicursal curves. I shall commence with *Euler's Problem and Theorems*, and shall apply the results briefly to the theories of *Mazes* and *Geometrical Trees*. The reciprocal unicursal problem of the *Hamilton Game* will be discussed in the latter half of the chapter.

EULER'S PROBLEM

Euler's problem has its origin in a memoir* presented by him in 1736 to the St. Petersburg Academy, in which he solved a question then under discussion, as to whether it was possible from any point in the town of Königsberg to take a walk in such a way as to cross every bridge in it once and only once and return to the starting point.

The town is built near the mouth of the river Pregel, which there takes the form indicated below and includes the island of Kneiphof. In the eighteenth century there were seven bridges in the positions shown in the diagram, and it is easily seen that with such an arrangement the problem is insoluble. (Since then, an eighth bridge has been built.) Euler, however, did not confine himself to the case of Königsberg, but discussed the general problem of any number of islands connected in any way by bridges. It is evident that the question will not

* 'Solutio problematis ad Geometriam situs pertinentis,' *Commentarii Academiae Scientiarum Petropolitanae* for 1736, Petrograd, 1741, vol. VIII, pp. 128—140. This has been translated into French by M. Ch. Henry; see Lucas, vol. I, part 2, pp. 21—33.

be affected if we suppose the islands to diminish to points and the bridges to lengthen out.　In this way we ultimately obtain

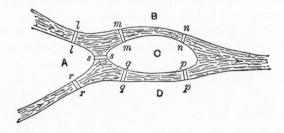

a geometrical figure or network.　In the Königsberg problem this figure is of the shape indicated below, the areas being represented by the points *A, B, C, D*, and the bridges being represented by the lines *l, m, n, p, q, r, s*.

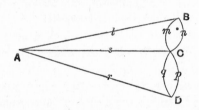

Euler's problem consists therefore in finding whether a given geometrical figure can be described by a point moving so as to traverse every line in it once and only once.　A more general question is to determine how many strokes are necessary to describe such a figure so that no line is traversed twice: this is covered by the rules hereafter given.　The figure may be either in three or in two dimensions, and it may be represented by lines, straight, curved, or tortuous, joining a number of given points, or a model may be constructed by taking a number of rods or pieces of string furnished at each end with a hook so as to allow of any number of them being connected together at one point.

The theory of such figures is included as a particular case

in the propositions proved by Listing in his *Topologie*.* I shall, however, adopt here the methods of Euler, and I shall begin by giving some definitions, as it will enable me to put the argument in a more concise form.

A *node* (or isle) is a point to or from which lines are drawn. A *branch* (or bridge or path) is a line connecting two consecutive nodes. An *end* (or hook) is the point at each termination of a branch. The *order* of a node is the number of branches which meet at it. A node to which only one branch is drawn is a *free* node or a free end. A node at which an even number of branches meet is an *even* node : evidently the presence of a node of the second order is immaterial. A node at which an odd number of branches meet is an *odd* node. A figure is closed if it has no free end : such a figure is often called a closed network.

A *route* consists of a number of branches taken in consecutive order and so that no branch is traversed twice. A *re-entrant* route terminates at a point from which it started. A figure is described *unicursally* when the whole of it is traversed in one route.

The following are Euler's results. (i) In any network the number of odd nodes is even. (ii) A figure which has no odd node can be described unicursally, in a re-entrant route, by a moving point which starts from any point on it. (iii) A figure which has two and only two odd nodes can be described unicursally by a moving point which starts from one of the odd nodes and finishes at the other. (iv) A figure which has more than two odd nodes cannot be described completely in one route ; to which Listing added the corollary that a figure which has $2n$ odd nodes, and no more, can be described completely in n separate routes. I now proceed to prove these theorems.

* *Die Studien*, Göttingen, 1847, part **x**. See also Tait on ' Listing's *Topologie*,' *Philosophical Magazine*, London, January, 1884, series 5, vol. XVII, pp. 30—46; and *Collected Scientific Papers*, Cambridge, vol II, 1900, pp. 85—98. The problem was discussed by J. C. Wilson in his *Traversing of Geometrical Figures*, Oxford, 1905.

First. *The number of odd nodes in any network is even.*

Suppose the number of branches to be b. Therefore the number of hooks is $2b$. Let k_n be the number of nodes of the nth order. Since a node of the nth order is one at which n branches meet, there are n hooks there.

$$\therefore \quad k_1 + 2k_2 + 3k_3 + 4k_4 + \ldots + nk_n + \ldots = 2b.$$

Hence $\qquad k_1 + 3k_3 + 5k_5 + \ldots \quad$ is even.

$$\therefore \quad k_1 + k_3 + k_5 + \ldots \quad \text{is even.}$$

Second. *A figure which has no odd node can be described unicursally in a re-entrant route.*

Since the route is to be re-entrant, it will make no difference where it commences. Suppose that we start from a node A. Every time our route takes us through a node we use up one hook in entering it and one in leaving it. There are no odd nodes, therefore the number of hooks at every node is even : hence, if we reach any node except A, we shall always find a hook which will take us into a branch previously untraversed. Hence the route will take us finally to the node A from which we started. If there are more than two hooks at A, we can continue the route over one of the branches from A previously untraversed, but in the same way as before we shall finally come back to A.

It remains to show that we can arrange our route so as to make it cover all the branches. Suppose each branch of the network to be represented by a string with a hook at each end, and that at each node all the hooks there are fastened together. The number of hooks at each node is even, and if they are unfastened, they can be re-coupled together in pairs, the arrangement of the pairs being immaterial. The whole network will then form one or more closed curves, since now each node consists merely of two ends hooked together.

If this random coupling gives us one single curve, then the proposition is proved ; for, starting at any point, we shall go along every branch and come back to the initial point. But if this random coupling produces anywhere an isolated loop, L, then where it touches some other loop, *M*, say at the node *P*, unfasten the four hooks there (viz., two of the loop *L* and two of the loop *M*) and re-couple them in any other order : then the loop *L* will become a part of the loop *M*. In this way, by altering the couplings, we can transform gradually all the separate loops into parts of only one loop.

For example, take the case of three isles, *A*, *B*, *C*, each connected with both the others by two bridges. The most unfavourable way of re-coupling the ends at *A*, *B*, *C* would be to make *ABA*, *ACA*, and *BCB* separate loops. The loops *ABA* and *ACA* are separate and touch at *A* ; hence we should re-couple the hooks at *A* so as to combine *ABA* and *ACA* into

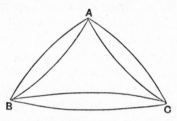

one loop *ABACA*. Similarly, by re-arranging the couplings of the four hooks at *B*, we can combine the loop *BCB* with *ABACA*, and thus make only one loop.

I infer from Euler's language that he had attempted to solve the problem of giving a practical rule which would enable one to describe such a figure unicursally without knowledge of its form, but that in this he was unsuccessful. He, however, added that any geometrical figure can be described completely in a single route provided each part of it is described twice and only twice, for, if we suppose that every branch is duplicated, there will be no odd nodes and the figure is unicursal. In this case any figure can be described completely without knowing its form : rules to effect this are given below.

Third. *A figure which has two and only two odd nodes can be described unicursally by a point which starts from one of the odd nodes and finishes at the other odd node.*

This at once reduces to the second theorem. Let A and Z be the two odd nodes. Consider the new figure derived by adding an extra branch from A to Z. In this new figure, all the nodes are even, including A and Z; hence, by Euler's second proposition, it can be described unicursally, and, if the route begins at Z, it will end at Z. We may suppose ZA to be the first branch of the route. The effect of removing this branch, and so restoring the original figure, is just to make the route begin at A; but it still ends at Z.

Fourth. *A figure having* 2n *odd nodes, and no more, can be described completely in* n *separate routes.*

If any route starts at an odd node, and if it is continued until it reaches a node where no fresh path is open to it, this latter node must be an odd one. For every time we enter an even node there is necessarily a way out of it; and similarly every time we go through an odd node we use up one hook in entering and one hook in leaving, but whenever we reach it as the end of our route, we use only one hook. If this route is suppressed there will remain a figure with $2n - 2$ odd nodes. Hence n such routes will leave one or more networks with only even nodes. But each of these must have some node common to one of the routes already taken, and therefore can be described as a part of that route. Hence the complete passage will require n, and not more than n, routes. It follows, as stated by Euler, that, if there are more than two odd nodes, the figure cannot be traversed completely in one route.

The Königsberg bridges lead to a network with four odd nodes; hence, by Euler's fourth proposition, it cannot be described unicursally in a single journey, though it can be traversed completely in two separate routes.

The first and second diagrams figured below contain only even nodes, and therefore each of them can be described unicursally. The first of these is a regular re-entrant pentagon; the second is the so-called sign-manual of Mohammed, said to have been originally traced in the sand by the point of his scimitar without taking it off the ground or retracing any part of the figure—which, as it contains only even nodes, is possible. The third diagram is taken from Tait's article: it contains only two odd nodes, and can therefore be described unicursally if we start from one of them, and finish at the other.

The re-entrant pentagon, figured below, has some interest from having been used by the Pythagoreans as a sign—known as the triple triangle or pentagram star—by which they could recognize one another. It was considered symbolical of health, and probably the angles were denoted by the letters of the word ὑγίεια, the diphthong ει being replaced by a θ.

 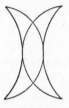 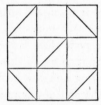

Iamblichus, who is our authority for this, tells us that a certain Pythagorean, when travelling, fell ill at a roadside inn where he had put up for the night; he was poor and sick, but the landlord, who was a kind-hearted fellow, nursed him carefully and spared no trouble or expense to relieve his pains. However, in spite of all efforts, the student got worse. Feeling that he was dying, and unable to make the landlord any pecuniary recompense, he asked for a board, on which he inscribed the pentagram star; this he gave to his host, begging him to hang it up outside so that all passers-by might see it, and assuring him that the result would recompense him for his charity. The scholar died and was honourably buried, and the board was duly exposed. After a considerable time had elapsed, a traveller one day riding by saw the sacred symbol; dismounting, he entered the inn, and after hearing the story, handsomely remunerated the landlord. Such is the anecdote, which, if not true, is at least well found.

As another example of a unicursal diagram, I may mention the geometrical figure formed by taking a $(2n + 1)$-gon and joining every angular point to every other angular point. The edges of an octahedron also form a unicursal figure. On the other hand, a chess-board, divided as usual by straight lines into 64 cells, has 28 odd nodes : hence it would require 14 separate pen-strokes to trace out all the boundaries without going over any more than once. Again, the diagram on page 169 has 20 odd nodes, and therefore would require 10 separate pen-strokes to trace it out.

I turn next to discuss in how many ways we can describe a unicursal figure, all of whose nodes are even.*

Let us consider first how the problem is affected by a path which starts from a node A of order $2n$ and returns to it, forming a closed loop L. If this loop were suppressed, we should have a figure with all its nodes even, the node A being now of the order $2(n-1)$. Suppose the original figure can be described in N ways, and the reduced figure in N' ways. Then each of these N' routes passes $(n-1)$ times through A, and in any of these passages we could describe the loop L in either sense as a part of the path. Hence $N = 2(n-1)N'$.

Similarly if the node A on the original figure is of the order $2(n+l)$, and there are l independent closed loops which start from and return to A, we shall have

$$N = 2^l n(n+1)(n+2)\ldots(n+l-1)N',$$

where N' is the number of routes by which the figure obtained by suppressing these l loops can be described.

By the use of these results, we may reduce any unicursal figure to one in which there are no closed loops of the kind above described. Let us suppose that in this reduced figure there are k nodes. We can suppress one of these nodes, say A, provided we replace the figure by two or more separate figures each of which has not more than $k-1$ nodes. For suppose

* See G. Tarry, *Association Française pour l'Avancement des Sciences*, 1886, pp. 49—53.

that the node A is of the order $2n$. Then the $2n$ paths which meet at A may be coupled in n pairs in $1 . 3 . 5 \ldots (2n - 1)$ ways and each pair will constitute either a path through A, or (in the special case where both members of the pair abut on another node B) a loop from A. This path or loop will form a portion of the route through A in which this pair of paths are concerned. Hence the number of ways of describing the original figure is equal to the sum of the number of ways of describing $1 . 3 . 5 \ldots (2n - 1)$ separate simpler figures.

It will be seen that the process consists in successively suppressing node after node. Applying this process continually we finally reduce the figure to a number of figures without loops and in each of which there are only two nodes. If in one of these figures these nodes are each of the order $2n$, it is easily seen that it can be described in $2 \times (2n - 1)!$ ways.

We know that a figure with only two odd nodes, A and B, is unicursal if we start at A (or B) and finish at B (or A). Hence the number of ways in which it can be described unicursally will be the same as the number required to describe the figure obtained from it by joining A and B. For if we start at A, it is obvious that at the B end of each of the routes which cover the figure we can proceed along BA to the node A whence we started.

This theory has been applied by Monsieur Tarry * to determine the number of ways in which a set of dominoes, running up to even numbers, can be arranged. This example will serve to illustrate the general method.

A domino consists of a small rectangular slab, twice as long as it is broad, whose face is divided into two squares, which are either blank or marked with 1, 2, 3 ... dots. An ordinary set contains 28 dominoes marked 6–6, 6–5, 6–4, 6–3, 6–2, 6–1, 6–0, 5–5, 5–4, 5–3, 5–2, 5–1, 5–0, 4–4, 4–3, 4–2, 4–1, 4–0, 3–3, 3–2, 3–1, 3–0, 2–2, 2–1, 2–0, 1–1, 1–0, and 0–0. Dominoes are used in various games, in most, if not all, of

* See the second edition of the French Translation of this work, Paris, 1908, vol. II, pp. 253—263; see also Lucas, vol. IV, pp. 145—150.

which the pieces are played so as to make a line such that consecutive squares of adjacent dominoes are marked alike. Thus if 6–3 is on the table, the only dominoes which can be placed next to the 6 end are 6–6, 6–5, 6–4, 6–2, 6–1, or 6–0. Similarly the dominoes 3–5, 3–4, 3–3, 3–2, 3–1, or 3–0, can be placed next to the 3 end. Assuming that the doubles are played in due course, it is easy to see that such a set of dominoes will form a closed circuit.* We want to determine the number of ways in which such a line or circuit can be formed.

Let us begin by considering the case of a set of 15 dominoes marked up to double-four. Of these 15 pieces, 5 are doubles. The remaining 10 dominoes may be represented by the sides and diagonals of a regular pentagon 01, 02, etc. The intersections of the diagonals do not enter into the representation,

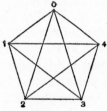

Figure A.

and accordingly are to be neglected. Omitting these from our consideration, the figure formed by the sides and diagonals of the pentagon has five even nodes, and therefore is unicursal. Any unicursal route (*e.g.* 0–1, 1–3, 3–0, 0–2, 2–3, 3–4, 4–1, 1–2, 2–4, 4–0) gives one way of arranging these 10 dominoes. Suppose there are a such routes. In any such route we may put each of the five doubles in either of two positions (*e.g.* in the route given above the double-two can be put between 0–2 and 2–3 or between 1–2 and 2–4). Hence the total number of unicursal arrangements of the 15 dominoes is 2^5a.

---

* Hence if we remove one domino, say 5–4, we know that the line formed by the rest of the dominoes must end on one side in a 5 and on the other in a 4.

If we arrange the dominoes in a straight line, then as we may begin with any of the 15 dominoes, the total number of arrangements is $15 \cdot 2^5 \cdot a$.

We have next to find the number of unicursal routes of the pentagon delineated above in figure A. At the node 0 there are four paths which may be coupled in three pairs. If 0 1 and 0 2 are coupled, as also 0 3 and 0 4, we get figure B. If 0 1 and 0 3 are coupled, as also 0 2 and 0 4, we get figure C. If 0 1 and 0 4 are coupled, as also 0 2 and 0 3, we get figure D.

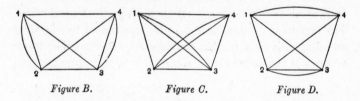

Figure B.   Figure C.   Figure D.

Let us denote the number of ways of describing figure B by b, of describing figure C by c, and so on. The effect of suppressing the node 0 in the pentagon A is to give us three quadrangles, B, C, D. And, in the above notation, we have $a = b + c + d$.

Take any one of these quadrangles, for instance D. We can suppress the node 1 in it by coupling the four paths which meet there in pairs. If we couple 1 2 with the upper of the paths 1 4, as also 1 3 with the lower of the paths 1 4, we get

Figure E.   Figure F.

the figure E. If we couple 1 2 with the lower of the paths 1 4, as also 1 3 with the upper of the paths 1 4, we again get the figure E. If we couple 1 2 and 1 3, as also the two paths 1 4, we get the figure F. Then as above, $d = 2e + f$. Similarly

$b = 2e + f,$ and $c = 2e + f.$ Hence $a = b + c + d = 6e + 3f.$

We proceed to consider each of the reduced figures E and F. First take E, and in it let us suppress the node 4. For simplicity of description, denote the two paths 4 2 by β and β', and the two paths 4 3 by γ and γ'. Then we can couple β and γ, as also β' and γ', or we can couple β and γ', as also β^{Λ} and γ : each of these couplings gives the figure G. Or we can couple β and β', as also γ and γ' : this gives the figure H. Thus $e = 2g + h$. Each of the figures G and H has only two nodes. Hence by the formulae given above, we have $g = 2 \cdot 3 \cdot 2 = 12$, and $h = 2 \cdot 2 \cdot 2 = 8$. Therefore $e = 2g + h = 32$. Next take the figure F. This has a loop at 4. If we suppress this

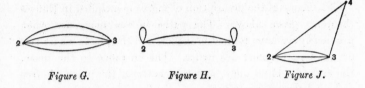

Figure G.   Figure H.   Figure J.

loop we get the figure J, and $f = 2j$. But the figure J, if we couple the two lines which meet at 4, is equivalent to the figure G. Thus $f = 2j = 2g = 24$. Introducing these results we have $a = 6e + 3f = 192 + 72 = 264$. And therefore $N = 15 \cdot 2^5 \cdot a = 126720$. This gives the number of possible arrangements in line of a set of 15 dominoes. In this solution we have treated an arrangement from right to left as distinct from one which goes from left to right : if these are treated as identical we must divide the result by 2. The number of arrangements in a closed ring is $2^5 a$, that is 8448.

We have seen that this number of unicursal routes for a pentagon and its diagonals is 264. Similarly the number for a heptagon is $h = 129{,}976320$. Hence the number of possible arrangements in line of the usual set of 28 dominoes, marked up to double-six, is $28 \cdot 3^7 \cdot h$, which is equal to 7,959229,931520. The number of unicursal routes covering a polygon of nine sides is $n = 2^{17} . 3^{11} . 5^2 . 711 . 40787$. Hence the number of possible arrangements in line of a set of 45 dominoes marked up to double-eight is $48 . 4^9 . n$.*

MAZES

Everyone has read of the labyrinth of Minos in Crete and of Rosamund's Bower. A few modern mazes exist here and there—notably one, a very poor specimen of its kind, at Hampton Court—and in one of these, or at any rate on a drawing of one, most people have at some time threaded their way to the interior. I proceed now to consider the manner in which any such construction may be completely traversed even by one who is ignorant of its plan.

The theory of the description of mazes is included in Euler's theorems given above. The paths in the maze are what previously we have termed branches, and the places where two or more paths meet are nodes. The entrance to the maze, the end of a blind alley, and the centre of the maze are free ends and therefore odd nodes.

If the only odd nodes are the entrance to the maze and the centre of it—which will necessitate the absence of all blind alleys—the maze can be described unicursally. This follows from Euler's third proposition. Again, no matter how many odd nodes there may be in a maze, we can always find a route which will take us from the entrance to the centre without retracing our steps, though such a route will take us through only a part of the maze. But in neither of the cases mentioned in this paragraph can the route be determined without a plan of the maze.

A plan is not necessary, however, if we make use of Euler's suggestion, and suppose that every path in the maze is duplicated. In this case we can give definite rules for the complete description of the whole of any maze, even if we are entirely

* These numerical conclusions have also been obtained by algebraical analysis: see M. Reiss, *Annali di Matematica*, Milan, 1871, vol. v, pp. 63—120.

ignorant of its plan. Of course, to walk twice over every path in a labyrinth is not the shortest way of arriving at the centre, but, if it is performed correctly, the whole maze is traversed, the arrival at the centre at some point in the course of the route is certain, and it is impossible to lose one's way.

I need hardly explain why the complete description of such a duplicated maze is possible, for now every node is even, and hence, by Euler's second proposition, if we begin at the entrance we can traverse the whole maze; in so doing we shall at some point arrive at the centre, and finally shall emerge at the point from which we started. This description will require us to go over every path in the maze twice, and as a matter of fact the two passages along any path will be always made in opposite directions.

If a maze is traced on paper, the way to the centre is generally obvious, but in an actual labyrinth it is not so easy to find the correct route unless the plan is known. In order to make sure of describing a maze without knowing its plan, it is necessary to have some means of marking the paths which we traverse and the direction in which we have traversed them —for example, by drawing an arrow at the entrance and end of every path traversed, or better perhaps by marking the wall on the right-hand side, in which case a path may not be entered when there is a mark on each side of it.

Of the various practical rules for threading a maze those enunciated by M. Trémaux seem to be the simplest.* These I proceed to explain. For brevity I shall describe a path or a node as old or new according as it has been traversed once before or not at all. Then the rules are : (i) whenever you come to a new node, take any path you like; (ii) whenever you come by a new path to an old node or to the closed end of a blind alley, turn back along the path by which you have just come; (iii) whenever you come by an old path to an old node, take a new path, if there is one, but if not, an old path; (iv) of course, a path traversed twice must not be entered. I should add that

* Lucas, vol. I, part iii, pp. 47 *et seq.*

on emerging at any node then, of the various routes which are permitted by these rules, it will be convenient always to select that which lies next to one's right hand, or always that which lies next to one's left hand.

Few if any mazes of the type I have been considering (namely, a series of interlacing paths through which some route can be obtained leading to a space or building at the centre of the maze) existed in classical or medieval times. One class of what the ancients called mazes or labyrinths seems to have comprised any complicated buildings with numerous vaults and passages.* Such a building might be termed a labyrinth, but it is not what is now usually understood by the word. The above rules would enable anyone to traverse the whole of any structure of this kind. I do not know if there are any accounts or descriptions of Rosamund's Bower other than those by Drayton, Bromton, and Knyghton : in the opinion of some, these imply that the bower was merely a house, the passages in which were confusing and ill-arranged.

Another class of ancient mazes consisted of a tortuous path confined to a small area of ground and leading to a tree or shrine in the centre.† This is a maze in which there is no chance of taking a wrong turning; but, as the whole area can be occupied by the windings of one path, the distance to be traversed from the entrance to the centre may be considerable, even though the piece of ground covered by the maze is but small.

The traditional form of the labyrinth constructed for the Minotaur is a specimen of this class. It was delineated on

---

* For instance, see the descriptions of the labyrinth at Lake Moeris given by Herodotus, bk. ii, c. 148; Strabo, bk. xvii, c. 1, art. 37; Diodorus, bk. i, cc. 61, 66; and Pliny, *Hist. Nat.*, bk. xxxvi, c. 13, arts. 84—89. On these and other references see A. Wiedemann, *Herodots zweites Buch*, Leipzig, 1890, p. 522 *et seq.* See also Virgil, *Aeneid*, bk. v, c. v, 588; Ovid, *Met.*, bk. viii, c. 5, 159; Strabo, bk. viii, c. 6.

† On ancient and medieval labyrinths—particularly of this kind—see an article by Mr. E. Trollope in *The Archaeological Journal*, 1858, vol. xv, pp. 216—235, from which much of the historical information given above is derived.

the reverses of the coins of Cnossus, specimens of which are not uncommon; one form of it is indicated in the accompanying diagram (figure i). The design really is the same as that drawn in figure ii, as can be easily seen by bending round a circle the rectangular figure there given.

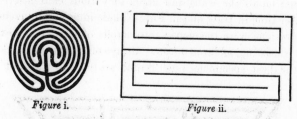

Figure i.   Figure ii.

Mr. Inwards has suggested * that this design on the coins of Cnossus may be a survival from that on a token given by the priests as a clue to the right path in the labyrinth there. Taking the circular form of the design shown above he supposed each circular wall to be replaced by two equidistant walls separated by a path, and thus obtained a maze to which the original design would serve as the key. The route thus indicated may be at once obtained by noticing that when a node is reached (*i.e.* a point where there is a choice of paths), the path to be taken is that which is next but one to that by which the node was approached. This maze may be also threaded by the simple rule of always following the wall on the right-hand side, or always that on the left-hand side. The labyrinth may be somewhat improved by erecting a few additional barriers, without affecting the applicability of the above rules, but it cannot be made really difficult. This makes a pretty toy, but though the conjecture on which it is founded is ingenious, it has no historical justification. Another suggestion is that the curved line on the reverse of the coins indicated the form of the rope held by those taking part in some rhythmic dance; while others consider that the form was gradually evolved from the widely prevalent swastika.

* *Knowledge*, London, October, 1892.

Copies of the maze of Cnossus were frequently engraved on Greek and Roman gems; similar but more elaborate designs are found in numerous Roman mosaic pavements.* A copy of the Cretan labyrinth was embroidered on many of the state robes of the later Emperors, and, apparently thence, was copied on to the walls and floors of various churches.† At a later time in Italy and in France these mural and pavement decorations were developed into scrolls of great complexity, but consisting, as far as I know, always of a single line. Some of the best specimens now extant are on the walls of the

Maze at Hampton Court.

cathedrals at Lucca, Aix in Provence, and Poitiers; and on the floors of the churches of Santa Maria in Trastevere at Rome, San Vitale at Ravenna, Notre Dame at St. Omer, and the cathedral at Chartres. It is possible that they were used to represent the journey through life as a kind of pilgrim's progress.

In England these mazes were usually, perhaps always, cut in the turf adjacent to some religious house or hermitage: and there are some slight reasons for thinking that, when traversed as a religious exercise, a *pater* or *ave* had to be repeated at every turning. After the Renaissance, such labyrinths were frequently termed Troy-Towns or Julian's Bowers. Some of the best specimens, which are still extant, or were so until recently, are those at Rockliff Marshes, Cumberland; Asenby,

---

* See, *e.g.*, Breton's *Pompeia*, p. 303.

† Ozanam, *Graphia aureae urbis Romae*, pp. 92, 178.

Yorkshire; Alkborough, Lincolnshire; Wing, Rutlandshire; Boughton-Green, Northamptonshire; Comberton, Cambridge-shire; Saffron Walden, Essex; and Chilcombe, near Winchester.

The modern maze seems to have been introduced—probably from Italy—during the Renaissance, and many of the palaces and large houses built in England during the Tudor and the Stuart periods had labyrinths attached to them. Those adjoining the royal palaces at Southwark, Greenwich, and Hampton Court were well known from their vicinity to

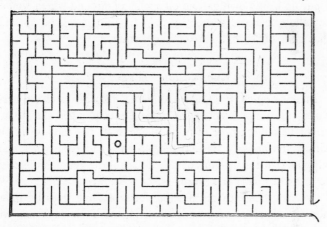

the capital. The last of these was designed by London and Wise in 1690, for William III, who had a fancy for such conceits: a plan of it is given in various guide-books. For the majority of the sight-seers who enter, it is sufficiently elaborate; but it is an indifferent construction, for it can be described completely by always following the hedge on one side (either the right hand or the left hand), and no node is of an order higher than three.

Unless at some point the route to the centre forks and subsequently the two forks reunite, forming a loop in which the centre of the maze is situated, the centre can be reached by the rule just given—namely, by following the wall on one side, either on the right hand or on the left hand. No labyrinth is worthy of the name of a puzzle which can be threaded in this way. Assuming that the path forks as described above, the more numerous the nodes and the higher their order the more difficult will be the maze, and the difficulty might be increased considerably by using bridges and tunnels so as to construct a labyrinth in three dimensions. In an ordinary garden and on a small piece of ground, often of an inconvenient shape, it is not easy to make a maze which fulfils these conditions. On page 259 is a plan of one which I put up in my own garden on a plot of ground which would not allow of more than 36 by 23 paths, but it will be noticed that none of the nodes are of a high order.

Geometrical Trees

Euler's original investigations were confined to a closed network. In the problem of the maze it was assumed that there might be any number of blind alleys in it, the ends of which formed free nodes. We may now progress one step further, and suppose that the network or closed part of the figure diminishes to a point. This last arrangement is known as a *tree*.

We can illustrate the possible form of these trees by rods, having a hook at each end. Starting with one such rod, we can attach at either end one or more similar rods. Again, on any free hook we can attach one or more similar rods, and so on. Every free hook, and also every point where two or more rods meet, are what hitherto we have called nodes. The rods are what hitherto we have termed branches or paths.

The theory of trees—which already plays a somewhat important part in certain branches of modern analysis, and possibly may contain the key to certain chemical and biological theories—originated in a memoir by Cayley,* written in

* *Philosophical Magazine*, March, 1857, series 4, vol. XIII, pp. 172—176; or *Collected Works*, Cambridge, 1890, vol. III, no. 203, pp. 242—246 : see also the paper on double partitions, *Philosophical Magazine*, November, 1860, series 4, vol. XX, pp. 337—341. On the number of trees with a given number

1856.   The discussion of the theory has been analytical rather than geometrical.   I content myself with noting the following results.

The number of trees with n given nodes is n^{n-2}.   If A_n is the number of trees with one special node, or *root*, and n other nodes (and therefore n branches), then

$$(1-x)^{-1}(1-x^2)^{-A_1}(1-x^3)^{-A_2}\dots$$
$$= 1 + A_1 x + A_2 x^2 + A_3 x^3 + \dots.$$

Using this formula we can find successively the values of $A_1, A_2, \dots$ The values of A_n when $n = 1, 2, 3, 4, 5, 6, 7$ arc 1, 2, 4, 9, 20, 48, 115.

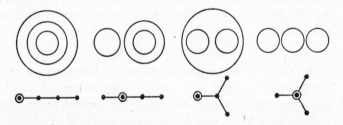

These results have an application to another topological problem : to find the number of ways in which n circles (or spheres) can be internal or external to one another.   For instance, two circles may be outside one another, or one inside the other.   The n circles can be put into correspondence with the nodes, other than the root, of a tree having n branches. Circles not contained in others correspond to nodes directly joined to the root.   Thereafter, every branch indicates that one circle is inside another.   This correspondence shows that the required number of ways is A_n.   In the above diagrams (for the case when $n = 3$), the root of each tree is ringed.

of nodes, see the *Quarterly Journal of Mathematics*, London, 1889, vol. XXIII, pp. 376—378.   The connection with chemistry was first pointed out in Cayley's paper on isomers, *Philosophical Magazine*, June, 1874, series 4, vol. XLVII, pp. 444—447, and was treated more fully in his report on trees to the British Association in 1875, *Reports*, pp. 257—305.

If we suppose the n circles to be numbered, so that the first might be inside the second, or the second inside the first, then the number of ways is increased to $(n + 1)^{n-1}$, this being the number of trees (regardless of roots) having $n + 1$ *given* nodes.

I turn next to consider some problems where it is desired to find a route which will pass once and only once through each node of a given geometrical figure. This is the reciprocal of the problem treated in the first part of this chapter, and is a far more difficult question. I am not aware that the general theory has been considered by mathematicians, though two special cases—namely, the *Hamiltonian* (or Icosian) *Game* and the *Knight's Path on a Chess-Board*—have been treated in some detail.

THE HAMILTONIAN GAME

The Hamiltonian Game consists in the determination of a route along the edges of a regular dodecahedron which will pass once and only once through every angular point. Sir William Hamilton,* who invented this game—if game is the right term for it—denoted the twenty angular points on the

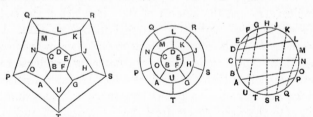

solid by letters which stand for various towns. The thirty edges constitute the only possible paths. The inconvenience of using a solid is considerable, and the dodecahedron may be represented conveniently in perspective by a flat board marked as shown in the first of the above diagrams. The second and

* See *Quarterly Journal of Mathematics*, London, 1862, vol. v, p. 305; or *Philosophical Magazine*, January, 1884, series 5, vol. XVII, p. 42; also Lucas, vol. II, part vii.

third diagrams will answer our purpose equally well and are easier to draw.

The first problem is to go " all round the world," that is, starting from any town, to go to every other town once and only once and to return to the initial town; the order of the n towns to be first visited being assigned, where n is not greater than five.

Hamilton's rule for effecting this was given at the meeting in 1857 of the British Association at Dublin. At each angular point there are three and only three edges. Hence, if we approach a point by one edge, the only routes open to us are one to the right, denoted by r, and one to the left, denoted by l. It will be found that the operations indicated on opposite sides of the following equalities are equivalent,

$$lr^2l = rlr,\ rl^2r = lrl,\ lr^3l = r^2,\ rl^3r = l^2.$$

Also the operation l^5 or r^5 brings us back to the initial point: we may represent this by the equations

$$l^5 = 1,\ r^5 = 1.$$

To solve the problem for a figure having twenty angular points we must deduce a relation involving twenty successive operations, the total effect of which is equal to unity. By repeated use of the relation $l^2 = rl^3r$ we see that

$$1 = l^5 = l^2l^3 = (rl^3r)l^3 = \{rl^3\}^2 = \{r(rl^3r)l\}^2$$
$$= \{r^2l^3rl\}^2 = \{r^2(rl^3r)lrl\}^2 = \{r^3l^3rlrl\}^2.$$

Therefore $\{r^3l^3(rl)^2\}^2 = 1$ ....(i),

and similarly $\{l^3r^3(lr)^2\}^2 = 1$ ....(ii).

Hence on a dodecahedron either of the operations

$$r\,r\,r\,l\,l\,l\,r\,l\,r\,l\,r\,r\,r\,l\,l\,l\,r\,l\,r\,l \ldots \text{(i)},$$
$$l\,l\,l\,r\,r\,r\,l\,r\,l\,r\,l\,l\,l\,r\,r\,r\,l\,r\,l\,r \ldots \text{(ii)},$$

indicates a route which takes the traveller through every town. The arrangement is cyclical, and the route can be commenced at any point in the series of operations by transferring the proper number of letters from one end to the other. The point at which we begin is determined by the order of certain towns which is given initially.

Thus, suppose that we are told that we start from F and then successively go to B, A, U, and T, and we want to find a route from T through all the remaining towns which will end at F. If we think of ourselves as coming into F from G, the path FB would be indicated by l, but if we think of ourselves as coming into F from E, the path FB would be indicated by r. The path from B to A is indicated by l, and so on. Hence our first paths are indicated either by $lllr$ or by $rllr$. The latter operation does not occur either in (i) or in (ii), and therefore does not fall within our solutions. The former operation may be regarded either as the 1st, 2nd, 3rd, and 4th steps of (ii), or as the 4th, 5th, 6th, and 7th steps of (i). Each of these leads to a route which satisfies the problem. These routes are

$$FBAUTPONCDEJKLMQRSHGF,$$
and $$FBAUTSRKLMQPONCDEJHGF.$$

It is convenient to make a mark or to put down a counter at each corner as soon as it is reached, and this will prevent our passing through the same town twice.

The operations denoted by l and r, and all combinations of them, form a closed set of sixty. For, if we start off along any one edge, the different operations take us in turn to each of the thirty edges in either direction. These sixty operations, or sixty symbols which have the same laws of combination, are said to constitute the *icosahedral group*, for which the relations

$$l^5 = 1, \ r^5 = 1, \ (l^3r)^2 = 1, \ (lr^3)^2 = 1$$

provide an *abstract definition*. This means that every true relation between the generators l and r (such as (i), or the relation $lr^2l = rlr$ mentioned above) is an algebraic consequence of these four. Hamilton himself has given * a simpler

* *Philosophical Magazine*, 1856, series 4, vol. XII, p. 446. (That short paper is the foundation for an important branch of mathematics: the theory of Abstract Groups.)

abstract definition for the same group (in terms of generators differently selected from the sixty operations).

A similar game may be played with other solids, provided that at each vertex three and only three edges meet. The reader can make for himself any number of plane figures representing such solids, similar to those drawn on page 262. (For some of these the problem is insoluble.*) But the "group-theoretical" method remains applicable only when the faces of the solid all have the same number of sides. Besides the tetrahedron and the cube, this restriction admits certain regular networks on surfaces of higher genus, such as the map of seven hexagons on the torus (page 235).

For solids having angular points where more than three edges meet—such as the octahedron where at each angular point four edges meet, or the icosahedron where at each angular point five edges meet—we should at each point have more than two routes open to us; hence (unless we suppress some of the edges) the symbolical notation would have to be extended before it could be applied to these solids. I offer the suggestion to anyone who is desirous of inventing a new game.

Another and a very elegant solution of the Hamiltonian dodecahedron problem has been given by M. Hermary. It consists in unfolding the dodecahedron into its twelve penta-gons, each of which is attached to the preceding one by only one of its sides; but the solution is geometrical, and not directly applicable to more complicated solids.

Hamilton suggested as another problem to start from any town, to go to certain specified towns in an assigned order, then to go to every other town once and only once, and to end the journey at some given town. He also suggested the con-sideration of the way in which a certain number of towns should be blocked so that there was no passage through them, in order to produce certain effects. These problems have not, so far as I know, been subjected to mathematical analysis.

* Dénes König, *Theorie der endlichen und unendlichen Graphen*, Leipzig, 1936, p. 28.

Hamilton's problem has been extended to certain cases where the number of towns is infinite (the required route having no beginning and no end). For a route along the edges of the tessellation of squares (4^4), see König's book on graphs.* A

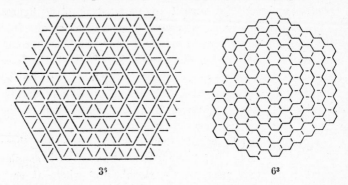

3^4 6^3

similar treatment of the other regular tessellations (3^6 and 6^3) is shown above.

The problem of the knight's path on a chess-board is somewhat similar in character to the Hamiltonian game. This I have already discussed in Chapter VI.

* Dénes König, *op. cit.*, p. 32.

CHAPTER X

KIRKMAN'S SCHOOL-GIRLS PROBLEM

THE Fifteen School-Girls Problem—first enunciated by T. P. Kirkman, and commonly known as *Kirkman's Problem* —consists in arranging fifteen things in different sets of triplets. It is usually presented in the form that a school-mistress was in the habit of taking her girls for a daily walk. The girls were fifteen in number, and were arranged in five rows of three each, so that each girl might have two companions. The problem is to dispose them so that for seven consecutive days no girl will walk with any of her school-fellows in any triplet more than once.

In the general problem, here discussèd, we require to arrange n girls, where n is an odd multiple of 3, in triplets to walk out for y days, where $y = (n-1)/2$, so that no girl will walk with any of her school-fellows in any triplet more than once.

The theory of the formation of all such possible triplets in the case of nine girls is comparatively easy, but the general theory involves considerable difficulties. Before describing any methods of solution, I will give briefly the leading facts in the history of the problem. For this and much of the material of this chapter I am indebted to O. Eckenstein. Detailed refer-ences to the authorities mentioned are given in the biblio-graphy mentioned in the footnote.*

The question was propounded in 1850, and in the same year

* The problem was first published in the *Lady's and Gentleman's Diary* for 1850, p. 48, and has been the subject of numerous memoirs. A bibliography of the problem by O. Eckenstein appeared in the *Messenger of Mathematics*, Cambridge, July, 1911, vol. XLI, pp. 33—36.

solutions were given for the cases when $n = 9, 15$, and 27; but the methods used were largely empirical.

The first writer to subject it to mathematical analysis was R. R. Anstice who, in 1852 and 1853, described a method for solving all cases of the form $12m + 3$ when $6m + 1$ is prime. He gave solutions for the cases when $n = 15, 27, 39$. Substantially, his process, in a somewhat simplified form, is covered by that given below under the heading Analytical Methods.

The next important advance in the theory was due to B. Peirce who, in 1860, gave cyclical methods for solving all cases of the form $12m + 3$ and $24m + 9$. But the processes used were complicated and partly empirical.

In 1871 A. H. Frost published a simple method applicable to the original problem when $n = 15$ and to all cases when n is of the form $2^{2m} - 1$. It has been applied to find solutions when $n = 15$ and $n = 63$.

In 1883 A. Bray (a name assumed by G. D. L. Harison) and E. Marsden gave three-step cyclical solutions for 21 girls. These were interesting because Kirkman had expressed the opinion that this case was insoluble.

Another solution when $n = 21$, by T. H. Gill, was given in the fourth edition of this book in 1905. His method though empirical appears to be applicable to all cases, but for high values of n it involves so much preliminary work by trial and error as to be of little value.

A question on the subject which I propounded in the *Educational Times* in 1906, attracted the attention of L. A. Legros, H. E. Dudeney and O. Eckenstein, and I received from them a series of interesting and novel solutions. As illustrations of the processes used, Dudeney published new solutions for $n = 27, 33, 51, 57, 69, 75, 87, 93, 111$; and Eckenstein for $n = 27, 33, 39, 45, 51, 57, 69, 75, 93, 99, 111, 123, 135$.

I now proceed to describe some of the methods applicable to the problem. We can use cycles and combinations of them. I confine my discussion to processes where the steps of the cycles do not exceed three symbols at a time. It will be convenient to begin with the easier methods, where, however, a certain amount of arrangement has to be made empirically, and then to go on to the consideration of the more general method.

One-Step Cycles. As illustrating solutions by one-step cyclical permutations I will first describe Legros's method. Solutions obtained by it can be represented by diagrams, and their use facilitates the necessary arrangements. It is always applicable when n is of the form $24m + 3$, and seems to be also applicable when n is of the form $24m + 9$. Somewhat similar methods were used by Dudeney, save that he made no use of geometrical constructions.

We have $n = 2y + 1 = 24m + 3$ or $n = 2y + 1 = 24m + 9$. We may denote one girl by k, and the others by the numbers $1, 2, 3, \ldots 2y$. Place k at the centre of a circle, and the numbers $1, 2, 3, \ldots 2y$ at equidistant intervals on the circumference. Thus the centre of the circle and each point on its circumference will indicate a particular girl. A solution in which the centre of the circle is used to denote one girl is termed a central solution.

The companions of k are to be different on each day. If we uppose that on the first day they are 1 and $y + 1$, on the second 2 and $y + 2$, and so on, then the diameters through k will give for each day a triplet in which k appears. On each day we have to find $2(y - 1)/3$ other triplets satisfying the conditions of the problem. Every triplet formed from the remaining $2y - 2$ girls will be represented by an inscribed triangle joining the points representing these girls. The sides of the triangles are the chords joining these $2y - 2$ points. These chords may be represented symbolically by [1], [2], [3], $\ldots$ [$y - 1$]; these numbers being proportional to the smaller arcs subtended. I will denote the sides of a triangle so represented by the letters p, q, r, and I will use the term triad or grouping to denote any group of p, q, r which determines the dimensions of an inscribed triangle. I shall place the numbers of a triad in square brackets. If p, q, r are proportional to the smaller arcs subtended, it is clear that if $p + q$ is less than y, we have $p + q = r$; and if $p + q$ is greater than y we have $p + q + r = 2y$. If we like to use arcs larger than the semi-circumference we may confine ourselves to the relation $p + q = r$. In the geometrical methods described below, we usually first determine the dimensions of the triangles to be used in the solution, and then find how they are to be arranged in the circle.

If $(y - 1)/3$ scalene triangles, whose sides are p, q, r, can be inscribed in the circle so that to each triangle corresponds an equal complementary triangle having its equal sides parallel to those of the first and with its vertices at free points, then the system of $2(y - 1)/3$ triangles with the corresponding diameter will give an arrangement for one day. If the system be permuted cyclically $y - 1$ times we get arrangements for the other $y - 1$ days. No two girls will walk together twice, for each chord occupies a different position after each permutation, and as all the chords forming the $(y - 1)/3$ triangles are unequal the same combination cannot occur twice. Since the triangles are placed in complementary pairs, one being y points in front of the other, it follows that after $y - 1$ permutations we shall come to a position like the initial one, and the cycle will be completed. If the circle be drawn and the triangles cut out to scale, the arrangement of the triangles is facilitated. The method will be better understood if I apply it to one or two of the simpler cases.

The first case is that of three girls, a, b, c, walking out for one day, that is, $n = 3$, $m = 0$, $y = 1$. This involves no discussion, the solution being $(a. b. c)$.

The next case is that of nine girls walking out for four days, that is, $n = 9$, $m = 0$, $y = 4$. The first triplet on the first day is $(1. k. 5)$. There are six other girls represented by the points 2, 3, 4, 6, 7, 8. These points can be joined so as to form triangles, and each triangle will represent a triplet. We want to find one such triangle, with unequal sides, with its vertices at three of these points, and such that the triangle formed by the other three points will have its sides equal and parallel to the sides of the first triangle.

The sides of a triangle are p, q, r. The only possible values are 1, 2, 3, and they satisfy the condition $p + q = r$. If a triangle of this shape is placed with its vertices at the points 3, 4, 6, we can construct a complementary equal triangle, four points further on, having 7, 8, 2 for its vertices. All the points in the figure are now joined, and form the three triplets for the first day, namely $(k.\,1.\,5)$, $(3.\,4.\,6)$, $(7.\,8.\,2)$. It is only necessary to rotate the figure one step at a time in order to obtain the triplets for the remaining three days. Another similar solution is obtained from the diameter $(1.\,k.\,5)$, and the triangles $(2.\,3.\,8)$, $(6.\,7.\,4)$. It is the reflection of the former solution.

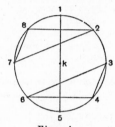

Figure i.

The next case to which the method is applicable is when $n = 27$, $m = 1$, $y = 13$. Proceeding as before, the 27 girls must be arranged with one of them, k, at the centre and the other 26 on the circumference of a circle. The diameter $(1.\,k.\,14)$ gives the first triplet on the first day. To obtain the other triplets we have to find four dissimilar triangles which satisfy the conditions mentioned above. The chords used as sides of these triangles may be of the lengths represented symbolically by [1], [2], ... [12]. We have to group these lengths so that $p + q = r$ or $p + q + r = 2y$; if the first condition can be satisfied it is the easier to use, as the numbers are smaller. In this instance the triads [3, 8, 11], [5, 7, 12], [2, 4, 6], [1, 9, 10] will be readily found. Now if four triangles with their sides of these lengths can be arranged in a system so that all the vertices fall on the ends of different diameters (exclusive of the ends of the diameter 1, k, 14), it follows that the opposite ends of those diameters can be joined by chords giving a series of equal triangles, symmetrically placed, each having its sides parallel to those of a triangle of the first system.   The following arrangement of triangles satisfies the conditions : (4. 11. 25), (5. 8. 23), (6. 7. 16), (9. 13. 15). The complementary system is (17. 24. 12), (18. 21. 10), (19. 20. 3), (22. 26. 2). These triplets with (k. 1. 14) give an arrangement for the first day ; and, by rotating the system cyclically, the arrangements for the remaining 12 days can be found immediately.

I proceed to give one solution of this type for every remaining case where n is less than 100.   From the result the triads or groupings used can be obtained. It is sufficient in each case to give an arrangement on the first day, since the arrangements on the following days are at once obtainable by cyclical permutations.

I take first the three cases, 33, 57, 81, where n is of the form $24m + 9$. In these cases the arrangements on the other days are obtained by one-step cyclical permutations.

For 33 girls, a solution is given by the system of triplets (2, 11. 16), (4. 6. 10), (5. 13. 30), (7. 8. 19), (9. 28. 31), and the complementary system (18. 27. 32), (20. 22. 26), (21. 29. 14), (23. 24. 3), (25. 12. 15). These 10 triplets, together with that represented by (k. 1. 17), will give an arrangement for the first day.

For 57 girls, a possible arrangement of triplets is (18. 13. 50), (20. 11. 28), (21. 52. 3), (8. 10. 51), (4. 25. 26), (2. 6. 12), (7. 19. 33), (27. 43. 16), (37. 14. 17). These, with the 9 complementary triplets, and the diameter triplet (1. k. 29), give an arrangement for the first day.

For 81 girls an arrangement for the first day consists of the diameter triplet (1. k. 41), the 13 triplets (3. 35. 42), (4. 10. 29), (5. 28. 56), (6. 26. 39), (7. 15. 17), (8. 11. 32), (13. 27. 49), (14. 19. 30), (20. 37. 38), (21. 25. 52), (24. 36. 62), (18. 33. 63), (31. 40. 74), and the 13 complementary triplets.

I take next the three cases, 51, 75, 99, where n is of the form $24m + 3$.   In these cases the arrangements on the other days are obtained either by one-step or by two-step cyclical permutations.

For 51 girls, an arrangement for the first day consists of the diameter triplet (k. 1. 26), the 8 triplets (2. 9. 36), (4. 7. 25), (6. 10. 19), (8. 14. 22), (12. 17. 45), (13. 24. 48), (15. 16. 46), (18, 28. 30), and the 8 complementary triplets.

For 75 girls, an arrangement for the first day consists of the diameter triplet (k. 1. 38), the 12 triplets (2. 44. 55), (4. 11. 19), (5. 50. 66), (6. 52. 57), (8. 46. 58), (10. 59. 65), (12. 60. 64), (14. 24. 68), (16. 25. 72), (17. 3. 74), (33. 34. 73), (30. 32. 63), and the 12 complementary triplets.

For 99 girls an arrangement for the first day consists of the diameter triplet (1. k. 50), the 16 triplets (2. 17. 47), (3. 9. 68), (4. 44. 82), (5. 12. 75), (6. 32. 42), (7. 23. 97), (8. 21. 30), (15. 20. 76), (16. 35. 85), (18. 45. 62), (22. 40. 63), (25. 37. 92), (28. 29. 80), (34. 38. 59), (39. 41. 73), (46. 49. 60), and the 16 complementary triplets.

It is also possible to obtain, for numbers of the form $24m + 3$, solutions which are uniquely two-step, but in these the complementary triangles are not placed symmetrically to each other. I give 27 girls as an instance, using the same triads as in the solution of this case given above. The triplets for the first day are (k. 1. 14), (2. 12. 3), (21. 5. 22), (20. 24. 26), (11. 15. 17), (8. 16. 19), (25. 7. 10), (6. 18. 13), and (23. 9. 4). From this the arrangements on the other days can be obtained by a two-step (but not by a one-step) cyclical permutation.

It is unnecessary to give more examples, or to enter on the question of how from one solution others can be deduced, or how many solutions of each case can be obtained in this way. The types of the possible triangles are found analytically, but their geometrical arrangement is empirical. The defect of this method is that it may not be possible to arrange a given grouping. Thus when $n = 27$, we easily obtain 24 different groupings, but two of them cannot be arranged geometrically to give solutions; and whether any particular grouping will give a solution can, in many cases, be determined only by long and troublesome empirical work. The same objection applies to the two-step and three-step methods which are described below.

Two-Step Cycles. The method used by Legros was extended by Eckenstein to cases where n is of the form $12m + 3$. When n is of this form and m is odd we cannot get sets of complementary triangles as is required in Legros's method; hence, to apply a similar method, we have to find $2(y - 1)/3$ different dissimilar inscribed triangles having no vertex in common and satisfying the condition $p + q = r$ or $p + q + r = 2y$. These solutions are also central. Since there are $2y$ points on the circumference of the circle, the permutations, if they are to be cyclical, must go in steps of two numbers at a time. In Legros's method we represent one triplet by a diameter. But obviously it will answer our purpose equally well to represent it by a triangle with k as vertex and two radii as sides, one

drawn to an even number and the other to an odd number :
in fact, this will include the diameter as a particular case.

I begin by considering the case where we use the diameter
(1. k. $y + 1$) to represent one triplet on the first day. Here
the chords used for sides of the triangles representing the other
triplets must be of lengths [1], [2], . . . [$y - 1$]. Also each given
length must appear twice, and the two equal lines so represented must start one from an even number and the other

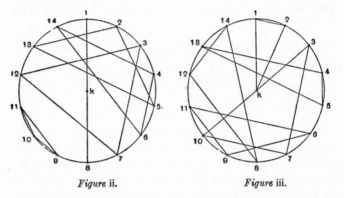

Figure ii.   *Figure* iii.

from an odd number, so as to avoid the same combination of
points occurring again when the system is rotated cyclically.
Of course, a vertex cannot be at the point 1 or y, as these
points will be required for the diameter triplet (1. k. $y + 1$).

These remarks will be clearer if we apply them to a definite
example. I take as an instance the case of 15 girls. As before,
we represent 14 of them by equidistant points numbered 1, 2,
3, . . 14 on the circumference of a circle, and one by a point k
at its centre. Take as one triplet the diameter (1. k. 8). Then
the sides p, q, r may have any of the values [1], [2], [3], [4], [5],
[6], and each value must be used twice. On examination it will
be found that there are only two possible groupings—namely,
[1, 1, 2], [2, 4, 6], [3. 3. 6], [5. 5. 4], and [1, 2, 3], [1, 4, 5],
[3, 5, 6], [2, 4, 6]. One of the solutions to which the first set of
groupings leads is defined by the diameter (1. k. 8) and the four
triplets (9. 10. 11), (4. 6. 14), (2. 5. 13), (3. 7. 12) ; see figure ii,

above : of the four triangles used, three are isosceles. The second set leads to solutions defined by the triplets $(k. 1. 8)$ $(4. 5. 7)$, $(13. 14. 9)$, $(3. 6. 11)$, $(10. 12. 2)$, or by the triplets $(k. 1. 8)$, $(6. 7. 9)$, $(3. 4. 13)$, $(5. 11. 14)$, $(10. 12. 2)$: in these solutions all the triangles used are scalene. If any one of these three sets of triplets is rotated cyclically two steps at a time, we get a solution of the problem for the seven days required. Each of these solutions by reflection and inversion gives rise to three others.

Next, if we take $(k. 1. 2)$ for one triplet on the first day, we shall have the points 3, 4, ... 14 for the vertices of the four triangles denoting the other triplets on that day. The sides must be of the lengths [1], [2], ... [7], of which [2], ... [6] must be used not more than twice and [1], [7] must be used only once. The [1] used must start from an even number, for otherwise the chord denoted by it would, when the system was rotated, occupy the position joining the points 1 and 2, which has been already used. The only possible groupings are [2, 4, 6], [2, 3, 5], [3, 4, 7], [1, 5, 6]; or [2, 4, 6], [2, 5, 7], [1, 4, 5], [3, 3, 6]; or [2, 4, 6], [2, 5, 7], [1, 3, 4], [3, 5, 6]. Each of these groupings gives rise to various solutions. For instance, the first grouping gives a set of triplets $(k. 1. 2)$, $(3. 7. 10)$, $(4. 5. 13)$, $(6. 9. 11)$, $(8. 12. 14)$. From this by a cyclical two-step permutation we get a solution. This solution is represented in figure iii. If we take $(k. 1. 4)$ or $(k. 1. 6)$ as one triplet on the first day, we get other sets of solutions.

Solutions involving the triplets $(k. 1. 2)$, $(k. 1. 4)$, $(k. 1. 6)$, $(k. 1. 8)$, and other analogous solutions can be obtained from the solutions illustrated in the above diagrams by rearranging the symbols denoting the girls. For instance, if in figure iii, where all the triangles used are scalene, we replace the numbers 2, 8, 3, 13, 4, 6, 5, 11, 7, 9, 10, 14 by 8, 2, 13, 3, 6, 4, 11, 5, 9, 7, 14, 10, we get the solution $(k. 1. 8)$, $(4. 5. 7)$, etc., given above. Again, if in figure iii we replace the symbols 1, 2, 3, 4, 5, 6, 7, 8, 9, 10, 11, 12, 13, 14, k by 12, 2, 10, 6, 1, 14, 5, 13, 9, 15, 4, 3, 11, 8, 7, we obtain a solution equivalent to that given by T. H. Gill and printed in the fourth edition of this book.   In this the arrangement on the first day is (1. 6. 11), (2. 7. 12), (3. 8. 13), (4. 9. 14), (5. 10. 15).   The arrangements on the other days are obtained as before by rotating the system so delineated round 7 as a centre two steps at a time.   Gill's arrangement is thus presented in its canonical form as a central two-step cyclical solution.

I proceed to give one solution of this type for every remaining case where n is less than 100.   In each case I give an arrangement on the first day; the arrangements for the other days can be got from it by a two-step cyclical permutation of the numbers.

In the case of 27 girls, one arrangement on the first day is (k. 1. 14), (19. 21. 20), (3. 9. 6), (13. 23. 18), (5. 17. 24), (7. 25. 16), (11. 15. 26), (10. 4. 2), (12. 22. 8).

In the case of 39 girls, one arrangement for the first day is (k. 1. 20), (35. 37. 36), (7. 13. 10), (19. 29. 24), (11. 25. 18), (3. 21. 12), (17. 33. 6), (15. 27. 2), (23. 31. 8), (5. 9. 26), (4. 16. 32), (14. 34. 38), (22. 28. 30).

In the case of 51 girls, one arrangement for the first day is (k. 1. 26), (21. 23. 22), (11. 17. 14), (35. 45. 40), (25. 39. 32), (15. 33. 24), (13. 41. 2), (5. 31. 18), (19. 49. 34), (27. 43. 10), (9. 47. 28), (29. 37. 8), (3. 7. 30), (4. 20. 46), (6. 36. 42), (12. 16. 44), (38. 48. 50).

In the case of 63 girls, one arrangement for the first day is (k. 1. 32), (57. 59. 58), (23. 29. 26), (37. 47. 42), (5. 53. 60), (17. 61. 8), (3. 43. 54), (7. 33. 20), (9. 39. 24), (27. 55. 10), (21. 45. 2), (11. 31. 52), (35. 51. 12), (13. 25. 50), (41. 49. 14), (15. 19. 48), (16. 18. 36), (6. 34. 38), (46. 56. 62), (22. 30. 44), (4. 28. 40).

In the case of 75 girls, one arrangement for the first day is (k. 1. 38), (23. 25. 24), (3. 9. 6), (29. 39. 34), (7. 21. 14), (51. 69. 60), (33. 55. 44), (11. 59. 72), (35. 65. 50), (37. 71. 54), (27. 63. 8), (15. 57. 36), (13. 41. 64), (43. 67. 18), (19. 73. 46), (31. 47. 2), (5. 17. 48), (53. 61. 20), (45. 49. 10), (30. 32. 52), (22. 26. 66), (56. 62. 70), (12. 28. 74), (16. 40. 58), (4. 42. 68).

In the case of 87 girls, one arrangement for the first day is (k. 1. 44), (61. 63. 62), (73. 79. 76), (35. 45. 40), (11. 83. 4), (25. 43. 34), (59. 81. 70), (7. 33. 20), (41. 71. 56), (23. 75. 6), (27. 65. 46), (13. 57. 78), (5. 51. 28), (3. 39. 64), (15. 47. 74), (9. 67. 38), (31. 55. 86), (19. 85. 52), (21. 37. 72), (17. 29. 66), (69. 77. 30), (49. 53. 8), (10. 12. 24), (22. 26. 84), (18. 54. 60), (2. 50. 80), (32. 42. 58), (14. 36. 82), (16. 48. 68).

In the case of 99 girls, one arrangement for the first day is (k. 1. 50), (47. 49. 48), (53. 59. 56), (55. 65. 60), (57. 71. 64), (23. 41. 32), (17. 39. 28), (63. 89. 76), (5. 35. 20), (3. 67. 84), (9. 69. 88), (29. 85. 8), (27. 79. 4), (25. 73. 98), (33. 77. 6), (21. 61. 90), (45. 81. 14), (51. 83. 18), (15. 43. 78), (13. 37. 74), (11. 31. 70), (75. 91. 34), (7. 19. 62), (87. 95. 42), (93. 97. 46), (58. 94. 96), (40. 44. 66), (10. 16. 26), (30. 38. 82), (68. 80. 2), (22. 36. 92), (24. 54. 72), (12. 52. 86).

This method may be also represented as a one-step cycle. For if we denote the girls by a point k at the centre of the circle, and points a_1, b_1, a_2, b_2, a_3, b_3, ... placed in that order on the circumference, we can re-write the solutions in the suffix notation, and then the cyclical permutation of the numbers denoting the suffixes is by one step at a time.

The one-step and two-step methods described above cover all cases except those where n is of the form $24m + 21$. These I have failed to bring under analogous rules, but we can solve them by recourse to the three-step cycles next described.

Three-Step Cycles. The fact that certain cases are soluble by one-step cycles, and others by two-step cycles, suggests the use of three-step cycles, and the fact that n is a multiple of 3 points to the same conclusion. On the other hand, if we denote the n girls by 1, 2, 3, ... n, and make a cyclical permutation of three steps at a time (or if we denote the girls by a_1, b_1, c_1, a_2, b_2, c_2, ..., and make a cyclical permutation of the suffixes one step at a time), we cannot get arrangements for more than $n/3$ days. Hence there will remain $(n - 1)/2 - n/3$ days, that is, $(n - 3)/6$ days, for which we have to find other arrangements. In fact, however, we can arrange the work so that in addition to the cyclical arrangements for $n/3$ days we can find $(n - 3)/6$ single triplets from each of which by a cyclical permutation of the numbers or suffixes an arrangement for one of these remaining days can be obtained; other methods are also sometimes available.

For instance, take the case of 21 girls. An arrangement for the first day is (1. 4. 10), (2. 5. 11), (3. 6. 12), (7. 14. 18), (8. 15. 16), (9. 13. 17), (19. 20. 21). From this by cyclical permutations of the numbers three steps at a time, we can get arrangements for 7 days in all. The arrangement for the 8th day can be got from the triplet (1. 6. 11) by a three-step cyclical permutation of the numbers in it. Similarly the arrangement for the 9th day can be got from the triplet (2. 4. 12), and that for the 10th day from the triplet (3. 5. 10), by three-step cyclical permutations.

This method was first used by A. Bray in 1883, and was subsequently developed by Dudeney and Eckenstein. It gives a solution for every value of n except 15, but it is not so easy to use as the methods already described, partly because the solution is in two parts, and partly because the treatment varies according as n is of the form $18m + 3$, or $18m + 9$, or $18m + 15$. Most of the difficulties in using it arise in the case when n is of the form $18m + 15$.

The geometrical representation is sufficiently obvious. In the methods used by Legros and Eckenstein, previously described, the girls were represented by $2y$ equidistant points on the circumference of a circle and a point at its centre. It is evident that we may with equal propriety represent all the girls by symbols placed at equidistant intervals round the circumference of a circle : such solutions are termed non-central. The symbols may be $1, 2, 3, \ldots n$, or letters $a_1, b_1, c_1,$ $a_2, b_2, c_2, \ldots.$ Any triplet will be represented by a triangle whose sides are chords of the circle. The arrangement on any day is to include all the girls, and therefore the triangles representing the triplets on that day are $n/3$ in number, and as each girl appears in only one triplet, no two triangles can have a common vertex.

The complete three-step solution will require the determination of a system of $(n - 1)/2$ inscribed triangles. In the first part of the solution $n/3$ of these triangles must be selected to form an arrangement for the first day, so that by rotating this arrangement three steps at a time we obtain triplets for $n/3$ days in all. In the second part of the solution we must assure ourselves that the remaining $(n - 3)/6$ triangles are such that from each of them, by a cyclical permutation of three steps at a time, an arrangement for one of the remaining $(n - 3)/6$ days is obtainable.

As before, we begin by tabulating the possible differences $[1], [2], [3], \ldots [(n - 1)/2]$, whose values denote the lengths of the sides p, q, r of the possible triangles ; also, we have either $p + q = r$ or $p + q + r = n$. From these values of p, q, r

are formed triads, and in these triads each difference must be used three times and only three times. Triangles of these types must be then formed and placed in the circle so that the side denoting any assigned difference p must start once from a number of the form $3m$, once from a number of the form $3m + 1$, and once from a number of the form $3m + 2$. Also an isosceles triangle, one of whose sides is a multiple of three, cannot be used : thus in any particular triad a 3, 6, 9, ... cannot appear more than once. Save in some exceptional cases of high values of n, every triangle, one of whose sides is a multiple of 3, must be used in the first part of the solution. In the whole arrangement every possible difference will occur n times, and, since any two assigned numbers can occur together only once, each difference when added to a number must start each time from a different number. I will not go into further details as to how these triangles are determined, but I think the above rules will be clear if I apply them to one or two easy examples.

For 9 girls, the possible differences are [1], [2], [3], [4], each of which must be used three times in the construction of four triangles the lengths of whose sides p, q, r are such that $p + q = r$ or $p + q + r = 9$. One possible set of triads formed from these numbers is [1, 2, 3], [1, 2, 3], [2, 3, 4], and [1, 4, 4]. Every triangle with a side of the length [3] must appear in the first part of the solutions ; thus the triplets used in the first part of the solution must be obtained from the first three of these triads. Hence we obtain as an arrangement for the first day the triplets (1. 3. 9), (2. 4. 7), (5. 6. 8). From this, three-step cyclical permutations give arrangements for other two days. The remaining triad [1, 4, 4] leads to a triplet (1. 2. 6) which, by a three-step cyclical permutation, gives an arrangement for the remaining day.

If we use the suffix notation, an arrangement for the first day is $a_1b_2a_3$, $b_1c_2b_3$, $c_1a_2c_3$. From this, by simple cyclical permutations of the suffixes, we get arrangements for the second and third days. Lastly, the triplet $a_1b_1c_1$ gives, by cyclical permutation of the suffixes, the arrangement for the fourth day—namely, $a_1b_1c_1$, $a_2b_2c_2$, $a_3b_3c_3$.

For 15 girls, the three-step process is inapplicable. The explanation of this is that two triads are required in the second part of the solution, and in neither of them may a 3 appear. The triads are to be formed from the differences [1], [2], ... [7], each of which is to be used three times, and the condition that in any particular triad only one 3 or one 6 may appear necessitates that six of the triads shall involve a 3 or a 6. Hence only one triad will be available for the second part of the solution.

I proceed to give one solution of this type for every remaining case where n is less than 100. I give some in the numerical, others in the suffix notation. The results will supply an indication of the process used.

First, I consider those cases where n is of the form $18m + 3$. In these cases it is always possible to find $2m$ triads each repeated thrice, and one equilateral triad, and to use the equilateral and m triads in the first part of the solution, the 3 triplets representing any one of these m triads being placed in the circle at equal intervals from each other in the first day's arrangement. From this, three-step or one-step cyclical permutations give arrangements for $6m + 1$ days in all. In the second part of the solution each of the m remaining triads is used thrice; it suffices to give the first triplet on each day, since from it the other triplets on that day are obtained by a three-step cyclical permutation.

For 21 girls an arrangement for the first day, for the first part of the solution, is (1. 4. 10), (8. 11. 17), (15. 18. 3), (2. 6. 7), (9. 13. 14), (16. 20. 21), (5. 12. 19). From this, three-step or one-step cyclical permutations give arrangements for 7 days in all. The first triplets used in the second part of the solution are (1. 3. 11), (2. 4. 12), (3. 5. 13). Each of these three triplets gives by a three-step cyclical permutation an arrangement for one of the remaining 3 days.

For 39 girls, arrangements for 13 days can be obtained from the following arrangement of triplets for the first day : (1. 4. 13), (14. 17. 26), (27. 30. 39), (2. 8. 23), (15. 21. 36), (28. 34. 10), (7. 11. 12), (20. 24. 25), (33. 37. 38), (3. 5. 19), (16. 18. 32), (29. 31. 6), (9. 22. 35). From each of the 6 triplets (1. 8. 18), (2. 9. 19), (3. 10. 20), (1. 9. 20), (2. 10. 21), (3. 11. 22), an arrangement for one of the remaining 6 days is obtainable.

For 57 girls, arrangements for 19 days can be obtained from the following arrangement of triplets for the first day: (1. 4. 25), (20. 23. 44), (39. 42. 6), (2. 8. 17), (21. 27. 36), (40. 46. 55), (3. 15. 33), (22. 34. 52), (41. 53. 14), (18. 19. 26), (37. 38. 45), (56. 57. 7), (13. 30. 35), (32. 49. 54), (51. 11. 16), (9. 29. 43), (28. 48. 5), (47. 10. 24), (12. 31. 50). From each of the 9 triplets (1. 3. 14), (2. 4. 15), (3. 5. 16), (1. 5. 30), (2. 6. 31), (3. 7. 32), (1. 11. 27),

(2. 12. 28), (3. 13. 29), an arrangement for one of the remaining 9 days is obtainable.

For 75 girls, arrangements for 25 days can be obtained from the following arrangement of triplets for the first day : (1. 4. 10), (26. 29. 35), (51. 54. 60), (3. 15. 36), (28. 40. 61), (53. 65. 11), (2. 17. 41), (27. 42. 66), (52. 67. 16), (13. 31. 58), (38. 56. 8), (63. 6. 33), (14. 21. 22), (39. 46. 47), (64. 71. 72), (7. 18. 20), (32. 43. 45), (57. 68. 70), (5. 9. 37), (30. 34. 62), (55. 59. 12), (19. 24. 50), (44. 49. 75), (69. 74. 25), (23. 48. 73). From each of the 12 triplets (1. 11. 30), (2. 12. 31), (3. 13. 32), (1. 15. 35), (2. 16. 36), (3. 17. 37), (1. 17. 39), (2. 18. 40), (3. 19. 41), (1. 18. 41), (2. 19. 42), (3. 20. 43), an arrangement for one of the remaining 12 days is obtainable.

For 93 girls, arrangements for 31 days can be obtained from the following arrangement of triplets for the first day : (1. 76. 79), (32. 14. 17), (63. 45. 48), (13. 25. 55), (44. 56. 86), (75. 87. 24), (29. 50. 74), (60. 81. 12), (91. 19. 43), (20. 26. 59), (51. 57. 90), (82. 88. 28), (3. 30. 39), (34. 61. 70), (65. 92. 8), (27. 64. 71), (58. 2. 9), (89. 33. 40), (35. 36. 52), (66. 67. 83), (4. 5. 21), (11. 15. 37), (42. 46. 68), (73. 77. 6), (16. 18. 41), (47. 49. 72), (78. 80. 10), (23. 31. 69), (54. 62. 7), (85. 93. 38), (22. 53. 84). From each of the 15 triplets (1. 14. 42), (2. 15. 43), (3. 16. 44), (1. 33. 44), (2. 34. 45), (3. 35. 46), (1. 11. 30), (2. 12. 31), (3. 13. 32), (1. 6. 41), (2. 7. 42), (3. 8. 43), (1. 15. 35), (2. 16. 36), (3. 17. 37), an arrangement for one of the remaining 15 days is obtainable by a three-step cyclical permutation.

Before leaving the subject of numbers of this type, I give two other solutions of the case when $n = 21$, one to illustrate the use of the suffix notation, and the other a cyclical solution which is uniquely three-step.

If we employ the suffix notation, the suffixes, with the type here used, are somewhat trying to read. Accordingly hereafter I shall write $a1$, $a2$, ..., instead of a_1, a_2, ... In the case of 21 girls, an arrangement for the first day is ($a1$. $a2$. $a4$), ($b1$. $b2$. $b4$), ($c1$. $c2$. $c4$), ($a3$. $b6$. $c5$), ($b3$. $c6$. $a5$), ($c3$. $a6$. $b5$), ($a7$. $b7$. $c7$). From this, by one-step cyclical permutations of the suffixes, we get arrangements for the 2nd, 3rd, 4th, 5th, 6th and 7th days. The arrangement for the 8th day can be obtained from the triplet ($a1$. $b2$. $c4$) by permuting the suffixes cyclically one step at a time. Similarly the arrangement for the 9th day can be obtained from the triplet ($b1$. $c2$. $a4$) and that for the 10th day from the triplet ($c1$. $a2$. $b4$). Thus with seven suffixes we keep 7 for each symbol in one triplet, and every other triplet depends on one or other of only two arrangements—namely, (1. 2. 4) or (3. 6. 5). If the solution be written out at length the principle of the method used will be clear.

Cyclical solutions which are uniquely three-step can also be obtained for numbers of the form $18m + 3$; in them the same triads can be used as before, but they are not placed at equal intervals in the circle. I give 21 girls as instance. The arrangements on the first 7 days can be obtained from the arrangement (1. 4. 10), (2. 20. 14), (15. 18. 3), (16. 17. 21), (8. 9. 13), (6. 7. 11), (5. 12. 19) by a three-step (but not by a one-step) cyclical permutation. From each of the triplets (1. 3. 11), (2. 4. 12), (3. 5. 13) an arrangement for one of the remaining 3 days is obtainable.

Next, I consider those cases where n is of the form $18m + 9$. Here, regular solutions in the suffix notation can be obtained in all cases except in that of 27 girls, but if the same solutions are expressed in the numerical notation, the triads are irregular. Accordingly, except when $n = 27$, it is better to use the suffix notation. I will deal with the case when $n = 27$ after considering the cases when $n = 45, 63, 81, 99$.

For 45 girls, an arrangement for the first day consists of the 5 triplets $(a1. \, a12. \, a13)$, $(a2. \, a9. \, a11)$, $(a5. \, a10. \, b15)$, $(a4. \, b3. \, c7)$, $(a8, b6. \, c14)$, and the 10 analogous triplets—namely, $(b1. \, b12. \, b13)$, $(c1. \, c12. \, c13)$, $(b2. \, b9. \, b11)$, $(c2. \, c9. \, c11)$, $(b5. \, b10. \, c15)$, $(c5. \, c10. \, a15)$, $(b4. \, c3. \, a7)$, $(c4. \, a3. \, b7)$, $(b8. \, c6. \, a14)$, $(c8. \, a6. \, b14)$. From these, by one-step cyclical permutations of the suffixes, the arrangements for 15 days can be got. Each of the 2 triplets $(c4. \, b3. \, a7)$, $(c8. \, b6. \, a14)$, the 4 analogous triplets—namely, $(a4. \, c3. \, b7)$, $(b4. \, a3. \, c7)$, $(a8. \, c6. \, b14)$, $(b8. \, a6. \, c14)$—and the triplet $(a1. \, b1. \, c1)$, gives, by a one-step cyclical permutation of the suffixes, an arrangement for one of the remaining 7 days.

For 63 girls, an arrangement for the first day consists of the 7 triplets $(a1. \, a10. \, a9)$, $(a5. \, a8. \, a3)$, $(a4. \, a19. \, a15)$, $(a7. \, a14. \, b21)$, $(a20. \, b11. \, c12)$, $(a16. \, b13. \, c18)$, $(a17. \, b2. \, c6)$, and the 14 analogous triplets. From these, by one-step cyclical permutations of the suffixes, the arrangements for 21 days can be got. Each of the 10 triplets, consisting of the 3 triplets $(c20. \, b11. \, a12)$, $(c16. \, b13, a18)$, $(c17. \, b2. \, a6)$, the 6 analogous triplets, and the triplet $(a1. \, b1. \, c1)$, gives, by a one-step cyclical permutation of the suffixes, an arrangement for one of the remaining 10 days.

For 81 girls, an arrangement for the first day consists of the 9 triplets $(a5. \, a7. \, a8)$, $(a3. \, a10. \, a14)$, $(a11. \, a21. \, a26)$, $(a4. \, a12. \, a25)$, $(a9. \, a18. \, b27)$, $(a22. \, b20. \, c19)$, $(a24. \, b17. \, c13)$, $(a16. \, b6. \, c1)$, $(a23. \, b15. \, c2)$, and the 18 analogous triplets. From these, by cyclical permutations of the suffixes, the arrangements for 27 days can be got. Each of the 13 triplets consisting of the 4 triplets $(c22. \, b20. \, a19)$, $(c24. \, b17. \, a13)$, $(c16. \, b6. \, a1)$, $(c23. \, b15. \, a2)$, the 8 analogous triplets, and the triplet $(a1. \, b1. \, c1)$, gives, by a cyclical permutation of the suffixes, an arrangement for one of the remaining 13 days.

For 99 girls, an arrangement for the first day consists of the 11 triplets $(a1. \, a3. \, a10)$, $(a2. \, a6. \, a20)$, $(a4. \, a12. \, a7)$, $(a8. \, a24. \, a14)$, $(a16. \, a15. \, a28)$, $(a11. \, a22. \, b33)$, $(a32. \, b30. \, c23)$, $(a31. \, b27. \, c13)$, $(a29. \, b21. \, c26)$, $(a25. \, b9. \, c19)$, $(a17. \, b18. \, c5)$, and the 22 analogous triplets. From these, by cyclical permutations of the suffixes, the arrangements for 33 days can be got. Each of the 16 triplets consisting of the 5 triplets $(c32. \, b30. \, a23)$, $(c31. \, b27. \, a13)$, $(c29. \, b21. \, a26)$, $(c25. \, b9. \, a19)$, $(c17. \, b18. \, a5)$, the 10 analogous triplets, and the triplet $(a1. \, b1. \, c1)$, gives, by a cyclical permutation of the suffixes, an arrangement for one of the remaining 16 days.

For 27 girls, an arrangement of triplets for the first day is $(1. \, 7. \, 10)$, $(14. \, 17. \, 8)$, $(27. \, 6. \, 9)$, $(13. \, 20. \, 25)$, $(11. \, 23. \, 18)$, $(12. \, 16. \, 24)$, $(21. \, 2. \, 4)$, $(15. \, 22. \, 26)$, $(19. \, 3. \, 5)$. From this, three-step cyclical permutations give arrangements for 9 days in all. The first triplets on the remaining 4 days are $(1. \, 2. \, 3)$, $(1. \, 6. \, 20)$, $(1. \, 11. \, 15)$, $(1. \, 17. \, 27)$, from each of which, by a three-step cyclical permutation, an arrangement for one of those days is obtainable.

Regular solutions in the numerical notation can also be obtained for all values of n, except 9, where n is of the form $18m + 9$. I give 27 girls as an instance. The first day's arrangement is $(1. \, 2. \, 4)$, $(10. \, 11. \, 13)$, $(19. \, 20. \, 22)$, $(8. \, 15. \, 23)$, $(17. \, 24. \, 5)$, $(26. \, 6. \, 14)$, $(3. \, 25. \, 9)$, $(12. \, 7. \, 18)$, $(21. \, 16. \, 27)$; from this arrangements for 9 days in all are obtained by one-step cyclical permutations. Each of the three triplets (1. 5. 15), (2. 6. 16), (3. 7. 17) gives an arrangement for one day by a three-step cyclical permutation. Finally the triplet (1. 10. 19), represented by an equilateral triangle, gives the arrangement on the last day by a one-step cyclical permutation.

Lastly, I consider those cases where n is of the form $18m + 15$. As before, the solution is divided into two parts. In the first part, we obtain an arrangement of the triplets for the first day, from which arrangements for $6m + 5$ days are obtained by three-step cyclical permutations. In the second part, we obtain the first triplet on each of the remaining $3m + 2$ days, from which the other triplets on that day are obtained by three-step cyclical permutations.

For 33 girls, an arrangement in the first part is (1. 13. 19), (23. 11. 5), (3. 15. 21), (2. 4. 7), (12. 14. 17), (28. 30. 33), (6. 16. 25), (10. 20. 29), (8. 18. 27), (24. 31. 32), (9. 22. 26). The triplets in the second part are (25. 32. 33), (26. 33. 1), (10. 23. 27), (11. 24. 28), (1. 12. 23).

For 51 girls, an arrangement in the first part is (17. 34. 51), (49. 16. 10), (11. 44. 50), (15. 33. 27), (19. 4. 46), (2. 38. 29), (21. 36. 45), (22. 25. 24), (5. 8. 7), (39. 42. 41), (43. 13. 20), (26. 47. 3), (9. 30. 37), (1. 14. 6), (35. 48. 40), (18. 31. 23), (28. 32. 12). The triplets in the second part are (29. 33. 13), (30. 34. 14), (1. 26. 12), (2. 27. 13), (3. 28. 14), (1. 11. 30), (2. 12. 31), (3. 13. 32).

For 69 girls, an arrangement in the first part is (23. 46. 69), (31. 34. 43), (11. 8. 68), (54. 57. 66), (58. 52. 28), (35. 29. 5), (45. 51. 6), (16. 1. 49), (62. 47. 26), (39. 24. 3), (4. 55. 42), (50. 32. 19), (27. 9. 65), (40. 67. 18), (17. 44. 64), (63. 21. 41), (10. 14. 15), (33. 37. 38), (56. 60. 61), (25. 53. 36), (2. 30. 13), (48. 7. 59), (22. 20. 12). The triplets in the second part are (23. 21. 13), (24. 22. 14), (1. 8. 33), (2. 9. 34), (3. 10. 35), (1. 17. 36), (2. 18. 37), (3. 19. 38), (1. 41. 15), (2. 42. 16), (3. 43. 17).

For 87 girls, an arrangement in the first part is (29. 58. 87), (76. 82. 73), (47. 53. 44), (15. 9. 18), (70. 1. 13), (41. 59. 71), (12. 30. 42), (4. 67. 31), (2. 26. 62), (60. 84. 33), (40. 79. 25), (11. 50. 83), (69. 21. 54), (43. 64. 63), (14. 35. 34), (72. 6. 5), (61. 16. 77), (32. 74. 48), (3. 45. 19), (28. 68. 66), (37. 86. 39), (10. 8. 57), (46. 80. 36), (22. 65. 75), (7. 17. 51), (85. 23. 78), (52. 20. 27), (49. 56. 81), (55. 38. 24). The triplets in the second part are (56. 39. 25), (57. 40. 26), (1. 5. 42), (2. 6. 43), (3. 7. 44), (1. 29. 6), (2. 30. 7), (3. 31. 8), (1. 9. 20), (2. 10. 21), (3. 11. 22), (1. 14. 36), (2. 15. 37), (3. 16. 38).

Before proceeding to the consideration of other methods I should add that it is also possible to obtain irregular solutions of cases where n is of any of these three forms. As an instance I give a three-step solution of 33 girls. A possible arrangement in the first part is (1. 4. 10), (14. 23. 26), (9. 15. 30), (3. 28. 33), (2. 6. 8), (11. 18. 27), (13. 24. 25), (5. 16. 20), (7. 17. 22), (21. 29. 31), (12. 19. 32). The triplets in the second part are (1. 2. 21), (1. 8. 30), (1. 3. 26), (1. 15. 20), (1. 17. 18). I describe this solution as irregular, since all, save one, of the triads used are different.

The Focal Method. Another method of attacking the problem, comparatively easy to use in practice, is applicable

when n is of the form $24m + 3p$, where $p = 6q + 3$. It is due to Eckenstein. Here it is convenient to use a geometrical representation by denoting $24m + 2p$ girls by equidistant numbered points on the circumference of a circle, and the remaining p girls by lettered points placed inside the circle; these p points are termed foci. The solution is in two parts. In the first part, we obtain an order from which the arrangements for $12m + p$ days are deducible by a two-step cycle of the numbers: in none of these triplets does more than one focus appear. In the second part, we find the arrangements for the remaining $3q + 1$ days; here the foci and the numbered points are treated separately, the former being arranged by any of the methods used for solving the case of $6q + 3$ girls, while of the latter a typical triplet is used on each of those days, from which the remaining triplets on that day are obtained by cyclical permutations.

This method covers all cases except when $n = 15, 21, 39$; and solutions by it for all values of n less than 200 have been written out. Sets of all the triplets required can be definitely determined. One way of doing this is by finding the primitive roots of the prime factors of $4m + 2q + 1$, though in the simpler cases the triplets can be written down empirically without much trouble. An advantage of this method is that solutions of several cases are obtained by the same work. Suppose that we have arranged suitable triangles in a circle, having on its circumference $12m + p$ or $3c$ equidistant points, and let y be the greatest integer satisfying the indeterminate equation $2x + 4y + 1 = c$, where $x = 0$ or $x = 1$, and α the highest multiple of 6 included in $x + y$, then solutions of not less than $y + 1 - \alpha$ cases can be deduced. Thus from a 27 circle arrangement, where $c = 9$, $y = 2$, $x = 0$, $\alpha = 0$, we can by this method deduce three solutions—namely, when $n = 57, 69, 81$; from a 39 circle arrangement where $c = 13$, $y = 3$, $x = 0$, $\alpha = 0$, we can deduce four solutions—namely, when $n = 81, 93, 105, 117$.

I have no space to describe the method fully, but I will

give solutions for two cases—namely, for 33 girls ($n = 33$, $m = 1$, $p = 3$) where there are 3 foci, and for 51 girls ($n = 51$, $m = 1$, $p = 9$) where there are 9 foci.

For 33 girls, we have 3 foci which we may denote by a, b, c, and 30 points which we may denote by the numbers 1 to 30 placed at equidistant intervals on the circumference of a circle. Then if the arrangement on the first day is (a. 5. 10), (b. 20, 25), (c. 15. 30), (1. 2. 14), (16. 17. 29), (4. 23. 26), (19. 8. 11), (9. 7. 3), (24. 22. 18), (6. 27. 13), (21. 12. 28), a two-step cyclical permutation of the numbers gives arrangements for 15 days; that on the second day being (a. 7. 12), (b. 22. 27), etc. The arrangement on the 16th day is (a. b. c), (1. 11. 21). (2. 12. 22), (3. 13. 23), ... (10. 20. 30).

For 51 girls, we have 9 foci, which we may denote by a, b, c, d, e, f, g, h, j, and 42 points denoted by 1, 2, ... 42, placed at equidistant intervals on the circumference of a circle. Then if the arrangement on the first day is (a. 5. 6), (b. 26. 27), (c. 3. 10), (d. 24. 31), (e. 19. 34), (f. 40. 13), (g. 39. 16), (h. 18. 37), (j. 21. 42), (9. 11. 22), (30. 32. 1), (35. 41. 2), (14. 20. 23), (17. 29. 12), (38. 8. 33), (7. 15. 25), (28. 36. 4), a two-step cyclical permutation of the numbers gives arrangements for 21 days. Next, arrange the 9 foci in triplets by any of the methods already given so as to obtain arrangements for 4 days. From the numbers 1 to 42 we can obtain four typical triplets not already used—namely, (1. 5. 21), (2. 6. 22), (3. 7. 23), (14. 28. 42). From each of these triplets we can, by a three-step cyclical permutation, obtain an arrangement of the 42 girls for one day, thus getting arrangements for 4 days in all. Combining these results of letters and numbers, we obtain arrangements for the 4 days. Thus an arrangement for the first day would be (a. c. j), (b. d. g), (e. f. h), (1. 5. 21), (4. 8. 24), (7. 11. 27), (10. 14. 30), (13. 17. 33), (16. 20. 36), (19. 23. 39), (22. 26. 42), (25. 29. 3), (28. 32. 6), (31. 35. 9), (34. 38. 12), (37. 41. 15), (40. 2. 18). For the second day the corresponding arrangement would be (d. f. c), (e. g. a), (h. j. b), (2. 6. 22), (5. 9. 25), etc.

Analytical Methods. The methods described above, under the headings One-Step, Two-Step and Three-Step Cycles, involve some empirical work. It is true that with a little practice it is not difficult to obtain solutions by them when n is a low number, but the higher the value of n the more troublesome is the process and the more uncertain its success. A general arithmetical process has, however, been given by which it is claimed that *some* solutions for *any* value of n can be always obtained. Most of the solutions given earlier in this chapter can be obtained in this way.

The essential feature of the method is the arrangement of the numbers by which the girls are represented in an order such that definite rules can be laid down for grouping them in pairs and triplets, so that the differences of the numbers in each pair or triplet either are all different or are repeated as often as may be required. The process depends on finding primitive roots of the prime factors of whatever number is taken as the base of the solution. When $(n-1)/2$ is prime, of the form $6u+1$, and is taken as base, the order is obtainable at once, and the rules for grouping the numbers are easy of application; owing to considerations of space, I here confine myself to such instances, but similar though somewhat longer methods are applicable to all cases.

I use the geometrical representation already explained. We have $n = 2y + 1$, and y is a prime of the form $6u + 1$. In forming the triplets we either proceed directly by arranging all the points in threes, or we arrange some of them in pairs and make the selection of the third point dependent on those of the two first chosen, leaving only a few triplets to be obtained otherwise. In the former case we have to arrange the numbers in triplets so that each difference will appear twice, and so that no two differences will appear together more than once. In the latter case we have to arrange the numbers so that the differences between the numbers in each pair comprise consecutive integers from 1 upwards and are all different. In both cases we commence by finding a primitive root of y, say x. The

residues to the modulus y of the $6u$ successive powers of x form
a series of numbers, $e1$, $e2$, $e3$, . . ., comprising all the integers
from 1 to $6u$, and when taken in the order of the successive
powers, they can be arranged in the manner required by definite
rules.

I will apply the method to the case of 27 girls from which
the general theory, in the restricted case where y is a prime
of the form $6u + 1$, will be sufficiently clear. In this case
we have $n = 27$, $y = 13$, $u = 2$, and $x = 2$. I take 13 as the
base of the analysis. I will begin by pairing the points, and
this being so, it is convenient to represent the girls by a point
k at the centre of a circle and points $a1$, $b1$, $a2$, $b2$, . . . at
equidistant intervals on the circumference. We reserve k, $a13$,
$b13$ for one triplet, and we have to arrange the other 24 points
so as to form 8 triangles of certain types. The residues are in
the order 2, 4, 8, 3, 6, 12, 11, 9, 5, 10, 7, 1, and these may be
taken as the suffixes of the remaining " a "s and " b "s.

First arrange these residues in pairs so that every difference
between the numbers in a pair occurs once. One rule by which
this can be effected is to divide the residues into two equal
sections and pair the numbers in the two sections. This gives
(2. 11), (4. 9), (8. 5), (3. 10), (6. 7), (12. 1) as possible pairs.
Another such rule is to divide the residue into six equal sections, and pair the numbers in the first and second sections,
those in the third and fourth sections, and those in the fifth
and sixth sections. This gives (2. 8), (4. 3), (6. 11), (12. 9),
(5. 7), (10. 1) as possible pairs. Either arrangement can be
used, but the first set of pairs leads only to scalene triangles.
In none of the pairs of the latter set does the sum of the
numbers in a pair add up to 13, and since this may allow the
formation of isosceles as well as of scalene triangles, and thus
increase the variety of the resulting solutions, I will use the
latter set of pairs. We use these basic pairs as suffixes of the
" a "s, and each pair thus determines two points of one of the
triangles required. We have now used up all the " a"s. The
third point associated with each of these six pairs of points

must be a " b," and the remaining six " b "s must be such that they can be arranged in suitable triplets.

Next, then, we must arrange the $6u$ residues $e1$, $e2$, $e3$ . . . in possible triplets. To do this arrange them cyclically in triplets, for instance, as shown in the first column of the left half of the table on page 289. We write in the second column the differences between the first and second numbers in each triplet, in the third column the differences between the second and third numbers in each triplet, and in the fourth column the differences between the third and first numbers in each triplet. If any of these differences d is greater than $3u$ we may replace it by the complementary number $y - d$: that this is permissible is obvious from the geometrical representation. By shifting cyclically the symbols in any vertical line in the first column we change these differences. We can, however, in this way always displace the second and third vertical lines in the first column so that the numbers in the second, third, and fourth columns include the numbers 1 to $3u$ twice over. This can be effected thus. If any term in the residue series is greater than $3u$, replace it by its complementary number $y - e$. In this way, from the residue series, we get a derivative series $d1$, $d2$, $d3$, . . . such that any $3u$ consecutive terms comprise all the integers from 1 to $3u$. The first half of this series may be divided into three equal divisions thus : (1) $d1$, $d4$, $d7$, . . . ; (2) $d2$, $d5$, $d8$, . . .; (3) $d3$, $d6$, $d9$, ... If the displacement is such that the first numbers in the second, third, and fourth columns are contained in different divisions, each difference must occur twice, and it will give a possible solution. Other possible regular arrangements give other solutions. Applying this to our case, we have the residue series, 2, 4, 8, 3, 6, 12, 11, 9, 5, 10, 7, 1. The derivative series is 2, 4, 5, 3, 6, 1, 2, 4, 5, 3, 6, 1. The three divisions are : (i) 2, 3; (ii) 4, 6,; (iii) 5, 1. The cyclical arrangement we started with and the consequent differences are shown in the left half of the accompanying table. A cyclical change as described above of the vertical lines of the symbols in the first column gives the arrangement in the right half of the table. Here each difference occurs twice, and accordingly this gives a possible arrangement of the triplets—namely, 2, 6, 5; 3, 9, 1; 11, 7, 8; 10, 4, 12. These are the suffixes of the "b"s. We have now to use six of these "b"s in connection with the basic "a"s already determined, keeping the other six "b"s for the remaining two triangles.

For instance we may obtain a scalene solution by taking as a suffix of the "b" associated with any pair of "a"s, a number equal to the sum of the suffixes of the "a"s. We

2. 4. 8	2	4	6	2. 6. 5	4	1	3
3. 6. 12	3	6	4	3. 9. 1	6	5	2
11. 9. 5	2	4	6	11. 7. 8	4	1	3
10. 7. 1	3	6	4	10. 4. 12	6	5	2

thus get as a solution (a2. a8. b10), (a4. a3. b7), (a6. a11. b4), (a12. a9. b8), (a5. a7. b12), (a10. a1. b11), (b2. b6. b5), (b3. b9, b1), (k. a13. b13). Or we might take as a suffix of the "b" associated with any pair of "a"s, the number midway between the suffixes of the "a"s on the 13 circle. This gives the following solution, in which the first six triangles are isosceles: (a2. a8. b5), (a4. a3. b10), (a6. a11. b2), (a12. a9. b4), (a5. a7. b6), (a10. a1. b12), (b3. b9. b1), (b11. b7. b8), (k. a13. b13).

In the case of 27 girls, we may equally well represent the points by k at the centre of the circle and 26 equidistant points 1, 2, ... 26 on the circumference. The points previously denoted by a and b with the suffix h are now denoted by the numbers $2h - 1$ and $2h$. Hence the basic pairs (2. 8), (4. 3), ... become (3. 15), (7. 5), (11. 21), (23. 17), (9. 13), (19. 1), and the corresponding scalene arrangement for the first day is (3. 15. 20), (7. 5. 14), ... (k. 25. 26). From this, by a two-step cyclical permutation of the numbers, an arrangement for 13 days can be got.

The case of 27 girls can also be treated by the direct formation of triplets. The triplets must be such that each difference is represented twice, but so that the groups of differences are different. There are analytical rules for forming such triplets somewhat analogous to those I have given for forming basic pairs, but their exposition would be lengthy, and I will not discuss them here. One set which will answer our purpose is (1. 12. 5), (2. 3. 10), (4. 6. 9), (8. 11. 7), giving respectively the differences [2, 6, 4], [1, 6, 5], [2, 3, 5], [3, 4, 1]. Now every difference d in a 13 circle will correspond to d or $13 - d$ in a 26 circle, and every residue e in a 13 circle will correspond to e or $13 + e$ in a 26 circle. Further, a triplet in the 26 circle must either have three even differences, or one even and two odd differences. Hence from the above sets we can get the following arrangement for the first day : (1. 25. 5) and (14. 12. 18) with differences [2, 6, 4], (15. 3. 10) and (2. 16. 23) with differences [12, 7, 5], (17. 6. 9) and (4. 19. 22) with differences [11, 3, 8], (21. 11. 20) and (8. 24. 7) with differences [10, 9, 1], (k. 13. 26). From this, by either a one-step or a two-step cyclical permutation of the numbers, an arrangement for 13 days can be got. I will not go into further details about the deduction of other similar solutions. A similar method is always applicable when n is of the form $24m + 3$.

The process by pairing when y is a prime of the form $6u + 1$ is extremely rapid. For instance, in the case of 15 girls we have $n = 15$, $y = 7$, $u = 1$, $x = 5$. The order of the residues is 5, 4, 6, 2, 3, 1. By our rule we can at once arrange basic pairs (5. 4), (6. 2), (3. 1). From these pairs we can obtain numerous solutions. Thus, using scalene triangles as above explained, we get as an arrangement for the first day ($a5. a4. b2$), ($a6. a2. b1$), ($a3. a1. b4$), ($b3. b5. b6$), ($k. a7. b7$), from which, by a one-step cyclical permutation of the numbers, arrangements for the seven days can be obtained. Using the basic pairs as bases of isosceles triangles, we get as an arrangement for the first day ($a5. a4. b1$), ($a6. a2. b4$), ($a3. a1. b2$), ($b3. b5. b6$), ($k. a7. b7$).

Again, take the case of 39 girls. Here we have $n = 39$, $y = 19$, $u = 3$, $x = 3$. The order of the residues is 3, 9, 8;

5, 15, 7 ; 2, 6, 18 ; 16, 10, 11 ; 14, 4, 12 ; 17, 13, 1. The basic pairs are (3. 5), (9. 15), (8. 7), (2. 16), etc. These are the suffixes of the "*a*"s. The possible triplets which determine what "*b*"s are to be associated with these, and what "*b*"s are to be left for the remaining three triangles, can be determined as follows : From the residue series we obtain the derivative series 3, 9, 8, 5, 4, 7, 2, 6, 1, etc. The divisions are (i) 3, 5, 2 ; (ii) 9, 4, 6 ; (iii) 8, 7, 1. A cyclical arrangement like that given above leads to the result in the left half of the following table, which does not satisfy our condition. A cyclical displacement of the symbols in the vertical lines in the first column leads to the arrangement given in the right half of the table, and shows

3. 9. 8	6	2	5	3. 15. 18	7	3	4
5. 15. 7	9	8	2	5. 6. 11	1	5	6
2. 6. 18	4	7	3	2. 10. 12	8	2	9
16. 10. 11	6	1	5	16. 4. 1	7	3	4
14. 4. 12	9	8	2	14. 13. 8	1	5	6
17. 13. 1	6	7	3	17. 9. 7	8	2	9

that (3. 15. 18), (5. 6. 11), etc., are possible triplets. From these results numerous solutions can be deduced in the same way as above. For instance, one solution is (*a*3. *a*.5 *b*4), (*a*9. *a*15. *b*12), (*a*8. *a*7. *b*17), (*a*2. *a*16. *b*9), (*a*6. *a*10. *b*8), (*a*18. *a*11. *b*5), (*a*14. *a*17. *b*6), (*a*4. *a*13. *b*18), (*a*12. *a*1. *b*16), (*b*3. *b*10. *b*1), (*b*2. *b*13. *b*7), (*b*14. *b*15. *b*11), (*k*. *a*19. *b*19).

In the case of 39 girls, we may also extend the method used above by which for 27 girls we obtained the solution (1. 25. 5), (14. 12. 18), ... We thus get a solution for 39 girls as follows : (1. 25. 18), (14. 38. 31), (27. 12. 5) ; (15. 16. 10), (28. 29. 23), (2. 3. 36) ; (17. 19. 35), (30. 32. 9), (4. 6. 22) ; (21. 24. 33), (34. 37. 7), (8. 11. 20) ; (13. 26. 39). From this the arrangements for the first 13 days are obtained either by a one-step or a three-step cyclical permutation of the numbers. The single triplets from each of which an arrangement for one of the other six days is obtainable are (1. 5. 15), (2. 6. 16),

(3. 7. 17) ; (1. 9. 20), (2. 10. 21), (3. 11. 22). From each of these the arrangement for one day is obtainable by a three-step cyclical permutation of the numbers.

These examples of the use of the Focal and Analytical Methods are given only by way of illustration, but they will serve to suggest the applications to other cases. When the number taken as base is composite, the formations of the series used in the Analytical Method may be troublesome, but the principle of the method is not affected, though want of space forbids my going into further details. Eckenstein, to whom the development of this method is mainly due, can, with the aid of a table of primitive roots and sets of numbers written on cards, within half an hour obtain a solution for any case in which n is less than 500, and can within one hour obtain a solution for any case in which n lies between 500 and 900.

Number of Solutions. The problem of 9 girls has been subjected to an exhaustive examination. The number of solutions is 840, if an arrangement on Monday, Tuesday, Wednesday and Thursday, and the same arrangement on (say) Monday, Tuesday, Thursday and Wednesday are regarded as identical. [If they are regarded as different the number of possible independent solutions is 20,160.] Any of these 840 solutions can, however, be deduced from any other of them by interchanges, and thus there is only one fundamental solution. The total number of possible arrangements of the girls in triplets for four days is $(280)^4/(4!)$; hence the probability of obtaining a solution by a chance arrangement is about 1 in 300,000.

In the case of 15 girls, the number of solutions, according to Mulder,* is $65 \times 13!$. The number of fundamental solutions, according to Mulder and Cole,† is seven. The total number of ways in which the girls can walk out for a week in triplets is

---

* P. Mulder, *Kirkman-Systemen* (Groningen Dissertation), Leiden, 1917.
† F. N. Cole, *Bulletin of the American Mathematical Society*, 1922, vol. XXVIII, pp. 435—437.

$(1401400)^7/(7!)$; so the probability that any chance way satisfies the conditions of the problem is less than one in 10^{27}.

Harison's Theorem. If we know solutions for Kirkman's Problem for $3l$ girls and for $3m$ girls we can find a solution for $3lm$ girls. The particular case of this when $l = 1$ was established by Walecki and given in the earlier editions of this work. Harison's proof, given in 1916, of the more general theorem is as follows :—

If the school-girls be denoted by the consecutive numbers from 1 to $3lm$ and the numbers be divided into $3l$ sets, each of m consecutive numbers, each of these sets can, by the method for the $3l$ problem, be divided in $(3l - 1)/2$ collections of groups of three sets, so that every set shall be included once in the same group with every other set.

In one of these collections, each group of three sets (involving $3m$ numbers) can, by the method for the $3m$ problem, be arranged in triplets for $(3m - 1)/2$ days, so as to have each number in each of the sets composing the group included once in the same triplet with every other number in the set to which it belongs and with every number in the other two sets in the group. This will give arrangements of all the numbers for that number of days.

In the remaining $(3l - 3)/2$ collections, each group can be arranged in triplets for m days, so as to have each number in each of the sets composing the group included once in the same triplet with each number of the other two sets. In the first arrangement in each collection, the first triplet in each group is composed of the first number of each set. In the second arrangement, the first triplet is composed of the first number of the first set, the second number of the second set, and the last number of the third set. In every other arrangement the first triplet is formed from the first triplet in the next preceding arrangement, by adding unity to the number of the second set, subtracting unity from the number of the third set, and leaving the number of the first set unchanged. In every arrangement the second and all subsequent triplets are formed cyclically from the next preceding triplet.

The arrangements thus made of the numbers in all the groups of all the collections will give arrangements of all the numbers for $(3lm-1)/2$ days, and will provide a solution of the problem.

Harison's Theorem provides solutions, alternative to those given above, for the cases when $n = 27, 45, 63, 75, 81, 99$. Also we can, by it, from the solutions already given for all values of n less than 100, at once deduce solutions for the cases when $n = 105, 117, 135, 147, 153, 165, 171, 189, 195$, etc.

Extension to n^2 Girls. Peirce suggested the corresponding problem of arranging n^2 girls in n groups, each group containing n girls on $n + 1$ days, so that no two girls will be together in a group on more than one day. We may conveniently represent the girls by a point k at the centre of a circle and $n^2 - 1$ equidistant points, numbered $1, 2, 3, \ldots$, on the circumference.

When $n = 2$, we may arrange initially the 4 points in two pairs, one pair consisting of k and one of the points (say) 3, and the other pair of the remaining points (1. 2). These two pairs give the arrangement for the first day. From them, the solution for the other days is obtained by one-step cyclical permutations.

When $n = 3$, we may arrange initially the 9 points in three triplets—namely, k and the ends of a diameter (k. 4. 8); a triangle (1. 2. 7); and the similar triangle (5. 6. 3) obtained by a four-step cyclical permutation. These three triplets give an arrangement for the first day. From them the solutions for the other days are obtained by one-step cyclical permutations.

When $n = 4$, we may arrange initially the 16 points in four quartets—namely, k and three equidistant points, (k. 5. 10. 15); a quadrilateral (1. 2. 4. 8); and the two similar quadrilaterals (6. 7. 9. 13) and (11. 12. 14. 3) obtained by five-step cyclical permutations. These four quartets give an arrangement for the first day. From them the solutions for the other days are obtained by one-step cyclical permutations.

When $n = 5$, we may arrange initially the 25 points in five quintets—namely, k and four equidistant points, (k. 6. 12. 18. 24); a pentagon (2. 3. 5. 13. 22); and the three similar pentagons (8. 9. 11. 19. 4), (14. 15. 17. 1. 10), (20. 21. 23. 7. 16) obtained by six-step cyclical permutations. These five quintets give an arrangement for the first day. From them the solutions for the other days are obtained by one-step cyclical permutations. There is a second solution (k. 6. 12. 18. 24), (1. 2. 15. 17. 22), etc.

Hitherto the case when $n = 6$ has baffled all attempts to find a solution.

When $n = 7$, we may initially arrange the 49 points in seven groups—namely (k. 8. 16. 24. 32. 40. 48), a group (1. 2. 5. 11. 31. 36. 38) and five similar groups obtained by successive additions of 8 to these numbers. There are three other solutions : in these the second group is either (2. 3. 17. 28. 38. 45. 47), or (3. 4. 6. 18. 23. 41. 45), or (3. 4. 14. 17. 26. 45. 47).

When $n = 8$, there are three solutions. If the first group is (k. 9. 18. 27. 36. 45. 54. 63), the second group is either (1. 2. 4. 8. 16. 21. 32. 42), or (2. 3. 16. 22. 24. 50. 55. 62), or (3. 4. 7. 19. 24. 26. 32. 56), the other groups in each solution being obtained by successive addition of 9 to the numbers in the second group.

When $n = 9$, one solution is as follows. Divide the girls into nine classes, each containing nine girls, denoted by $a1, a2, \ldots a9$; $b1, b2, \ldots b9$; and similarly for the letters c, d, e, f, g, h, k. The arrangement on the first day is made up of the a group, the b group, etc. The arrangement on the second day is of nine groups, as follows : first group, $k1, a5, b3, c8, d7, e9, f4, g6, h2$; second group, $k2, a3, b6, c4, d1, e8, f9, g5, h7$; third group, $k3, a8, b4, c7, d5, e2, f1, g9, h6$; fourth group, $k4, a7, b1, c5, d8, e6, f3, g2, h9$; fifth group, $k5, a9, b8, c2, d6, e1, f7, g4, h3$; sixth group, $k6, a4, b9, c1, d3, e7, f2, g8, h5$; seventh group, $k7, a6, b5, c9, d2, e4, f8, g3, h1$; eighth group, $k8, a2, b7, c6, d9, e3, f5, g1, h4$; ninth group, $k9, a1, b2, c3, d4, e5, f6, g7, h8$. The arrangements for the other eight days are got by shifting the numbers attached to the letters $a, b, \ldots h$ (but not k) in each group cyclically. Thus the first group on the third day will be, $k1$, $a3$, $b8$, $c7$, $d9$, $e4$, $f6$, $g2$, $h5$.

When n is composite, no general method of attacking the problem has been discovered, though solutions for various particular cases have been given. But when n is prime, we can proceed thus. Denote the n^2 girls by the suffixed letters

$k1$,	$k2$,	....	kn.	$k1$,	$a1$,	$b2$,	$c3$,	....
$a1$,	$a2$,	....	an.	$k2$,	$a2$,	$b4$,	$c6$,	....
$b1$,	$b2$,	....	bn,	$k3$,	$a3$,	$b6$,	$c9$,	....
....				....				
....				kn,	an,	bn,	cn,	....
Arrangement on First Day				*Arrangement on Second Day*				

shown in the left half of the above table. Take this as giving the arrangement on the first day. Then on the second day we may take as an arrangement that shown in the right half of the table. From the arrangement on the second day, the arrangements for the other days are obtained by one-step cyclical permutations of the suffixes of a, b, etc.; the suffixes of k being unaltered.

Kirkman's Problem in Quartets. The problem of arranging $4m$ girls, where m is of the form $3n + 1$, in quartets to walk out for $(4m - 1)/3$ days, so that no girl will walk with any of her school-fellows in any quartet more than once, has been attacked. Methods similar to those given above are applicable, and solutions for all cases where m does not exceed 49 have been written out. One example will suffice: for 16 girls (*i.e.* when $m = 4$, $n = 1$), arrangements in quartets for five days can be obtained from the following arrangement for the first day, (k. 5. 10. 15), (8. 2. 1. 4), (13. 7. 6. 9), (3. 12. 11. 14); from which three-step cyclical permutations of the numbers give arrangements for the other days. I conjecture that similar methods are applicable to corresponding problems about quintets, sextets, etc.

Bridge Problem. Another analogous question is where we deal with arrangements in pairs instead of triplets. One problem of this kind is to arrange $4m$ members of a bridge club for $4m - 1$ rubbers so that (i) no two members shall play together as partners more than once, and (ii) each member shall meet every other member as opponent twice. The general theory has been discussed by E. H. Moore, O. Eckenstein and G. A. Miller. A typical method for obtaining cyclic solutions is as follows. Denote the members by a point k at the centre of a circle and by $4m - 1$ equidistant points, numbered 1, 2, 3, . . ., on the circumference. We can join the points 2, 3, 4, . . . by chords, and these chords with (k. 1) give possible partners at the m tables in the first rubber. A one-step cyclical permutation of the numbers will give the arrangements for the other rubbers if, in the initial arrangement, (i) the lengths of the chords representing every pair of partners are unequal and thus appear only once, and (ii) the lengths of the chords representing every pair of opponents appear only twice. Since the chords representing pairs of partners are unequal, their lengths are uniquely determined, but the selection of the chords is partly empirical. Solutions for many values of m have been given. In the following examples for $m = 2$, 3, 4, I give an arrangement of the card-tables for the first rubber, the arrangements for the subsequent rubbers being thence obtained by one-step cyclical permutations of the numbers. If $m = 2$, such an initial arrangement is (k. 1 against 5. 6) and (2. 4 against 3. 7). If $m = 3$, one such initial arrangement is (k. 1 against 5. 6), (2. 11 against 3. 9) and (4. 8 against 7. 10). If $m = 4$, one such initial arrangement is (k. 1 against 6. 11), (2. 3 against 5. 9), (4. 12 against 13. 15), and (7. 10 against 8. 14). There are also solutions by other methods.

Sylvester's Corollary. To the original theorem J. J. Sylvester added the corollary that the school of 15 girls could walk out in triplets on 91 days until every possible triplet had walked abreast once, and he published a solution in 1861.

The generalized problem of finding the number of ways in

which x girls walking in rows of a abreast can be arranged so that every possible combination of b of them may walk abreast once and only once is as yet unsolved. Suppose that this number of ways is y. It is obvious that, if all the x girls are to walk out each day in rows of a abreast, then x must be an exact multiple of a, and the number of rows formed each day is x/a. If such an arrangement can be made for z days, then we have a solution of the problem to arrange x girls to walk out in rows of a abreast for z days so that they all go out each day and so that every possible combination of b girls may walk together once and only once. For instance, if $x = 2n$, $a = 2$, $b = 2$, we have $y = n(2n - 1)/2$, $z = 2n - 1$. If $x = 15$, $a = 3$, $b = 2$, we have $y = 35$; and these 35 rows can be divided into 7 sets, each of which contains all the symbols; hence $z = 7$.

ADDENDUM

Note. Page 267. Here is an explicit solution of Kirkman's Problem in its original form.

Sun.	Mon.	Tues.	Wed.	Thurs.	Fri.	Sat.
1, 2, 3	1, 4, 5	1, 6, 7	1, 8, 9	1, 10, 11	1, 12, 13	1, 14, 15
4, 8, 12	2, 8, 10	2, 9, 11	2, 12, 14	2, 13, 15	2, 4, 6	2, 5, 7
5, 10, 15	3, 13, 14	3, 12, 15	3, 5, 6	3, 4, 7	3, 9, 10	3, 8, 11
6, 11, 13	6, 9, 15	4, 10, 14	4, 11, 15	5, 9, 12	5, 11, 14	4, 9, 13
7, 9, 14	7, 11, 12	5, 8, 13	7, 10, 13	6, 8, 14	7, 8, 15	6, 10, 12

Michael Goldberg has pointed out that these triplets are " safe combinations " in the game of Nim (page 37).

CHAPTER XI

MISCELLANEOUS PROBLEMS

I PROPOSE to discuss in this chapter the mathematical theory of a few common mathematical amusements and games. I might have dealt with them in the first four chapters, but, since most of them involve mixed geometry and algebra, it is rather more convenient to deal with them apart from the problems and puzzles which have been described already ; the arrangement is, however, based on convenience rather than on any logical distinction.

The majority of the questions here enumerated have no connection one with another, and I jot them down almost at random.

I shall discuss in succession the *Fifteen Puzzle*, the *Tower of Hanoï*, *Chinese Rings*, and some miscellaneous *Problems connected with a Pack of Cards*.

THE FIFTEEN PUZZLE *

Some years ago the so-called *Fifteen Puzzle* was on sale in all toy-shops. It consists of a shallow wooden box—one side being marked as the top—in the form of a square, and contains fifteen square blocks or counters numbered 1, 2, 3, . . . up to 15. The box will hold just sixteen such counters, and, as it contains only fifteen, they can be moved about in the box relatively to one another. Initially they are put in the box in any order, but leaving the sixteenth cell or small square empty ; the

---

* There are two articles on the subject in the *American Journal of Mathematics*, 1879, vol. II, by Professors Woolsey Johnson and Storey ; but the whole theory is deducible immediately from the proposition I give in the text.

puzzle is to move them so that finally they occupy the position
shown in the first of the annexed figures.

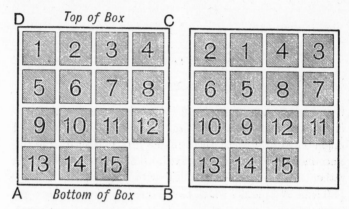

We may represent the various stages in the game by supposing that the blank space, occupying the sixteenth cell, is
moved over the board, ending finally where it started.

The route pursued by the blank space may consist partly of
tracks followed and again retraced, which have no effect on the
arrangement, and partly of closed paths travelled round, which
necessarily are cyclical permutations of an odd number of
counters.   No other motion is possible.

Now, a cyclical permutation of n letters is equivalent to
$n-1$ simple interchanges; accordingly an odd cyclical
permutation is equivalent to an even number of simple interchanges.   Hence, if we move the counters so as to bring the
blank space back into the sixteenth cell, the new order must
differ from the initial order by an even number of simple
interchanges.   If therefore the order we want to get can be
obtained from this initial order only by an odd number of
interchanges, the problem is incapable of solution; if it can be
obtained by an even number, the problem is possible.

Thus the order in the second of the diagrams given above is
deducible from that in the first diagram by six interchanges—
namely, by interchanging the counters 1 and 2, 3 and 4, 5 and

6, 7 and 8, 9 and 10, 11 and 12. Hence the one can be deduced from the other by moving the counters about in the box.

If, however, in the second diagram the order of the last three counters had been 13, 15, 14, then it would have required seven interchanges of counters to bring them into the order given in the first diagram. Hence in this case the problem would be insoluble.

The easiest way of finding the number of simple interchanges necessary in order to obtain one given arrangement from another is to make the transformation by a series of cycles. For example, suppose that we take the counters in the box in any definite order, such as taking the successive rows from left to right, and suppose the original order and the final order to be respectively

$$1, 13, 2, 3, 5, 7, 12, 8, 15, \quad 6, \quad 9, \quad 4, 11, 10, 14,$$
and $\quad 11, \quad 2, 3, 4, 5, 6, \quad 7, 1, \quad 9, 10, 13, 12, \quad 8, 14, 15.$

We can deduce the second order from the first by 12 simple interchanges. The simplest way of seeing this is to arrange the process in three separate cycles as follows :—

$$1, 11, 8; \quad \mid \quad 13, 2, 3, \quad 4, 12, 7, \quad 6, 10, 14, 15, \quad 9; \quad \mid \quad 5.$$
$$11, \quad 8, 1; \quad \mid \quad 2, 3, 4, 12, \quad 7, 6, 10, 14, 15, \quad 9, 13; \quad \mid \quad 5.$$

Thus, if in the first row of figures 11 is substituted for 1, then 8 for 11, then 1 for 8, we have made a cyclical interchange of 3 numbers, which is equivalent to 2 simple interchanges (namely, interchanging 1 and 11, and then 1 and 8). Thus the whole process is equivalent to one cyclical interchange of 3 numbers, another of 11 numbers, and another of 1 number. Hence it is equivalent to $(2 + 10 + 0)$ simple interchanges. This is an even number, and thus one of these orders can be deduced from the other by moving the counters about in the box.

It is obvious that, if the initial order is the same as the required order except that the last three counters are in the order 15, 14, 13, it would require one interchange to put them in the order 13, 14, 15 ; hence the problem is insoluble.

If, however, the box is turned through a right angle, so as to make AD the top, this rotation will be equivalent to 13 simple interchanges. For, if we keep the sixteenth square always blank, then such a rotation would change any order such as

1, 2, 3, 4, 5, 6, 7, 8, 9, 10, 11, 12, 13, 14, 15,

to   13, 9, 5, 1, 14, 10, 6, 2, 15, 11, 7, 3, 12, 8, 4,

which is equivalent to 13 simple interchanges. Hence it will change the arrangement from one where a solution is impossible to one where it is possible, and *vice versa*.

Again, even if the initial order is one which makes a solution impossible, yet if the first cell and not the last is left blank, it will be possible to arrange the fifteen counters in their natural order. For, if we represent the blank cell by b, this will be equivalent to changing the order

1, 2, 3, 4, 5, 6, 7, 8, 9, 10, 11, 12, 13, 14, 15, b,

to b, 1, 2, 3, 4, 5, 6, 7, 8, 9, 10, 11, 12, 13, 14, 15 :

this is a cyclical interchange of 16 things, and therefore is equivalent to 15 simple interchanges. Hence it will change the arrangement from one where a solution is impossible to one where it is possible, and *vice versa*.

So, too, if it were permissible to turn the 6 and the 9 upside down, thus changing them to 9 and 6 respectively, this would be equivalent to one simple interchange, and therefore would change an arrangement where a solution is impossible to one where it is possible.

It is evident that the above principles are applicable equally to a rectangular box containing mn cells or spaces and $mn - 1$ counters which are numbered. Of course, m may be equal to n. When m and n are both even (and in certain other cases, such as $m = 3$, $n = 5$), the operation of turning the box through a right angle is equivalent to an odd number of simple interchanges, and thus will change an impossible position to a possible one, and *vice versa*. Similarly, if m and n are not both odd, and it is impossible to solve the problem when the last call is left blank, then it will be possible to solve it by leaving the first cell blank.

The problem may be made more difficult by limiting the possible movements by fixing bars inside the box which will prevent the movement of a counter transverse to their directions. We can conceive also of a similar cubical puzzle, but we could not work it practically except by sections.

The Tower of Hanoï

I may mention next the ingenious puzzle known as the *Tower of Hanoï*. It was brought out in 1883 by M. Claus (Lucas).

It consists of three pegs fastened to a stand, and of eight circular discs of wood or cardboard, each of which has a hole in the middle through which a peg can be passed. These discs are of different radii, and initially they are placed all on one peg, so that the biggest is at the bottom, and the radii of the successive discs decrease as we ascend : thus the smallest disc is at the top. This arrangement is called the *Tower*. The problem is to shift the discs from one peg to another in such a way that a disc shall never rest on one smaller than itself, and finally to transfer the tower (*i.e.* all the discs in their proper order) from the peg on which they initially rested to one of the other pegs.

The method of effecting this is as follows. (i) If initially there are n discs on the peg A, the first operation is to transfer gradually the top $n - 1$ discs from the peg A to the peg B, leaving the peg C vacant : suppose that this requires x separate transfers. (ii) Next, move the bottom disc to the peg C. (iii) Then, reversing the first process, transfer gradually the $n - 1$ discs from B to C, which will necessitate x transfers. Hence, if it requires x transfers of simple discs to move a tower of $n - 1$ discs, then it will require $2x + 1$ separate transfers of single discs to move a tower of n discs. Now, with 2 discs it requires 3 transfers, *i.e.* $2^2 - 1$ transfers; hence with 3 discs the number of transfers required will be $2(2^2 - 1) + 1$, that is, $2^3 - 1$. Proceeding in this way, we see that with a tower of n discs it will require $2^n - 1$ transfers of single discs to effect the complete transfer. Thus the eight discs of the puzzle will require 255 single transfers. It will be noticed that every alternate move consists of a transfer of the smallest disc from one peg to another, the pegs being taken in cyclical order; further, if the discs be numbered consecutively 1, 2, 3, ... beginning with the smallest, all those with odd numbers rotate in one direction, and all those with even numbers in the other direction.

Obviously, the discs may be replaced by cards numbered 1, 2, 3, ... n; and if n is not greater than 10, playing-cards may be conveniently used.

De Parville gave an account of the origin of the toy which is a sufficiently pretty conceit to deserve repetition.* In the great temple at Benares, says he, beneath the dome which marks the centre of the world, rests a brass plate in which are fixed three diamond needles, each a cubit high and as thick as the body of a bee. On one of these needles, at the creation, God placed sixty-four discs of pure gold, the largest disc resting on the brass plate, and the others getting smaller and smaller up to the top one. This is the Tower of Bramah. Day and night unceasingly the priests transfer the discs from one diamond needle to another according to the fixed and immutable laws of Bramah, which require that the priest on duty must not move more than one disc at a time and that he must place this disc on a needle so that there is no smaller disc below it. When the sixty-four discs shall have been thus transferred from the needle on which at the creation God placed them to one of the other needles, tower, temple, and Brahmins alike will crumble into dust, and with a thunderclap the world will vanish.

The number of separate transfers of single discs which the Brahmins must make to effect the transfer of the tower is

* *La Nature*, Paris, 1884, part I, pp. 285—286.

$2^{64} - 1$, that is, is 18,446744,073709,551615 : a number which, even if the priests never made a mistake, would require many thousands of millions of years to carry out.

CHINESE RINGS *

A somewhat more elaborate toy, known as *Chinese Rings*, which is on sale in most English toy-shops, is represented in the accompanying figure. It consists of a number of rings hung upon a bar in such a manner that the ring at one end (say *A*)

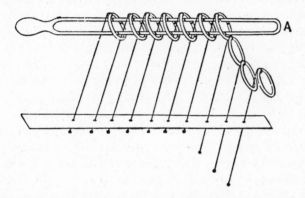

can be taken off or put on the bar at pleasure ; but any other ring can be taken off or put on only when the one next to it towards *A* is on, and all the rest towards *A* are off the bar. The order of the rings cannot be changed.

Only one ring can be taken off or put on at a time. [In the toy, as usually sold, the first two rings form an exception to the rule. Both these can be taken off or put on together. To simplify the discussion I shall assume at first that only one ring is taken off or put on at a time.] I proceed to show that, if there are *n* rings, then, in order to disconnect them from the

* This was described by Cardan in 1550 in his *De Subtilitate*, bk. xv, paragraph 2, ed. Sponius. vol. III, p. 587; by Wallis in his *Algebra*, Latin edition, 1693, *Opera*, vol. II, chap. cxi, pp. 472—478; and allusion is made to it also in Ozanam's *Récréations*, 1723 edition, vol. IV, p. 439.

bar, it will be necessary to take a ring off or to put a ring on either $\frac{1}{3}(2^{n+1} - 1)$ times or $\frac{1}{3}(2^{n+1} - 2)$ times, according as n is odd or even.

Let the taking a ring off the bar or putting a ring on the bar be called a *step*. It is usual to number the rings from the free end A. Let us suppose that we commence with the first m rings off the bar and all the rest on the bar; and suppose that then it requires $x - 1$ steps to take off the next ring—that is, it requires $x - 1$ additional steps to arrange the rings so that the first $m + 1$ of them are off the bar and all the rest are on it. Before taking these steps we can take off the $(m + 2)$th ring, and thus it will require x steps from our initial position to remove the $(m + 1)$th and $(m + 2)$th rings.

Suppose that these x steps have been made, and that thus the first $m + 2$ rings are off the bar and the rest on it, and let us find how many additional steps are now necessary to take off the $(m + 3)$th and $(m + 4)$th rings. To take these off, we begin by taking off the $(m + 4)$th ring: this requires 1 step. Before we can take off the $(m + 3)$th ring we must arrange the rings so that the $(m + 2)$th ring is on and the first $m + 1$ rings are off: to effect this, (i) we must get the $(m + 1)$th ring on and the first m rings off, which requires $x - 1$ steps, (ii) then we must put on the $(m + 2)$th ring, which requires 1 step, (iii) and lastly we must take the $(m + 1)$th ring off, which requires $x - 1$ steps: these movements require in all $\{2(x - 1) + 1\}$ steps. Next we can take the $(m + 3)$th ring off, which requires 1 step; this leaves us with the first $m + 1$ rings off, the $(m + 2)$th on, the $(m + 3)$th and $(m + 4)$th off, and all the rest on. Finally, to take off the $(m + 2)$th ring, (i) we get the $(m + 1)$th ring on and the first m rings off, which requires $x - 1$ steps, (ii) we take off the $(m + 2)$th ring, which requires 1 step, (iii) we take the $(m + 1)$th ring off, which requires $x - 1$ steps: these movements require $\{2(x - 1) + 1\}$ steps.

Therefore, if when the first m rings are off it requires x steps to take off the $(m + 1)$th and $(m + 2)$th rings, then the number of additional steps required to take off the $(m + 3)$th

and $(m+4)$th rings is $1 + \{2(x-1)+1\} + 1 + \{2(x-1)+1\}$
—that is, is $4x$.

To find the whole number of steps necessary to take off an odd number of rings we proceed as follows.

To take off the first ring requires 1 step;

$\therefore$ to take off the first 3 rings requires 4 additional steps;

$\therefore$,, ,, 5 ,, ,, 4^2 ,, ,,

In this way we see that the number of steps required to take off the first $2n+1$ rings is $1 + 4 + 4^2 + \ldots + 4^n$, which is equal to $\frac{1}{3}(2^{2n+2} - 1)$.

To find the number of steps necessary to take off an even number of rings we proceed in a similar manner.

To take off the first 2 rings requires 2 steps;

$\therefore$ to take off the first 4 rings requires 2×4 additional steps;

$\therefore$,, ,, ,, 6 ,, ,, 2×4^2 ,, ,,

In this way we see that the number of steps required to take off the first $2n$ rings is $2 + (2 \times 4) + (2 \times 4^2) + \ldots + (2 \times 4^{n-1})$, which is equal to $\frac{1}{3}(2^{2n+1} - 2)$.

If we take off or put on the first two rings in one step instead of two separate steps, these results become respectively 2^{2n} and $2^{2n-1} - 1$.

I give the above analysis because it is the direct solution of a problem attacked unsuccessfully by Cardan in 1550 and by Wallis in 1693, and which at one time attracted some attention.

I proceed next to give another solution, more elegant, though rather artificial. This, which is due to Monsieur Gros,* depends on a convention by which any position of the rings is denoted by a certain number expressed in the binary scale of notation in such a way that a step is indicated by the addition or subtraction of unity.

Let the rings be indicated by circles : if a ring is on the bar, it is represented by a circle drawn above the bar; if the ring is off the bar, it is represented by a circle below the bar. Thus figure i below represents a set of seven rings, of which the first

* *Théorie du Baguenodier*, by L. Gros, Lyons, 1872. I take the account of this from Lucas, vol. I, part 7.

two are off the bar, the next three are on it, the sixth is off it, and the seventh is on it.

Denote the rings which are on the bar by the digits 1 or 0 alternately, reckoning from left to right, and denote a ring which is off the bar by the digit assigned to that ring on the bar which is nearest to it on the left of it, or by a 0 if there is no ring to the left of it.

Thus the three positions indicated below are denoted respectively by the numbers written below them. The position represented in figure ii is obtained from that in figure i by putting the first ring on to the bar, while the position represented in figure iii is obtained from that in figure i by taking the fourth ring off the bar.

It follows that every position of the rings is denoted by a number expressed in the binary scale : moreover, since in going from left to right every ring on the bar gives a variation (that is, 1 to 0, or 0 to 1) and every ring off the bar gives a continuation, the effect of a step by which a ring is taken off or put on the bar is either to subtract unity from this number or to add unity to it. For example, the number denoting the position of the rings in figure ii is obtained from the number denoting that in figure i by adding unity to it. Similarly the number denoting the position of the rings in figure iii is obtained from the number denoting that in figure i by subtracting unity from it.

| 1101000 | 1101001 | 1100111 |
| Figure i. | Figure ii. | Figure iii. |

The position when all the seven rings are off the bar is denoted by the number 0000000 : when all of them are on the bar, by the number 1010101. Hence to change from one position to the other requires a number of steps equal to the difference between these two numbers in the binary scale. The first of these numbers is 0 : the second is equal to $2^6 +$

$2^4 + 2^2 + 1$—that is, to 85. Therefore 85 steps are required. In a similar way we may show that to put on a set of $2n + 1$ rings requires $(1 + 2^2 + \ldots + 2^{2n})$ steps—that is, $\frac{1}{3}(2^{2n+2} - 1)$ steps—and to put on a set of $2n$ rings requires $(2 + 2^3 + \ldots + 2^{2n-1})$ steps—that is, $\frac{1}{3}(2^{2n+1} - 2)$ steps.

I append a table indicating the steps necessary to take off the first four rings from a set of five rings. The diagrams in the middle column show the successive position of the rings

Initial position		10101
After 1st step		10110 ⎫
,, 2nd ,,		10111 ⎬
,, 3rd ,,		11000
,, 4th ,,		11001 ⎫
,, 5th ,,		11010 ⎬
,, 6th ,,		11011
,, 7th ,,		11100
,, 8th ,,		11101
,, 9th ,,		11110 ⎫
,, 10th ,,		11111 ⎬

after each step. The number following each diagram indicates that position, each number being obtained from the one above it by the addition of unity. The steps which are bracketed together can be made in one movement, and, if thus effected, the whole process is completed in 7 movements instead of 10 steps: this is in accordance with the formula given above.

Gros asserted that it is possible to take from 64 to 80 steps a minute, which in my experience is a rather high estimate. If we accept the lower of these numbers, it would be possible to take off 10 rings in less than 8 minutes; to take off 25 rings would require more than 582 days, each of ten hours' work; and to take off 60 rings would necessitate no less than 768614,336404,564650 steps, and would require nearly 55000,000000 years' work—assuming, of course, that no mistakes were made.

PROBLEMS CONNECTED WITH A PACK OF CARDS

An ordinary pack of playing-cards can be used to illustrate many questions depending on simple properties of numbers, or involving the relative position of the cards. In problems of this kind, the principle of solution generally consists in re-arranging the pack in a particular manner so as to bring the card into some definite position. Any such rearrangement is a species of shuffling.

I shall treat in succession of problems connected with *Shuffling a Pack, Arrangements by Rows and Columns*, the *Determination of a Pair out of* $\frac{1}{2}n(n+1)$ *Pairs, Gergonne's Pile Problem*, the *Window Reader*, and the game known as the *Mouse Trap*.

SHUFFLING A PACK

Any system of *shuffling a pack* of cards, if carried out consistently, leads to an arrangement which can be calculated; but tricks that depend on it generally require considerable technical skill.

Suppose, for instance, that a pack of n cards is shuffled, as is not unusual, by placing the second card on the first, the third below these, the fourth above them, and so on. The theory of this system of shuffling is due to Monge.* The following are some of the results, and are not difficult to prove directly.

* Monge's investigations are printed in the *Mémoires de l'Académie des Sciences*, Paris, 1773, pp. 390—412. Among those who have studied the subject afresh I may in particular mention V. Bouniakowski, *Bulletin physico-mathématique de St. Pétersbourg*, 1857, vol. xv. pp. 202—205, summarized in the *Nouvelles annales de mathématiques*, 1858, *Bulletin*, pp. 66—67; T. de St. Laurent, *Mémoires de l'Académie de Gard*, 1865; L. Tanner, *Educational Times Reprints*, 1880, vol. xxxii, pp. 73—75; M. J. Bourget, *Liouville's Journal*, 1882, pp. 413—434; H. F. Baker, *Transactions of the British Association for* 1910, pp. 526—528; and P. H. Cowell, *The Field* 2 April, 1921, p. 444.

One shuffle of a pack of $2p$ cards will move the card which was in the x_0th place to the x_1th place, where $x_1 = \frac{1}{2}(2p + x_0 + 1)$ if x_0 is odd, and $x_1 = \frac{1}{2}(2p - x_0 + 2)$ if x_0 is even. For instance, if a complete pack of 52 cards is shuffled as described above, the eighteenth card will remain the eighteenth card. If an écarté pack of 32 cards is so shuffled, the seventh and the twentieth cards will change places.

By repeated applications of the above formulae we can show that the effect of m such shuffles is to move the card which was initially in the x_0th place to the x_mth place, where

$$2^{m+1}x_m = (4p+1)(2^{m-1} \pm 2^{m-2} \pm \ldots \pm 2 \pm 1) \pm 2x_0 + 2^m \pm 1,$$

the sign $\pm$ representing an ambiguity of sign.

Again, in any pack of n cards, after a certain number of shufflings, not greater than n, the cards will return to their primitive order. This will always be the case as soon as the original top card occupies that position again. To determine the number of shuffles required for a pack of $2p$ cards, it is sufficient to put $x_m = x_0$ and find the smallest value of m which satisfies the resulting equation for all values of x_0 from 1 to $2p$.

The result can, however, be obtained more easily if the cards are numbered from the bottom of the original pack. Doing this, we can show that if after s shuffles a card is in the rth place from the bottom, its original number from the bottom was the difference between $2^s \times r$ and the nearest multiple of $4p + 1$. Hence, if m shuffles are required to restore the original order, m is the least number for which $2^m + 1$ or $2^m - 1$ is divisible by $4p + 1$. The number for a pack of $2p + 1$ cards is the same as that for a pack of $2p$ cards. With an écarté pack of 32 cards, six shuffles are sufficient; with a pack of 2^n cards, $n + 1$ shuffles are sufficient; with a full pack of 52 cards, twelve shuffles are sufficient; with a pack of 13 cards, ten shuffles are sufficient; while with a pack of 50 cards, fifty shuffles are required; and so on.

W. H. H. Hudson * has also shown that, whatever is the law

---

* *Educational Times Reprints*, London, 1865, vol. II, p. 105.

of shuffling, yet if it is repeated again and again on a pack of n cards, the cards will ultimately fall into their initial positions after a number of shufflings not greater than the greatest possible L.C.M. of all numbers whose sum is n.

For suppose that any particular position is occupied after the 1st, 2nd, ..., pth shuffles by the cards A_1, A_2, ..., A_p respectively, and that initially the position is occupied by the card A_0. Suppose further that after the pth shuffle A_0 returns to its initial position, therefore $A_0 = A_p$. Then at the second shuffling A_2 succeeds A_1 by the same law by which A_1 succeeded A_0 at the first; hence it follows that previous to the second shuffling A_2 must have been in the place occupied by A_1 previous to the first. Thus the cards which after the successive shuffles take the place initially occupied by A_1 are A_2, A_3, ..., A_p, A_1—that is, after the pth shuffle A_1 has returned to the place initially occupied by it : and so for all the other cards A_2, A_3, ..., A_{p-1}.

Hence the cards A_1, A_2, ..., A_p form a cycle of p cards, one or other of which is always in one or other of p positions in the pack, and which go through all their changes in p shufflings. Let the number n of the pack be divided into p, q, r, ... such cycles, whose sum is n; then the L.C.M. of p, q, r, ... is the utmost number of shufflings necessary before all the cards will be brought back to their original places. In the case of a pack of 52 cards, the greatest L.C.M. of numbers whose sum is 52 is 180180.

ARRANGEMENTS BY ROWS AND COLUMNS

A not uncommon trick, which rests on a species of shuffling, depends on the obvious fact that if n^2 cards are arranged in the form of a square of n rows, each containing n cards, then any card will be defined if the row and the column in which it lies are mentioned.

This information is generally elicited by first asking in which row the selected card lies, and noting the extreme left-hand card of that row. The cards in each column are then taken up, face upwards, one at a time, beginning with the lowest card of each column and taking the columns in their order from right to left—each card taken up being placed on the top of those previously taken up. The cards are then dealt out again in rows, from left to right, beginning with the top left-hand corner, and a question is put as to which row contains the card. The selected card will be that card in the row mentioned which is in the same vertical column as the card which was originally noted.

The trick is improved by allowing the pack to be cut as often as is liked before the cards are re-dealt, and then giving one cut at the end so as to make the top card in the pack one of those originally in the top row. For instance, take the case of 16

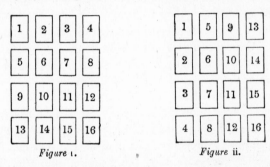

Figure i.   *Figure* ii.

cards. The first and second arrangements may be represented by figures i and ii. Suppose we are told that in figure i the card is in the third row, it must be either 9, 10, 11, 12 : hence, if we know in which row of figure ii it lies, it is determined. If we allow the pack to be cut between the deals, we must secure somehow that the top card is either 1, 2, 3, or 4, since that will leave the cards in each row of figure ii unaltered though the positions of the rows will be changed.

DETERMINATION OF A SELECTED PAIR OF CARDS OUT OF $\frac{1}{2}n(n + 1)$ GIVEN PAIRS *

Another common trick is to throw twenty cards on to a table in ten couples, and ask someone to select one couple. The cards

---

* Bachet, problem XVII, avertissement, pp. 146 *et seq.*

are then taken up, and dealt out in a certain manner into four rows each containing five cards.   If the rows which contain the given cards are indicated, the cards selected are known at once.

This depends on the fact that the number of homogeneous products of two dimensions which can be formed out of four things is 10.   Hence the homogeneous products of two dimensions formed out of four things can be used to define ten things.

Suppose that ten couples of cards are placed on a table and

someone selects one couple.   Take up the cards in their couples.   Then the first two cards form the first couple, the next two the second couple, and so on.   Deal them out in four rows each containing five cards according to the scheme shown above.

The first couple (1 and 2) are in the first row.   Of the next couple (3 and 4), put one in the first row and one in the second. Of the next couple (5 and 6), put one in the first row and one in the third, and so on, as indicated in the diagram.   After filling up the first row proceed similarly with the second row, and so on.

Enquire in which rows the two selected cards appear.   If only one line, the mth, is mentioned as containing the cards, then the required pair of cards are the mth and $(m + 1)$th cards in that line.   These occupy the clue squares of that line. Next, if two lines are mentioned, then proceed as follows.   Let the two lines be the pth and the qth and suppose $q > p$. Then that one of the required cards which is in the qth line will be the $(q - p)$th card which is below the first of the clue squares in the pth line. The other of the required cards is in the pth line, and is the $(q - p)$th card to the right of the second of the clue squares.

Bachet's rule, in the form in which I have given it, is applicable to a pack of $n(n + 1)$ cards divided into couples, and dealt in n rows each containing $n + 1$ cards; for there are $\frac{1}{2}n(n + 1)$ such couples, also there are $\frac{1}{2}n(n + 1)$ homogeneous products of two dimensions which can be formed out of n things. Bachet gave the diagrams for the cases of 20, 30, and 42 cards : these the reader will have no difficulty in constructing for himself, and I have enunciated the rule for 20 cards in a form which covers all the cases.

I have seen the same trick performed by means of a sentence and not by numbers. If we take the case of ten couples, then, after collecting the pairs, the cards must be dealt in four rows each containing five cards, in the order indicated by the sentence *Matas dedit nomen Cocis.* This sentence must be imagined as written on the table, each word forming one line. The first card is dealt on the M. The next card (which is the pair of the first) is placed on the second m in the sentence—that is, third in the third row. The third card is placed on the a. The fourth card (which is the pair of the third) is placed on the second a—that is, fourth in the first row. Each of the next two cards is placed on a t, and so on. Enquire in which rows the two selected cards appear. If two rows are mentioned, the two cards are on the letters common to the words that make these rows. If only one row is mentioned, the cards are on the two letters common to that row.

The reason is obvious : let us denote each of the first pair by an a, and similarly each of any of the other pairs by an e, i, o, c, d, m, n, s, or t respectively. Now the sentence *Matas dedit nomen Cocis* contains four words each of five letters; ten letters are used, and each letter is repeated only twice. Hence, if two of the words are mentioned, they will have one letter in common, or, if one word is mentioned, it will have two like letters.

To perform the same trick with any other number of cards we should require a different sentence.

The number of homogeneous products of three dimensions which can be formed out of four things is 20, and of these the number consisting of products in which three things are alike and those in which three things are different is 8. This leads to a trick with 8 trios of things, which is similar to that last given—the cards being arranged in the order indicated by the sentence *Lanata levete livini novoto*.

I believe that these arrangements by sentences are well-known, but I am not aware who invented them.

Gergonne's Pile Problem

Before discussing Gergonne's theorem I will describe the familiar three-pile problem, the theory of which is included in his results.

The Three-Pile Problem.* This trick is usually performed as follows. Take 27 cards and deal them into three piles, face upwards. By "dealing" is to be understood that the top card is placed as the bottom card of the first pile, the second card in the pack as the bottom card of the second pile, the third card as the bottom card of the third pile, the fourth card on the top of the first one, and so on: moreover, I assume that throughout the problem the cards are held in the hand face upwards. The result can be modified to cover any other way of dealing.

Request a spectator to note a card, and remember in which pile it is. After finishing the deal, ask in which pile the card is. Take up the three piles, placing that pile between the other two. Deal again as before, and repeat the question as to which pile contains the given card. Take up the three piles again, placing the pile which now contains the selected card between the other two. Deal again as before, but in dealing note the middle card of each pile. Ask again, for the third

* The trick is mentioned by Bachet, problem XVIII, p. 143, but his analysis of it is insufficient.

time, in which pile the card lies, and you will know that the
card was the one which you noted as being the middle card of
that pile. The trick can be finished then in any way that you
like. The usual method—but a very clumsy one—is to take
up the three piles once more, placing the named pile between
the other two as before, when the selected card will be the
middle one in the pack—that is, if 27 cards are used it will be
the 14th card.

The trick is often performed with 15 cards or with 21 cards,
in either of which cases the same rule holds.

Gergonne's Generalization. The general theory for a pack
of m^m cards was given by M. Gergonne.* Suppose the pack is
arranged in m piles, each containing m^{m-1} cards, and that, after
the first deal, the pile indicated as containing the selected card
is taken up ath; after the second deal, is taken up bth; and so
on, and finally after the mth deal, the pile containing the card
is taken up kth. Then when the cards are collected after the
mth deal, the selected card will be nth from the top where

$$\text{if } m \text{ is even, } n = km^{m-1} - jm^{m-2} + \ldots + bm - a + 1,$$
$$\text{if } m \text{ is odd, } \ n = km^{m-1} - jm^{m-2} + \ldots - bm + a.$$

For example, if a pack of 256 cards (*i.e.* $m = 4$) was given,
and anyone selected a card out of it, the card could be determined by making four successive deals into four piles of
64 cards each, and after each deal asking in which pile the
selected card lay. The reason is that after the first deal you
know it is one of 64 cards. In the next deal these 64 cards
are distributed equally over the four piles, and therefore, if
you know in which pile it is, you will know that it is one of
16 cards. After the third deal you know it is one of 4 cards.
After the fourth deal you know which card it is.

Moreover, if the pack of 256 cards is used, it is immaterial
in what order the pile containing the selected card is taken up
after a deal. For, if after the first deal it is taken up ath,

---

* Gergonne's *Annales de Mathématiques*, Nîmes, 1813—1814, vol. IV,
pp. 276—283.

after the second bth, after the third cth, and after the fourth dth, the card will be the $(64d - 16c + 4b - a + 1)$th from the top of the pack, and thus will be known. We need not take up the cards after the fourth deal, for the same argument will show that it is the $(64 - 16c + 4b - a + 1)$th in the pile then indicated as containing it. Thus if $a = 3, b = 4, c = 1, d = 2$, it will be the 62nd card in the pile indicated after the fourth deal as containing it, and will be the 126th card in the pack as then collected.

In exactly the same way a pack of 27 cards may be used, and three successive deals, each into three piles of 9 cards, will suffice to determine the card. If after the deals the pile indicated as containing the given card is taken up ath, bth, and cth, respectively, then the card will be the $(9c - 3b + a)$th in the pack or will be the $(9 - 3b + a)$th card in the pile indicated after the third deal as containing it.

The method of proof will be illustrated sufficiently by considering the usual case of a pack of 27 cards, for which $m = 3$, which are dealt into three piles each of 9 cards.

Suppose that, after the first deal, the pile containing the selected card is taken up ath: then (i) at the top of the pack there are $a - 1$ piles each containing 9 cards; (ii) next there are 9 cards, of which one is the selected card; and (iii) lastly there are the remaining cards of the pack. The cards are dealt out now for the second time: in each pile the bottom $3(a - 1)$ cards will be taken from (i), the next 3 cards from (ii), and the remaining $9 - 3a$ cards from (iii).

Suppose that the pile now indicated as containing the selected card is taken up bth: then (i) at the top of the pack are $9(b - 1)$ cards; (ii) next are $9 - 3a$ cards; (iii) next are 3 cards, of which one is the selected card; and (iv) lastly are the remaining cards of the pack. The cards are dealt out now for the third time: in each pile the bottom $3(b - 1)$ cards will be taken from (i), the next $3 - a$ cards will be taken from (ii), the next card will be one of the 3 cards in (iii), and the remaining $8 - 3b + a$ cards are from (iv).

Hence, after this deal, as soon as the pile is indicated, it is known that the card is the $(9 - 3b + a)$th from the top of that pile. If the process is continued by taking up this pile as cth, then the selected card will come out in the place $9(c - 1) + (8 - 3b + a) + 1$ from the top—that is, will come out as the $(9c - 3b + a)$th card.

Since, after the third deal, the position of the card in the pile then indicated is known, it is easy to notice the card, in which case the trick can be finished in some way more effective than dealing again.

If we put the pile indicated always in the middle of the pack, we have $a = 2$, $b = 2$, $c = 2$, hence $n = 9c - 3b + a = 14$, which is the form in which the trick is usually presented, as was explained above on page 316.

I have shown that if a, b, c are known, then n is determined. We may modify the rule so as to make the selected card come out in any assigned position—say the nth. In this case we have to find values of a, b, c which will satisfy the equation $n = 9c - 3b + a$, where a, b, c can have only the values 1, 2, or 3.

Hence, if we divide n by 3 and the remainder is 1 or 2, this remainder will be a; but, if the remainder is 0, we must decrease the quotient by unity so that the remainder is 3, and this remainder will be a. In other words, a is the smallest positive number (exclusive of zero) which must be subtracted from n to make the difference a multiple of 3.

Next let p be this multiple—i.e. p is the next lowest integer to $n/3$: then $3p = 9c - 3b$, therefore $p = 3c - b$. Hence b is the smallest positive number (exclusive of zero) which must be added to p to make the sum a multiple of 3, and c is that multiple.

A couple of illustrations will make this clear. Suppose we wish the card to come out 22nd from the top, therefore $22 = 9c - 3b + a$. The smallest number which must be subtracted from 22 to leave a multiple of 3 is 1, therefore $a = 1$. Hence $22 = 9c - 3b + 1$, therefore $7 = 3c - b$. The smallest number which must be added to 7 to make a multiple of 3 is 2, therefore $b = 2$. Hence $7 = 3c - 2$, therefore $c = 3$. Thus $a = 1, b = 2, c = 3$.

Again, suppose the card is to come out 21st. Hence $21 = 9c - 3b + a$. Therefore a is the smallest number which subtracted from 21 makes a multiple of 3, therefore $a = 3$. Hence $6 = 3c - b$. Therefore b is the smallest number which added to 6 makes a multiple of 3, therefore $b = 3$. Hence $9 = 3c$, therefore $c = 3$. Thus $a = 3, b = 3, c = 3$.

If any difficulty is experienced in this work, we can proceed thus. Let $a = x + 1$, $b = 3 - y$, $c = z + 1$; then x, y, z may have only the values 0, 1, or 2. In this case Gergonne's equation takes the form $9z + 3y + x = n - 1$. Hence, if $n - 1$ is expressed in the ternary scale of notation, x, y, z will be determined, and therefore a, b, c will be known.

The rule in the case of a pack of m^m cards is exactly similar. We want to make the card come out in a given place. Hence, in Gergonne's formula, we are given n and we have to find $a, b, \ldots, k$. We can effect this by dividing n continually by m, with the convention that the remainders are to be alternately positive and negative, and that their numerical values are to be not greater than m or less than unity.

An analogous theorem with a pack of lm cards can be constructed. C. T. Hudson and L. E. Dickson * have discussed the general case where such a pack is dealt n times, each time into l piles of m cards; and they have shown how the piles must be taken up in order that after the nth deal the selected card may be rth from the top.

The principle will be sufficiently illustrated by one example treated in a manner analogous to the cases already discussed. For instance, suppose that an écarté pack of 32 cards is dealt into four piles each of 8 cards, and that the pile which contains some selected card is picked up ath. Suppose that on dealing

---

* *Educational Times Reprints*, 1868, vol. IX, pp. 89—91; and *Bulletin* of the American Mathematical Society, New York, April, 1895, vol. I, pp. 184—186.

again into four piles, one pile is indicated as containing the
selected card, the selected card cannot be one of the bottom
$2(a-1)$ cards, or of the top $8-2a$ cards, but must be one of
the intermediate 2 cards, and the trick can be finished in any
way, as for instance by the common conjuring ambiguity of
asking someone to choose one of them, leaving it doubtful
whether the one he takes is to be rejected or retained.

M. R. Goormaghtigh* has determined the condition which
l and m must satisfy in order that a selected card may be
located by dealing three times into l piles of m, the indicated
pile being taken up second every time. The condition is
$[(m+h)/l] = [(m+k)/l]$ $(= p$, say), where $h = [m/l]$ and
and $k = [(2m-1)/l]$. The selected card is then the $(p+1)$th
in the pile indicated after the third deal. For an ordinary
pack of 52 cards, we may take $l = 4$, $m = 13$; then $h = 3$,
$k = 6$, and $p = 4$, so that after three deals the selected card
will be the fifth in the indicated pile.

THE WINDOW READER

Some years ago a set of 8 numbered and perforated cards
was brought out which enabled an operator to state a number
chosen by a spectator. Of the 8 cards each of the first 7 was
pierced with window-like openings, each of the last 7 contained
some of the numbers less than 100 headed by the word *Yes*,
each of the last 3 had also certain digits on its back, and the
first of the cards was headed with the word *Top*. Each card
if turned upside down bore on what was then its top the word
No.

The cards were employed to determine any number less
than 100 chosen by someone—say, A. They were used by B
thus. B first laid on the table the card numbered 1 with the
side marked *Top* uppermost. B then took the second card,
and asked A if the chosen number was on it; if A said yes,
B placed the card 2 on the top of the card 1 with the *Yes*
uppermost; and if A said no, B turned the card round and

* *Sphinx*, 1936, pp. 113—115.

placed it with the *No* uppermost. *B* then asked if the chosen number was on the third card, and placed it on the top of 2 with the appropriate end uppermost; and so on with the rest of the cards 4 to 8. Finally, on turning the whole pile over, the chosen number was seen through the windows.

The puzzle must have been widely circulated. It was sold in Italy and Germany as well as in London. The method used is fairly obvious, and I will leave to any reader, sufficiently interested, the task of constructing cards suitable for the purpose.

Evidently, however, any number not exceeding 128 can be determined by only 7 cards, each bearing 64 selected numbers. For the first card serves to divide the numbers into two sets of 64 numbers, numbers on the second card can be chosen so as to divide each of these into two sets of 32 cards, the third divides each of these into two sets of 16 cards, and so on. The numbers must be written on the cards and the windows cut so that after arranging the cards in their proper order, and turning the pack over, the chosen number appears on the back of the seventh card as seen through the windows cut in the first 6 cards. To arrange the numbers in this way presents no difficulty, but the geometrical problem of cutting the windows is less easy. I give one solution.

If we work with 7 cards, one way of preparing them is as follows. We write under the word *Yes* on the first card, the 64 numbers 1 to 32, 65 to 96; on the second card, the numbers 1 to 16, 33 to 48, 65 to 80, 97 to 112; on the third card, the numbers in four arithmetical progressions starting from 1, 2, 5, 6, each of 16 terms, with 8 as difference; on the fourth card, the numbers in eight arithmetical progressions starting from 1, 2, 3, 4, 5, 6, 7, 8, each of 8 terms, with 16 as difference; on the fifth card, the odd numbers from 1 to 127; on the sixth card, the numbers in four arithmetical progressions starting from 1, 2, 3, 4, each of 16 terms, with 8 as difference; and on the seventh card the consecutive numbers from 1 to 64; on this card, however, the *No* must be written on the left-hand edge of the card, and not on its lowest edge. On the back of the last card we must now write the numbers from 1 to 128 in their natural order, 1 to 32 occupying the first quarter, 33 to 64 the fourth quarter, 65 to 96 the second quarter rotated through a right angle, and 97 to 128 the third quarter also rotated through a right angle. The spacing of the figures requires care, but is not difficult if the principle of construction is grasped and squared paper used.

The windows should be cut as follows. We will suppose that we use squared paper dividing each card into four equal quadrants with margins. In the first card, we form the window by cutting out the whole of the second quadrant. In the second card, we get two windows by cutting out the top half of the second quadrant and the top half of the third quadrant. In the third card, we get two windows by cutting out the right half of the second quadrant and the right half of the third quadrant. In the fourth card, we divide the second and third quadrants into four equal horizontal strips, and from each of these quadrants cut out the first and third strips. In the fifth card, we divide the second and third quadrants into four equal vertical strips, and from each of these quadrants cut out the second and fourth of these strips. In the sixth card, we divide the second and third quadrants into eight horizontal strips, and from each of these quadrants cut out the first, third, fifth, and seventh strips.

It will be noticed that no windows are cut in the first or fourth quarter of any card; hence they are free for insertion of the 64 numbers written on the face of each card. The construction here given is due to my friend R. A. L. Cole.

Possibly the puzzle is better presented by omitting all numbers exceeding 100, for the introduction of 128 at once suggests the method of construction. With that restriction I think the use of only 7 cards is better and more elegant than the form in which I have seen it on sale.

THE MOUSE TRAP. TREIZE

I will conclude this chapter with the bare mention of another game of cards, known as the *Mouse Trap*, the discussion of which involves some rather difficult algebraic analysis.

It is played as follows. A set of cards, marked with the numbers 1, 2, 3, . . ., n, is dealt in any order, face upwards, in the form of a circle. The player begins at any card and counts round the circle always in the same direction. If the kth card has the number k on it—which event is called a *hit*—the player takes up the card and begins counting afresh. According to Cayley, the player wins if he thus takes up all the cards, and the cards win if at any time the player counts up to n without being able to take up a card.

For example, if a pack of only 4 cards is used, and these cards come in the order 3214, then the player would obtain the second card 2 as a hit, next he would obtain 1 as a hit, but if he went on for ever, he would not obtain another hit. On the other hand, if the cards in the pack were initially in the order 1423, the player would obtain successively all four cards in the order 1, 2, 3, 4.

The problem may be stated as the determination of what hits and how many hits can be made with a given number of cards; and what permutations will give a certain number of hits in a certain order.

Cayley * showed that there are 9 arrangements of a pack of 4 cards in which no hit will be made, 7 arrangements in which only one hit will be made, 3 arrangements in which only two hits will be made, and 5 arrangements in which four hits will be made.

Prof. Steen † has investigated the general theory for a pack of n cards. He has shown how to determine the number of arrangements in which x is the first hit [Arts. 3—5]; the number of arrangements in which 1 is the first hit and x is the

* *Quarterly Journal of Mathematics*, 1878, vol. xv, pp. 8—10.
† *Ibid.*, vol. xv, pp. 230—241.

second hit [Art. 6]; and the number of arrangements in which
2 is the first hit and x the second hit [Arts. 7—8]; but beyond
this point the theory has not been carried.   It is obvious that,
if there are $n - 1$ hits, the nth hit will necessarily follow.

The French game of *treize* is very similar.   It is played
with a full pack of fifty-two cards (knave, queen, and king
counting as 11, 12, and 13 respectively)   The dealer calls out
1, 2, 3, . . ., 13, as he deals the 1st, 2nd, 3rd, . . ., 13th cards
respectively.   At the beginning of a deal the dealer offers to
lay or take certain odds that he will make a hit in the thirteen
cards next dealt.   (Cf. page 47.)

CHAPTER XII

THREE CLASSICAL GEOMETRICAL PROBLEMS

AMONG the more interesting geometrical problems of antiquity are three questions which attracted the special attention
of the early Greek mathematicians. Our knowledge of
geometry is derived from Greek sources, and thus these
questions have attained a classical position in the history of
the subject. The three questions to which I refer are : (i)
the duplication of a cube—that is, the determination of the
side of a cube whose volume is double that of a given cube ;
(ii) the trisection of an angle; and (iii) the squaring of a
circle—that is, the determination of a square whose area is
equal to that of a given circle; each problem to be solved by
a geometrical construction involving the use of straight lines
and circles only—that is, by Euclidean geometry.

This limitation to the use of straight lines and circles
implies that the only instruments available in Euclidean
geometry are compasses and rulers. But the compasses must
be capable of opening as wide as is desired, and the ruler
must be of unlimited length. Further, the ruler must not be
graduated, for if there were two fixed marks on it we could
obtain constructions equivalent to those obtained by the use
of the conic sections.

With the Euclidean restriction all three problems are insoluble.* To duplicate a cube the length of whose side is a,
we have to find a line of length x, such that $x^3 = 2a^3$. Again,

---

* See F. C. Klein, *Vorträge über ausgewählte Fragen der Elementargeometrie*,
Leipzig, 1895; and F. G. Texeira, *Sur les Problèmes célèbres de la Géométrie
Élémentaire non resolubles avec la Règle et le Compas*, Coimbra, 1915. It is
said that the earliest rigorous proof that the problems were insoluble by
Euclidean geometry was given by P. L. Wantzell in 1837.

to trisect a given angle, we may proceed to find the sine of the angle—say a—then, if x is the sine of an angle equal to one-third of the given angle, we have $4x^3 = 3x - a$. Thus the first and second problems, when considered analytically, require the solution of a cubic equation; and since a construction by means of circles (whose equations are of the form $x^2 + y^2 + ax + by + c = 0$) and straight lines (whose equations are of the form $ax + \beta y + \gamma = 0$) cannot be equivalent to the solution of a cubic equation, it is inferred that the problems are insoluble if in our constructions we are restricted to the use of circles and straight lines. If the use of the conic sections is permitted, both of these questions can be solved in many ways. The third problem is different in character, but under the same restrictions it also is insoluble.

I propose to give some of the constructions which have been proposed for solving the first two of these problems. To save space I shall not draw the necessary diagrams, and in most cases I shall not add the proofs: the latter present but little difficulty. I shall conclude with some historical notes on approximate solutions of the quadrature of the circle.

THE DUPLICATION OF THE CUBE *

The problem of the duplication of the cube was known in ancient times as the Delian problem, in consequence of a legend that the Delians had consulted Plato on the subject. In one form of the story, which is related by Philoponus,† it is asserted that the Athenians in 430 B.C., when suffering from the plague of eruptive typhoid fever, consulted the oracle at Delos as to how they could stop it. Apollo replied that they must double the size of his altar, which was in the form of a cube. To the unlearned suppliants nothing seemed more easy,

---

* See *Historia Problematis de Cubi Duplicatione* by N. T. Reimer, Göttingen, 1798; and *Historia Problematis Cubi Duplicandi* by C. H. Biering, Copenhagen, 1844; also *Das Delische Problem*, by A. Sturm, Linz, 1895-7. Some notes on the subject are given in my *History of Mathematics*.

† *Philoponus ad Aristotelis Analytica Posteriora*, bk. i, chap. vii.

and a new altar was constructed either having each of its edges double that of the old one (from which it followed that the volume was increased eight-fold) or by placing a similar cube altar next to the old one. Whereupon, according to the legend, the indignant god made the pestilence worse than before, and informed a fresh deputation that it was useless to trifle with him, as his new altar must be a cube and have a volume exactly double that of his old one. Suspecting a mystery, the Athenians applied to Plato, who referred them to the geometricians. The insertion of Plato's name is an obvious anachronism. Eratosthenes * relates a somewhat similar story, but with Minos as the propounder of the problem.

In an Arab work, the Greek legend was distorted into the following extraordinarily impossible piece of history, which I cite as a curiosity of its kind. "Now in the days of Plato," says the writer, "a plague broke out among the children of Israel. Then came a voice from heaven to one of their prophets, saying, 'Let the size of the cubic altar be doubled, and the plague will cease'; so the people made another altar like unto the former, and laid the same by its side. Nevertheless the pestilence continued to increase. And again the voice spake unto the prophet, saying, 'They have made a second altar like unto the former, and laid it by its side, but that does not produce the duplication of the cube.' Then applied they to Plato, the Grecian sage, who spake to them, saying, 'Ye have been neglectful of the science of geometry, and therefore hath God chastised you, since geometry is the most sublime of all the sciences.' Now, the duplication of a cube depends on a rare problem in geometry, namely . . ." And then follows the solution of Apollonius, which is given later.

If a is the length of the side of the given cube and x that of the required cube, we have $x^3 = 2a^3$—that is, $x : a = \sqrt[3]{2} : 1$.

---

* *Archimedis Opera cum Eutocii Commentariis*, ed. Torelli, Oxford, 1792, p. 144; ed. Heiberg, Leipzig, 1880–1, vol. III, pp. 104—107.

It is probable that the Greeks were aware that the latter ratio is incommensurable—in other words, that no two integers can be found whose ratio is the same as that of $\sqrt[3]{2} : 1$—but it did not therefore follow that they could not find the ratio by geometry : in fact, the side and diagonal of a square are instances of lines whose numerical measures are incommensurable.

I proceed now to give some of the geometrical constructions which have been proposed for the duplication of the cube.* With one exception, I confine myself to those which can be effected by the aid of the conic sections.

Hippocrates † (*circ.* 420 B.C.) was perhaps the earliest mathematician who made any progress towards solving the problem. He did not give a geometrical construction, but he reduced the question to that of finding two means between one straight line (a), and another twice as long ($2a$). If these means are x and y, we have $a : x = x : y = y : 2a$, from which it follows that $x^3 = 2a^3$. It is in this form that the problem is always presented now. Formerly any process of solution by finding these means was called a mesolabum.

One of the first solutions of the problem was that given by Archytas ‡ in or about the year 400 B.C. His construction is equivalent to the following. On the diameter OA of the base of a right circular cylinder describe a semicircle whose plane is perpendicular to the base of the cylinder. Let the plane containing this semicircle rotate round the generator through O, then the surface traced out by the semicircle will cut the cylinder in a tortuous curve. This curve will itself be cut by a right cone, whose axis is OA and semi-vertical angle is (say) 60°, in a point P, such that the projection of OP on the base

---

* On the application to this problem of the traditional Greek methods of analysis by Hero and Philo (leading to the solution by the use of Apollonius's circle), by Nicomedes (leading to the solution by the use of the conchoid), and by Pappus (leading to the solution by the use of the cissoid), see *Geometrical Analysis* by J. Leslie, Edinburgh, second edition, 1811, pp. 247—250, 453.   † Proclus, ed. Friedlein, pp. 212—213.

‡ *Archimedis Opera*, ed. Torelli, p. 143 ; ed. Heiberg, vol. III, pp. 98—103.

of the cylinder will be to the radius of the cylinder in the ratio of the side of the required cube to that of the given cube.   Of course, the proof given by Archytas is geometrical; and it is interesting to note that in it he shows himself familiar with the results of the propositions Euc. III, 18, III, 35, and XI, 19. To show analytically that the construction is correct, take OA as the axis of x, and the generator of the cylinder drawn through O as axis of z, then with the usual notation, in polar co-ordinates, if a is the radius of the cylinder, we have for the equation of the surface described by the semicircle $r = 2a \sin \theta$; for that of the cylinder $r \sin \theta = 2a \cos \phi$; and for that of the cone $\sin \theta \cos \phi = \frac{1}{2}$. These three surfaces cut in a point such that $\sin^3 \theta = \frac{1}{2}$, and therefore $(r \sin \theta)^3 = 2a^3$. Hence the volume of the cube whose side is $r \sin \theta$ is twice that of the cube whose side is a.

The construction attributed to Plato * (*circ.* 360 B.C.) depends on the theorem that, if CAB and DAB are two right-angled triangles, having one side, AB, common, their other sides, AD and BC, parallel, and their hypotenuses, AC and BD, at right angles, then if these hypotenuses cut in P, we have $PC : PB = PB : PA = PA : PD$. Hence, if such a figure can be constructed having $PD = 2PC$, the problem will be solved.   It is easy to make an instrument by which the figure can be drawn.

The next writer whose name is connected with the problem is Menaechmus,† who in or about 340 B.C. gave two solutions of it.

In the first of these he pointed out that two parabolas having a common vertex, axes at right angles, and such that the latus rectum of the one is double that of the other, will intersect in another point whose abscissa (or ordinate) will give a solution.   If we use analysis, this is obvious; for, if the equations of the parabolas are $y^2 = 2ax$ and $x^2 = ay$, they intersect in a point whose abscissa is given by $x^3 = 2a^3$.   It is

---

* *Archimedis Opera*, ed. Torelli, p. 135; ed. Heiberg, vol. III, pp. 66—71.
† *Ibid.*, ed. Torelli, pp. 141—143; ed. Heiberg, vol. III, pp. 92—99.

probable that this method was suggested by the form in which Hippocrates had cast the problem—namely, to find x and y so that $a : x = x : y = y : 2a$, whence we have $x^2 = ay$ and $y^2 = 2ax$.

The second solution given by Menaechmus was as follows. Describe a parabola of latus rectum l. Next describe a rectangular hyperbola, the length of whose real axis is $4l$, and having for its asymptotes the tangent at the vertex of the parabola and the axis of the parabola. Then the ordinate and the abscissa of the point of intersection of these curves are the mean proportionals between l and $2l$. This is at once obvious by analysis. The curves are $x^2 = ly$ and $xy = 2l^2$. These cut in a point determined by $x^3 = 2l^3$ and $y^3 = 4l^3$. Hence

$$l : x = x : y = y : 2l.$$

The solution of Apollonius,* which was given about 220 B.C., was as follows. The problem is to find two mean proportionals between two given lines. Construct a rectangle $OADB$, of which the adjacent sides OA and OB are respectively equal to the two given lines. Bisect AB in C. With C as centre describe a circle cutting OA produced in a and cutting OB produced in b, so that aDb shall be a straight line. If this circle can be so described, it will follow that $OA : Bb = Bb : Aa = Aa : OB$—that is, Bb and Aa are the two mean proportionals between OA and OB. It is impossible to construct the circle by Euclidean geometry, but Apollonius gave a mechanical way of describing it.

The only other construction of antiquity to which I will refer is that given by Diocles and Sporus.† It is as follows. Take two sides of a rectangle OA, OB, equal to the two lines between which the means are sought. Suppose OA to be the greater. With centre O and radius OA describe a circle. Let

---

* *Archimedis Opera*, ed. Torelli, p. 137; ed. Heiberg, vol. III, pp. 76—79. The solution is given in my *History of Mathematics*, London, 1901, p. 84.

† *Ibid.*, ed. Torelli, pp. 138, 139, 141; ed. Heiberg, vol. III, pp. 78—84, 90—93.

OB produced cut the circumference in *C* and let *AO* produced cut it in *D*. Find a point *E* on *BC* so that if *DE* cuts *AB* produced in *F* and cuts the circumference in *G*, then *FE* = *EG*. If *E* can be found, then *OE* is the first of the means between *OA* and *OB*. Diocles invented the cissoid in order to determine *E*, but it can be found equally conveniently by the aid of conics.

In more modern times several other solutions have been suggested. I may allude in passing to three given by Huygens,* but I will enunciate only those proposed respectively by Vieta, Descartes, Gregory of St. Vincent, and Newton.

Vieta's construction is as follows.† Describe a circle, centre *O*, whose radius is equal to half the length of the larger of the two given lines. In it draw a chord *AB* equal to the smaller of the two given lines. Produce *AB* to *E* so that *BE* = *AB*. Through *A* draw a line *AF* parallel to *OE*. Through *O* draw a line *DOCFG*, cutting the circumference in *D* and *C*, cutting *AF* in *F*, and cutting *BA* produced in *G*, so that *GF* = *OA*. If this line can be drawn then *AB* : *GC* = *GC* : *GA* = *GA* : *CD*.

Descartes pointed out ‡ that the curves

$$x^2 = ay \text{ and } x^2 + y^2 = ay + bx$$

cut in a point (*x*, *y*) such that *a* : *x* = *x* : *y* = *y* : *b*. Of course, this is equivalent to the first solution given by Menaechmus, but Descartes preferred to use a circle rather than a second conic.

Gregory's construction was given in the form of the following theorem.§ The hyperbola drawn through the point of intersection of two sides of a rectangle so as to have the two other sides for its asymptotes meets the circle circumscribing the rectangle in a point whose distances from the asymptotes are

---

* *Opera Varia*, Leyden, 1724, pp. 393—396.

† *Opera Mathematica*, ed. Schooten, Leyden, 1646, prop. v, pp. 242—243.

‡ *Geometria*, bk. iii, ed. Schooten, Amsterdam, 1659, p. 91.

§ Gregory of St. Vincent, *Opus Geometricum Quadraturae Circuli*, Antwerp, 1647, bk. vi, prop. 138, p. 602.

the mean proportionals between two adjacent sides of the rectangle. This is the geometrical expression of the proposition that the curves $xy = ab$ and $x^2 + y^2 = ay + bx$ cut in a point (x, y) such that $a : x = x : y = y : b$.

One of the constructions proposed by Newton is as follows.* Let OA be the greater of two given lines. Bisect OA in B. With centre O and radius OB describe a circle. Take a point C on the circumference so that BC is equal to the other of the two given lines. From O draw ODE cutting AC produced in D, and BC produced in E, so that the intercept $DE = OB$. Then $BC : OD = OD : CE = CE : OA$. Hence OD and CE are two mean proportionals between any two lines BC and OA.

The Trisection of an Angle †

The trisection of an angle is the second of these classical problems, but tradition has not enshrined its origin in romance. The following two constructions are among the oldest and best known of those which have been suggested; they are quoted by Pappus,‡ but I do not know to whom they were due originally.

The first of them is as follows. Let AOB be the given angle. From any point P in OB draw PM perpendicular to OA. Through P draw PR parallel to OA. On MP take a point Q so that if OQ is produced to cut PR in R then $QR = 2 . OP$. If this construction can be made, then $AOR = \frac{1}{3}AOB$. The solution depends on determining the position of R. This was effected by a construction which may be expressed analytically thus. Let the given angle be $\tan^{-1}(b/a)$. Construct the hyperbola $xy = ab$, and the circle $(x - a)^2 +$

---

* *Arithmetica Universalis*, Ralphson's (second) edition, 1728, p. 242; see also pp. 243, 245.

† On the bibliography of the subject see the supplements to *L'Intermédiaire des Mathématiciens*, Paris, May and June, 1904.

‡ Pappus, *Mathematicae Collectiones*, bk. IV, props. 32, 33 (ed. Commandino, Bonn, 1670, pp. 97—99). On the application to this problem of the traditional Greek methods of analysis see *Geometrical Analysis*, by J. Leslie, Edinburgh, second edition, 1811, pp. 245—247.

$(y - b)^2 = 4(a^2 + b^2)$. Of the points where they cut, let x be the abscissa which is greatest, then $PR = x - a$, and $\tan^{-1}(b/x) = \frac{1}{3}\tan^{-1}(b/a)$.

The second construction is as follows. Let AOB be the given angle. Take $OB = OA$, and with centre O and radius OA describe a circle. Produce AO indefinitely and take a point C on it external to the circle, so that if CB cuts the circumference in D then CD shall be equal to OA. Draw OE parallel to CDB. Then, if this construction can be made, $AOE = \frac{1}{3}AOB$. The ancients determined the position of the point C by the aid of the conchoid: it could be also found by the use of the conic sections.

I proceed to give a few other solutions, confining myself to those effected by the aid of conics.

Among other constructions given by Pappus * I may quote the following. Describe a hyperbola whose eccentricity is two. Let its centre be C and its vertices A and A'. Produce CA' to S so that $A'S = CA'$. On AS describe a segment of a circle to contain the given angle. Let the orthogonal bisector of AS cut this segment in O. With centre O and radius OA or OS describe a circle. Let this circle cut the branch of the hyperbola through A' in P. Then $SOP = \frac{1}{3}SOA$.

In modern times one of the earliest of the solutions by a direct use of conics was suggested by Descartes, who effected it by the intersection of a circle and a parabola. His construction † is equivalent to finding the points of intersection, other than the origin, of the parabola $y^2 = \frac{1}{4}x$ and the circle $x^2 + y^2 - \frac{13}{4}x + 4ay = 0$. The ordinates of these points are given by the equation $4y^3 = 3y - a$. The smaller positive root is the sine of one-third of the angle whose sine is a. The demonstration is ingenious.

One of the solutions proposed by Newton is practically equivalent to the third one which is quoted above from Pappus. It is as follows.‡ Let A be the vertex of one

---

* Pappus, *Mathematicae Collectiones*, bk. IV, prop. 34, pp. 99—104.

† *Geometria*, bk. III, ed. Schooten, Amsterdam, 1659, p. 91.

‡ *Arithmetica Universalis*, problem XLII, Ralphson's (second) edition, London, 1728, p. 148; see also pp. 243—245.

branch of a hyperbola whose eccentricity is two, and let S be the focus of the other branch. On AS describe the segment of a circle containing an angle equal to the supplement of the given angle. Let this circle cut the S branch of the hyperbola in P. Then PAS will be equal to one-third of the given angle.

The following elegant solution is due to Clairaut.* Let AOB be the given angle. Take $OA = OB$, and with centre O and radius OA describe a circle. Join AB, and trisect it in H, K, so that $AH = HK = KB$. Bisect the angle AOB by OC cutting AB in L. Then $AH = 2 \cdot HL$. With focus A, vertex H, and directrix OC, describe a hyperbola. Let the branch of this hyperbola which passes through H cut the circle in P. Draw PM perpendicular to OC and produce it to cut the circle in Q. Then by the focus and directrix property we have $AP : PM = AH : HL = 2 : 1$, $\therefore AP = 2 \cdot PM = PQ$. Hence, by symmetry, $AP = PQ = QB$. $\therefore AOP = POQ = QOB$.

I may conclude by giving the solution which Chasles † regards as the most fundamental. It is equivalent to the following proposition. If OA and OB are the bounding radii of a circular arc AB, then a rectangular hyperbola having OA for a diameter and passing through the point of intersection of OB with the tangent to the circle at A will pass through one of the two points of trisection of the arc.

Several instruments have been constructed by which mechanical solutions of the problem can be obtained.

The Quadrature of the Circle ‡

The object of the third of the classical problems was the determination of a side of a square whose area should be equal to that of a given circle.

* I believe that this was first given by Clairaut, but I have mislaid my reference. The construction occurs as an example in the *Geometry of Conics*, by C. Taylor, Cambridge, 1881, No. 308, p. 126.

† *Traité des sections coniques*, Paris, 1865, art. 37, p. 36.

‡ See Montucla's *Histoire des Recherches sur la Quadrature du Cercle*, edited by P. L. Lacroix, Paris, 1831; also various articles by A. De Morgan,

The investigation, previous to the last two hundred years, of this question was fruitful in discoveries of allied theorems, but in more recent times it has been abandoned by those who are able to realize what is required. The history of this subject has been treated by competent writers in such detail that I shall content myself with a very brief allusion to it.

Archimedes showed * (what possibly was known before) that the problem is equivalent to finding the area of a right-angled triangle whose sides are equal respectively to the perimeter of the circle and the radius of the circle. Half the ratio of these lines is a number, usually denoted by π.

That this number is incommensurable had been long suspected, and has been now demonstrated. The earliest analytical proof of it was given by Lambert † in 1761; in 1803 Legendre ‡ extended the proof to show that π^2 was also incommensurable; and in 1882 Lindemann § showed that π cannot be the root of a rational algebraical equation.

An earlier attempt by James Gregory to give a geometrical demonstration of this is worthy of notice. Gregory proved ‖ that the ratio of the area of any arbitrary sector to that of

---

and especially his *Budget of Paradoxes*, London, 1872. A popular sketch of the subject has been compiled by H. Schubert, *Die Quadratur des Zirkels*, Hamburg, 1889; and since the publication of the earlier editions of these *Recreations* Prof. F. Rudio of Zurich has given an analysis of the arguments of Archimedes, Huygens, Lambert, and Legendre on the subject, with an introduction on the history of the problem, Leipzig, 1892.

* *Archimedis Opera*, Κύκλου μέτρησις, prop. I, ed. Torelli, pp. 203—205; ed. Heiberg, vol. I, pp. 258—261, vol. III, pp. 269—277.

† *Mémoires de l'Académie de Berlin* for 1761, Berlin, 1768, pp. 265—322.

‡ Legendre's *Geometry*, Brewster's translation, Edinburgh, 1824, pp. 239—245.

§ Ueber die Zahl π, *Mathematische Annalen*, Leipzig, 1882, vol. XX, pp. 213—225. The proof leads to the conclusion that, if x is a root of a rational integral algebraical equation, then e^x cannot be rational: hence, if πi was the root of such an equation, $e^{\pi i}$ could not be rational; but $e^{\pi i}$ is equal to -1, and therefore is rational; hence πi cannot be the root of such an algebraical equation, and therefore neither can π.

‖ *Vera Circuli et Hyperbolae Quadratura*, Padua, 1668: this is reprinted in Huygens's *Opera Varia*, Leyden, 1724, pp. 405—462.

the inscribed or circumscribed polygons is not expressible by a finite number of algebraical terms. Hence he inferred that the quadrature was impossible. This was accepted by Montucla, but it is not conclusive, for it is conceivable that some particular sector might be squared, and this particular sector might be the whole circle.

In connection with Gregory's proposition above cited, I may add that Newton * proved that in any closed oval an arbitrary sector bounded by the curve and two radii cannot be expressed in terms of the co-ordinates of the extremities of the arc by a finite number of algebraical terms. The argument is condensed and difficult to follow : the same reasoning would show that a closed oval curve cannot be represented by an algebraical equation in polar co-ordinates. From this proposition no conclusion as to the quadrature of the circle is to be drawn, nor did Newton draw any. In the earlier editions of this work I expressed an opinion that the result presupposed a particular definition of the word oval, but on more careful reflection I think that the conclusion is valid without restriction.

With the aid of the quadratrix, or the conchoid, or the cissoid, the quadrature of the circle is easy, but the construction of those curves assumes a knowledge of the value of π, and thus the question is begged.

I need hardly add that, if π represented merely the ratio of the circumference of a circle to its diameter, the determination of its numerical value would have but slight interest. It is, however, a mere accident that π is defined usually in that way, and it really represents a certain number which would enter into analysis from whatever side the subject was approached.

I recollect a distinguished professor explaining how different would be the ordinary life of a race of beings born, as easily they might be, so that the fundamental processes of arithmetic, algebra and geometry were different from those which seem

* *Principia*, bk. I, section VI, emma XXVIII.

to us so evident; but, he added, it is impossible to conceive of a universe in which e and π should not exist.

I have quoted elsewhere an anecdote, which perhaps will bear repetition, that illustrates how little the usual definition of π suggests its properties. De Morgan was explaining to an actuary what was the chance that a certain proportion of some group of people would at the end of a given time be alive; and quoted the actuarial formula, involving π, which, in answer to a question, he explained stood for the ratio of the circumference of a circle to its diameter. His acquaintance, who had so far listened to the explanation with interest, interrupted him and exclaimed, "My dear friend, that must be a delusion; what can a circle have to do with the number of people alive at the end of a given time?" In reality the fact that the ratio of the length of the circumference of a circle to its diameter is the number denoted by π does not afford the best analytical definition of π, and is only one of its properties.

The use of a single symbol to denote this number 3·14159 ... seems to have been introduced about the beginning of the eighteenth century. William Jones * in 1706 represented it by π; a few years later † John Bernoulli denoted it by c; Euler in 1734 used p, and in 1736 used c; Christian Goldback in 1742 used π; and after the publication of Euler's *Analysis* the symbol π was generally employed.

The numerical value of π can be determined by either of two methods with as close an approximation to the truth as is desired.

The first of these methods is geometrical. It consists in calculating the perimeters of polygons inscribed in and circumscribed about a circle, and assuming that the circumference of the circle is intermediate between these perimeters.‡ The

---

* *Synopsis Palmariorum Matheseos*, London, 1706, pp. 243, 263 *et seq.*

† See notes by G. Eneström in the *Bibliotheca Mathematica*, Stockholm, 1889, vol. III, p. 28; *ibid.*, 1890, vol. IV, p. 22.

‡ The history of this method has been written by K. E. I. Selander, *Historik öfver Ludolphska Talet*, Upsala, 1868.

approximation would be closer if the areas and not the perimeters were employed. The second and modern method rests on the determination of converging infinite series for π.

We may say that the π-calculators who used the first method regarded π as equivalent to a geometrical ratio, but those who adopted the modern method treated it as the symbol for a certain number which enters into numerous branches of mathematical analysis.

It may be interesting if I add here a list of some of the approximations to the value of π given by various writers.* This will indicate incidentally those who have studied the subject to the best advantage.

The ancient Egyptians † took 256/81 as the value of π; this is equal to $3 \cdot 1605 \ldots$; but the rougher approximation of 3 was used by the Babylonians ‡ and by the Jews.§ It is not unlikely that these numbers were obtained empirically.

We come next to a long roll of Greek mathematicians who attacked the problem. Whether the researches of the members of the Ionian School, the Pythagoreans, Anaxagoras, Hippias, Antipho, and Bryso led to numerical approximations for the value of π is doubtful, and their investigations need not detain us. The quadrature of certain lunes by Hippocrates of Chios is ingenious and correct, but a value of π cannot be thence deduced; and it seems likely that the later members of the Athenian School concentrated their efforts on other questions.

* For the methods used in classical times and the results obtained, see the notices of their authors in M. Cantor's *Geschichte der Mathematik*, Leipzig, vol. I, 1880. For medieval and modern approximations, see the article by A. De Morgan on the Quadrature of the Circle in vol. XIX of the *Penny Cyclopaedia*, London, 1841; with the additions given by B. de Haan in the *Verhandelingen* of Amsterdam, 1858, vol. IV, p. 22: the conclusions were tabulated, corrected, and extended by Dr. J. W. L. Glaisher in the *Messenger of Mathematics*, Cambridge, 1873, vol. II, pp. 119—128; and *ibid.*, 1874, vol. III, pp. 27—46.

† *Ein mathematisches Handbuch der alten Aegypter* (*i.e.* the Rhind papyrus), by A. Eisenlohr, Leipzig, 1877, arts. 100—109, 117, 124.

‡ Oppert, *Journal Asiatique*, August, 1872, and October, 1874.

§ 1 Kings, ch. 7, ver. 23; 2 Chronicles, ch. 4, ver. 2.

It is probable that Euclid,* the illustrious founder of the Alexandrian School, was aware that π was greater than 3 and less than 4, but he did not state the result explicitly.

The mathematical treatment of the subject began with Archimedes, who proved that π is less than $3\frac{1}{7}$ and greater than $3\frac{10}{71}$—that is, it lies between $3.1428\ldots$ and $3.1408\ldots$ He established † this by inscribing in a circle and circumscribing about it regular polygons of 96 sides, then determining by geometry the perimeters of these polygons, and finally assuming that the circumference of the circle was intermediate between these perimeters: this leads to a result from which he deduced the limits given above. This method is equivalent to using the proposition $\sin\theta < \theta < \tan\theta$, where $\theta = \pi/96$: the values of $\sin\theta$ and $\tan\theta$ were deduced by Archimedes from those of $\sin\frac{1}{3}\pi$ and $\tan\frac{1}{3}\pi$ by repeated bisections of the angle. With a polygon of n sides this process gives a value of π correct to at least the integral part of $(2\log n - 1.19)$ places of decimals. The result given by Archimedes is correct to two places of decimals. His analysis leads to the conclusion that the perimeters of these polygons for a circle whose diameter is 4970 feet would lie between 15610 feet and 15620 feet—actually it is about 15613 feet 9 inches.

Apollonius discussed these results, but his criticisms have been lost.

Hero of Alexandria gave ‡ the value 3, but he quoted § the result 22/7: possibly the former number was intended only for rough approximations.

The only other Greek approximation that I need mention is that given by Ptolemy,‖ who asserted that $\pi = 3° 8' 30''$. This is equivalent to taking $\pi = 3 + \frac{8}{60} + \frac{30}{3600} = 3\frac{17}{120} = 3.1416$.

---

* These results can be deduced from Euc. IV, 15, and IV, 8: see also book XII, prop. 16.

† *Archimedis Opera*, Κύκλου μέτρησις, prop. III, ed. Torelli, Oxford, 1792, pp. 205—216; ed. Heiberg, Leipzig, 1880, vol. I, pp. 263—271.

‡ *Mensurae*, ed. Hultsch, Berlin, 1864, p. 188.

§ *Geometria*, ed. Hultsch, Berlin, 1864, pp. 115, 136.

‖ *Almagest*, bk. VI, chap. 7; ed. Halma, vol. I, p. 421.

The Roman surveyors seem to have used 3, or sometimes 4, for rough calculations. For closer approximations they often employed $3\frac{1}{8}$ instead of $3\frac{1}{7}$, since the fractions then introduced are more convenient in duodecimal arithmetic. On the other hand, Gerbert * recommended the use of 22/7.

Before coming to the medieval and modern European mathematicians, it may be convenient to note the results arrived at in India and the East.

Baudhayana † took 49/16 as the value of π.

Arya-Bhata,‡ *circ.* 530, gave 62832/20000, which is equal to 3·1416. He showed that, if a is the side of a regular polygon of n sides inscribed in a circle of unit diameter, and if b is the side of a regular inscribed polygon of $2n$ sides, then $b^2 = \frac{1}{2} - \frac{1}{2}(1 - a^2)^{\frac{1}{2}}$. From the side of an inscribed hexagon, he found successively the sides of polygons of 12, 24, 48, 96, 192, and 384 sides. The perimeter of the last is given as equal to $\sqrt{9\cdot8694}$, from which his result was obtained by approximation.

Brahmagupta,§ *circ.* 650, gave $\sqrt{10}$, which is equal to 3·1622.... He is said to have obtained this value by inscribing in a circle of unit diameter regular polygons of 12, 24, 48, and 96 sides, and calculating successively their perimeters, which he found to be $\sqrt{9\cdot65}$, $\sqrt{9\cdot81}$, $\sqrt{9\cdot86}$, $\sqrt{9\cdot87}$ respectively; and to have assumed that as the number of sides is increased indefinitely the perimeter would approximate to $\sqrt{10}$.

Bhaskara, *circ.* 1150, gave two approximations. One ‖— possibly copied from Arya-Bhata, but said to have been calculated afresh by Archimedes's method from the perimeters of regular polygons of 384 sides—is 3927/1250, which is equal

* *Œuvres de Gerbert*, ed. Olleris, Clermont, 1867, p. 453.

† The *Sulvasutras* by G. Thibaut, *Asiatic Society of Bengal*, 1875, arts. 26—28.

‡ *Leçons de calcul d'Aryabhata*, by L. Rodet in the *Journal Asiatique*, 1879, series 7, vol. XIII, pp. 10, 21.

§ *Algebra... from Brahmegupta and Bhascara*, trans. by H. T. Colebrooke, London, 1817, chap. XII, art. 40, p. 308.

‖ *Ibid.*, p. 87.

to 3·1416 : the other * is 754/240, which is equal to 3·1416, but it is uncertain whether this was not given only as an approximate value.

Among the Arabs the values 22/7, $\sqrt{10}$, and 62832/20000 were given by Alkarism,† circ. 830; and no doubt were derived from Indian sources. He described the first as an approximate value, the second as used by geometricians, and the third as used by astronomers.

In Chinese works the values 3, 22/7, 157/50 are said to occur; probably the last two results were copied from the Arabs. The Japanese ‡ approximations were closer.

Returning to European mathematicians, we have the following successive approximations to the value of π : many of those prior to the eighteenth century having been calculated originally with the view of demonstrating the incorrectness of some alleged quadrature.

Leonardo of Pisa,§ in the thirteenth century, gave for π the value 1440/458⅓, which is equal to 3·1418 . . . . In the fifteenth century, Purbach ‖ gave or quoted the value 62832/20000, which is equal to 3·1416; Cusa believed that the accurate value was $\frac{3}{4}(\sqrt{3} + \sqrt{6})$, which is equal to 3·1423 . . . ; and, in 1464, Regiomontanus ¶ is said to have given a value equal to 3·14243.

Vieta,** in 1579, showed that π was greater than

* Algebra . . . from Brahmegupta and Bhascara, trans. by H. T. Colebroke, London, 1817, chap. XII, art. 40, p. 95.

† The Algebra of Mohammed ben Musa, ed. by F. Rosen, London, 1831, pp. 71—72.

‡ On Japanese approximations and the methods used, see P. Harzer, Transactions of the British Association for 1905, p. 325.

§ Boncompagni's Scritti di Leonardo, vol. II (Practica Geometriae), Rome, 1862, p. 90. Leonardo was nicknamed Fibonacci (see page 57).

‖ Appendix to the De Triangulis of Regiomontanus, Basle, 1541, p. 131.

¶ In his correspondence with Cardinal Nicholas de Cusa, De Quadratura Circuli, Nuremberg, 1533, wherein he proved that the cardinal's result was wrong. I cannot quote the exact reference, but the figures are given by competent writers and I have no doubt are correct.

** Canon Mathematicus seu ad Triangula, Paris, 1579, pp. 56, 66: probably this work was printed for private circulation only; it is very rare.

31415926535/10^{10}, and less than 31415926537/10^{10}. This was deduced from the perimeters of the inscribed and circumscribed polygons of 6×2^{16} sides, obtained by repeated use of the formula $2 \sin^2 \frac{1}{2}\theta = 1 - \cos \theta$. He also gave * a result equivalent to the formula

$$\frac{2}{\pi} = \frac{\sqrt{2}}{2} \frac{\sqrt{(2 + \sqrt{2})}}{2} \frac{\sqrt{\{2 + \sqrt{(2 + \sqrt{2})}\}}}{2} \cdots$$

The father of Adrian Metius,† in 1585, gave 355/113, which is equal to 3·14159292 . . ., and is correct to six places of decimals. This was a curious and lucky guess, for all that he proved was that π was intermediate between 377/120 and 333/106, whereon he jumped to the conclusion that he would obtain the true fractional value by taking the mean of the numerators and the mean of the denominators of these fractions.

In 1593 Adrian Romanus ‡ calculated the perimeter of the inscribed regular polygon of 1073,741824 (*i.e.* 2^{30}) sides, from which he determined the value of π correct to 15 places of decimals.

L. van Ceulen devoted no inconsiderable part of his life to the subject. In 1596 § he gave the result to 20 places of decimals : this was calculated by finding the perimeters of the inscribed and circumscribed regular polygons of 60×2^{33} sides, obtained by the repeated use of a theorem of his discovery equivalent to the formula $1 - \cos A = 2 \sin^2 \frac{1}{2}A$. I possess a finely executed engraving of him of this date, with the result printed round a circle which is below his portrait. He died in 1610, and by his directions the result to 35 places of decimals (which was as far as he had calculated it) was engraved

---

* *Vietae Opera*, ed. Schooten, Leyden, 1646, p. 400.

† *Arithmeticae libri duo et Geometriae*, by A. Metius, Leyden, 1626, pp. 88—89. [Probably issued originally in 1611.]

‡ *Ideae Mathematicae*, Antwerp, 1593 : a rare work, which I have never been able to consult.

§ *Van den Circkel*, Delft, 1596, fol. 14, p. 1; or *De Circulo*, Leyden, 1619, p. 3.

on his tombstone * in St. Peter's Church, Leyden. His post-
humous arithmetic † contains the result to 32 places; this
was obtained by calculating the perimeter of a polygon, the
number of whose sides is 2^{62}, *i.e.* 4,611686,018427,387904.
Van Ceulen also compiled a table of the perimeters of various
regular polygons.

Willebrord Snell,‡ in 1621, obtained from a polygon of 2^{30}
sides an approximation to 34 places of decimals. This is less
than the numbers given by van Ceulen, but Snell's method
was so superior that he obtained his 34 places by the use of a
polygon from which van Ceulen had obtained only 14 (or
perhaps 16) places. Similarly, Snell obtained from a hexagon
an approximation as correct as that for which Archimedes had
required a polygon of 96 sides, while from a polygon of 96
sides he determined the value of π correct to seven decimal
places instead of the two places obtained by Archimedes.
The reason is that Archimedes, having calculated the lengths
of the sides of inscribed and circumscribed regular polygons
of n sides, assumed that the length of $1/n$th of the perimeter
of the circle was intermediate between them; whereas Snell
constructed from the sides of these polygons two other lines
which gave closer limits for the corresponding arc. His
method depends on the theorem $3 \sin \theta/(2 + \cos \theta) < \theta <$
$(2 \sin \tfrac{1}{3}\theta + \tan \tfrac{1}{3}\theta)$, by the aid of which a polygon of n sides
gives a value of π correct to at least the integral part of
$(4 \log n - \cdot 2305)$ places of decimals, which is more than twice
the number given by the older rule. Snell's proof of his
theorem is incorrect, though the result is true.

Snell also added a table § of the perimeters of all regular

* The inscription is quoted by Prof. de Haan in the *Messenger of Mathematics*, 1874, vol. III, p. 25.

† *De Arithmetische en Geometrische Fondamenten*, Leyden, 1615, p. 163; or
p. 144 of the Latin translation by W. Snell, published at Leyden in 1615 under
the title *Fundamenta Arithmetica et Geometrica*. This was reissued, together
with a Latin translation of the *Van den Circkel*, in 1619, under the title *De
Circulo*; in which see pp. 3, 29—32, 92.

‡ *Cyclometricus*, Leyden, 1621, p. 55.

§ It is quoted by Montucla, ed. 1831, p. 70.

inscribed and circumscribed polygons, the number of whose
sides is 10×2^n where n is not greater than 19 and not less
than 3. Most of these were quoted from van Ceulen, but
some were recalculated. This list has proved useful in refuting
circle-squarers. A similar list was given by James Gregory.*

In 1630 Grienberger,† by the aid of Snell's theorem, carried
the approximation to 39 places of decimals. He was the last
mathematician who adopted the classical method of finding
the perimeters of inscribed and circumscribed polygons.
Closer approximations serve no useful purpose. Proofs of the
theorems used by Snell and other calculators in applying this
method were given by Huygens in a work‡ which may be
taken as closing the history of this method.

In 1656 Wallis§ proved that

$$\frac{\pi}{2} = \frac{2}{1} \cdot \frac{2}{3} \cdot \frac{4}{3} \cdot \frac{4}{5} \cdot \frac{6}{5} \cdot \frac{6}{7} \cdot \frac{8}{7} \cdots,$$

and quoted a proposition given a few years earlier by Viscount
Brouncker to the effect that

$$\frac{4}{\pi} = 1 + \frac{1^2}{2} + \frac{3^2}{2} + \frac{5^2}{2} + \cdots,$$

but neither of these theorems was used to any large extent
for calculation.

Subsequent calculators have relied on converging infinite
series, a method that was hardly practicable prior to the
invention of the calculus, though Descartes ‖ had indicated a
geometrical process which was equivalent to the use of such

* *Vera Circuli et Hyperbolae Quadratura*, prop. 29, quoted by Huygens,
Opera Varia, Leyden, 1724, p. 447.

† *Elementa Trigonometrica*, Rome, 1630, end of preface.

‡ *De Circula Magnitudine Inventa*, 1654; *Opera Varia*, pp. 351—387. The
proofs are given in G. Pirie's *Geometrical Methods of Approximating to the
Value* of π, London, 1877, pp. 21—23.

§ *Arithmetica Infinitorum*, Oxford, 1656, prop. 191. An analysis of the
investigation by Wallis was given by Cayley, *Quarterly Journal of Mathematics*, 1889, vol. XXIII, pp. 165—169.

‖ See Euler's paper in the *Novi Commentarii Academiae Scientiarum*
Petrograd, 1763, vol. VIII, pp. 157—168.

a series. The employment of infinite series was proposed by James Gregory,* who established the theorem that

$$\theta = \tan\theta - \tfrac{1}{3}\tan^3\theta + \tfrac{1}{5}\tan^5\theta - \dots,$$

the result being true only if θ lies between $-\tfrac{1}{4}\pi$ and $\tfrac{1}{4}\pi$.

The first mathematician to make use of Gregory's series for obtaining an approximation to the value of π was Abraham Sharp,† who, in 1699, on the suggestion of Halley, determined it to 72 places of decimals (71 correct). He obtained this value by putting $\theta = \tfrac{1}{6}\pi$ in Gregory's series.

Machin,‡ earlier than 1706, gave the result to 100 places (all correct). He calculated it by the formula

$$\tfrac{1}{4}\pi = 4\tan^{-1}\tfrac{1}{5} - \tan^{-1}\tfrac{1}{239}.$$

De Lagny,§ in 1719, gave the result to 127 places of decimals (112 correct), calculating it by putting $\theta = \tfrac{1}{6}\pi$ in Gregory's series.

Hutton,‖ in 1776, and Euler,¶ in 1779, suggested the use of the formula $\tfrac{1}{4}\pi = \tan^{-1}\tfrac{1}{2} + \tan^{-1}\tfrac{1}{3}$ or $\tfrac{1}{4}\pi = 5\tan^{-1}\tfrac{1}{7} + 2\tan^{-1}\tfrac{3}{79}$, but neither carried the approximation as far as had been done previously.

Vega, in 1789,** gave the value of π to 143 places of decimals (126 correct); and, in 1794,†† to 140 places (136 correct).

* See the letter to Collins, dated Feb. 15, 1671, printed in the *Commercium Epistolicum*, London, 1712, p. 25, and in the Macclesfield Collection, *Correspondence of Scientific Men of the Seventeenth Century*, Oxford, 1841, vol. II, p. 216.

† See *Life of A. Sharp* by W. Cudworth, London, 1889, p. 170. Sharp's work is given in one of the preliminary discourses (pp. 53 *et seq.*) prefixed to H. Sherwin's *Mathematical Tables*. The tables were issued at London in 1705 : probably the discourses were issued at the same time, though the earliest copies I have seen were printed in 1717.

‡ W. Jones's *Synopsis Palmariorum*, London, 1706, p. 243; and Maseres, *Scriptores Logarithmici*, London, 1796, vol. III, pp. vii—ix, 155—164.

§ *Histoire de l'Académie* for 1719, Paris, 1721, p. 144.

‖ *Philosophical Transactions*, 1776, vol. LXVI, pp. 476—492.

¶ *Nova Acta Academiae Scientiarum Petropolitanae* for 1793, Petrograd, 1798, vol. XI, pp. 133—149 : the memoir was read in 1779.

** *Nova Acta Academiae Scientiarum Petropolitanae* for 1790, Petrograd, 1795, vol. IX, p. 41.

†† *Thesaurus Logarithmorum* (*logarithmisch-trigonometrischer Tafeln*), Leipzig, 1794, p. 633.

Towards the end of the eighteenth century F. X. von Zach saw in the Radcliffe Library, Oxford, a manuscript by an unknown author which gives the value of π to 154 places of decimals (152 correct).

In 1837, the result of a calculation of π to 154 places of decimals (152 correct) was published.*

In 1841 Rutherford † calculated it to 208 places of decimals (152 correct), using the formula $\frac{1}{4}\pi = 4 \tan^{-1}\frac{1}{5} - \tan^{-1}\frac{1}{70} + \tan^{-1}\frac{1}{99}$.

In 1844 Dase ‡ calculated it to 205 places of decimals (200 correct), using the formula $\frac{1}{4}\pi = \tan^{-1}\frac{1}{2} + \tan^{-1}\frac{1}{5} + \tan^{-1}\frac{1}{8}$.

In 1847 Clausen § carried the approximation to 250 places of decimals (248 correct), calculating it independently by the formulae $\frac{1}{4}\pi = 2 \tan^{-1}\frac{1}{3} + \tan^{-1}\frac{1}{7}$ and $\frac{1}{4}\pi = 4 \tan^{-1}\frac{1}{5} - \tan^{-1}\frac{1}{239}$.

In 1853 Rutherford ‖ carried his former approximation to 440 places of decimals (all correct), and William Shanks prolonged the approximation to 530 places. In the same year Shanks published an approximation to 607 places : ¶ and in 1873 he carried the approximation to 707 places of decimals.** These were calculated from Machin's formula.

In 1853 Richter, presumably in ignorance of what had been done in England, found the value of π to 333 places †† of decimals (330 correct); in 1854 he carried the approximation to 400 places; ‡‡ and in 1855 carried it to 500 places.§§

Of the series and formulae by which these approximations

---

* J. F. Callet's *Tables, etc., Précis Élémentaire*, Paris, tirage, 1837. Tirage, 1894, p. 96.

† *Philosophical Transactions*, 1841, p. 283.

‡ *Crelle's Journal*, 1844, vol. XXVII, p. 198.

§ Schumacher, *Astronomische Nachrichten*, vol. XXV, col. 207.

‖ *Proceedings of the Royal Society*, Jan. 20, 1853, vol. VI, pp. 273—275.

¶ *Contributions to Mathematics*, W. Shanks, London, 1853, pp. 86—87.

** *Proceedings of the Royal Society*, 1872–3, vol. XXI, p. 318; 1873–4, vol. XXII, p. 45.

†† *Grünert's Archiv*, vol. XXI, p. 119.

‡‡ *Ibid.*, vol. XXIII, p. 476 : the approximation given in vol. XXII, p. 473, is correct only to 330 places.

§§ *Ibid.*, vol. XXV, p. 472; and *Elbinger Anzeigen*, No. 85.

have been calculated, those used by Machin and Dase are perhaps the easiest to employ. Other series which converge rapidly are the following :

$$\frac{\pi}{6} = \frac{1}{2} + \frac{1}{2} \cdot \frac{1}{3 \cdot 2^3} + \frac{1 \cdot 3}{2 \cdot 4} \cdot \frac{1}{5 \cdot 2^5} + \cdots,$$

and

$$\frac{\pi}{4} = 22 \tan^{-1} \frac{1}{28} + 2 \tan^{-1} \frac{1}{443} - 5 \tan^{-1} \frac{1}{1393} - 10 \tan^{-1} \frac{1}{11018};$$

the latter of these is due to Mr. Escott.*

As to those writers who believe that they have squared the circle, their number is legion and, in most cases, their ignorance profound, but their attempts are not worth discussing here. " Only prove to me that it is impossible," said one of them, " and I will set about it immediately "; and doubtless the statement that the problem is insoluble has attracted much attention to it.

Among the geometrical ways of approximating to the truth the following is one of the simplest. Inscribe in the given circle a square, and to three times the diameter of the circle add a fifth of a side of the square; the result will differ from the circumference of the circle by less than one-seventeen-thousandth part of it.

An approximate value of π has been obtained experimentally by the theory of probability. On a plane a number of equidistant parallel straight lines, distance apart a, are ruled; and a stick of length l, which is less than a, is dropped on the plane. The probability that it will fall so as to lie across one of the lines is $2l/\pi a$. If the experiment is repeated many hundreds of times, the ratio of the number of favourable cases to the whole number of experiments will be very nearly equal to this fraction : hence the value of π can be found. In 1855 Mr. A. Smith † of Aberdeen made 3204 trials, and deduced $\pi = 3 \cdot 1553$. A pupil of Prof. De Morgan,† from 600 trials,

---

* For a comparison of about thirty such formulae, see D. H. Lehmer, *American Mathematical Monthly*, 1938, vol. XLV, pp. 657—664.

† A. De Morgan, *Budget of Paradoxes*, London, 1872, pp. 171, 172.

deduced $\pi = 3 \cdot 137$. In 1864 Captain Fox * made 1120 trails with some additional precautions, and obtained as the mean value $\pi = 3 \cdot 1419$.

Other similar methods of approximating to the value of π have been indicated. For instance, it is known that if two numbers are written down at random, the probability that they will be prime to each other is $6/\pi^2$. Thus, in one case † where each of 50 students wrote down 5 pairs of numbers at random, 154 of the pairs were found to consist of numbers prime to each other. This gives $6/\pi^2 = 154/250$, from which we get $\pi = 3 \cdot 12$.

* *Messenger of Mathematics*, Cambridge, 1873, vol. ii, pp. 113, 114.

† Note on π by R. Chartres, *Philosophical Magazine*, London, series 6, vol. xxxix, March, 1904, p. 315.

CHAPTER XIII

CALCULATING PRODIGIES

AT rare intervals there have appeared lads who possess extraordinary powers of mental calculation.* In a few seconds they gave the answers to questions connected with the multiplication of numbers and the extraction of roots of numbers, which an expert mathematician could obtain only in a longer time and with the aid of pen and paper. Nor were their powers always limited to such simple problems. More difficult questions, dealing for instance with factors, compound interest, annuities, the civil and ecclesiastical calendars, and the solution of equations, were solved by some of them with facility as soon as the meaning of what was wanted had been grasped. In most cases these lads were illiterate, and usually their rules of working were of their own invention.

The performances were so remarkable that some observers held that these prodigies possessed powers differing in kind from those of their contemporaries. For such a view there is no foundation. Any lad with an excellent memory and a natural turn for arithmetic can, if he continuously gives his undivided attention to the consideration of numbers, and indulges in constant practice, attain great proficiency in mental arithmetic, and of course the performances of those that are specially gifted are exceptionally astonishing.

In this chapter I propose to describe briefly the doings of

* Most of the facts about calculating prodigies have been collected by E. W. Scripture, *American Journal of Psychology*, 1891, vol. IV, pp. 1—59; by F. D. Mitchell, *ibid.*, 1907, vol. XVIII, pp. 61—143; and G. E. Müller, *Zur Analyse der Gedächtnistätigkeit und des Vorstellungsverlaufes*, Leipzig, 1911. I have used these papers freely, and in some cases where authorities are quoted of which I have no first-hand information have relied exclusively on them. These articles should be consulted for bibliographical notes on the numerous original authorities.

the more famous calculating prodigies. It will be seen that their performances were of much the same general character, though carried to different extents; hence in the later cases it will be enough to indicate briefly peculiarities of the particular calculators.

I confine myself to self-taught calculators, and thus exclude the consideration of a few public performers who by practice, arithmetical devices, and the tricks of the showman have simulated like powers. I also concern myself only with those who showed the power in youth. As far as I know, the only self-taught mathematician of advanced years whom I thus exclude is John Wallis, 1616—1703, the Savilian Professor at Oxford, who in middle-life developed, for his own amusement, his powers in mental arithmetic. As an illustration of his achievements, I note that on 22 December, 1669, he, when in bed, occupied himself in finding (mentally) the integral part of the square root of 3×10^{40}; and several hours afterwards wrote down the result from memory. This fact having attracted notice, two months later he was challenged to extract the square root of a number of fifty-three digits; this he performed mentally, and a month later he dictated the answer, which he had not meantime committed to writing. Such efforts of calculation and memory are typical of calculating prodigies.

One of the earliest of these prodigies of whom we have records was *Jedediah Buxton*, who was born in or about 1707 at Elmton, Derbyshire. Although a son of the village school-master, his education was neglected, and he never learnt to write or cipher. With the exception of his power of dealing with large numbers, his mental faculties were of a low order : he had no ambition, and remained throughout his life a farm labourer, nor did his exceptional skill with figures bring him any material advantage other than that of occasionally receiving small sums of money from those who induced him to exhibit his peculiar gift. He does not seem to have given public exhibitions. He died in 1772.

He had no recollection as to when or how he was first
attracted by mental calculations, and of his performances in
early life we have no reliable details. Mere numbers, however,
seem always to have had a strange fascination for him. If
the size of an object was stated, he began at once to compute
how many inches or hair-breadths it contained; if a period of
time was mentioned, he calculated the number of minutes in
it; if he heard a sermon, he thought only of the number of
words or syllables in it. No doubt his powers in these matters
increased by incessant practice, but his ideas were childish,
and do not seem to have gone beyond pride in being able to
state accurately the results of such calculations. He was
slow-witted, and took far longer to answer arithmetical
questions than most of these prodigies. The only practical
accomplishment to which his powers led him was the ability
to estimate by inspection the acreage of a field of irregular
shape.

His fame gradually spread through Derbyshire. Among
many questions put to him by local visitors were the following, which fairly indicate his powers when a young man:
How many acres are there in a rectangular field 351 yards
long and 261 wide? answered in 11 minutes. How many
cubic yards of earth must be removed in order to make a
pond 426 feet long, 263 feet wide, and 2½ feet deep? answered in
15 minutes. If sound travels 1,142 feet in one second, how
long will it take to travel 5 miles? answered in 15 minutes.
Such questions involve no difficulties of principle.

Here are a few of the harder problems solved by Buxton
when his powers were fully developed. He calculated to what
sum a farthing would amount if doubled 140 times: the
answer is a number of pounds sterling which requires thirty-
nine digits to represent it, with 2s. 8d. over. He was then asked
to multiply this number of thirty-nine digits by itself: to
this he gave the answer two and a half months later, and he
said he had carried on the calculation at intervals during that
period. In 1751 he calculated how many cubic inches there are

in a right-angled block of stone 23,145,789 yards long, 5,642,732 yards wide, and 54,965 yards thick; how many grains of corn would be required to fill a cube whose volume is 202,680,000,360 cubic miles; and how many hairs one inch long would be required to fill the same space—the dimensions of a grain and a hair being given. These problems involve high numbers, but are not intrinsically difficult, though they could not be solved mentally unless the calculator had a phenomenally good memory. In each case he gave the correct answer, though only after considerable effort. In 1753 he was asked to give the dimensions of a cubical cornbin which holds exactly one quarter of malt. He recognized that to answer this required a process equivalent to the extraction of a cube root, which was a novel idea to him, but in an hour he said that the edge of the cube would be between $25\frac{1}{2}$ and 26 inches, which is correct: it has been suggested that he got this answer by trying various numbers.

Accounts of his performances were published, and his reputation reached London, which he visited in 1754. During his stay there he was examined by various members of the Royal Society, who were satisfied as to the genuineness of his performances. Some of his acquaintances took him to Drury Lane Theatre to see Garrick, being curious to see how a play would impress his imagination. He was entirely unaffected by the scene, but on coming out informed his hosts of the exact number of words uttered by the various actors, and of the number of steps taken by others in their dances.

It was only in rare cases that he was able to explain his methods of work, but enough is known of them to enable us to say that they were clumsy. He described the process by which he arrived at the product of 456 and 378: shortly it was as follows:—If we denote the former of these numbers by a, he proceeded first to find $5a =$ (say) b; then to find $20b =$ (say) c; and then to find $3c =$ (say) d. He next formed $15b =$ (say) e, which he added to d. Lastly he formed $3a$, which, added to the sum last obtained, gave the result. This is equivalent to saying that he used the multiplier 378 in the form $(5 \times 20 \times 3) + (5 \times 15) + 3$. Mitchell suggests that this may mean that Buxton counted by multiples of 60 and of 15, and thus reduced the multiplication to addition. It may be so, for it is difficult to suppose that he did not realize that successive multiplications by 5 and 20 are equivalent to a multiplication by 100, of which the result can be at once obtained. Of billions, trillions, etc., he had never heard, and in order to represent the high numbers required in some of the questions proposed to him, he invented a notation of his own, calling 10^{18} a tribe and 10^{36} a cramp.

As in the case of all these calculators, his memory was exceptionally good, and in time he got to know a large number of facts (such as the products of certain constantly recurring numbers, the number of minutes in a year, and the number of hair-breadths in a mile), which greatly facilitated his calculations. A curious and perhaps unique feature in his case was that he could stop in the middle of a piece of mental calculation, take up other subjects, and after an interval, sometimes of weeks, could resume the consideration of the problem. He could answer simple questions when two or more were proposed simultaneously.

Another eighteenth-century prodigy was *Thomas Fuller*, a negro, born in 1710 in Africa. He was captured there in 1724, and exported as a slave to Virginia, U.S.A., where he lived till his death in 1790. Like Buxton, Fuller never learnt to read or write, and his abilities were confined to mental arithmetic. He could multiply together two numbers, if each contained not more than nine digits, could state the number of seconds in a given period of time, the number of grains of corn in a given mass, and so on—in short, answer the stock problems commonly proposed to these prodigies, as long as they involved only multiplications and the solutions of problems by rule of three. Although more rapid than Buxton, he was a slow worker as compared with some of those whose doings are described below.

I mention next the case of two mathematicians of note who showed similar aptitude in early years. The first of these was *André Marie Ampère*, 1775—1836, who, when a child some four years old, was accustomed to perform long mental calculations, which he effected by means of rules learnt from playing with arrangements of pebbles. But though always expert at mental arithmetic, and endowed with a phenomenal memory for figures, he did not specially cultivate this arithmetical power. It is more difficult to say whether *Carl Friedrich Gauss*, 1777—1855, should be reckoned among these calculating prodigies. He had, when three years old, taught himself some arithmetical processes, and astonished his father by correcting him in his calculations of certain payments for overtime; perhaps, however, this is only evidence of the early age at which his consummate abilities began to develop. Another remarkable case is that of *Richard Whately*, 1787—1863, afterwards Archbishop of Dublin. When he was about five or six years old he showed considerable skill in mental arithmetic : it disappeared in about three years. " I soon," said he, " got to do the most difficult sums, always in my head, for I knew nothing of figures beyond numeration, nor had I any names for the different processes I employed. But I believe my sums were chiefly in multiplication, division, and the rule of three. . . . I did these sums much quicker than anyone could upon paper, and I never remember committing the smallest error. I was engaged either in calculating or in castle-building . . . morning, noon, and night. . . . When I went to school, at which time the passion was worn off, I was a perfect dunce at ciphering, and so have continued ever since." The archbishop's arithmetical powers were, however, greater in after-life than he here allows.

The performances of *Zerah Colburn* in London, in 1812, were more remarkable. Colburn,* born in 1804, at Cabut, Vermont, U.S.A., was the son of a small farmer. While still

* To the authorities mentioned by E. W. Scripture and F. D. Mitchel should be added *The Annual Register*, London, 1812, pp. 507 *et seq.*

less than six years old he showed extraordinary powers of mental calculation, which were displayed in a tour in America. Two years later he was brought to England, where he was repeatedly examined by competent observers. He could instantly give the product of two numbers each of four digits, but hesitated if both numbers exceeded 10,000. Among questions asked him at this time were to raise 8 to the 16th power; in a few seconds he gave the answer 281,474,976,710,656, which is correct. He was next asked to raise the numbers 2, 3, ... 9 to the 10th power : and he gave the answers so rapidly that the gentleman who was taking them down was obliged to ask him to repeat them more slowly; but he worked less quickly when asked to raise numbers of two digits like 37 or 59 to high powers. He gave instantaneously the square roots and cube roots (when they were integers) of high numbers, *e.g.* the square root of 106,929 and the cube root of 268,336,125; such integral roots can, however, be obtained easily by various methods. More remarkable are his answers to questions on the factors of numbers. Asked for the factors of 247,483, he replied 941 and 263; asked for the factors of 171,395, he gave 5, 7, 59, and 83; asked for the factors of 36,083, he said there were none. He, however, found it difficult to answer questions about the factors of numbers higher than 1,000,000. His power of factorizing high numbers was exceptional, and depended largely on the method of two-digit terminals described below. Like all these public performers, he had to face buffoons who tried to make fun of him, but he was generally equal to them. Asked on one such occasion how many black beans were required to make three white ones, he is said to have at once replied, " Three, if you skin them "—this, however, has much the appearance of a pre-arranged show.

It was clear to observers that the child operated by certain rules, and during his calculations his lips moved as if he was expressing the process in words. Of his honesty there seems to have been no doubt. In a few cases he was able to explain the method of operation. Asked for the square of 4,395, he hesitated, but on the question being repeated, he gave the correct answer—namely, 19,316,025. Questioned as to the cause of his hesitation, he said he did not like to multiply four figures by four figures, but said he, " I found out another way; I multiplied 293 by 293 and then multiplied this product twice by the number 15." On another occasion when asked for the product of 21,734 by 543, he immediately replied 11,801,562; and on being questioned explained that he had arrived at this by multiplying 65,202 by 181. These remarks suggest that whenever convenient he factorized the numbers with which he was dealing.

In 1814 he was taken to Paris, but amid the political turmoil of the time his exhibitions fell flat. His English and American friends, however, raised money for his education, and he was sent in succession to the Lycée Napoleon in Paris and Westminster School in London. With education his calculating powers fell off, and he lost the frankness which when a boy had charmed observers. His subsequent career was diversified and not altogether successful. He commenced with the stage, then tried schoolmastering, then became an itinerant preacher in America, and finally a " professor " of languages. He wrote his own biography, which contains an account of the methods he used. He died in 1840.

Contemporary with Colburn we find another instance of a self-taught boy, *George Parker Bidder*, who possessed quite exceptional powers of this kind. He is perhaps the most interesting of these prodigies, because he subsequently received a liberal education, retained his calculating powers, and in later life analysed and explained the methods he had invented and used.

Bidder was born in 1806 at Moreton Hampstead, Devonshire, where his father was a stone-mason. At the age of six he was taught to count up to 100, but though sent to the village school, learnt little there, and at the beginning of his career was ignorant of the meaning of arithmetical terms and of numerical symbols. Equipped solely with this knowledge of counting, he taught himself the results of addition, subtraction, and multiplication of numbers (less than 100) by arranging and rearranging marbles, buttons, and shot in patterns. In after-life he attached great importance to such concrete representations, and believed that his arithmetical powers were strengthened by the fact that at that time he knew nothing about the symbols for numbers. When seven years old he heard a dispute between two of his neighbours about the price of something which was being sold by the pound, and to their astonishment remarked that they were both wrong, mentioning the correct price. After this exhibition the villagers delighted in trying to pose him with arithmetical problems.

His reputation increased and, before he was nine years old, his father found it profitable to take him about the country to exhibit his powers. A couple of distinguished Cambridge graduates (Thomas Jephson, then tutor of St. John's, and John Herschel) saw him in 1817, and were so impressed by his general intelligence that they raised a fund for his education, and induced his father to give up the rôle of showman; but after a few months Bidder senior repented of his abandonment of money so easily earned, insisted on his son's return, and began again to make an exhibition of the boy's powers. In 1818, in the course of a tour, young Bidder was pitted against Colburn, and on the whole proved the abler calculator. Finally the father and son came to Edinburgh, where some members of that University intervened and persuaded his father to leave the lad in their care to be educated. Bidder remained with them, and in due course graduated at Edinburgh, shortly afterwards entering the profession of civil engineering, in which he rose to high distinction. He died in 1878.

With practice Bidder's powers steadily developed. His earlier performances seem to have been of the same type as those of Buxton and Colburn which have been already described. In addition to answering questions on products of numbers and the number of specified units in given quantities, he was, after 1819, ready in finding square roots, cube roots, etc., of high numbers, it being assumed that the root is an integer, and later explained his method, which is easy of application : this method is the same as that used by Colburn. By this time he was able also to give immediate solutions of easy problems on compound interest and annuities which seemed to his contemporaries the most astonishing of all his feats. In factorizing numbers he was less successful than Colburn, and was generally unable to deal at sight with numbers higher than 10,000. As in the case of Colburn, attempts to be witty at his expense were often made, but he could hold his own. Asked at one of his performances in London in 1818 how many bulls' tails were wanted to reach to the moon, he immediately answered one, if it is long enough.

Here are some typical questions put to and answered by him in his exhibitions during the years 1815—1819 : they are taken from authenticated lists which comprise some hundreds of such problems : few, if any, are inherently difficult. His rapidity of work was remarkable, but the time limits given were taken by unskilled observers, and can be regarded as only approximately correct. Of course, all the calculations were mental without the aid of books, pencil, or paper. In 1815, being then nine years old, he was asked : If the moon be distant from the earth 123,256 miles, and sound travels at the rate of 4 miles a minute, how long would it be before the inhabitants of the moon could hear of the battle of Waterloo ? answer, 21 days 9 hours 34 minutes, given in less than one minute. In 1816, being then ten years old, just learning to write, but unable to form figures, he answered questions such as the following : What is the interest on £11,111 for 11,111 days at 5 per cent. a year ? answer, £16,911 11s., given in one minute. How many hogsheads of cider can be made from a million of apples, if 30 apples make one quart ? answer, 132 hogsheads 17 gallons 1 quart and 10 apples over, given in 35 seconds

If a coach-wheel is 5 feet 10 inches in circumference, how many times will it revolve in running 800,000,000 miles? answer, 724,114,285,704 times and 20 inches remaining, given in 50 seconds. What is the square root of 119,550,669,121? answer 345,761, given in 30 seconds. In 1817, being then eleven years old, he was asked: How long would it take to fill a reservoir whose volume is one cubic mile if there flowed into it from a river 120 gallons of water a minute? answered in 2 minutes. Assuming that light travels from the sun to the earth in 8 minutes, and that the sun is 98,000,000 miles off, if light takes 6 years 4 months travelling from the nearest fixed star to the earth, what is the distance of that star, reckoning 365 days 6 hours to each year and 28 days to each month?— asked by Sir William Herschel: answer, 40,633,740,000,000 miles. In 1818, at one of his performances, he was asked: If the pendulum of a clock vibrates the distance of $9\frac{3}{4}$ inches in a second of time, how many inches will it vibrate in 7 years 14 days 2 hours 1 minute 56 seconds, each year containing 365 days 5 hours 48 minutes 55 seconds? answer, 2,165,625,744$\frac{3}{4}$ inches, given in less than a minute. If I have 42 watches for sale and I sell the first for a farthing, and double the price for every succeeding watch I sell, what will be the price of the last watch?   answer, £2,290,649,224 10s. 8d. If the diameter of a penny piece is $1\frac{3}{8}$ inches, and if the world is girdled with a ring of pence put side by side, what is their value sterling, supposing the distance to be 360 degrees, and a degree to contain 69·5 miles? answer, £4,803,340, given in one minute. Find two numbers whose difference is 12 and whose product, multiplied by their sum, is equal to 14,560? answer, 14 and 26. In 1819, when fourteen years old, he was asked: Find a number whose cube less 19 multiplied by its cube shall be equal to the cube of 6: answer, 3, given instantly. What will it cost to make a road for 21 miles 5 furlongs 37 poles 4 yards, at the rate of £123 14s. 6d. a mile? answer, £2,688 13s. 9$\frac{3}{4}$d., given in 2 minutes. If you are now 14 years old and you live 50 years longer and spend half-a-crown a day, how many farthings will you spend in your life? answer, 2,805,120, given in 15 seconds. Mr. Moor contracted to illuminate the city of London with 22,965,321 lamps; the expense of trimming and lighting was 7 farthings a lamp, the oil consumed was $\frac{2}{3}$ths of a pint for every three lamps, and the oil cost 3s. 7$\frac{1}{2}d$. a gallon; he gained 16$\frac{1}{2}$ per cent. on his outlay: how many gallons of oil were consumed, what was the cost to him, and what was the amount of the contract? answer, he used 212,641 gallons of oil, the cost was £205,996 16s. 1$\frac{3}{4}d$., and the amount of the contract was £239,986 13s. 2d.

It should be noted that Bidder did not visualize a number like 984 in symbols, but thought of it in a concrete way as so many units which could be arranged in 24 groups of 41 each. It should also be observed that he, like Inaudi, whom I mention later, relied largely on the auditory sense to enable him to recollect numbers. " For my own part," he wrote, in later life, " though much accustomed to see sums and quantities expressed by the usual symbols, yet if I endeavour to get any number of figures that are represented on paper fixed in my memory, it takes me a much longer time and a very great deal more exertion than when they are expressed or enumerated verbally." For instance, suppose a question put to find the product of two numbers each of nine digits, if they were " read to me, I should not require this to be done more than once; but if they were represented in the usual way, and put into my hands, it would probably take me four times to peruse them before it would be in my power to repeat them, and after all they would not be impressed so vividly on my imagination."

Bidder retained his power of rapid mental calculation to the end of his life, and as a constant parliamentary witness in matters connected with engineering it proved a valuable accomplishment. Just before his death an illustration of his powers was given to a friend who, talking of then recent discoveries, remarked that if 36,918 waves of red light which only occupy one inch are required to give the impression of red, and if light travels at 190,000 miles a second, how immense must be the number of waves which must strike the eye in one second to give the impression of red. " You need not work it out," said Bidder; " the number will be 444,433,651,200,000."

Other members of the Bidder family have also shown exceptional powers of a similar kind as well as extraordinary memories. Of Bidder's elder brothers, one became an actuary, and on his books being burnt in a fire, he rewrote them in six months from memory, but, it is said, died of consequent brain fever; another was a Plymouth Brother, and knew the whole Bible by heart, being able to give chapter and verse for any text quoted. Bidder's eldest son, a lawyer of eminence, was able to multiply together two numbers each of fifteen digits. Neither in accuracy nor rapidity was he equal to his father, but, then, he never steadily and continuously devoted himself to developing his abilities in this direction. He remarked that in his mental arithmetic, he worked with pictures of the figures, and said, " If I perform a sum mentally it always proceeds in a visible form in my mind; indeed I can conceive no other way possible of doing mental arithmetic " : this, it will be noticed, is opposed to his father's method. Two of his children, one son and one daughter, representing a third generation, inherited analogous powers.

I mention next the names of *Henri Mondeux*, and *Vito Mangiamele*. Both were born in 1826 in humble circumstances, were shepherds, and became when children noticeable for feats in calculation which deservedly procured for them local fame. In 1839 and 1840 respectively they were brought to Paris, where their powers were displayed in public, and tested by Arago, Cauchy, and others. Mondeux's performances were the more striking. One question put to him was to solve the equation $x^3 + 84 = 37x$: to this he at once gave the answer 3 and 4, but did not detect the third root, namely, — 7. Another question asked was to find solutions of the indeterminate equation $x^2 - y^2 = 133$: to this he replied immediately 66 and 67; asked for a simpler solution he said after an instant 6 and 13. I do not, however, propose to discuss their feats in detail, for there was at least a suspicion that these lads were not frank, and that those who were exploiting them had taught them rules which enabled them to simulate powers they did not really possess. Finally both returned to farm work, and ceased to interest the scientific world. If Mondeux was self-taught, we must credit him with a discovery of some algebraic theorems which would entitle him to rank as a mathematical genius, but in that case it is inconceivable that he never did anything more, and that his powers appeared to be limited to the particular problems solved by him.

Johann Martin Zacharias Dase, whom I next mention, is a far more interesting example of these calculating prodigies. Dase was born in 1824 at Hamburg. He had a fair education, and was afforded every opportunity to develop his powers, but save in matters connected with reckoning and numbers he made little progress, and struck all observers as dull. Of geometry and any language but German he remained ignorant to the end of his days. He was trustworthy, and filled various small official posts in Germany. He gave exhibitions of his calculating powers in Germany, Austria, and England. He died in 1861.

When exhibiting in Vienna in 1840, he made the acquaintance of Strasznicky, who urged him to apply his powers to scientific purposes. This Dase gladly agreed to do, and so became acquainted with Gauss, Schumacher, Petersen, and Encke. To his contributions to science I allude later. In mental arithmetic the only problems to which I find allusions are straightforward examples like the following: Multiply 79,532,853 by 93,758,479 : asked by Schumacher, answered in 54 seconds. In answer to a similar request to find the product of two numbers each of twenty digits, he took 6 minutes; to find the product of two numbers each of forty digits, he took

40 minutes; to find the product of two numbers each of a hundred digits, he took 8 hours 45 minutes. Gauss thought that perhaps on paper the last of these problems could be solved in half this time by a skilled computator. Dase once extracted the square root of a number of a hundred digits in 52 minutes. These feats far surpass all other records of the kind, the only calculations comparable to them being Buxton's squaring of a number of thirty-nine digits, and Wallis's extraction of the square root of a number of fifty-three digits. Dase's mental work, however, was not always accurate, and once (in 1845) he gave incorrect answers to every question put to him, but on that occasion he had a headache, and there is nothing astonishing in his failure.

Like all these calculating prodigies, he had a wonderful memory, and an hour or two after a performance could repeat all the numbers mentioned in it. He had also the peculiar gift of being able after a single glance to state the number (up to about 30) of sheep in a flock, of books in a case, and so on; and of visualizing and recollecting a large number of objects. For instance, after a second's look at some dominoes he gave the sum (117) of their points; asked how many letters were in a certain line of print chosen at random in a quarto page, he instantly gave the correct number (63); shown twelve digits, he had in half a second memorized them and their positions so as to be able to name instantly the particular digit occupying any assigned place. It is to be regretted that we do not know more of these performances. Those who are acquainted with the delightful autobiography of Robert-Houdin will recollect how he cultivated a similar power, and how valuable he found it in the exercise of his art.

Dase's calculations, when also allowed the use of paper and pencil, were almost incredibly rapid, and invariably accurate. When he was sixteen years old Strasznicky taught him the use of the familiar formula $\pi/4 = \tan^{-1}(\frac{1}{2}) + \tan^{-1}(\frac{1}{5}) + \tan^{-1}(\frac{1}{8})$, and asked him thence to calculate π. In two months he carried the approximation to 205 places of decimals, of which 200

are correct.* Dase's next achievement was to calculate the
natural logarithms of the first 1,005,000 numbers to 7 places of
decimals; he did this in his off-time from 1844 to 1847, when
occupied by the Prussian survey. During the next two years
he compiled in his spare time a hyperbolic table which was
published by the Austrian Government in 1857. Later he
offered to makes tables of the factors of all numbers from
7,000,000 to 10,000,000, and, on the recommendation of Gauss,
the Hamburg Academy of Sciences agreed to assist him so that
he might have leisure for the purpose, but he lived only long
enough to finish about half the work.

Truman Henry Safford, born in 1836 at Royalton, Vermont,
U.S.A., was another calculating prodigy. He was of a somewhat different type, for he received a good education, graduated
in due course at Harvard, and ultimately took up astronomy,
in which subject he held a professional post. I gather that
though always a rapid calculator, he gradually lost the
exceptional powers shown in his youth. He died in 1901.

Safford never exhibited his calculating powers in public, and
I know of them only through the accounts quoted by Scripture
and Mitchell, but they seem to have been typical of these
calculators. In 1842, he amused and astonished his family by
mental calculations. In 1846, when ten years old, he was
examined, and here are some of the questions then put to him :
Extract the cube root of a certain number of seven digits;
answered instantly. What number is that which being divided
by the product of its digits, the quotient is three, and if 18 be
added the digits will be inverted? answer 24, given in about a
minute. What is the surface of a regular pyramid whose
slant height is 17 feet, and the base a pentagon of which each
side is 33·5 feet? answer 3354·5558 square feet, given in
two minutes. Asked to square a number of eighteen digits,
he gave the answer in a minute or less, but the question was
made the more easy as the number consisted of the digits

---

* The result was published in *Crelle's Journal*, 1844, vol. xxvii, p. 198 :
on closer approximations and easier formulae, see Chapter XII.

365 repeated six times. Like Colburn, he factorized high numbers with ease. In such examples his processes were empirical;
he selected (he could not tell how) likely factors and tested the
matter in a few seconds by actual division.

More recently there have been four calculators of some note :
Ugo Zamebone, an Italian, born in 1867; *Pericles Diamandi*, a
Greek, born in 1868; *Carl Rückle*, a German; and *Jacques
Inaudi*, born in 1867. The three first mentioned were of the
normal type, and I do not propose to describe their perform-
ances, but Inaudi's performances merit a fuller treatment.

Jacques Inaudi * was born in 1867 at Onorato in Italy. He
was employed in early years as a shepherd, and spent the long
idle hours in which he had no active duties in pondering on
numbers, but used for them no concrete representations such
as pebbles. His calculating powers first attracted notice
about 1873. Shortly afterwards his elder brother sought his
fortune as an organ-grinder in Provence, and young Inaudi,
accompanying him, came into a wider world, and earned a
few coppers for himself by street exhibitions of his powers.
His ability was exploited by showmen, and thus in 1880 he
visited Paris, where he gave exhibitions : in these he impressed
all observers as being modest, frank, and straightforward.
He was then ignorant of reading and writing : these arts he
subsequently acquired.

His earlier performances were not specially remarkable as
compared with those of similar calculating prodigies, but with
continual practice he improved. Thus at Lyons in 1873 he
could multiply together almost instantaneously two numbers
of three digits. In 1874 he was able to multiply a number of
six digits by another number of six digits. Nine years later he
could work rapidly with numbers of nine or ten digits. Still
later, in Paris, asked by Darboux to cube 27, he gave the
answer in 10 seconds. In 13 seconds he calculated how many

---

* See Charcot and Darboux, *Mémoires de l'Institut, Comptes Rendus*, 1892,
vol. CXIV, pp. 275, 528, 578; and Binet, *Révue des deux Mondes*, 1892, vol.
CXI, pp. 905—924.

seconds are contained in 18 years 7 months 21 days 3 hours : and he gave immediately the square root of one-sixth of the difference between the square of 4,801 and unity. He also calculated with ease the amount of wheat due according to the traditional story to Sessa, who, for inventing chess, was to receive 1 grain on the first cell of a chess-board, 2 on the second, 4 on the third, and so on in geometrical progression.

He could find the integral roots of equations and integral solutions of problems, but proceeded only by trial and error. His most remarkable feat was the expression of numbers less than 10^5 in the form of a sum of four squares, which he could usually do in a minute or two; this power was peculiar to him. Such problems were repeatedly solved at private performances, but the mental strain caused by them was considerable.

A performance before the general public rarely lasted more than 12 minutes, and was a much simpler affair. A normal programme included the subtraction of one number of twenty-one digits from another number of twenty-one digits : the addition of five numbers each of six digits : the multiplying of a number of four digits by another number of four digits : the extraction of the cube root of a number of nine digits, and of the fifth root of a number of twelve digits : the determination of the number of seconds in a period of time, and the day of the week on which a given date falls. Of course, the questions were put by members of the audience. To a professional calculator these problems are not particularly difficult. As each number was announced, Inaudi repeated it slowly to his assistant, who wrote it on a blackboard, and then slowly read it aloud to make sure that it was right. Inaudi then repeated the number once more. By this time he had generally solved the problem, but if he wanted longer time he made a few remarks of a general character, which he was able to do without interfering with his mental calculations. Throughout the exhibition he faced the audience : the fact that he never even glanced at the blackboard added to the effect.

It is probable that the majority of calculating prodigies rely on the speech-muscles as well as on the eye and the ear to help them to recollect the figures with which they are dealing. It was formerly believed that they all visualized the numbers proposed to them, and certainly some have done so. Inaudi, however, trusted mainly to the ear and to articulation. Bidder also relied partly on the ear, and when he visualized a number, it was not as a collection of digits, but as a concrete collection of units divisible, if the number was composite, into definite groups. Rückle relied mainly on visualizing the numbers. So it would seem that there are different types of the memories of calculators. Inaudi could reproduce mentally the sound of the repetition of the digits of the number in his own voice, and was confused, rather than helped, if the numbers were shown to him in writing. The articulation of the digits of the number also seemed necessary to enable him fully to exhibit his powers, and he was accustomed to repeat the numbers aloud before beginning to work on them—the sequence of sounds being important. A number of twenty-four digits being read to him, in 59 seconds he memorized the sound of it, so that he could give the sequence of digits forwards or backwards from selected points—a feat which Mondeux had taken 5 minutes to perform. Numbers of about a hundred digits were similarly memorized by Inaudi in 12 minutes, by Diamandi in 25 minutes, and by Rückle in under 5 minutes. This power is confined to numbers, and calculators cannot usually recollect a ong sequence of letters. Numbers were ever before Inaudi: he thought of little else, he dreamt of them, and sometimes even solved problems in his sleep. His memory was excellent for numbers, but normal or subnormal for other things. At the end of a séance he could repeat the questions which had been put to him and his answers, involving hundreds of digits in all. Nor was his memory in such matters limited to a few hours. Once, eight days after he had been given a question on a number of twenty-two digits, he was unexpectedly asked about it, and at once repeated the number. He was repeatedly examined, and we know more of his work than of any of his predecessors, with the possible exception of Bidder.

Most of these calculating prodigies find it difficult or impossible to explain their methods. But we have a few analyses by competent observers of the processes used : notably one by Bidder on his own work; another by Colburn on his work; and others by Müller and Darboux on the work of Rückle and Inaudi respectively. That by Bidder is the most complete, and the others are on much the same general lines.

Bidder's account of the processes he had discovered and used is contained in a lecture * given by him in 1856 to the Institution of Civil Engineers. Before describing these processes there are two remarks of a general character which should, I think, be borne in mind when reading his statement. In the first place, he gives his methods in their perfected form, and not necessarily in that which he used in boyhood : moreover, it is probable that in practice he employed devices to shorten the work which he did not set out in his lecture. In the second place, it is certain, in spite of his belief to the contrary, that he, like most of these prodigies, had an exceptionally good memory, which was strengthened by incessant practice. One example will suffice. In 1816, at a performance, a number was read to him backwards : he at once gave it in its normal form. An hour later he was asked if he remembered it : he immediately repeated it correctly. The number was : 2,563,721,987,653,461,598,746,231,905,607,541,128,975,231.

Of the four fundamental processes, addition and subtraction present no difficulty and are of little interest. The only point to which it seems worth calling attention is that Bidder, in adding three or more numbers together, always added them one at a time, as is illustrated in the examples given below. Rapid mental arithmetic depended, in his opinion, on the arrangement of the work, whenever possible, in such a way that only

* *Institution of Civil Engineers, Proceedings*, London, 1856, vol. xv, pp. 251—280. An early draft of the lecture is extant in MS.; the variations made in it are interesting, as showing the history of his mental development, but are not sufficiently important to need detailed notice here.

B.B

one fact had to be dealt with at a time. This is also noticeable in Inaudi's work.

The multiplication of one number by another was, naturally enough, the earliest problem Bidder came across, and by the time he was six years old he had taught himself the multiplication table up to 10 times 10. He soon had practice in harder sums, for, being a favourite of the village blacksmith, and constantly in the smithy, it became customary for the men sitting round the forge-fire to ask him multiplication sums. From products of numbers of two digits, which he would give without any appreciable pause for thought, he rose to numbers of three and then of four digits. Halfpence rewarded his efforts, and by the time he was eight years old, he could multiply together two numbers each of six digits. In one case he even multiplied together two numbers each of twelve digits, but, he says, " it required much time," and " was a great and distressing effort."

The method that he used is, in principle, the same as that explained in the usual text-books, except that he added his results as he went on. Thus to multiply 397 by 173 he proceeded as follows :—

We have	$100 \times 397 = 39700,$		
to this must be added	$70 \times 300 = 21000$	making	60,700,
,, ,, ,, ,, ,,	$70 \times 90 = 6300$	,,	67,000,
,, ,, ,, ,, ,,	$70 \times 7 = 490$	,,	67,490,
,, ,, ,, ,, ,,	$3 \times 300 = 900$	,,	68,390,
,, ,, ,, ,, ,,	$3 \times 90 = 270$	,,	68,660,
,, ,, ,, ,, ,,	$3 \times 7 = 21$	,,	68,681.

We shall underrate his rapidity if we allow as much as a second for each of these steps, but even if we take this low standard of his speed of working, he would have given the answer in 7 seconds. By this method he never had at one time more than two numbers to add together, and the factors are arranged so that each of them has only one significant digit : this is the common practice of mental calculators. It will also be observed that here, as always, Bidder worked from left to right : this, though not usually taught in our schools, is the natural and most convenient way. In effect he formed the product of $(100 + 70 + 3)$ and $(300 + 90 + 7)$, or $(a + b + c)$ and $(d + e + f)$ in the form $ad + ae \ldots + cf$.

The result of a multiplication like that given above was attained so rapidly as to seem instantaneous, and practically gave him the use of a multiplication table up to 1000 by 1000. On this basis, when dealing with much larger numbers—for instance, when multiplying 965,446,371 by 843,409,133—he worked by numbers forming groups of 3 digits, proceeding as if 965, 446, etc., were digits in a scale whose radix was 1000 : in middle life he would solve a problem like this in about 6 minutes. Such difficulty as he experienced in these multiplications seems to have been rather in recalling the result of the previous step than in making the actual multiplications.

Inaudi also multiplied in this way, but he was content if one of the factors had only one significant digit : he also sometimes made use of negative quantities : for instance, he thought of 27×729 as $27(730 - 1)$; so, too, he thought of 25×841 in the form $84100/4$; and in squaring numbers he was accustomed to think of the number in the form $a + b$, choosing a and b of convenient forms, and then to calculate the result in the form $a^2 + 2ab + b^2$.

In multiplying concrete data by a number Bidder worked on similar lines to those explained above in the multiplication of two numbers. Thus to multiply £14 15s. $6\frac{3}{4}d$. by 787 he proceeded thus :

We have $\qquad$ £$(787)(14) = $ £11018 0s. 0d.
to which we add $(787)(15)$ shillings $= $ £590 5s. 0d. making £11608 5s. 0d.
to which we add $(787)(27)$ farthings $= $ £22 2s. $8\frac{1}{4}d$. making £11630 7s. $8\frac{1}{4}d$.

Division was performed by Bidder much as taught in schoolbooks, except that his power of multiplying large numbers at sight enabled him to guess intelligently and so save unnecessary work. This also was Inaudi's method. A division sum with a remainder presents more difficulty. Bidder was

better skilled in dealing with such questions than most of
these prodigies, but even in his prime he never solved such
problems with the same rapidity as those with no remainder.
In public performances difficult questions on division are
generally precluded by the rules of the game.

If, in a division sum, Bidder knew that there was no
remainder, he often proceeded by a system of two-digit
terminals. Thus, for example, in dividing (say) 25,696 by
176, he first argued that the answer must be a number of
three digits, and obviously the left-hand digit must be 1.
Next he had noticed that there are only 4 numbers of two
digits (namely, 21, 46, 71, 96) which when multiplied by 76
give a number which ends in 96. Hence the answer must
be 121, or 146, or 171, or 196; and experience enabled him
to say without calculation that 121 was too small and 171
too large. Hence the answer must be 146. If he felt any
hesitation, he mentally multiplied 146 by 176 (which he
said he could do " instantaneously "), and thus checked the
result. It is noticeable that when Bidder, Colburn, and some
other calculating prodigies knew the last two digits of a
product of two numbers, they also knew, perhaps subcon-
sciously, that the last two digits of the separate numbers were
necessarily of certain forms. The theory of these two-digit
arrangements has been discussed by Mitchell.

Frequently also in division, Bidder used what I will call a
digital process, which *a priori* would seem far more laborious
than the normal method, though in his hands the method was
extraordinarily rapid : this method was, I think, peculiar to
him. I define the digital of a number as the digit obtained by
finding the sum of the digits of the original number, the sum
of the digits of this number, and so on, until the sum is less
than 10. The digital of a number is the same as the digital of
the product of the digitals of its factors. Let us apply this in
Bidder's way to see if 71 is an exact divisor of 23,141. The
digital of 23,141 is 2. The digital of 71 is 8. Hence if 71 is
a factor, the digital of the other factor must be 7, since 7 times

8 is the only multiple of 8 whose digital is 2. Now the only number which multiplied by 71 will give 41 as terminal digits is 71. And since the other factor must be one of three digits and its digital must be 7, this factor (if any) must be 871. But a cursory glance shows that 871 is too large. Hence 71 is not a factor of 23,141. Bidder found this process far more rapid than testing the matter by dividing by 71. As another example let us see if 73 is a factor of 23,141. The digital of 23,141 is 2; the digital of 73 is 1; hence the digital of the other factor (if any) must be 2. But since the last two digits of the number are 41, the last two digits of this factor (if any) must be 17. And since this factor is a number of three digits and its digital is 2, such a factor, if it exists, must be 317. This on testing (by multiplying it by 73) is found to be a factor.

When he began to exhibit his powers in public, questions concerning weights and measures were, of course, constantly proposed to him. In solving these he knew by heart many facts which frequently entered into such problems, such as the number of seconds in a year, the number of ounces in a ton, the number of square inches in an acre, the number of pence in a hundred pounds, the elementary rules about the civil and ecclesiastical calendars, and so on. A collection of such data is part of the equipment of all calculating prodigies.

In his exhibitions Bidder was often asked questions concerning square roots and cube roots, and at a later period higher roots. That he could at once give the answer excited unqualified astonishment in an uncritical audience; if, however, the answer is integral, this is a mere sleight of art which anyone can acquire. Without setting out the rules at length, a few examples will illustrate his method.

He was asked to find the square root of 337,561. It is obvious that the root is a number of three digits. Since the given number lies between 500^2 or 250,000 and 600^2 or 360,000, the left-hand digit of the root must be a 5. Reflection had shown him that the only numbers of two digits whose squares end in 61 are 19, 31, 69, 81, and he was familiar with this fact. Hence the answer was 519, or 531, or 569, or 581. But he argued that as 581 was nearly in the same ratio to 500 and 600 as 337,561 was to 250,000 and 360,000, the answer must be 581, a result which he verified by direct multiplication in a couple of seconds. Similarly in extracting the square root of 442,225, he saw at once that the left-hand digit of the answer was 6, and since the number ended in 225, the last two digits of the answer were 15 or 35, or 65 or 85. The position of 442,225 between $(600)^2$ and $(700)^2$ indicates that 65 should be taken. Thus the answer is 665, which he verified before announcing it. Other calculators have worked out similar rules for the extraction of roots.

For exact cube roots the process is more rapid. For example, asked to extract the cube root of 188,132,517, Bidder saw at once that the answer was a number of three digits, and since $5^3 = 125$ and $6^3 = 216$, the left-hand digit was 5. The only number of two digits whose cube ends in 17 is 73. Hence the answer is 573. Similarly the cube root of 180,362,125 must be a number of three digits, of which the left-hand digit is a 5, and the two right-hand digits were either 65 or 85. To see which of these was required, he mentally cubed 560, and seeing it was near the given number, assumed that 565 was the required answer, which he verified by cubing it. In general a cube root that ends in a 5 is a trifle more difficult to detect at sight by this method than one that ends in some other digit, but since 5^3 must be a factor of such numbers, we can divide by that and apply the process to the resulting number. Thus the above number 180,362,125 is equal to $5^3 \times 1,442,897$, of which the cube root is at once found to be 5(113)—that is, 565.

For still higher exact roots the process is even simpler, and for fifth roots it is almost absurdly easy, since the last digit of the number is always the same as the last digit of the root. Thus if the number proposed is less than 10^{10}, the answer consists of a number of two digits. Knowing the fifth powers to 10, 20, ... 90, we have, in order to know the first digit of the answer, only to see between which of these powers the number proposed lies, and the last digit being obvious, we can give the answer instantly. If the number is higher, but less than 10^{15}, the answer is a number of three digits, of which the middle digit can be found almost as rapidly as the others. This is rather a trick than a matter of mental calculation.

In his later exhibitions, Bidder was sometimes asked to extract roots, correct to the nearest integer, the exact root involving a fraction. If he suspected this, he tested it by " casting out the nines," and if satisfied that the answer was not an integer, proceeded tentatively as best he could. Such a question, if the answer is a number of three or more digits, is a severe tax on the powers of a mental calculator, and is usually disallowed in public exhibitions.

Colburn's remarkable feats in factorizing numbers led to similar questions being put to Bidder, and gradually he evolved some rules, but in this branch of mental arithmetic I do not think he ever became proficient. Of course, a factor which is a power of 2 or of 5 can be obtained at once and powers of 3 can be obtained almost as rapidly. For factors near the square root of a number he always tried the usual method of expressing the number in the form $a^2 - b^2$, in which case the factors are obvious. For other factors he tried the digital method already described.

Bidder was successful in giving almost instantaneously the answers to questions about compound interest and annuities : this was peculiar to him, but his method is quite simple, and may be illustrated by his determination of the compound interest on £100 at 5 per cent. for 14 years. He argued that the simple interest amounted to £(14)(5), *i.e.* to £70. At the end of the first year the capital was increased by £5, the annual interest on this was 5s. or one crown, and this ran for 13 years, at the end of the second year another £5 was due, and the 5s. interest on this ran for 12 years. Continuing this argument, he had to add to the £70 a sum of $(13 + 12 + \ldots + 1)$ crowns, *i.e.* $(13/2)(14)(5)$ shillings, *i.e.* £22 15s. 0d.,

which, added to the £70 before mentioned, made £92 15s. 0d.
Next the 5s. due at the end of the second year (as interest on
the £5 due at the end of the first year) produced in the same
way an annual interest of 3d. All these three-pences amount
to $(12/3)(13/2)(14)(3)$ pence, i.e. £4 11s. 0d., which, added
to the previous sum of £92 15s. 0d., made £97 6s. 0d. To this
we have similarly to add $(11/4)(12/3)(13/2)(14)(3/20)$ pence,
i.e. 12s. 6d., which made a total of £97 18s. 6d. To this again
we have to add $(10/5)(11/4)(12/3)(13/2)(14)(3/400)$ pence,
i.e. 1s. 3d., which made a total of £97 19s. 9d. To this again
we have to add $(9/6)(10/5)(11/4)(12/3)(13/2)(14)(3/8000)$
pence, i.e. 1d., which made a total of £97 19s. 10d. The
remaining sum to be added cannot amount to a farthing, so
he at once gave the answer as £97 19s. 10d. The work in this
particular example did in fact occupy him less than one
minute—a much shorter time than most mathematicians would
take to work it by aid of a table of logarithms. It will be
noticed that in the course of his analysis he summed various
series.

In the ordinary notation, the sum at compound interest
amounts to $£(1{\cdot}05)^{14} \times 100$. If we denote £100 by P and ·05
by r, this is equal to $P(1 + r)^{14}$ or $P(1 + 14r + 91r^2 + \ldots)$,
which, as r is small, is rapidly convergent. Bidder in effect
arrived by reasoning at the successive terms of the series, and
rejected the later terms as soon as they were sufficiently small.

In the course of this lecture Bidder remarked that if his
ability to recollect results had been equal to his other intellectual powers, he could easily have calculated logarithms.
A few weeks later he attacked this problem, and devised a
mental method of obtaining the values of logarithms to seven
or eight places of decimals. He asked a friend to test his
accuracy, and in answer to questions gave successively the
logarithms of 71, 97, 659, 877, 1297, 8963, 9973, 115249,
175349, 290011, 350107, 229847, 369353, to eight places of
decimals; taking from thirty seconds to four minutes to make
the various calculations. All these numbers are primes. The

greater part of the answers were correct, but in a few cases there was an error, though generally of only one digit : such mistakes were at once corrected on his being told that his result was wrong. This remarkable performance took place when Bidder was over 50.

His method of calculating logarithms is set out in a paper * by W. Pole. It was, of course, only necessary for him to deal with prime numbers, and Bidder began by memorizing the logarithms of all primes less than 100. For a prime higher than this he took a composite number as near it as he could, and calculated the approximate addition which would have to be added to the logarithm : his rules for effecting this addition are set out by Pole, and, ingenious though they are, need not detain us here. They rest on the theorems that, to the number of places of decimals quoted, if $\log n$ is p, then $\log (n + n/10^2)$ is $p + \log 1\cdot01$, *i.e.* is $p + 0\cdot00432137$, $\log (n + n/10^3)$ is $p + 0\cdot00043408$, $\log (n + n/10^4)$ is $p + 0\cdot00004343$, $\log (n + n/10^5)$ is $p + 0\cdot00000434$, and so on.

The last two methods, dealing with compound interest and logarithms, are peculiar to Bidder, and show real mathematical skill. For the other problems mentioned his methods are much the same in principle as those used by other calculators, though details vary. Bidder, however, has set them out so clearly that I need not discuss further the methods generally used.

A curious question has been raised as to whether a law for the rapidity of the mental work of these prodigies can be found. Personally I do not think we have sufficient data to enable us to draw any conclusion, but I mention briefly the opinions of others. We shall do well to confine ourselves to the simplest case : that of the multiplication of a number of n digits by another number of n digits. Bidder stated that in solving such a problem he believed that the strain on his mind (which he assumed to be proportional to the time taken

* *Institution of Civil Engineers, Proceedings*, London, 1890—1891, vol. CIII, p. 250.

in answering the question) varied as n^4, but in fact it seems in his case according to this time test to have varied approximately as n^5. In 1855 he worked at least half as quickly again as in 1819, but the law of rapidity for different values of n is said to have been about the same. In Dase's case, if the time occupied is proportional to n^x, we must have x less than 3. From this, some have inferred that probably Dase's methods were different in character to those used by Bidder, and it is suggested that the results tend to imply that Dase visualized recorded numerals, working in much the same way as with pencil and paper, while Bidder made no use of symbols, and recorded successive results verbally in a sort of cinematograph way; but it would seem that we shall need more detailed observations before we can frame a theory on this subject.

The cases of calculating prodigies here mentioned, and, as far as I know, the few others of which records exist, do not differ in kind. In most of them the calculators were uneducated and self-taught. Blessed with excellent memories for numbers, self-confident, stimulated by the astonishment their performances excited, the odd coppers thus put in their pockets and the praise of their neighbours, they pondered incessantly on numbers and their properties; discovered (or in a few cases were taught) the fundamental arithmetical processes, applied them to problems of ever increasing difficulty, and soon acquired a stock of information which shortened their work. Probably *constant practice* and *undivided devotion to mental calculation* are essential to the maintenance of the power, and this may explain why a general education has so often proved destructive to it. The performances of these calculators are remarkable, but, in the light of Bidder's analysis, are not more than might be expected occasionally from lads of exceptional abilities.

CHAPTER XIV

CRYPTOGRAPHY AND CRYPTANALYSIS

THE art of writing secret messages—intelligible to those who are in possession of the key and unintelligible to all others—has been studied for centuries. The usefulness of such messages, especially in time of war, is obvious; on the other hand, their solution may be a matter of great importance to those from whom the key is concealed. But the romance connected with the subject, the not uncommon desire to discover a secret, and the implied challenge to the ingenuity of all from whom it is hidden have attracted to the subject the attention of many to whom its utility is a matter of indifference.

Although it is possible to communicate information in many different ways, we shall be concerned here only with secret communications which are in writing or in some other permanent form. Thus, small muscular movements, such as breathing long and short in the Morse dot and dash system, or signalling with a fan or stick, will not concern us. The essential feature is that the information conveyed remain hidden from all those who may have been enabled to obtain copies of the messages transmitted but are not in possession of the key. Thus we would consider secret those messages which are outwardly intelligible, but really convey a different, hidden meaning.* On the other hand, a communication in a foreign language or in any recognized notation like shorthand is *not* a secret message.

The famous diary of Samuel Pepys is commonly said to have been written in cipher, but in reality it was written in

---

* The reader is referred, for two classic examples of this type, to *Cryptographie Pratique*, A. de Grandpré, Paris, 1905, p. 57.

shorthand according to a system invented by J. Shelton.* It is, however, somewhat difficult to read, for the vowels were usually omitted, and Pepys used some arbitrary signs for terminations, particles, and certain frequent words. Further, in certain places, where the matter was such that it could hardly be expressed with decency, he changed from English to a foreign language, or inserted non-significant symbols. Shelton's system had been forgotten when attention was first attracted to the diary. Accordingly, we may say that, to those who first tried to read it, it was written in cipher; but Pepys' contemporaries would have properly described the diary as being written in shorthand, although it involved a few modifications of his own invention.

The mere fact that a message is concealed or secretly conveyed does not make it a secret message. The majority of stories dealing with secret communication are concerned with the artfulness with which the message is concealed or conveyed, and have nothing to do with cryptography. Many of the ancient instances of secret communication are of this type. Herodotus tells of the practice of shaving a slave's head and inscribing the message on his scalp; then sending the slave to deliver the message after his hair had grown back again. More modern illustrations are to be found in messages conveyed by pigeons or written on the paper wrapping of a cigarette.

Cryptographic Systems. Every method for converting a plain-text message into a secret message consists of two parts: (1) a basic, invariant method, called the *general system*, and (2) a variable, keying element usually consisting of a word, phrase, or sequence of numbers, called the *specific key*. It is ordinarily assumed that the *enemy* (any person who has obtained unauthorized possession of the messages and is

---

* *Tachy-graphy*, by J. Shelton, first edition 1620, sixth edition used by Pepys 1641. A somewhat similar system by W. Cartwright was issued by J. Rich under the title *Semographie*, London, 1644.

attempting to solve them) has full knowledge of the general system. (This assumption is based on the fact that no large communication system can hope to keep its general procedure secret very long, nor can it attempt to vary its procedure at will, in view of the great difficulty of training personnel in new methods.) The relative security of any cryptographic system is then considered to be proportional to the length of time required to determine the specific key. In this connection it must be appreciated that it is ordinarily not practicable to change specific keys more than once a day. Consequently, if all the messages (or most of them, at any rate) are intercepted, the enemy would sometimes have several hundred messages available for the determination of one specific key. This fact is often overlooked, and many systems whose security is quite low are given exaggerated importance, in the minds of their inventors, because they may be very difficult or even impossible to solve when only one message is available.

According to the method of treating the original message, general systems are divided into two main classes. If the characters of the plain-text message are merely rearranged without suffering any change in identity—*i.e.* if some permutation is applied to the original characters—the system is called *transposition*. If, however, the characters themselves are replaced by equivalents in the form of letters, or figures, or arbitrary symbols, without introducing any change in their original sequence, the system is called *substitution*. Both of these systems may be combined in a single cryptogram, by applying one to the result obtained by the other.

In the short treatment of the subject which will be given in this chapter, an attempt will be made to present a brief description of the classic systems of enciphering messages. In each case, a few words will be added with reference to the method of solution. The reader should note in this connection the difference in the use of the words *deciphering* and *solving*. The former refers to the procedure followed by the bona-fide correspondent who is in possession of all the details of the system and who merely reverses the steps followed in enciphering. The latter refers to the method used by an enemy of obtaining an unauthorized translation by applying the principles of the science now called *Cryptanalysis*.

Transposition Systems. Practically every transposition system involves a geometric figure in which the plain-text message is inscribed according to one route and then transscribed according to another route.

The following is an example of encipherment, in a system commonly called *route transposition*. Suppose the message to be transmitted is

I MUST HAVE ANOTHER HUNDRED DOLLARS

The general system, we will say, requires a completely filled rectangle of eight columns, so that it is necessary to add dummy letters if the number of letters in the message is not a multiple of eight. We therefore add two such letters, say XX, at the end of the message, in order to have 32 letters in all. We will assume next that the route for inscription is horizontal, starting at the upper left-hand corner and proceeding alternately to the right and to the left. The following arrangement will then be obtained.

I	M	U	S	T	H	A	V
R	E	H	T	O	N	A	E
H	U	N	D	R	E	D	D
X	X	S	R	A	L	L	O

If the method of transcription is vertical, beginning at the upper right-hand corner and proceeding alternately down and up, the final cipher message, prepared for transmission, would be VEDOL DAAHN ELARO TSTDR SNHUM EUXXH RI. The reversal of the above steps, in deciphering, would involve no particular difficulty.

It is not amiss to observe at this point that, because of international telegraphic regulations governing the cost of transmitting messages the final text of cryptograms is usually divided up into regular groups of five letters.   This consideration is obviously of no consequence from a cryptanalytic standpoint.

A system of the type just described possesses very little security and has the further disadvantage of not being readily adaptable to change.   Even if the dimensions of the rectangle and the routes of inscription and transcription were to be changed regularly, an enemy would have little difficulty in reading intercepted messages.   The procedure in solution is essentially one of trial, but the number of possibilities is so limited that with a little experience a solution can be obtained in a very short time.

A very widely used variation of route transposition is known as *columnar transposition*.   In this system the geometric figure is again a rectangle but with the message inscribed in the *normal* manner of writing.   The transcription is vertical, the columns being selected in the order determined by a numerical key, the width of the rectangle being equal to the length of the key.   To illustrate, suppose the key is 3–2–7–1–4–6–5 and the message is THE PRISONERS HAVE SEIZED THE RAILWAY STATION.

The first step would be to write the message in a rectangle whose columns are headed by the key numbers.

3	2	7	1	4	6	5
T	H	E	P	R	I	S
O	N	R	S	H	A	
V	E	S	E	I	Z	E
D	T	H	E	R	A	I
L	W	A	Y	S	T	A
T	I	O	N			

It is inadvisable to complete the last row of the rectangle with dummy letters, as that would give the enemy a clue to the length of the key. Then, transcribing the columns in order according to the numerical key and simultaneously preparing the message for transmission by dividing it up into five-letter groups, we have:

PREEY NHNET WITOV DLTRS IRSSA EIAIH ZATEE SHAO

The first step in deciphering is to determine how many long columns there are—that is, how many letters occur on the last row of the rectangle. This is accomplished by dividing the number of letters in the message by the length of the key; the remainder obtained from this division is the desired number. When it has been calculated, the cipher letters can be put into their proper positions, and the message will reappear.

In cases where the key is fairly long and it is inadvisable to reduce it to writing, it is found convenient to derive the numerical sequence from an easily remembered key word or phrase. This may be done in any one of several ways, the most common being to assign numbers to the letters in accordance with their normal alphabetical order. To illustrate, suppose the key word is CRYPTOGRAPHY. The letter A which appears in it is numbered 1. Then, since there is no B in the word, the letter C is numbered 2. The next letter, alphabetically, is G, and this is numbered 3, etc. This procedure is continued until a number has been assigned to every letter in the word. Whenever a letter appears more than once, the several appearances are numbered consecutively from left to right. The complete numerical key thus obtained is

C	R	Y	P	T	O	G	R	A	P	H	Y
2	8	11	6	10	5	3	9	1	7	4	12

The procedure in solving a columnar transposition is based on the fact that the letters of an entire column have been transcribed as a unit. Let us suppose that we are trying to

solve the cipher message ju t obtained. The first step is to
fit together two groups of consecutive letters which will form
good plain-text combinations. The most frequent *digraph*
(two-letter combination) in English is TH, and so we might
begin by setting every T next to every H, in turn. In each
such case, several letters just preceding and just following the
T and the H would also be juxtaposed. For example, if we
place the first T in the message against the last H, we have
the following combinations :

$$
\begin{array}{cc}
Y & A \\
N & T \\
H & E \\
N & E \\
E & S \\
\mathit{T} & \mathit{H} \\
W & A \\
I & O \\
T & \\
O & \\
\end{array}
$$

The number of letters to be placed in each column is as yet
unknown, but certain limitations are sometimes imposed by
the positions of the particular letters being used. In the above
instance, the O at the foot of the first column may be discarded,
since the long columns of a transposition rectangle exceed the
short ones by one letter. The T just above the O will be correct
only if it is the last letter of the message, for it would end the
last long column. As another example of how limitations
may be placed upon the length of the columns corresponding
to a given assumption, suppose we had placed the first T
of the message against the first H, which is only three letters
removed. Then only three digraphs would have been obtained.
Consequently with this assumption no column of the rectangle
could contain more than four letters.

There would be one pair of columns such as those given
above for every possible TH combination, and it is next
necessary to choose that pair which is composed of the best
selection of high-frequency combinations. The experienced
cryptanalyst can do this at sight, but the same result can be
obtained by a purely mathematical process. Extended

studies of the relative frequencies of single letters, digraphs,
trigraphs, and polygraphs have been made by various authors.
These relative frequencies may be considered an invariant
property of the corresponding plain-text combinations, since
they are derived from studies of a very large amount of text.
By assigning to each digraph a weight equal to its relative
frequency, it then becomes a very simple matter to select that
pair of colums which yields the greatest average weight per
digraph.

Such a test will show that the arrangement already set up
is an exceptionally good one. The only digraphs which are
not high-frequency combinations are YA and WA, and the
former may be beyond the limits of the column. If we assume
that this arrangement is correct, we then try to add a third
column, either on the right or on the left, so as to obtain good
plain-text trigraphs.

Now, IO is almost always followed by N. In addition the
TH suggests the word THE. This prompts us to seek an
E followed at two intervals by an N, and we find just one such
place in the cipher message. Note how the addition of the
corresponding letters to the combinations already obtained
delimits the columns.

```
H E P
N E R
E S E
T H E
W A Y
I O N
T
```

Should there be several possibilities instead of only one,
these may again be compared by summing the weights of the
trigraphs in each case and choosing the arrangement which
gives the greatest average. In the present case, however, it
is obvious that we are on the right track, and the solution will
follow very readily.

The procedure which has just been carried out is greatly
facilitated by a knowledge of particular words which would
be likely to appear in the message. Such a knowledge is quite

usual in military cryptanalysis, for example. Indeed, many writers on Cryptanalysis refer frequently to the *Probable word* or *Intuitive* method as a means of solution for many different systems.

What has been said thus far about the method of solving columnar transpositions has implied that the cryptanalyst is in possession of only one message. It has already been pointed out that in actual practice there may be many messages in the same key available for study. In such cases several methods can be used to obtain a rapid solution.

Among these the following is of note, since it is applicable to any transposition system whatever. Suppose two or more messages of *identical lengths* are subjected to the same transposition. Then, no matter how complicated the system may be, it is obvious that letters which were in corresponding positions in the plain-text will be in corresponding positions in the cipher text. Suppose the cipher messages are superimposed so that the first letters of all the messages are in one column, the second letters of all the messages are in a second column, etc. Then if it is assumed that two particular letters of one message are sequent in the plain-text, the letters in the corresponding positions of each of the other messages will combine in the same order. They will thus afford a check on the correctness of the first assumption, in the same way that the combinations arising from two columns in columnar transposition served as a check on the juxtaposition of a particular pair of letters in those columns. To each of these digraphs a third letter may be added to form trigraphs, etc. The idea is essentially one of *anagramming* the entire columns of the superimposed messages, and the mathematical method of summing frequencies may be used to advantage.

A good start can often be obtained by choosing an invariant combination, such as QU, or a digraph composed of two letters which have a great affinity for one another, such as TH or RE. If one of the letters of the digraph is infrequent—as, for example, in VE—the number of possibilities is very considerably reduced. Given a minimum of four messages of identical lengths, one can safely be assured of obtaining a solution of those messages. However, it is not always true that this solution will permit the cryptanalyst to translate additional messages of different lengths. In order to accomplish this, he would have to obtain some information about the general system and the specific key from the messages already solved.

A second procedure which is very fruitful in solving columnar transpositions is applicable to two or more messages involving a long repetition. Such repetitions are often found in the messages of large communication systems where there is a tendency to use stereotyped phraseology. In order to appreciate the procedure more fully, let us encipher, with the numerical key 8–6–4–1–5–3–2–7 the following two messages containing the repetition THE FIRST AND SECOND DIVISIONS.

8	6	4	1	5	3	2	7
W	H	A	T	A	R	E	T
H	E	O	R	D	E	R	S
F	O	R	T	H	E	F	I
R	S	T	A	N	D	S	E
C	O	N	D	D	I	V	I
S	I	O	N	S			

8	6	4	1	5	3	2	7
T.	H	E	F	I	R	S	T
A	N	D	S	E	C	O	N
D	D	I	V	I	S	I	O
N	S	W	I	L	L	L	E
A	V	E	A	T	O	N	C
E							

The two cryptograms available for study by the cryptanalyst are

　　　　1　　　　2　　　　3　　　　4　　　　5
1. TR*TAD* N*ERFS* V*REED* I*AORT* N*OADH* N*DS*HE
　　　　6　　　　7　　　　8
　　OS*OIT* S*IEIW* HF*RCS*

　　　　1　　　　2　　　　3　　　　4　　　　5　　　　6　　　　7　　　　8
2. *FSVIA* *SOILN* *RCSLO* *EDIWE* *IEILT* *HNDSV* *TNOEC* *TADN*A E

He would notice and underline the italicised repetitions.

Note how the letters which make up the repetition appear

in the two messages. The number of portions into which it has been broken up is equal to the number of columns in the rectangle, and the figure over each repeated portion is the key number which heads the corresponding column. The letters *RCS* in cipher message 1 are at the foot of their column. They indicate that the repeated phrase is at the end of the corresponding plain-text message. On the other hand, the letters *FSV*, which are at the head of their column in cipher message 2, indicate that the repetition is at the beginning of the corresponding plain-text message. As a result of this information, the length of each column is at once ascertainable. In the first message, for example, column 1 contains the letters *TRTADN*, column 2 contains the letters *ERFSV*, etc. In the second message column 1 contains the letters *FSVIA*, column 2 contains the letters *SOILN*, etc. We thus have determined which are the long columns and which are the short columns of each of the two messages.

In addition to the above information, which in itself is of considerable value, one can almost always get portions of the key, and sometimes the whole key, from these repetitions. In order to appreciate how this is done, let us assume for a moment that the original rectangles are known. Note then that the letter T, which is the first letter of the repetition, appears in the fourth column of message 1 and in the first column of message 2. As a result, any letter of the repetition will appear, in message 1, three columns to the right of the position of the corresponding letter in message 2.

The letters *FSV* which begin the second cipher message must come from the column headed by number 1 of the key. The letters *FSV* of message 1 come from the column headed by number 2. But, if these letters in the first message are three places in advance of the corresponding letters of the second message, it follows that the numerical key contains the sequence 1–?–?–2 (where the question marks indicate undetermined numbers). The portion of the repetition which appears in the second message in the column headed by the number 2 is *SOI*, and corresponds in message 1 to the column headed by the number 6. Hence, by the same reasoning as before, the key must contain the sequence 1–?–?–2–?–?–6. Column 6 in the second message corresponds to column 5 in the first. Remembering that the key is of length 8, we may now say that it contains the sequence 1–5–?–2–?–?–6–?.

Continuing in this way, we build up the entire key 1–5–3–2–7–8–6–4, which is a cyclic permutation of the correct key. If it is applied to the first cipher message, the result will be:

1	5	3	2	7	8	6	4
T	A	R	E	T	W	H	A
R	D	E	R	S	H	E	O
T	H	E	F	I	F	O	R
A	N	D	S	E	R	S	T
D	D	I	V	I	C	O	N
N	S				S	I	O

and the proper starting-point is at once determined by inspection. Another method of determining the beginning of the cycle is to note how the cipher messages break up into long and short columns. Since the columns which have one extra letter are all at the left in the original rectangle, the cycle begins with the first long column that follows a short column.

The reader will appreciate from what has preceded that we were enabled to derive the entire key because of the fact that the relative displacement of corresponding letters in the two repetitions was prime to the length of the key. If these two numbers had had a common factor, the key would have broken up into as many partial cycles as the greatest common divisor of the two numbers. It would then have become necessary to join the partial cycles into one complete cycle. This would have introduced several possible solutions, but a moment's trial would have determined the correct one.

Now, we assumed, in obtaining the solution just described, that the relative displacement was known. This is sometimes the case. For example, consider two messages whose endings are identical. After the length of the key has been determined by the number of sections into which the repetition breaks up, the number of long columns in each of the rectangles is at once obtained. The difference between these two numbers is the sought displacement. In the two messages just studied it is also possible to determine the relative displacement between the two repetitions, because of the fact that one repetition is at the beginning and the other at the end of their respective messages. Since the repetition is 26 letters long, its last letter must be in the second column of the second message. Moreover, this same letter is in the last long column—*i.e.* the fifth column—of the first message. The displacement is therefore three columns.

If the relative positions of the repetitions are the same, so that there is no displacement, as would happen if they were both at the beginnings of their messages, no information whatever about the actual numerical key would be obtainable by this method.

In those cases where the relative displacement is indeterminate, the assumption of each possibility in turn would still require a relatively small number of tests before the correct answer would be obtained.

The security of columnar transposition is very greatly increased if the resulting cipher is put through a second columnar transposition. This second step may use the same or a different numerical key. In either case, the superimposition of one columnar transposition upon a second yields a result obtainable from the original plain-text by a single transposition, but this latter process is much more complicated than columnar transposition. Such a system is usually called *double transposition*, and a single message so enciphered has a very high degree of security. However, two or more messages of identical lengths can be solved without difficulty in the manner already explained. The numerical keys involved in a double transposition can be obtained if the cryptanalyst is in possession of a single cipher message with its translation.

As a last example of transposition, a few words will be said about a classic system known as the *grille*, an example of which is shown below. It is a perforated card, usually square, which when put over a sheet of paper permits only certain portions of the sheet to be visible. In encipherment, the letters of the message are entered through these perforations. In decipherment, the message is written out in a diagram of the proper dimensions, the grille is superimposed, and only the desired letters of the plain-text will show through.

1	2	3	4	5	1
5	1	2	3	1	2
4	3	1	1	2	3
3	2	1	1	3	4
2	1	3	2	1	5
1	5	4	3	2	1

Grilles may be used in two different ways. With the first of these methods, the final cipher text will involve only the letters of the original plain-text message. One way of accomplishing this is to arrange the grille in such a way that if it is used successively in different positions, every cell of the underlying sheet of paper will be occupied. In the second method, on the other hand, it would be arranged that only certain cells will be filled, and the encipherer then has the further task of surrounding these significant letters with *false text*. This is generally a very difficult procedure, and has the further disadvantage of making the cipher text considerably longer than the plain-text. The inscription and transcription in grille systems may, of course, follow any prearranged routes.

The grille shown above is an example of a *revolving grille* of 36 cells. If it is successively rotated through 90° after the cells exposed by each position have been filled, every cell will be found to have been filled when the grille has returned to its starting position. The numbers which have been entered in the various cells indicate the method of construction. From each concentric band of cells, one cell must be cut to correspond to each number. If the number of cells on a side is odd, the central square of the grille must remain uncut.

Grilles are not very practicable when there is any considerable amount of communication. Besides, their security is quite low. For example, all messages enciphered with a given revolving grille would break up into portions of identical lengths, each of which has been treated identically. The method of anagramming columns is therefore applicable.

In all of the transposition systems which have been described thus far the unit of cryptographic treatment has been a single letter. There is no reason why it could not be changed to a regular group of letters, or to syllabic groupings, or even to whole words.. Such systems are by no means uncommon. An outstanding historical instance was the use of a route transposition on words by the Federal Army in the American Civil War, 1861—1865, equivalents being substituted for proper names.   Also grilles of a rectangular shape, with rather long perforations, are sometimes used, so that a syllable or even a whole word can be entered at a time.

Substitution Systems. The simplest type of substitution system is that in which the same plain-text letter is always represented by the same equivalent.   It is probably the best-known type of cipher, and seems to be the very first idea that comes to the mind of a beginner in Cryptography.   Just what form the equivalent takes is obviously of no consequence, and yet it is surprising how many people get the notion that the use of complicated arbitrary symbols yields a more secure system than would be obtained with letters or figures.

The simplest way to employ such a system is to set down the equivalents in the form of a *substitution alphabet*, which consists of a *plain-sequence* and a *cipher sequence*, superimposed one above the other. The plain-text letter is found in the plain sequence, and replaced by the corresponding character in the cipher sequence.

For example, if we employ the substitution alphabet

Plain   A B C D E F G H I J K L M N O P Q R S T U V W X Y Z
Cipher A D G J M P S V Y B E H K N Q T W Z C F I L O R U X

the sentence COME HOME ALL IS FORGIVEN would be enciphered GQKMV QKMAH HYCPQ ZSYLM N.

In the usual method of writing a substitution alphabet, the plain sequence is the *normal* alphabet. In such cases, the assignment of the cipher sequence alone is sufficient to define the entire substitution alphabet. Depending upon the manner in which the cipher sequence is constructed, substitution alphabets are divided into three different classes.

1. *Standard Alphabets.* Here the cipher sequence is a cyclic permutation of either the normal alphabet or the normal alphabet *reversed*. This is the oldest type of substitution alphabet known. Some writers call cipher systems using a standard alphabet *the system of Julius Caesar*. However, Caesar used but one of the possible standard alphabets; his cipher sequence was always the normal alphabet beginning with the letter D.*

2. *Systematically Mixed Alphabets.* The difficulty arising from the use of standard alphabets is obvious. One or two

---

* Of some of Caesar's correspondence, Suetonius says (cap. 56) *si quis investigare et persequi velit, quartam elementorum literam, id est, d pro a, et perinde reliqua commutet.* And of Augustus he says (cap. 88) *quoties autem per notas scribit, b pro a, c pro b, ac deinceps eadem ratione, sequentes literas ponit pro x autem duplex a.* ("If anyone wishes to investigate and follow it up, let him replace the fourth letter of the alphabet, that is, D, by A and in like manner with the others." "Whenever he writes in cipher, he puts B for A. C for B and continues in the same way; for X, however, he puts AA.")

identifications are sufficient to determine the whole alphabet. To circumvent this difficulty and still avoid the necessity of reducing the cipher sequence to writing, some systematic procedure must be employed for disarranging the normal alphabet. Cryptographic literature is full of devices for accomplishing this end, but only one will be described here, merely for the sake of example. Let a key word be'chosen which has no repeated letters in it—say FISHER. Write all the remaining letters of the alphabet in order in a rectangular array under the key word.

2	4	6	3	1	5
F	I	S	H	E	R
A	B	C	D	G	J
K	L	M	N	O	P
Q	T	U	V	W	X
Y	Z				

Then transpose the letters of this figure by columns according to the numerical key based on the word FISHER. The resulting cipher sequence is

E G O W F A K Q Y H D N V I B L T Z R J P X S C M U

3. *Random Alphabets.* Here the letters of the cipher sequence are chosen at random, and in such a sequence no aid in determining unknown letters can be obtained from known identifications. The objection to this type of sequence is, of course, that it must be reduced to writing.

The method of solution of a system which uses only one substitution alphabet or, as we shall call it, a *monoalphabetic* system, is fairly well known. It is based on the relative frequencies of the individual letters of the alphabet, together with the relative frequencies of their combinations with one another.

In English, the relative frequencies of occurrence of the individual letters, most frequent digraphs, and trigraphs are as follows : *

E ·131	R ·067	F ·028	G ·014	Q ·001
T ·090	S ·065	U ·028	B ·013	Z ·001
O ·082	H ·059	M ·026	V ·010	
A ·078	D ·044	P ·022	K ·004	
N ·073	L ·036	Y ·015	X ·003	
I ·068	C ·029	W ·015	J ·001	

TH ·034	ER ·019	IN ·014	AT ·013	HA ·012
HE ·026	ON ·019	ED ·014	OF ·013	EN ·011
AN ·019	RE ·017	ND ·014	OR ·012	NT ·011

THE ·015	HAT ·003	FOR ·003	NDE ·003
AND ·005	EDT ·003	ION ·003	HAS ·002
THA ·004	ENT ·003	TIO ·003	MEN ·002

Further aids are : (1) the determination of the vowels as being those high-frequency letters which rarely combine with one another, and hence show definite interval relationships : (2) the selection of unusual combinations of letters which suggest certain definite plain-text words or phrases. Examples : THAT, WHICH, AS SOON AS, BEGINNING, etc. These are detected in the cipher text by the intervals between the repeated letters, their appearance being referred to as *word patterns*; (3) the search for probable words, which are always very helpful to a cryptanalyst.

Once a few identifications have been made by using any one of the above ideas, a complete solution follows very readily.

The relatively low security possessed by a monoalphabetic system is the result of the fact that each plain-text letter has only one equivalent. If we insist that this equivalent may not represent any other letter, and wish at the same time to provide additional equivalents for the individual letters, it becomes necessary to have more than 26 cipher characters. If, for example, we use every two-digit number as a cipher unit, we have 100 possible equivalents : if we use a two-letter combination as a cipher unit, we have 676 possible equivalents.

* P. Valerio, *De la Cryptographie*, Paris. 1893, pp. 202, 204.

It then becomes possible with the introduction of additional cipher equivalents to represent each plain-text letter by any one of several *variant* values. If the number of equivalents assigned to each letter is proportional to its relative frequency of occurrence in plain-text, the resulting system has much more security than an ordinary monoalphabet.

However, it may be solved without too much trouble. The procedure is to reduce the cipher text to monoalphabetic terms by determining which cipher characters are equivalent to one another. This is done in two ways : (1) it will be found by frequency studies that certain characters combine in the same sort of way with all the others. A detailed study of all their appearances will establish the equivalence of those characters which represent the same plain-text letter; (2) a careful study of repetitions will disclose places where the same word has been differently enciphered. Thus, one might find such occurrences as

$$11 \quad 22 \quad 27 \quad 75 \quad 89 \quad 16 \quad 31$$
$$11 \quad 22 \quad 27 \quad 61 \quad 89 \quad 16 \quad 31$$
$$11 \quad 22 \quad 45 \quad 75 \quad 82 \quad 16 \quad 31$$

The obvious conclusion is that 27 and 45, 61 and 75, 82 and 89 are equivalent pairs. An extended study along these lines will yield considerable information, and before many equivalents have been established, the cryptanalyst will be able to take advantage of frequency considerations and word patterns to obtain plain-text identifications.

A cipher system in which one plain-text letter is replaced by two or more cipher characters is called *polyliteral*. Sometimes polyliteral systems are used without taking advantage of variant values. Francis Bacon's cipher, for example, was pentaliteral, each plain-text letter being replaced by a five-letter group consisting of A's and B's only. Since that allowed 32 possibilities (2^5), there were 6 symbols to spare. These were not used by Bacon. The Morse code is an example of a polyliteral system in which the cipher equivalents are not all of the same length.*

A more effective way to suppress frequency than by the use of variants is to make use of more than one substitution alphabet. Such systems are often called *polyalphabetic*, and take two very distinct forms, according as the alphabets are used periodically or aperiodically.

As a simple example of the first type, suppose the correspondents have constructed five different random alphabets.

Plain	A	B	C	D	E	F	G	H	I	J	K	L	M	N	O	P	Q	R	S	T	U	V	W	X	Y	Z
1	R	K	S	L	D	P	A	V	E	C	O	G	J	U	B	N	I	F	X	Z	W	H	Y	M	Q	T
2	J	Y	B	I	W	Q	H	X	D	P	T	F	A	Z	G	O	C	L	S	U	E	K	N	V	M	R
3	F	K	U	D	N	H	T	A	Z	L	G	Q	Y	R	B	I	J	V	M	O	C	W	E	X	S	P
4	N	T	Q	I	C	G	S	E	J	O	P	A	W	B	V	U	X	D	L	F	R	H	K	Z	M	Y
5	K	E	M	A	J	B	T	L	V	D	N	U	F	S	C	Q	G	O	X	I	P	Y	W	Z	R	H

Cipher (bracketed at left of rows)

The plain-text message is written out in five columns, and the first alphabet is used to encipher the letters of the first column, the second alphabet is used to encipher the letters of the second column, etc. The effect of this procedure is that the ath alphabet enciphers every letter whose position in the plain-text is a number of the form $5k + a$. With the alphabets given above, the message THREE SHIPS SAILED TODAY would be enciphered ZXVCJ XXZUX XJZAJ LUBIK Q.

Instead of having a fixed number of alphabets, the correspondents may provide arrangements for varying their alphabets by regular changes of a key word. One means of attaining this end will now be explained. It is described by most of the older authors, and is called by some of them the *double key* system. One key word—for example, COPYRIGHT—is used

* The Morse alphabet is listed here for those who are not familiar with it.

A . –	G – – .	M – –	S . . .	Y – . – –
B – . . .	H	N – .	T –	Z – – . .
C – . – .	I . .	O – – –	U . . –	
D – . .	J . – – –	P . – – .	V . . . –	
E .	K – . –	Q – – . –	W . – –	
F . . – .	L . – . .	R . – .	X – . . –	

to construct the following diagram, known as a Vigenère Square (see below). If we consider each row of the square a cipher sequence, and the normal alphabet above the square the plain sequence, the diagram gives us 26 substitution alphabets. Let each of these alphabets be designated by the letter in the first column of the square. Then a second key word—say AUGUST—is employed to select the particular alphabets to be used and the order in which to use them. The first substitution alphabet would be the A alphabet, and

A	B	C	D	E	F	G	H	I	J	K	L	M	N	O	P	Q	R	S	T	U	V	W	X	Y	Z
C	O	P	Y	R	I	G	H	T	A	B	D	E	F	J	K	L	M	N	Q	S	U	V	W	X	Z
Z	C	O	P	Y	R	I	G	H	T	A	B	D	E	F	J	K	L	M	N	Q	S	U	V	W	X
X	Z	C	O	P	Y	R	I	G	H	T	A	B	D	E	F	J	K	L	M	N	Q	S	U	V	W
W	X	Z	C	O	P	Y	R	I	G	H	T	A	B	D	E	F	J	K	L	M	N	Q	S	U	V
V	W	X	Z	C	O	P	Y	R	I	G	H	T	A	B	D	E	F	J	K	L	M	N	Q	S	U
U	V	W	X	Z	C	O	P	Y	R	I	G	H	T	A	B	D	E	F	J	K	L	M	N	Q	S
S	U	V	W	X	Z	C	O	P	Y	R	I	G	H	T	A	B	D	E	F	J	K	L	M	N	Q
Q	S	U	V	W	X	Z	C	O	P	Y	R	I	G	H	T	A	B	D	E	F	J	K	L	M	N
N	Q	S	U	V	W	X	Z	C	O	P	Y	R	I	G	H	T	A	B	D	E	F	J	K	L	M
M	N	Q	S	U	V	W	X	Z	C	O	P	Y	R	I	G	H	T	A	B	D	E	F	J	K	L
L	M	N	Q	S	U	V	W	X	Z	C	O	P	Y	R	I	G	H	T	A	B	D	E	F	J	K
K	L	M	N	Q	S	U	V	W	X	Z	C	O	P	Y	R	I	G	H	T	A	B	D	E	F	J
J	K	L	M	N	Q	S	U	V	W	X	Z	C	O	P	Y	R	I	G	H	T	A	B	D	E	F
F	J	K	L	M	N	Q	S	U	V	W	X	Z	C	O	P	Y	R	I	G	H	T	A	B	D	E
E	F	J	K	L	M	N	Q	S	U	V	W	X	Z	C	O	P	Y	R	I	G	H	T	A	B	D
D	E	F	J	K	L	M	N	Q	S	U	V	W	X	Z	C	O	P	Y	R	I	G	H	T	A	B
B	D	E	F	J	K	L	M	N	Q	S	U	V	W	X	Z	C	O	P	Y	R	I	G	H	T	A
A	B	D	E	F	J	K	L	M	N	Q	S	U	V	W	X	Z	C	O	P	Y	R	I	G	H	T
T	A	B	D	E	F	J	K	L	M	N	Q	S	U	V	W	X	Z	C	O	P	Y	R	I	G	H
H	T	A	B	D	E	F	J	K	L	M	N	Q	S	U	V	W	X	Z	C	O	P	Y	R	I	G
G	H	T	A	B	D	E	F	J	K	L	M	N	Q	S	U	V	W	X	Z	C	O	P	Y	R	I
I	G	H	T	A	B	D	E	F	J	K	L	M	N	Q	S	U	V	W	X	Z	C	O	P	Y	R
R	I	G	H	T	A	B	D	E	F	J	K	L	M	N	Q	S	U	V	W	X	Z	C	O	P	Y
Y	R	I	G	H	T	A	B	D	E	F	J	K	L	M	N	Q	S	U	V	W	X	Z	C	O	P
P	Y	R	I	G	H	T	A	B	D	E	F	J	K	L	M	N	Q	S	U	V	W	X	Z	C	O
O	P	Y	R	I	G	H	T	A	B	D	E	F	J	K	L	M	N	Q	S	U	V	W	X	Z	C

would be used to encipher each letter whose position in the plain-text is given by a number of the form $6k + 1$; the second substitution alphabet would be the U alphabet, and would be used to encipher each letter whose position in the plain text is given by a number of the form $6k + 2$; etc. The resulting cipher would be a polyalphabet of six alphabets, of which only five are distinct. With these two keywords the message NEED REINFORCEMENTS AT ONCE would be enciphered VZBXD EMTDA DBFHB TFCAJ STVE.

The first step in solving periodic polyalphabetic systems is to determine the number of alphabets. In order to understand how this is accomplished, suppose a word is repeated several times in a message. Any two appearances for which the relative positions of this word are the same with regard to the key will yield identical cipher text. Two appearances placed differently with respect to the key will not yield cipher repetitions. Hence, the intervals separating cipher repetitions are multiples of the length of the key. The exact length of the key is the greatest common divisor of all the intervals separating such repetitions. Suppose this number has been determined. Then if the message is written out in as many columns as the length of the key, all the letters in any one column will have been enciphered in a single substitution alphabet.

The second step is the analysis of these different mono-alphabets. It involves essentially the same procedure as that described in connection with monoalphabetic systems. If some of the alphabets are the same, this can be determined by statistical methods, and the corresponding frequencies combined. In addition, if the different alphabets are related as in a Vigenère square, certain properties of symmetry can be used to advantage, so that identifications in one alphabet will simultaneously yield identifications in others.

Quite recently there has been considerable research carried on in an attempt to invent cipher machines for the automatic encipherment and decipherment of messages. Most of them employ periodic polyalphabetic systems. The most recent machines are electrical in operation, and in many cases the period is a tremendously large number; in addition, the number of independent alphabets is often of the same order as the period. These machine systems are much more rapid and much more accurate than hand methods. They can even be combined with printing and transmitting apparatus so that, in enciphering, a record of the cipher message is kept and the message transmitted; in deciphering, the secret message is received and translated, all automatically. So far as present cryptanalytic methods are concerned, the cipher systems derived from some of these machines are very close to practical insolvability.

The study of aperiodic polyalphabetic systems would lead us into very involved cryptanalysis, and therefore only two such systems will be mentioned.

1. Suppose a Vigenère square has been constructed, giving 26 different alphabets, each designated by a single letter. Then the letters of the plain-text message itself may serve as the key. For example, suppose the first alphabet is, by prearrangement, known to be the A alphabet. Then the first letter is enciphered in this alphabet. Thereafter, each succeeding letter is enciphered in the alphabet designated by the plain-text letter just preceding. Such a system is called *auto-key*. With the Vigenère square based on the word COPYRIGHT, and A the first substitution alphabet, the message BRIDGE DYNAMITED would be enciphered BOETM BKALN UZXEK.

2. The system known as *running key* is similar to the above except that the key is quite distinct from the message. In this system the key may be the text of a book or periodical beginning on some prearranged page and line. Or, it may be a random collection of letters of which each correspondent has a copy.

Aperiodic systems such as the first of the two just described have a very serious disadvantage from the standpoint of practicability. If for any reason an error should be introduced into a message, causing a single letter to be incorrectly received, every subsequent letter will be affected. Since the average number of errors involved in just the transmission of a message may be as high as 5%, this makes it difficult, and sometimes impossible, to read a cipher message.

The increased security gained in polyalphabetic systems is basically due to the fact that they suppress monoalphabetic frequencies. But these will reappear if the cryptanalyst can find ways of breaking up the message into its component monoalphabets. This possibility will always exist if the unit of cryptographic treatment is a single letter, as it has been in all the substitution systems described thus far. We are thus led to the idea of *polygraphic substitution*—the replacement of a plain-text polygraph by a cipher group of the same number of letters.

As a first example we give the classic *digraphic* system known as the *Playfair Cipher*. In this system, 25 cells arranged in form of a square are filled in some prearranged manner with the letters of the alphabet (one letter, say Q, is omitted). The square given below contains a systematically mixed sequence based on the word MANCHESTER.

M	A	N	C	H
E	S	T	R	B
D	F	G	I	J
K	L	O	P	U
V	W	X	Y	Z

The plain-text message is divided into pairs of letters, and in order to prevent any pair consisting of the same two letters, a dummy letter like Z is introduced whenever necessary. Thus, if the first word of a message is BATTALION, it would be broken up as follows BA TZ TA LI ON. In encipherment, if both letters of a digraph appear in the same horizontal (or vertical) line of the square, each of them is replaced by the letter in the square immediately to its right (or below it), the letters in each row and column being treated as in cyclical order. If the letters of a pair do not appear in the same row or column, they must necessarily be at opposite angles of some rectangle, and they are then replaced by those at the other angles of the rectangle, each by that which is on the same horizontal line. Thus the message WILL MEET YOU AT NOON would first be written WI LZ LM EZ ET YO UA TN OZ ON. With the square shown above, the message would then be enciphered YFUWK ABVSR XPLHG TUXXT.

The security of this system, or, for that matter, of any digraphic system, is quite low. There exists sufficient variation in the relative frequencies of plain-text digraphs to permit a cryptanalyst to obtain a great deal of information from considerations of frequency alone. The correct identification of only a few digraphs is sufficient to insure solution. In addition, the cryptanalyst can make considerable use of probable words and of word patterns. Of course, he is limited in the latter to patterns based on digraphs. Examples : *RE* FE *RE* NC E, P *RE* PA *RE*, *DE* CI *DE*.

In the Playfair Cipher there are further aids. If it has been determined that TH is replaced by BN, then HT is replaced by NB. In general if $A_1A_2 = B_1B_2$, then $A_2A_1 = B_2B_1$. Moreover, if these four letters A_1, A_2, B_1, B_2 are known to be the vertices of a rectangle, the following additional identifications will result at once : $B_1B_2 = A_1A_2$; $B_2B_1 = A_2A_1$. These facts are quite helpful in special frequency studies—for example, in distinguishing the equivalent of a high-frequency digraph such as TH whose reversal (HT) is infrequent from one such as ER, whose reversal (RE) is frequent. If may be pointed out that in Playfair ciphers the complete square can be reconstructed from just a few identifications.

The security of polygraphic substitution increases **very**

rapidly as the unit of crytographic treatment increases in size. When the unit becomes as large as five or six letters, the security is very high. Unfortunately, a serious practical difficulty enters at this point. An error in one letter of a cipher group will give an incorrect translation for the entire unit of plain-text letters, so that, in effect, it garbles five or six letters at once. Since it is not possible to introduce means for correcting errors in such a system, four or five errors in the transmission of a message may render the entire message unintelligible. Such a difficulty is prohibitive. From a theoretical standpoint, however, such a system is quite interesting, and a very general mathematical treatment of it has been given by Professor Lester S. Hill.*

In every cryptographic system that has been considered thus far, the cipher text has been at least as long as the plain-text. The chief concern was secrecy, and considerations of economy did not enter. But such considerations are often of prime importance, and have led to the development of very highly specialized substitution systems called *code*. In these systems each correspondent is given a copy of a *code book* containing a long list of words, phrases, and sentences, each of which has an arbitrary equivalent set alongside it. These equivalents are most often five-letter groups, although regular groupings of a smaller number of letters and, more rarely, groups of figures are sometimes used. Provision is made for spelling out words which may not appear in the code *vocabulary*, by assigning equivalents to the individual letters of the alphabet and to the most frequent syllables.

Generally, a code book is constructed for a particular industry or for a group of people having special interests, and, as a consequence, long phrases, and even whole sentences, apt to be often repeated, are included in the vocabulary, and can be replaced by one code group. It results quite frequently that a code message is only one-fourth or one-fifth as long as the corresponding plain-text message.

* Concerning certain linear transformation apparatus of cryptography, *American Mathematical Monthly*, 1931, vol. xxxviii, pp. 135–154.

By way of illustration we reproduce below a portion, under the *caption* ARRIVAL, from the Western Union Traveller's Cable Code.

ADAUX   Am awaiting arrival of . . .
ADAVY   Arrived all right
ADAXA   Arrived all right, address letters to care of . . .
ADBAE   Arrived all right, telegraph (cable) me in care of . . .
ADBEI   Arrived all right, pleasant passage, advise friends
ADBIM   Arrived all right, pleasant passage, am writing
etc.

This power of condensation brings with it the difficulty that an error in a single code group may cause the loss of a considerable portion of plain-text. In order to avoid the necessity of having the message repeated, provision is made for the correction of errors. What is done is to select the code groups from a special type of code construction table,* which assures that every code group will differ from every other by at least two letters. It results therefrom that a code group is completely determined by any four of its letters. If, then, one letter is garbled in transmission, the resulting group will not be found in the book, and the decoder is thus informed of the presence of an error. By assuming each letter in turn to be the incorrect one, there will be at most five possible translations for the garbled word, and the context will indicate the correct translation. This procedure is based on the assumption that only one letter of the code group which has been incorrectly received is wrong, and, fortunately, this is almost always true.

A further improvement in code-word construction tables, which assists in the correction of errors, assures that no two code words in the book will differ by only an interchange of two letters. The necessity for such a feature arises in the

---

* An example of such a table, together with some interesting notes about code, will be found in a paper entitled " Notes on Code Words," W. F. Friedman and C. J. Mendelsohn, *American Mathematical Monthly*, 1932, vol. XXXIX, pp. 394—409.

tendency of some clerks, particularly typists, to introduce such an error, without realizing it, when working rapidly.

Secrecy in code communication is largely dependent upon keeping the code book out of unauthorized hands. But code books are often compromised without passing out of the hands of their rightful owners; for example, they may be copied or photographed. If there is any possibility whatever of such compromise, recourse may be had to *superencipherment*. This means applying some one or more of the possible cipher systems to the code text, treating the code message as though it were plain-text. These systems and the specific keys applying to them may be changed as often as desired.

Determination of Cryptographic System. It has been remarked that in most cryptanalytic studies it is assumed that the enemy is in possession of the general system. Naturally this is not always true, and the cryptanalyst sometimes has the problem of determining what general system applies to a set of messages under consideration. This is one of the most difficult problems of the entire field, and in order to prevent the present discussion from becoming too involved, a few words will be said about the methods for distinguishing general systems from one another *when only one process is involved*. Given a set of messages for study, the first step is to make a systematic search for repetitions, and to study the external appearance of the messages. If we limit ourselves to repetitions at least five or six letters in length, we can feel assured that we are omitting any repetitions which may be accidental. Suppose it is found that the lengths of all the repetitions which appear and the intervals separating them are all multiples of the same number n. Then the system is either polyliteral, polygraphic, or code.

If we tabulate all the n-letter groups which occur and make a frequency distribution of their appearances, we can then distinguish between these three systems as follows. A polyliteral system which does not use variants will involve at most

26 different groups, whose frequencies will correspond with the normal frequencies of the individual letters of plain-text. If variants are used, this can be determined by establishing equivalents in the manner already described. Code systems differ from polygraphic systems, in that the *n*-letter groups of code are regular in form and structure, possess a two-letter difference, and may be made to fit a code-word construction table, whose size limits the total number of groups. In a polygraphic system, on the other hand, *every n-letter combination* is a bona-fide cipher group. The number of these groups actually obtained in the set of messages at hand is of the same order as the number of distinct plain-text polygraphs of *n* letters to be expected in such an amount of text.

If the cipher unit is not a group of two or more letters, the system is monographic, and must be either transposition or substitution. If it is transposition, it is merely a permutation of the original letters of the message, and the relative frequency of each individual letter will be the same as in plain-text. Hence, the proportion of vowels must be the same as in plain-text—*i.e.* about 40%. Very few, if any, long repetitions will be found, as the transposition process has a tendency to break up words and scatter the individual letters throughout the message.

If the system is not transposition, it must be substitution. A monoalphabetic substitution can be distinguished by the fact that the frequencies of the individual letters are of the same relative magnitudes and show the same degree of variation as plain-text frequencies. The noticeable difference in the cipher lies in the fact that the high frequencies may be exhibited by letters which are infrequent in plain-text, and, similarly, letters which are very frequent in a plain-text may be infrequent in the cipher-text. The proportion of vowels generally is much less than in plain-text, since the vowels are all high-frequency letters in plain-text. Then, too, a monoalphabet will contain a considerable number of repetitions, since every plain-text repetition yields a cipher repetition;

and these repetitions will contain recognizable word patterns. The intervals between them will, of course, have no common factor.

If the general system is one of polyalphabetic substitution, the frequency distribution will be quite *flat*—that is, the cipher letters will all have approximately equal frequencies. This is the result of the use of more than one alphabet, causing a particular cipher equivalent sometimes to represent a frequent plain-text letter, and at other times an infrequent one. It remains to determine whether the alphabets are being used periodically or aperiodically. If they are used periodically, the intervals between repetitions will all be multiples of the period. When the messages are broken up into sections equal to the length of the period, and these sections are superimposed, the letters in a single column will constitute a monoalphabet. If, however, the intervals between repetitions show no common factor, then the system is aperiodic.

Further study of any one of these systems with a view towards solution depends upon the particular system encountered, and upon any other elements of pertinent information which may be available to the cryptanalyst as a result of the particular situation.

A Few Final Remarks. In most cases, the information contained in a set of cryptograms is valuable only for a very short period. In fact, a system is generally considered sufficiently secure if the delay caused the enemy in its attempts at solution is long enough to make the information valueless. However, it sometimes happens that the application of the principles of Cryptanalysis will result in obtaining material of definite historic importance. Consider, for example, as a first type of material, the ancient systems of writing. In the real sense of the word, these were not intended to be *secret* writing. Nevertheless they had to be treated as such when attempts were made to read them. On the other hand, historians are sometimes vitally interested in reading secret messages written many years ago. We might cite, in connection with this type of material, the diplomatic code messages transmitted during the period of the American Revolution.

Under each of the two heads mentioned above there is considerable material available for study, even to-day. In connection with ancient systems of writing there is the outstanding example of the Mayan *glyphs*. To be sure, some progress in their identification has been made. The numbers, the calendric symbols, the glyphs representing the various Mayan gods and a few others have been identified. But a considerable amount of work still remains to be done.

In conclusion, a word might be said about instances of attempts to solve ciphers whose very existence has been a matter of question. We might cite, in particular, all the work that has been done in connection with the Bacon–Shakespeare controversy. Very little knowledge of Cryptanalysis is necessary to appreciate that the solutions which have been obtained are entirely subjective and that no two independent investigators using the methods proposed would arrive at identical results. It is quite possible for an investigator to become so obsessed with an idea that he actually forces it to work out by selecting a system sufficiently flexible to permit any desired result. A tragic instance of this phenomenon is provided by the case of Prof. W. R. Newbold,[*] who imagined that he had succeeded in reading the Voynich Manuscript. The latter is a beautifully written and profusely illustrated medieval treatise of over two hundred pages, discovered in Italy by Wilfrid M. Voynich, about 1912. It remains an outstanding challenge to linguists and cryptanalysts.

---

[*] *The Cipher of Roger Bacon*, Philadelphia, 1928. There are photostatic copies of the Voynich Manuscript in the British Museum and the New York Public Library. (It is no longer attributed to Roger Bacon.)

ADDENDUM

References for Further Study

BAZERIES, ÉTIENNE,
Les chiffres secrets dévoilés, Paris, 1901.

Encyclopædia Britannica :
" Codes and Ciphers."

FIGL, A.,
Systeme des chiffrierens, Graz, 1926.

GIVIERGE, COL. M.,
Cours de Cryptographie, Paris, 1925.

GRANDPRÉ, A. DE,
La cryptographie pratique, Paris, 1905.

LANGE, ANDRÉ, and SOUDART, E. A.,
Traité de Cryptographie, Paris, 1925.

LANGIE, ANDRÉ,
De la cryptographie, Paris, 1918. (English translation by Macbeth, *Cryptography*, New York, 1922.)

VALERIO, P.,
De la cryptographie : Part I, Paris, 1893; Part II, Paris, 1896.

YARDLEY, HERBERT O.,
The American Black Chamber, Indianapolis, 1931.

INDEX

Aces Paradox, 44.
Agrippa, Cornelius, 194.
Ahrens, W., 194.
Aix, Labyrinth at, 258.
Alcuin, 2, 116.
Alexander, J. W., 232.
Alkarism on π, 342.
Alkborough, Labyrinth at, 259.
Alphabet, Morse, 398.
Amicable Numbers, 67.
Ampère, A. M., 355.
Anallagmatic Pavements, 108–111.
Analysis Situs, chaps. VIII, IX.
Anaxagoras, 339.
Andreas, J. M., preface, 126, 153, 170, 215, 238.
Andreini, A., 147, 159.
Andrews, W. S., 194, 212.
Angle Trisection, 333–335.
Anstice, R. R., 268.
Antipho, 339.
Antiprism, 129.
Apollonius, 331, 340.
Arago, F. J. D., 362.
Archimedean Solids, 135–140, 158.
Archimedes, 328–331, 336, 340.
Archytas on Delian Problem, 329.
Arithmetic, Higher, 52–75.
Arithmetical Fallacies, 41–44.
Arithmetical Prodigies, chap. XIII.
—— Puzzles, 4–50.
—— Recreations, chaps. I, II, XI.
—— Restorations, 20–26.
Arnoux, G., 207, 210.
Arya-Bhata on π, 341.
Asenby, Labyrinth at, 258.
Augustus, 394.
Auto-key System, 401.
Automorphic Numbers, 60.
Axis of Symmetry, 130, 135.

Bachet's *Problèmes*, 2, 4, 6, 8, 11, 12, 16, 18, 28, 30, 33, 50, 116, 313, 316.
Bacon, Francis, 397, 409.
Bacon, Roger, 409.

Badoureau, A., 145.
Baker, H. F., 310.
Ball, W. W. R., preface, 327.
Ball-Piling, 148–151.
Barbette, E., 212.
Barrau, J. A., 110.
Baudhayana on π, 341.
Bazeries, E., 410.
Beeger, N. G. W. H., 72.
Bell, E. T., 57, 63.
Bennett, G. T., 69.
Bergholt, E. G. B., 49, 211.
Bernoulli, John, 41, 338.
Bernoulli Numbers, 71.
Bertrand, J. L. F., 41.
Bertrand, L. (of Geneva), 176.
Berwick, W. E. H., 23.
Besicovitch, A. S., 99, 100.
Bewley, E. D., 49.
Bhaskara on π, 341.
Bidder, G. P., 357–362, 368–378.
Bidder Family, The, 362.
Biering, C. H., 327.
Bilguer, von, on Chess Pieces, 164.
Binary Powers, Fermat on, 68.
Binet, A., 366.
Birthdays Problem, 45.
Bishop's Re-entrant Path, 186.
Bordered Magic Squares, 200.
Boughton Green, Labyrinth at, 259.
Bouniakowski, V., on Shuffling, 310.
Bourlet, C. E. E., 31.
Bouton, C. L., 36.
Brahmagupta on π, 341.
Bray, A., on Kirkman's Problem, 268, 278.
Breton on Mosaics, 258.
Bridge Problem, 297.
Bromton, 256.
Brouncker, Viscount, on π, 345.
Brown, B. H., 27.
Brückner, M., 153.
Brun, 64.
Bryso, 339.
Busschop, P., 89.
Buxton, Jedediah, 351–354.

Cæsar, Julius, 394.

CALCULATING PRODIGIES, chap.
XIII.
CALENDAR PROBLEMS, 26.
Callet, J. F., on π, 347.
Cantor, M., on π, 339.
Cardan, G., 2, 305, 307.
Cards, Problems with, 18–20, 47, 49,
190, 304, 310–325.
Cartwright, W., 380.
Cauchy, A. L., 144, 362.
Cayley, A., 101, 145, 223, 260, 324,
345.
Cazalas, E., 191.
Cells of a Chess-board, 161.
Ceulen, van, on π, 343.
Characteristic, Euler-Poincaré, 233.
Charcot, J. M., 366.
Chartres, Labyrinth at, 258.
Chartres, R., 41, 83, 349.
Chasles on Trisection of Angle, 335.
Cheney, W. F., 94.
Chernick, J., 212.
CHESS-BOARD, GAMES ON, 122–125,
chap. VI.
—— Knight's move on, 174–185.
—— Notation of, 161.
CHESS, MAXIMUM PIECES PROBLEM,
171.
—— MINIMUM PIECES PROBLEM,
171.
—— Number of Initial Moves, 162.
—— PIECES, VALUE OF, 162–165.
CHIFU-CHEMULPO PUZZLE, 115, 127.
Chilcombe, Labyrinth at, 259.
Chinese, 196, 342.
CHINESE RINGS, 305–310.
Chrystal, G., 41, 57.
Ciccolini, T., on Chess, 181.
CIPHERS, chap. XIV.
CIRCLE, QUADRATURE OF, 335–349.
Cissoid, the, 329, 332, 337.
Clairaut on Trisection of Angle, 335.
Claus, 303.
Clausen on π, 347.
Clerk Maxwell, J., 5, 101.
CLOSE-PACKING, hexagonal, 150.
—— spherical, 149.
Cnossos, coins of, 257.
Coccoz, M., 78, 212.
Code-Book Ciphers, 404–406.
Code, Morse, 398.
Colburn, Z., 355–359, 369, 372, 375.
Cole, F. N., 292.
Cole, R. A. L., 323.
Collini on Knight's Path, 180.
COLOUR-CUBE PROBLEM, 112.
COLOURING MAPS, chap. VIII.

Comberton, Labyrinth at, 259.
COMPASS PROBLEMS, 96.
Compound Polyhedra, 134, 136, 146.
Conchoid, the, 329, 334, 337.
CONTINUED FRACTIONS, 55, 58, 59,
86.
Contour-lines, 101.
Convergents to a Continued Frac-
tion, 56, 58, 87.
Counters, Games with, 104–106,
119–125.
Coxeter, H. S. M., 152, 158.
Cretan Labyrinth, 258.
CRYPTOGRAPHY AND CRYPTANALYSIS,
chap. XIV.
CUBE, DUPLICATION OF, 93, 327–333.
Cubes, Coloured, 112.
—— Magic, 217–221.
—— Skeleton, 49.
—— Tessellation of, 147, 152.
Cuboctahedron, 136, 147.
Cudworth, W., on Sharp, 346.
Cunningham, A. J. C., 69.
Cusa on π, 342.
Cutting Cards, Problems on, 19.
CYCLOTOMY, 94–96.

D'Alembert, J., 43.
Darboux, G., 366, 369.
Dase, J. M. Z., 347, 363–365, 378.
Davenport, H., 45, 110.
DECIMALS, 53–55.
Decimation, 32–36.
De Coatpont, 89.
De Fonteney on Ferry Problem, 117.
De Fouquières, 105.
De Grandpré, A., 379.
De Haan, B., on π, 339, 344.
Dehn, M., 93.
De Lagny on π, 346.
De la Hire, P., 202, 203.
De la Loubère, S., 195, 203.
Delannoy, 117, 121.
De Lavernède, J. E. T., 181.
Delens, P., 21.
DELIAN PROBLEM, 93, 327–333.
Deltoid, the, 100.
De Lury, D. B., 44.
De Moivre, A., 175.
De Montmort, 1, 46, 175.
De Morgan, A., 223, 335, 338, 339,
349.
Denary Scale of Notation, 11–16,
20–26, 53.
De Parville on Tower of Hanoï, 304.
De Polignac, A., 64, 184.
Derangements, 46, 325.

Derrington, on Queens Problem, 170.
De St. Laurent, T., 310.
Descartes, 332, 334, 345.
DIABOLIC MAGIC SQUARES, 203, 206, 208–212.
Diamandi, P., 366, 368.
DICE, CUBIC AND OCTAHEDRAL, 215.
Dickson, L. E., 67, 73, 320.
Digital Process, 372.
DIGITS, MISSING, 20–26.
Diocles on Delian Problem, 331.
Diodorus on Lake Moeris, 256.
Dirichlet, Lejeune, 71.
DISSECTION PROBLEMS, 87–94.
Dodecahedron, Great, 144, 234, 236.
—— Pentagonal, 131, 231, 238, 262–265.
—— Rhombic, 136, 150.
—— Stellated, 144.
Dodgson, C. L., on Parallels, 77.
DOMINOES, 31, 214, 250–254.
Donchian, P. S., preface, 140.
Double Transposition, 391.
Doubly-Magic Squares, 212.
Drayton, 256.
DUAL MAPS, 234.
Dudeney, H. E., 35, 39, 49, 59, 79, 88, 92, 96, 116, 118, 125, 186, 189, 211, 215, 268.
DUPLICATION OF CUBE, 93, 327–333.
Dürer, A., 194, 203.

e, 47, 56, 87, 336.
Eckenstein, O., 267, 268, 273, 284, 292, 297.
EIGHT QUEENS PROBLEM, 165–170.
Eisenlohr, A., on Ahmes, 339.
Elements, the Four, 132.
Enantiomorphism, 130, 134, 139, 146, 159, 215, 238, 241.
Enciphering and Deciphering, 381.
Encke, J. F., 363.
Eneström, G., on π, 338.
Eratosthenes, 328.
Errera, A., 230.
Escott, E. B., 215, 348.
Estermann, T., 65.
Etten, H. van, 12.
Euclid, 62, 67, 131, 340.
Euclidean Construction, 95–97, 139, 326.
Euler, L., 59, 62, 63, 67, 68, 70, 174–179, 203, 338, 346.
Eulerian Cubes, 192, 220.
—— Squares, 190–192, 213.
Euler's Officers Problem, 190.

Euler's Theorem, 131, 145.
—— (Proof), 233.
EULER'S UNICURSAL PROBLEM, 242–247.
Euzet, M., 89.
Exploration Problems, 32.

Factorization, 61, 63.
FALLACIES, ARITHMETICAL, 41–44.
—— GEOMETRICAL, 76–84.
Fedorow, E. von, 140.
Fermat Numbers, 69, 95.
FERMAT ON BINARY POWERS, 68.
Fermat's Criterion for Primes, 63.
FERMAT'S LAST THEOREM, 69–73.
FERRY-BOAT PROBLEMS, 116–118.
Fibonacci Numbers, 57, 86.
FIFTEEN GIRLS PROBLEM, chap. X.
FIFTEEN PUZZLE, 299–303.
FINITE ARITHMETICS, 60, 109, 190.
Fisher, R. A., 189.
FIVE DISC PROBLEM, 97.
Fonteney on Ferry Problem, 117.
Fouquières, Becq de, on Games, 105.
FOUR-COLOUR MAP THEOREM, 222–231.
Four "4's" Problem, 15.
Four Digits Problem, 15.
Fourrey, E., 27.
Fox, Captain, on π, 349.
Franklin, C. H. H., 143.
Franklin, P., 230, 237.
Frénicle (de Bessy), B., 200.
Friedman, W. F., 405.
Frost, A. H., 203, 268.
Fry, T. C., 45.
Fuller, T., 354.

GALOIS ARITHMETICS, 73–75, 109, 191, 220.
Galton, F., 41.
GAMES, Dynamical, 114–128.
—— Statical, 104–114.
—— with Counters, 104–106, 119–125.
Gauss, C. F., 94, 355, 363.
Genus, 234.
GEODESIC PROBLEMS, 118.
GEOGRAPHY, PHYSICAL, 101.
GEOMETRICAL FALLACIES, 76–84.
—— PROBLEMS, THREE CLASSICAL, chap. XII.
—— RECREATIONS, chaps. III, IV, V, XI.
GERGONNE'S PROBLEM, 316–321.
Gerwien, P., 89.
Ghersi, I., 185.

Gill, T. H., on Kirkman's Problem, 268, 276.
Glaisher, J. W. L., 166, 339.
Goldbach's Theorem. 65.
Goldberg, Michael, 39, 89, 96, 154, 298.
Golden Section, 57, 131.
Goormaghtigh, M. R., 231.
Gosset, Thorold, 170.
Grandpré, A. de, 379, 410.
Great Dodecahedron, 144, 234, 236.
—— Icosahedron, 144.
GREAT NORTHERN PUZZLE, 114, 127.
Greenwich, Labyrinth at, 259.
Gregory, Jas., 336, 345, 346.
Gregory of St Vincent, 332.
Gregory's Series, 346.
Grienberger on π, 345.
Grille, The, 392.
Gros, L., on Chinese Rings, 307–309.
Group, Icosahedral, 157, 264.
GUARINI'S PROBLEM, 188.
Guitel, E., 89.
Günther, S., 165, 194.
Guthrie on Colouring Maps, 223.

Haan, B. de, on π, 339, 344.
Halley on π, 346.
HAMILTONIAN GAME, 262–266.
Hampton Court, Maze at, 259.
HANOÏ, TOWER OF, 303–305.
Harison, G. D. L., 268, 293.
Harzer, P., on π, 342.
Haussner, 65.
Heath, R. V., 12, 200, 201, 213, 216, 221.
Heath, T., 131, 134.
Heawood, P. J., on Maps, 224, 227–232, 235.
Heffter, L., on Maps, 237.
Hegesippus on Decimation, 32.
Henry, Ch., on Euler's Problem, 242.
Hermary, 265.
Herodotus on Lake Moeris, 256.
Hero of Alexandria, 329, 340.
Herschel, Sir John, 358.
Herschel, Sir William, 360.
Hess, E., 154.
Hexagon Problem, 111.
Hexagons, Interlocked, 215–217.
Hilbert, D., 235.
Hill, L. S., 404.
HILLS AND DALES, 102.
Hippias, 339.
Hippocrates of Chios, 329, 339.
Hoppenot, F., 58, 63.
Houdin, J. E. R., 364.

Hudson, C. T., 320.
Hudson, W. H. H., 311.
Hutton, C., 3, 346.
Huygens, C., 332, 336, 345.
Hyper-cubes, 140.
Hypocychoid, The Three-cusped, 100.

Icosahedron, Regular, 131, 238–241.
—— Rhombic, 143.
—— Stellated, 144–146.
ICOSIAN GAME, 262–266.
Icosidodecahedron, 136.
Inaudi, J., 366–369.
Ingham, A. E., 62, 235.
Interlocked Hexagons, 215–217.
Intermediate Convergents, 87.
Inwards on the Cretan Maze, 257.

Jaenisch, C. F. de, 172, 185.
Jephson, T., 358.
Johnson, W., on Fifteen Puzzle, 299.
Jones, W., on π, 338, 346.
Josephus Problem, 32–36.
Julian's Bowers, 258.
Julius Cæsar, 394.

Kagno, I. N., 237.
KAKEYA, 99.
KALEIDOSCOPE, 154–160.
Kamke, E., 44.
Kayles, 39.
Kempe, A. B., on Colouring Maps, 224.
Kepler, J., 133.
KEPLER-POINSOT POLYHEDRA, 143–145, 234.
Khajuraho, 203.
KING'S RE-ENTRANT PATH, 185.
Kirkman, T. P., 267.
KIRKMAN'S PROBLEM, chap. X.
Klein, F. C., 86, 326.
KNIGHT'S RE-ENTRANT PATH, 174–185.
KNIGHTS OF THE ROUND TABLE, 49.
Knyghton, 256.
König, Dénes, 265, 266.
Königsberg Problem, 242.
Kraïtchik, M., 13, 28, 60, 63, 65, 68, 69, 95, 107, 185, 200, 202, 207, 208.
Kummer, E. E., 71.

Labyrinths, 254–260.
Lagny, de, on π, 346.
La Hire, P., 202, 203.
La Loubère, S., 195, 203.

Lambert, J. H., on π, 336.
Lamé, G., 71.
Landry, F., 69.
Laquière on Knight's Path, 184.
Latin Cubes, 192.
LATIN SQUARES, 189.
Lattice Points, 86.
Lavernède, J. E. T. de, 181.
Leake, 12, 16, 28.
Lebesgue, 71.
Legendre, A. M., 71, 176, 185, 336.
Legros, L. A., 269.
Lehmer, D. H., 56, 62, 66, 72, 348.
Lehmer, D. N., 58, 63, 64.
LEHMER'S MACHINE, 61.
Leibniz, 1, 63.
Leonardo of Pisa on π, 342.
Leslie, J., 329, 333.
Leurechon, J., 2, 12.
Licks, H. E., 57.
Linde, A. van der, 174.
Lindemann on π, 336.
Lines, L., 136.
Lines of Slope, 101.
Listing, J. B., 126, 244.
London and Wise, 259.
Lo-shu, 196.
Loubère, S. De la, 195, 203.
Loyd, S., 29.
Lucas, E., 50, 60, 63, 65, 117, 122, 125, 144, 255, 303.
Lucca, Labyrinth at, 258.

Macaulay, W. H., 93.
McClintock, E., 203.
Machin's Series for π, 346.
MacMahon, P. A., 51, 111, 112, 189.
MAGIC CUBES, 217–221.
MAGIC SQUARES, chap. VII.
Magic Square Puzzles, 214.
Mangiamele, V., 362.
MAP COLOUR THEOREMS, 222–231, 235–237.
Margossian, 208, 221.
Marks, 74, 191.
Marsden, E., on Kirkman's Problem, 268.
Mascheroni, L., 96.
Maxwell, J. Clerk, 5, 101.
Mayan Glyphs, 409.
Mazes, 254–260.
Medieval Problems, 27–36.
Meissel, 63.
Menaechmus, 330.
Ménage Problem, 50.
Mendelsohn, C. J., 405.

MENTAL ARITHMETIC, chap. XIII.
MERSENNE'S NUMBERS, 65.
Mesolabum, 329.
Metius, A., on π, 343.
Méziriac, see Bachet.
Mikami, Y., 201.
Miller, G. A., 297.
Miller, J. C. P., 137.
Minding on Knight's Path, 185.
Minos, 254, 328.
Minotaur, 256.
MIRRORS, 154–160.
MISSING DIGITS, 20–26.
Mitchell, F. D., 350–354.
Möbius, A. F., 158, 223.
Models, Geometrical, 130, 134, 152, 158.
Mohammed's Sign-Manual, 248.
Mohr, Georg, 96.
Moivre, A. de, 175.
Mondeux, H., 362, 368.
Monge, on Shuffling Cards, 310–312.
Monoalphabetic Systems, 395–397.
Montmort, de, 1, 46, 175.
Montucla, J. F., 3, 89, 335, 337, 344.
Moore, E. H., 38, 297.
Mordell, L. J., 69.
Morehead, J. C., 69.
Morgan, A. de, see De Morgan.
Moroń, Z., 93.
Morse Code, 398.
Mosaic Pavements, 107, 258.
Moschopulus, 194.
MOUSETRAP, GAME OF, 324.
Mulder, P., on Kirkman's Problem, 292.
Müller (Regiomontanus), 342.
Müller, G. E., 350, 369.
Muncey, J. N., 211.
Mydorge, 2.

NASIK MAGIC SQUARES, 203, 206, 208–212.
Nauck, F., 165.
Neville, E. H., 98.
Newbold, W. R., 409.
Newton, Isaac, 333, 334, 337.
Nicomedes, 329.
NIM, 36–38, 298.
Nine Digits Problem, 15, 40.
Normal Piling, 149, 151.
Noughts and Crosses, 104.
NUMBERS, PERFECT, 67.
—— PUZZLES WITH, 4–50.
—— THEORY OF, 57–75, 231.

Octahedron, 131, 147, 215.

Oppert, on π, 339.
Orientability of Surfaces, 232.
Oughtred's *Recreations*, 12, 16, 28.
Ovid, 256.
Ozanam, A. F., on Labyrinths, 258.
Ozanam's *Récréations*, 2, 3, 12, 28, 85, 116, 175, 305.

π, 336–349.
Pacioli di Burgo, 2.
Pairs-of-Cards Trick, 313–316.
Paley, R. E. A. C., 110.
PANDIAGONAL MAGIC SQUARES, 203, 206, 208–212.
Pappus, 134, 329, 333, 334.
PARADROMIC RINGS, 125, 232.
Parmentier on Knight's Path, 174.
Pars, L. A., 227–230.
Parville, de, 304.
PAWNS, GAMES WITH, 122–125.
PEIRCE'S PROBLEM OF n^2 GIRLS, 294–296.
Pentagram, 143, 248.
Pepys, S., 379.
Perelman, 40.
PERFECT NUMBERS, 67.
Perigal, H., 88.
PERMUTATION PROBLEMS, 48–50.
Petersburg Paradox, 44.
Petersen, A. C., 363.
Petersen, J., on Graphs, 226.
Petrie, J. F., 146, 152, 157.
Petrie Polygon, 135, 144.
Philo, 329.
Philoponus on Delian Problem, 327.
Photo-electric Number-sieve, 61..
PHYSICAL GEOGRAPHY, 101.
PILE PROBLEMS, 316–321.
Pipping on Goldbach's Theorem, 65.
Pirie, G., on π, 345.
Planck, C., 203, 204, 210.
Plane of Symmetry, 130, 135.
Planets, 133, 194.
PLATONIC SOLIDS, 130–135, 238.
Plato on Delian Problem, 327, 330.
Playfair Cipher, 402.
Pliny, 256.
Poitiers, Labyrinth at, 258.
Pole, W., 377.
Polignac, A. de, 64, 184.
Pólya, G., 107, 160.
Polyalphabetic Systems, 398–402.
Polygraphic Substitution, 402–404.
POLYHEDRA, chap. V.
Polyliteral Systems, 397.
Portier, B., on Magic Squares, 212.
Poussin, De la Vallée, 64.

Powers, R. E., 65, 66.
Pratt on Knight's Path, 180.
Prime Pairs, 64.
PRIMES, 62–65, 211.
Probabilities, 43–47, 84, 293, 325, 348.
Ptolemy, 340.
Purbach on π, 342.
PUZZLES, Arithmetical, 4–50.
—— Geometrical, 77–128.
Pyramidal Numbers, 59, 151.
Pythagoras' Theorem, 57, 87.

Quadratic Residues, 109.
QUADRATURE OF CIRCLE, 335–349.
QUEENS PROBLEM, EIGHT, 165–170.
Queens, Problems with, 187, 189.

Railway Puzzles (Shunting), 114–116.
Ramification, 260–262.
Ravenna, Labyrinth at, 258.
Reciprocal Polyhedra, 132–136, 152, 234.
—— Tesselations, 108, 134.
RE-ENTRANT CHESS PATHS, 174–187.
Reflexible Figures, 129.
Regiomontanus on π, 342.
Regular Polygons, 130.
—— Polyhedra, 130.
—— Tesselations, 107, 134, 152, 266.
Reimer, N. T., 327.
Reiss, M., 125, 254.
Renton, W., 84.
Residues, 60, 109.
RESTORATIONS OF DIGITS, 20–26.
Reynolds, C. N., 230.
Reynolds, Osborne, 151.
Rhind Papyrus, 339.
Rhombicuboctahedron and Rhombicosidodecahedron, 137.
Rich, J., 380.
Richmond, H. W., 95.
Richter on π, 347.
Riemann, G. F. B., 64.
RIGHT-ANGLED TRIANGLES, 57, 88.
Rilly, A., 185, 212.
Robert-Houdin, J. E., 364.
Robinson, G. de B., 158.
Rockliff Marshes, Labyrinth at, 258.
Rodet, L., on Arya-Bhata, 341.
Roget, P. M., 181–184.
Romanus, on π, 343.
Rome, Labyrinth at, 258.
ROOK'S RE-ENTRANT PATH, 186.
Rosamund's Bower, 256.
Rosen, F., on Arab values of π, 342.

Rosser, J. B., 72, 203, 204.
ROTATING RINGS OF TETRAHEDRA, 153, 215, 235.
Round Table, Knights of, 49.
ROUTES ON CHESS-BOARD, 174–188.
Rückle, C., 366, 368, 369.
Rudis, F., on π, 336.
Running-key System, 401.
Rutherford on π, 347.

Safford, T. H., 365.
Saffron Walden, Labyrinth at, 259.
St. Laurent, T. de, on Cards, 310.
St. Omer, Labyrinth at, 258.
St. Petersburg Paradox, 44.
St. Vincent, Gregory of, 332.
Sauveur, J., 203.
Sayles, H. A., 211.
Scale of Notation, Denary, 11–16.
—— Transforming to Another, 55.
Schiffner, E., 53.
Schläfli, L., 140, 145.
SCHOOL-GIRLS, FIFTEEN, chap. X.
Schooling, J. H., 10.
Schots, M. H., 213.
Schubert, H., on π, 336.
Schuh, H., 22.
Schumacher, H. C., 363.
Scripture, E. W., 350.
SECRET COMMUNICATIONS, chap. XIV.
Selander, K. E. I., on π, 338.
SEVEN-COLOUR MAP THEOREM, 235.
Shanks, W., on π, 347.
Sharp, A., 129, 142, 346.
Shelton, J., 380.
Sherwin's Tables, 346.
SHUFFLING CARDS, 310–312.
Shuldham, C. D., 211.
SHUNTING PROBLEMS, 114–116.
Sinkov, A., preface, chap. XIV.
Sixty-five Puzzle, 85.
Skeleton Cubes, 49.
Smith, A., on π, 348.
Smith, D. E., 196, 201, 203.
Snell, W., on π, 344.
Snub Solids, 138.
Solitaire, 124.
Sommerville, D. M. Y., 140.
Southwark, Labyrinth at, 259.
Sovereign, Change for, 48.
SPONGES, REGULAR, 151–153.
Sporus on Delian Problem, 331.
SQUARING THE CIRCLE, 335–349.
Standard Alphabets, 394.
STATICAL GAMES, 104–114.
Steen on the Mousetrap, 324.

Steinhaus, H., 232, 238.
Steinitz, E., 136.
Stella Octangula, 134, 136, 146.
Stellated Polyhedra, 144–146.
Storey on the Fifteen Puzzle, 299.
STOTT, MRS. A. BOOLE, 139.
Strabo on Lake Moeris, 256.
Strachey, R., 196.
Strasznicky, 363, 364.
String Figures, preface.
Sturm, A., 327.
SUBSTITUTION, 393–404.
Suetonius, 394.
Super-Dominoes, 111.
SURFACES, UNBOUNDED, 232.
Swastika, 257.
Swinden, B. A., 36.
Sylvester, J. J., 67, 105, 108, 297.
SYMMETRICAL MAGIC SQUARES, 203.
SYMMETRY, 130, 135, 151.

Tait, P. G., 34, 120, 224–227, 230–231, 244.
Tangrams, 113.
Tanner, L., on Shuffling Cards, 310.
Tarry, G., 117, 212, 249–253.
Tartaglia, 2, 28, 33, 51, 116.
Taylor, B., 175.
Taylor, Ch., 335.
Taylor, H. M., 91, 162.
Ten Digits Problem, 15, 40.
TESSELLATION, PLANE, 106–112, 138, 148, 155, 266.
—— SOLID, 112, 146–152, 159.
Tetrahedral Numbers, 59, 151.
Tetrahedron, 131, 147.
Texeira, F. G., 326.
Theaetetus, 131.
THEORY OF NUMBERS, 57–75, 231.
Thibaut, G., on Baudhayana, 341.
THREE-IN-A-ROW, 104.
THREE-PILE PROBLEM, 316.
TOPOLOGY, chaps. VIII, IX.
Torus, 216, 222, 235, 265.
TOWER OF HANOÏ, 303–305.
TRANSPOSITION, COLUMNAR, 383 391.
—— ROUTE, 382.
Trastevere, Labyrinth at, 258.
Travers, J., 93, 201.
Trebly-Magic Squares, 213.
TREES, GEOMETRICAL, 260–262.
Treize, Game of, 325.
Trémaux on Mazes, 255.
Triacontahedron, 136.
TRIANGULAR NUMBERS, 59.
TRICKS WITH NUMBERS, 3–50.

TRISECTION OF ANGLE, 333–335.
Troitsky, 13.
Trollope, E., on Mazes, 256.
Troy-towns, 258.
Truncated Solids, 138, 147, 153.
Turton, W. H., 81, 173.
Tutte, W. T., 93, 103.
Two Digit Process, 372.

UNICURSAL PROBLEMS, chap. IX.
Uniform Polyhedra, 135, 158.

Valerio, P., 396, 410.
Vallée Poussin, Ch. J. de la, 64.
Van Ceulen on π, 343.
Vandermonde, 179.
Vandiver, H. S., 72.
Van Etten, H., 12.
Vase Problem, 28.
Veblen, O., 208.
Vega on π, 346.
Vieta, F., 332, 342.
Vigenère Square, 399.
Vinogradoff, L. A., 65.
Virgil, 256.
Volpicelli, P., on Knight's Path, 174.
Von Bilguer on Chess Pieces, 164.
Voting, 49, 107.
Voynich, W. M., 409.

Walecki on Kirkman's Problem, 293.

Walker, G. T., 41.
Walker, R. J., 203, 204.
Wallis, J., 307, 345, 351.
Wantzell, P. L., 326.
Warnsdorff on Knight's Path, 180.
Watch Problem, 17.
Watersheds and Watercourses, 102.
Watson, G. N., 60.
WEIGHTS PROBLEM, 50.
Western, A. E., on Binary Powers, 69.
Whateley, R., 355.
Wheeler, A. H., 93, 94, 146.
Wiedemann, A., on Lake Moeris, 256.
Wieferich, A., 72.
Wijthoff, see Wythoff.
William III of England, 259.
Wilson's Theorem, 63.
WINDOW READER, 321–323.
Wing, Labyrinth at, 259.
Winn, C. E., 230.
Winter, F., 112.
Wythoff, W. A., 38, 158.

Yardley, H. O., 410.
Yates, F., 189.

Zach, F. X. von, on π, 347.
Zamebone, U., 366.
Zonohedra, 140.

THE END

Carolyn M. Byerly and Karen Ross

Women
&Media

A Critical Introduction

Blackwell
Publishing

BLACKWELL PUBLISHING
350 Main Street, Malden, MA 02148-5020, USA
9600 Garsington Road, Oxford OX4 2DQ, UK
550 Swanston Street, Carlton, Victoria 3053, Australia

First published 2006 by Blackwell Publishing Ltd

1   2006

Library of Congress Cataloging-in-Publication Data is available for this title.

ISBN-13: 9781405116060 (hardback)
ISBN-10: 1405116064 (hardback)
ISBN-13: 9781405116077 (paperback)
ISBN-10: 1405116072 (paperback)

A catalog record for this title is available from the British Library.

Set in 10.5 on 13 pt Minion
by SNP Best-set Typesetter Ltd, Hong Kong
Printed and bound in the United Kingdom
by TJ International Ltd, Padstow, Cornwall

The publisher's policy is to use permanent paper from mills that operate a
sustainable forestry policy, and which has been manufactured from pulp
processed using acid-free and elementary chlorine-free practices. Furthermore,
the publisher ensures that the text paper and cover board used have met
acceptable environmental accreditation standards.

For further information on
Blackwell Publishing, visit our website:
www.blackwellpublishing.com

Contents

Preface and acknowledgments   vi
About the authors   ix

1   Introduction   1

Part I   Research on women and media: a short history   **15**
2   Women in/as entertainment   17
3   Images of women in news and magazines   37
4   Women as audience   56
5   Women and production: gender and the political economy
     of media industries   75

Part II   Women, media, and the public sphere:
shifting the agenda   **97**
6   Toward a Model of Women's Media Action   99
7   First path: politics to media   129
8   Second path: media profession to politics   155
9   Third path: advocate change agent   185
10   Fourth path: women's media enterprises   208

11   Conclusion   231

Bibliography   240
Appendix: research participants   273
Name index   278
Subject index   284

Preface and Acknowledgments

We didn't set out to write this book. Three years ago, we were well on our way to completing a different book, an edited collection, which, as it got under way, seemed to call out for a companion theoretical volume, one that mapped out not only women's problematic relationship to media but also their responses as researchers, as activists, as media professionals. Jayne Fargnoli at Blackwell, who would become our editor for the first volume, *Women and Media: International Perspectives* (2004) would also be the person to make the call to us for the companion text. We hope that we have answered it adequately in this volume. As colleagues and friends who had already worked together on various small-scale projects and then on our jointly edited book, we trusted our cross-Atlantic working relationship. Even so, we were often challenged to manage this project, which seemed to expand beyond the undertaking that we initially envisaged. As we began our work, the more we talked to women about their experiences, the more we wanted to reveal and examine how those in quite different geographical and cultural settings had grappled with ways to amplify women's voices and presence in media. Building on existing research, we set out to locate and interview women in sufficient numbers to enable us to paint a broad picture of their work and accomplishments, as well as their analyses of these experiences.

Throughout this project, we worked under tight deadlines that competed with other commitments in our lives. In addition, we had the strain of realizing that while we shared a common language, we sometimes worked in uncommon vernaculars and theoretical approaches that challenged us to find ways to speak in a clear, more unified, voice to our readers. Thus, the research and writing presented in this volume represent our personal growth as scholars and friends, as well as the collective encouragement, support, and participation of many women and men around the world who assisted us.

We are very grateful for the time and financial support afforded our work by our respective universities, the University of Maryland and Howard University (USA), and Coventry University (UK). And we have many other people to thank, without whose generous gifts of time, information, and other help this book would not exist. Ammu Joseph (Bangalore, India) was, in many ways, a partner in our project's development and enabled the interviews in India to take shape and place. We are, of course, enormously grateful to our 90 informants in 20 nations, whose names and affiliations appear in the Appendix. These women shared their experiences as media activists in candid and wonderful detail, enabling us to understand, describe, analyze, and theorize the ways in which they have worked to open up public spaces for feminist dialogue and, in many cases, to make media structures more egalitarian over the past 30 years. This book is dedicated to them and to all the other women (and men) who have provoked inspiration and shown dogged determination to ensure that women have a public voice through media.

We are also grateful to others who supported us in various ways: Frieda Werden of Women's International Newsgathering Service (WINGS), in Vancouver, staff at the Center for Arab Women's Training and Research (CAWTAR), in Tunis, and numerous other individuals for assistance in locating research informants; Sudip Mazumdar and Kalpana Sharma in India, for logistical support; Jill Gibbs, for her dedicated, thorough work on transcriptions; Takisha Watson and Lauren Vance for additional help with transcriptions; the anonymous reviewers of our manuscript for their helpful comments; and Geoffrey Palmer, Ken Provencher, and others at Blackwell for bringing the book to print. Finally, but not lastly, we offer thanks to Kay and Greta, Barry and Pearl (our partners and canine companions, respectively) for the daily encouragement that they have provided on the home front and their (almost) total lack of complaint.

Carolyn M. Byerly and Karen Ross

About the Authors

Carolyn M. Byerly, PhD, is Associate Professor in the Graduate Program of Mass Communication and Media Studies, Department of Journalism, Howard University, Washington DC (USA). She teaches seminars in mass communication theory, research methods, media effects, and political communication. Recent publications include *Women and Media: International Perspectives* (edited with Karen Ross, Blackwell, 2004), "After 9/11: Formation of an Oppositional Discourse" (*Feminist Media Studies*, Fall 2005), and "Women and the Concentration of Media Ownership" (in R. R. Rush, C. E. Oukrop, and P. J. Creedon, *Seeking Equity for Women in Journalism and Mass Communication Education*, Erlbaum, 2004).

Karen Ross PhD, is Professor of Mass Communication at Coventry University (UK). She teaches research methods, gender politics and media, and audience studies and has written extensively on issues of in/equality in communication and culture. Her previous books include *Gender and Newsroom Cultures: Identities at Work* (with Marjan de Bruin, 2004), *Women and Media: International Perspectives* (edited with Carolyn M. Byerly, Blackwell, 2004), and *Media and Audiences* (with Virginia Nightingale, 2003). She is currently working on two studies relating to press coverage of elections from a gender perspective.

1

Introduction

Groups of women manipulating and producing media constitute active and widespread movements at the community level. These groups use video, radio or theater for communicating among themselves for lobbying and rights advocacy, restoration of their group and personal history, or for promoting community organization.

Pilar Riaño (1991)

Scholarly developments reflect the wider world. The emergence of feminist scholarship during the 1970s was an academic response to women's liberation movements in both local and global contexts. After two world wars and a series of national liberation movements[1] in the first half of the century, women had begun to find their own voices and seek a more active role in public and academic life. Modern-day women's movements began to take shape during the early 1960s in both developed and developing nations, in part through the work of United Nations committees concerned with improving women's status. A network of women's independent non-governmental organizations – some of them growing out of women's peace-action and opposition to war – also provided entry points for women's cross-cultural collaboration. To be sure, women's impetus to become involved in movements for self-determination varied from place to place and person to person. In some cases, they had been inspired by national development in which women desired to participate more actively. In other cases, inspiration came from having had a taste of public life, and from the ability to develop a vision for their own and other women's leadership. Feminist historians in a number of nations have chronicled and examined the events and personal motives that led to both local and global feminist movements by the early 1970s. For example, Amrita Basu's (1995) *The Challenge of Local Feminisms*, Elise Boulding's (1992) *The Underside of History*, and Maitrayee Chaudhuri's (2004) edited volume *Feminism in India* document the evolution of women's movements around the world, pointing out that activists from all cultures and social classes have been involved and that feminist progress is likely to endure, even as the backlash of patriarchy appears predictably everywhere to hold it back.

What is clear to us, as feminist media scholars, is that the media have played a central but not yet fully examined role in these events. The present text seeks to reveal more about the interconnections between the media and feminist movements, and, in turn, the ways in which women's communication through media extended beyond those movements into the larger societies. Thus, the title of this book, *Women and Media: A Critical Introduction*, signals the book's dual goals of taking stock of the existing (and expansive) literature on women and media while also moving beyond it. The title also conveys our intent to take a critical approach to our subject, examining gendered relations of power and both the hegemonic tendencies and emancipatory potentials of media structures. Feminist media scholarship to date has focused primarily on women's representation in the mainstream media; hence, much is known about how the portrayal of women in film, television, news, and other media has changed (or remained the same) within and across nations. Similarly, there is a growing body of work on how female audience members "read" and respond to messages and images of women. A smaller part of the literature includes feminist analyses of media structures, where men's ownership and creative control are still the norm everywhere, and where women have had a tough time gaining access to production, either as trained professionals or citizens.

Still only marginally represented in national and international feminist media studies, however, are analyses of women's own media enterprises, feminist campaigns to reform large-scale media industries, and feminist media networks. We situate our own contribution in the last (and least defined) of these inquiries, but draw heavily on the wider body of women-and-media literature to accomplish our goals. We have looked particularly to the experiences of feminist activists and media professionals for an understanding of women's agency in the use of (many kinds of) media, to develop and disperse social critiques and to spread ideas about women, from a feminist perspective. Women's media activism represents an historically significant but under-investigated and under-theorized aspect of women's relationship to contemporary media, both those media that are owned and operated by powerful men and those that women have established themselves. Also relatively under-scrutinized are the various support activities, such as community-level media monitoring, academic research, and advocacy groups that mobilize citizen action around specific women-and-media issues. We believe that these aspects of the women-and-media relationship begin to reveal the process of struggle that women have engaged in for use of media to gain a public voice, presence, and influence.

The vision for this project grew out of our respective work as feminist media scholars, whose projects through the years have sought to enlarge our realities as white academics, and to move beyond the borders of our respective Western nations, the United States and the United Kingdom. In both different and overlapping ways, we have tried to examine the perspectives, situations, challenges, and successes of women in both our own and other nations with respect to their media endeavors. In the process, we have gained a growing awareness of how much women have done in their struggles to use media to speak freely, publicly, and forcefully in their respective locales. The work of women media activists, among whom we include many who carry out their daily work in mainstream industries, is ongoing and compelling, and we believe it is central to reshaping societies everywhere. We have tried to provide a glimpse into some of these processes and outcomes in the pages to come.

Expanding Feminisms

The word *feminism* (and its derivative *feminist*), which appears throughout this book, has undergone considerable scrutiny, argument, and transformation in meaning over the years.[2] Third world women, women of color, working-class women, and others have debated the word for several decades, questioning whether a term associated with Western (white, bourgeois) origins can legitimately apply to women of other backgrounds and situations. In the process, the term has come to encompass a wide range of experiences and positionalities. We use the words feminist and feminism to refer to women's liberation movements since the 1970s that have been aimed at securing women's right to participate in their societies, including the ability to enter into public deliberation, institution building, and other processes associated with citizenship. We recognize that women's movements have varied histories, shaped by culture, economics, political structures, and (in some cases) colonial relations. Maitrayee Chaudhuri (2004: xv–xvi) observes, for instance, that feminism in India has to be "located within the broader framework of an unequal international world," but she also asks whether hesitation to use the term might exclude women "from the feminist heritage." Such questions may arise even within a nation whose traditional feminism has been assumed to be white and European. African American feminist theorist Patricia Hill Collins (1990) has reminded us that the USA is not free from its own internal colonial history, and that that history has shaped black women's feminism:

> The dialectic of oppression and activism, the tension between the suppression of Black women's ideas and our intellectual activism in the race of that suppression, comprises the politics of Black feminist thought. More important, understanding this dialectical relationship is critical in assessing how Black feminist thought – its definitions, core themes, and epistemological significance – is fundamentally embedded in a political context that has challenged its very right to exist. (Hill Collins 1990: 5–6)

In addition, both white feminist scholars (e.g., Linda K. Kerber & Jane Sherron De Hart 2000) and black feminist scholars (e.g., Angela Y. Davis 1981) have explored American feminism's birth in the nineteenth-century anti-slavery movement, a moment that joined their activism in a common cause and that gives testimony to a complex multiracial US feminist history. Similarly, American feminist historian Sally Roesch Wagner (1996) has acknowledged her own cultural blindness in overlooking the deeply significant ways in which Native American women's experiences intertwine with modern US feminism. Wagner's collaborative research with women of the Iroquois nation, a confederacy of six Native American tribes in upstate New York, suggests that women's rights leaders who formed the nucleus of the 1848 Seneca Falls Convention[3] (and the work that grew out of it) took their vision for egalitarianism in male–female relationships, women's right to own property, and notions of freedom from men's violence from the Iroquois people who lived around them.

Chandra Talpade Mohanty (1991) sought to construct a definition of *third world feminism*, but she had to begin with questions such as: "What is the third world?" "Do third world women make up a real constituency?" and "Are women's political struggles in the third world necessarily 'feminist'?" She traced the term's meaning through a number of writers from former colonial states who showed ways in which colonial histories, social class, race, and other signifiers of power become embedded in contemporary understandings of third world feminism. Mohanty's thoughtful, comprehensive book reminds us of what she calls "the urgency and necessity to rethink feminist praxis and theory within a cross-cultural, international framework and to discuss (a) the assumption of third world women as a social category in feminist work, and (b) definitions and contests over feminism among third world women" (Mohanty 1991: 39). Some African and African American women have preferred to call themselves *womanists* instead of feminists, adopting the term popularized by US author Alice Walker in the 1980s to signify a woman who is committed to the survival of her whole people, men and woman (Walker 1981). Cheryl Johnson-Odim (1991) acknowledges that the coining of new terms (such as "womanist") demonstrates a commitment to connect feminists' struggles to those of black and third world communities that are fighting racism, economic exploitation, and other oppression. At the same time, she acknowledges that some white radical women have also understood these connections and worked for broader liberation. Johnson-Odim, who adopts a feminist identity, believes that in the process of building an international feminist movement, third world women have wrestled with both the meaning of feminism and its agenda, thereby integrating class, race, and anti-imperialism concerns into its meaning structure.

Recent writings by third world women reveal the comprehensive understanding – that is, the overlap of gender and other concerns – that Johnson-Odim refers to. For example, South African scholars Amanda Kemp, Nozizwe Madlala, Asha Moodley, and Elaine Salo (1995) found that as women have sought to constitute themselves as participants in the emerging pluralistic South African society, since the 1990s, they shaped their understanding that "ideologies of womanhood had as much to do with race as they do with sex" (p. 133). These authors also factor in concerns about national development, which they assert is bound up with women's advancement and hence their work as social activists. Thus, in articulating a politics of equality and advancement for women, black South African feminists, they say, also must raise issues such as access to clean water and housing – things not specifically defined as "feminist" (ibid.).

In this book, we take the position that such consciousness and inclusivity must inform feminist theory and the research that flows from it, regardless of national boundaries. Therefore, we have tried to inform own our text with the knowledge and lessons shared by these and other feminist scholars, realizing with some humility that that we are still evolving and that our work may still contain blind spots. Similarly, while we have tried to make spaces in the text for women of widely ranging cultural and national contexts to speak, we make no pretense at claiming that these informants speak for all women of their respective nations or cultures. Limitations of time and space constrained our investigation and writing. Thus, what we hope to offer is groundwork for others to build on in years to come. In addition, while we make the space for others to speak, we have tried to avoid speaking for them. Throughout the book, we try to distinguish our own voices from those of the participants in our cross-cultural research, reported in Chapters 7–10. Our analysis of those participants' information was undertaken with scholarly rigor and (we hope) fairness, although we recognize that scholarship is always fraught with certain risks of error in interpretation.

An Overview of the Chapters

The book is divided into two parts. Part I reviews the existing literature on women and media, emphasizing research and theoretical work undertaken since 1970. One goal of these chapters is to point out the dialectical nature of women's relationship to media industries over these decades. The term "dialectical process" is a Hegelian concept that Marx and later critical theorists borrowed to refer to patterns of upheaval by opposing forces within any hegemonic system such as capitalism.[4] Feminist applications have focused on seeing women's emergence from subjugation in patriarchal systems as such a process, drawing particularly on Marx and Engels's understanding of history as "a natural flux of action and reaction, of opposites yet inseparable and interpenetrating" (Firestone 1970: 2–3). In earlier work (Byerly 1999), we have explained women's relationship to media as uneven and contradictory, characterized by feminism becoming deeply embedded in media messages and the industries that produce them but, at the same time, women as subject remaining marginalized and misrepresented in media content, and women professionals remaining outside production apparatuses. A second goal of Part I is to consider the ways in which feminist media scholars from cultural and media studies and political-economy positions have theorized the women-and-media relationship.

Inasmuch as feminist media scholarship has (as previously noted) focused heavily on women's representation in popular media, we dedicate Chapters 2 and 3 to a synthesis of this work. As Part I reveals, most feminist media scholarship has been framed by what we have characterized elsewhere as a paradigm of the misogynist media (Byerly 1999). The central concerns in this paradigm are women's exclusion and misrepresentation in media content, professions, and policies. Documenting and analyzing the historical patterns of exclusion and misrepresentation that women have endured in the larger print and broadcast media (in spite of active and enormously effective women's liberation movements) has been essential in order to reveal the causes of these problems and to advance strategies for change. Even research that brings to light the ways in which women have progressed – for example, advancing in media professions or increasing news attention for women's achievements – inevitably acknowledges the still overwhelming amount to be done in order to redress what Gallagher (1995) has deemed women's "unfinished story."

Chapter 2 focuses on women's representation in film and television, considering entertainment and fiction-based media, predominantly film and television. In this chapter, we take a genre approach, which includes crime, soaps, and fantasy narratives, to signal the primary issues that have concerned feminist media scholars. A significant amount of the work on representation has been done within a feminist cultural studies framework, focusing specifically on commercially made films, and foregrounding considerations of ways in which audiences negotiate meanings in texts. What we attempt to show in this chapter is the endurance of gendered stereotyping, even as more contemporary renditions of women and femininity are finally providing a little more diversity in the media landscape. There is no doubt that the roles available to women have changed considerably over the past few decades, and that images and plotlines that are now routine would simply have been inconceivable 30 years ago. To a large extent, this really is a case of art following life, since women's progress must eventually be mirrored on the large and small screen. While women's representation today is certainly "better," in many ways, than ever before, women still experience actual prejudice and discrimination in terms of unequal treatment, unequal pay, and unequal value in real life. So too do these themes continue to occur in media portraits.

Chapter 3 looks at the representation of women in fact-based programming, especially news, together with an analysis of women's magazines, discussing the ways in which feminist media scholars have endeavored to expose the patriarchal ideology lying beneath these texts. The first part of the chapter focuses on news media, and we explore the key tropes associated with women's subject positions in relation to journalistic narratives, as well as the ways in which women's voices, both elite and public, are allowed (or not) to speak. The chapter considers women and/in advertising, in particular focusing on women's magazines. What our discussion demonstrates is that the media's framing (in every sense of the word) of women in highly restricted and mostly negative ways is not simply the consequence of the idiosyncrasies of this newspaper or that TV channel or that radio station but, rather, is a *global* phenomenon that has endured over time and media form, and continues to do so. The type of story that most frequently features woman as a victim, usually of male sexual violence, says something profound about the role of women in society. Where are the stories of women's success in business, in politics, in education, in science? What we hope to show in these two chapters is the uneven nature of women's progress on both the large and small screen. We argue here for women's greater control over the representations of their and our lives, so that the wonderful diversity of all our experiences becomes incorporated in the popular media landscape.

Chapter 4 explores the ways in which women as an audience have been addressed, and it begins with a sustained discussion of research on women audiences for soap opera, before moving on to consider research on other aspects of women's audiencehood, including film-going, crime genres, news, and magazines. The history of feminist engagement with the female audience is, in some ways, exemplified by the overdetermination of research studies on soaps which, as we will see later, is itself a product of feminist scholars' recognition of what women watched and enjoyed. The last section of the chapter concentrates on women's use of and relationship to new technologies, since the rise of technologies such as the Internet is forcing a new (re)consideration of the ways in which we function as an audience. Importantly, the level of interactivity that is enabled by technologies such as the Internet or digital television means that the viewer really can exert control over how she watches, listens, and reads popular media: finally, there is a reality to the rhetoric of audience power. In this chapter, we show the different ways in which women use, make sense of, understand, and interact with media products such as television, films, magazines, and the Internet. It is through the exploration of social context and women's lived experience, and the tensions between the two, that we can better comprehend how women negotiate their position as audience against the reality of their own lives.

Chapter 5 uses a feminist political-economy framework of analysis to consider the ways in which ownership of media industries by wealthy (mostly white) men have served to limit women's involvement in creative ranks, affecting women of color in particular. The chapter also critiques media productions (particularly films) by women, questioning whether progress is really achieved when liberal feminist media producers work within the narrow confines of topics and messages intended for conventional audiences so as to maintain their profits.

The second part of the book discusses and analyzes the empirical data that we collected for this book, and thus provides an elaboration of the various ways in which women activists and media workers have contributed to en-gendering the media and the broader public sphere. From our own earlier research, as well as our connections to feminists engaged in various kinds of media activism in different nations, we knew that a parallel world of women's communicative action had long lived alongside the "common" discourse. Women's movements (both within and across nations) have placed media reform and support for women's alternative media high on their agendas and, as a result, there has been measurable progress as well as recalcitrance in relation to changes within media structures. An additional outcome has been an explosion of women's initiatives to establish book publishing, radio and television production, news, magazine, documentary film, Internet, and other enterprises, in order to create new channels for women to speak publicly about their lives and concerns about the world – in their own voices.

Part II presents new research on women's media activism, and poses the Model of Women's Media Action, toward gaining a more comprehensive understanding of how women have tried to use media in order to enter more fully into democratic processes. Chapter 6 explains how women's media activism has shaped a feminist public sphere that overlaps and spreads feminist discourse into the dominant public sphere. In Chapter 6, we offer a new Model of Women's Media Action, reframing the women-and-media relationship from the 1970s to the present and identifying the ways in which feminist agency has manifested itself through the work of women media activists. Succeeding chapters further develop the Model of Women's Media Action as we interpret our empirical research with feminist journalists, filmmakers, researchers, and a range of other women in 20 nations. Women's media activism, we show, can be organized into four main paths, or approaches, and in Chapters 7–10 we develop those four paths through the personal narratives of participants in the study. Chapter 7 is concerned with the work of women media activists who have learned to "do" media as a part of their feminist political work. Chapter 8 discusses the work of women media professionals who decided to take a feminist approach to their work after they began their careers. Chapter 9 discusses the work of women who have worked outside media structures to conduct media monitoring and research, or to wage campaigns for media reform of some kind. Chapter 10 focuses on the work of women who have established a range of women's media enterprises. Chapter 11 summarizes what is known about women's treatment by and relationship to media industries, and identifies contributions that media activism has made in these last decades in advancing women's public participation and feminist movements' impact on their societies. In addition, we explore new strands of research that might grow out of our own project and the Model of Women's Media Action that it has produced.

Real Women, Real Lives

Central to this book is the work of women who have critiqued, monitored, shaped the content of, and otherwise sought to place media at the greater service of all women in gaining a bigger public voice and political role in their societies. The stories of 90 informants in 20 nations, who shared their experiences as women media activists with us in a two-year cross-cultural study, are at the heart of the book. Their work expands what we know of women's struggle to gain media access and to speak in their own voices, often against great odds, and two brief stories drawn from our interviews illustrate this well.

Preeti Mehra, journalist, New Delhi. January mornings are cold in New Delhi, India, when the fog settles in, sending dampness into unheated homes and chilling the bones of the inhabitants. Preeti Mehra, a veteran journalist in her forties, pulled her wool tunic closer around her to ward off the dampness and leaned back in her chair to talk about her years working for major English-language Indian newspapers in India. The autonomous women's movement, which had emerged in India by the mid-1970s, had drawn women such as Preeti Mehra, who saw close links between the movement's goals and her work as a reporter. She began to find ways to get women into news stories, both routine events and more dramatic coverage of riots, earthquakes, and disasters. "Women were so marginalized," she remembers, and helping them gain visibility became part of her daily challenge. In the late 1980s, she joined Women in the Media in Bombay, a group of about thirty women journalists. Members organized public events to focus on sexist media images and then strategized among themselves about how to overcome a lack of news coverage of women. They also protested about discrimination against women journalists. Mehra was among those who joined *dharnas* (sit-ins) outside newspaper offices to protest against sexual harassment and other problems. She participated in filing a complaint with the Bombay police to stop publication of a Marathi-language magazine titled "How do you rape?" – a manual whose pseudo-medical language barely masked its titillating subtext. The legal case went on for years, she said, generating a public discussion about violence against women and helping to mobilize other women around media issues.

Although Women in the Media disbanded around 1993, several of its members – including some who had become high profile and powerful in the news business – would go on to found the national-level Network of Women in Media in India, in 2002. With 13 chapters, NWMI members continue to find ways to combat sexism in the profession at the local level, and they speak out on broader issues such as media globalization, which they believe affect women across India.

Ramesh Sepehrrad, political activist, Washington, DC. On another continent, on a humid June afternoon, 35-year-old Ramesh Sepehrrad pushed up her glasses and explained how she came to women's media activism through advocating for women's human rights in Iran. In the 1990s, Sepehrrad and a small group of Iranian feminist exiles living in the USA founded the National Committee of Women for a Democratic Iran (NCWDI), based in Washington, DC. The group immediately established an English-language website to raise general awareness about the widespread discrimination, official abuse, and murder of women in Iran under the Islamic fundamentalist regime that had ruled since 1979. The NCWDI posted articles containing details about women's imprisonment, hanging, and stoning to death, gathered from Farsi-language Iranian Internet sites, Amnesty International and other reports, and informants living in Iran. The goals were to mobilize opposition to women's treatment, but also "to make sure that the political voice of women was heard in the dialogue about democratization in Iran," Sepehrrad said. The website also had the effect of drawing interest among women living inside Iran, who provided additional details of day-to-day life for women under the regime. In 2004, the NCWDI merged with the Women's Forum Against Fundamentalism in Iran (WFAFI), a broad-based international organization, headquartered in Boston, which advocates for women's rights and religious pluralism in Iran and other nations with fundamentalist governments.

The WFAFI is affiliated with groups in Europe, such as the European Organization Against Fundamentalism, in Germany, and the Revolutionary

Association of Women in Afghanistan, based in Pakistan. The WFAFI represents an interesting study in women's media activism, through which it conducts nearly all of its work. The organization seeks both female and male followers within the Iranian diaspora (whose members live all over the world), as well as from feminist, human rights, religious-pluralist, and other communities through a sophisticated website (www.wfafi.org), a monthly electronic newsletter called *E-Zan* (the Farsi word for woman is *zan*), and, since late 2004, a weekly Farsi-language radio program called *Voice of Women*. VOW, a 30-minute program on women's rights, broadcasts into Iran via shortwave radio on Saturday evenings, when women's listenership is highest. VOW broadcasts are produced in the USA and transmitted through a network of booster systems located in Europe. Sepehrrad, a specialist in information technology who is pursuing a doctorate in political science, pointed out the amount of cooperation-building that took place among women's and other groups internationally to bring the details of this project together. Feminist media activism fits within a larger scope of political work for Sepehrrad, who hopes one day to return to Iran and live under a secular, democratic government.

These stories exemplify the complexity of women's media activism internationally. In each case, a feminist has worked individually and collectively using media to inform, motivate, and mobilize some kind of political action on women's behalf. Preeti Mehra has followed the second path associated with the integration of media activism into her career as a journalist. Ramesh Sepehrrad has followed a different path – that of an outside advocate using a multimedia approach on behalf of women's organizations concerned with women's human rights in Iran.

The Longer View of Women and Media

As we said at the beginning of this introduction, the feminist scholarship whose goal is to assess women's relationship to both mainstream and other media forms has a deep connection to women's status in the real world. No one has made this connection clearer than Noeleen Hayzer, executive director of the UN Fund for Women (UNIFEM), on International Women's Day, March 8, 2004:

> As a result of constant advocacy by women's rights groups over the last 20 years, more and more countries have some type of legislation concerning

violence against women. At least 45 nations have specific laws against domestic violence, 21 more are drafting new laws, and many others have amended criminal laws to include domestic violence. To make a real difference, we have to transform words into action and results. This requires governments and the international community at large to stand by their commitments and to allocate resources to translate them into action . . . I call on the world community to pay close attention to what women are telling us about the situation they live in – their needs, hopes and visions of a better future. It is our responsibility to amplify their voices and to use them to guide our work and policies. Only then can we hope to achieve a world in which both men and women are able to lead the best lives they can.[5]

Notes

1   The Indian freedom movement led to India's independence from Great Britain in 1947. Similar independence movements in African and Asian nations that were seeking independence from their European colonial rulers followed in the decades of the 1950s, 1960s, and 1970s.
2   Throughout the book, we use the term *feminism* interchangeably with *women's movement(s)* and *women's liberation movement(s)*.
3   The Seneca Falls Convention, held in Seneca Falls, New York, in July 1948, marked the beginning of the nineteenth-century American women's rights movement. Lucretia Mott, Elizabeth Cady Stanton, and other convention planners had been active in the anti-slavery movement. A year before, during their attendance at a world anti-slavery convention in England, they had been barred from sitting on the main floor of that meeting or speaking. They vowed to initiate their own movement to address women's status in American society upon their return. The Seneca Falls Convention was the result.
4   For a useful description of the development of dialectics, see Kellner (1989).
5   See   www.unifem.org/speeches.php?f_page_pid=77&f_pritem_pid=161 (accessed October 17, 2004).

PART I

*Research on Women and Media:
A Short History*

2

Women in/as Entertainment

In most action movies, women are in the way.
Arnold Schwarzenegger,
Playboy, January 1988

The ways in which women are routinely portrayed in mass media have been the focus of much feminist media scholarship over the past 30 years. Gaye Tuchman, Arlene Kaplan Daniels, and James Benet's (1978) foundational collection of empirical and theoretical articles in *Hearth and Home* was among the earliest to problematize women's media representations. The text cited not only women's routine omission – or symbolic annihilation – from mass media, but also the ways in which women were stereotyped. While Tuchman et al. focused mainly on the women-and-media problems in North America, its themes were by no means geographically unique. Mieke Ceulemans and Guido Fauconnier's (1979) UNESCO-funded cross-cultural study located women's representations within several sociopolitical and cultural contexts. Like Tuchman et al.'s work, they found that advertising, television, films, news, and other genres in Western nations, as well as those in Africa, Asia, and Latin America, disproportionately emphasized women's traditional domestic roles or treated them as sex objects. Similarly, Margaret Gallagher's (1979) UNESCO-funded study emphasized the underlying reason why women's image would continue to concern women for decades to come: "The . . . media are potentially powerful agents of socialization and social change – presenting models, conferring status, suggesting appropriate behaviors, encouraging stereotypes" (p. 3).

Media representations thus became a major front for both popular and academic feminist struggle, continuing up to the present time with contemporary concerns such as bride sites on the Internet and pornography downloads via cell phones. In fact, feminists could argue that the media's influence is even greater now than before, with 24/7 news channels, hundreds of satellite and digital services offering everything from natural history to hard-core pornography, and picture messaging via mobile phones. And popular media such as film, television, newspapers, and magazines continue to frame (in every sense of the word) women within a narrow repertoire of types that bear little or no relation to how real women live their real lives. However, the situation is not entirely gloomy and as feminist campaigns have demanded media reform over the representations of women, and as women and men with feminist consciences have made their way into media professions, there have been important changes almost everywhere in the world. What is important to emphasize at the outset of this discussion, then, is the dialectical nature of the process – progress inevitably occurs alongside recalcitrance, and backlash is a predictable part of these events.

In this chapter, then, we consider women's representation in entertainment and fiction-based media, predominantly film and television, and we take a genre approach that includes crime, soaps, and fantasy narratives as vehicles through which to signal the primary concerns of feminist media scholars. As women's status and social practices have shifted through women's movements worldwide, these have (and often have not) been reflected in changing patterns of gendered representation. This is an extremely broad field and our intention here is not to be exhaustive in our overview – which is, in any case, impossible – but, rather, to illustrate some of the key trends that have been exposed by feminist media scholars' interrogations of popular media praxis over the past few decades. A significant amount of the work on representation has been done within a feminist cultural studies framework, focusing specifically on commercially made films, and foregrounding considerations of ways in which audiences negotiate meanings in texts.

The Early Days

Many of the early feminist analyses of mediated representations of women in fictional genres were focused on the medium of film. For Maggie Humm

(1997), the power of the feminist project was precisely its ability to demonstrate the ways in which the category "woman" was politically constructed and routinely oppressed. In an interesting analysis of four films spanning the 1930s to the 1970s – *Camille* (1936), *Blonde Venus* (1932), *Lady from Shanghai* (1946), and *Looking for Mr. Goodbar* (1977) – E. Ann Kaplan (1983) sets out to reveal the ways in which the male gaze operates from the vantage point of power and renders women silent and marginal. One of the crucial ways in which women's lives were implicitly regulated in cinematic portrayals was through the very device of appealing to them as women spectators via the invention of the "woman's film." This was, arguably, a marketing ploy established in the US studio era of the 1930s and 1940s as a way of targeting a niche (female) audience that had hitherto failed to be attracted to the cinema in large numbers, with the release of films such as *Leave Her to Heaven* (1945) and *The Reckless Moment* (1949).

Given the era in which they were made, these films contained an inherent contradiction, offering women the spectacle of a lifestyle outside the conventions of respectable femininity, but at the same time making clear the errors of that particular way (Basinger 1994). This temptation, though, is merely illusion, since the film industry at that time, and for at least two decades beyond, was circumscribed by a set of guidelines (the Production Code) that attempted to maintain standards of sexual and moral probity, although by the end of the 1960s both the Production Code and this kind of "woman's film" had all but disappeared (Neale 2000). Molly Haskell (1973) suggests that the genre was framed within an avowedly conservative aesthetic that encouraged the (woman) spectator to accept rather than reject her lot, whilst taking on a pitying stance toward the tragic heroine. Interestingly, the use of cinema as a tool of moral conscription was not a uniquely American phenomenon and, as Lant (1991) suggests, British wartime films trod a careful line between valorizing women's contribution to the war effort but also reassuring men of their continued femininity. Regulation of moral conduct through cinematic representations of women and women's role was also widely used in Spain during the same period. In her discussion of Spanish director Josefina Molina's success in subverting gender stereotypes in films such as *Función de Noche* (*Evening Performance*, 1981), María Suárez Lafuente (2003: 395) suggests that:

Women's psyche had suffered the devastating effects of 40 years of a film industry dedicated to epic and local-color films, where women were the embodiment of discipline and self-sacrifice to the glory of God and country, or else cheap comedies where the female body was a mere sexual object for the male gaze. Spanish cinema was part of the state apparatus to keep men entertained and under control, and to provide women with the correct and incorrect models of national femininity. It is no exaggeration to say that during the 1950s and the 1960s women were educated in the official social morals and manners primarily through their Sunday visit to the cinema.

The Eyes of Laura Mulvey

Early explorations of the highly gendered nature of looking relations – the gaze – between the audience and the text are largely credited to Laura Mulvey, writing in the 1970s, and contemporary feminist media research and theorizing about media artifacts owes a rather large debt to her foundational work, *Visual Pleasure and Narrative Cinema*, published in 1975. In that essay, written 30 years ago, she theorized the relationship between the production of a film (i.e., its basic techniques, structure, and principal mode of address), the audience (spectator), and viewing pleasure. Mulvey's legacy in terms of her impact on the field and her enduring influence on contemporary work is her insistence that film is deliberately structured to produce a male gaze that makes voyeurs of us all, and it is this masculinized gaze that "is the main mechanism of filmic control" (Humm 1997: 14). For Mulvey, herself heavily influenced by psychoanalytic theory, the gaze is inherently eroticized (in Lacanian terms, "scopophilic"), since the principal players, in the form of the camera*man*, the audience, and the hero, are assumed to be male, and the principal object in the form of the film's co-star/love interest is assumed to be female.

What Mulvey did in that essay, for the very first time, was to argue that film was inexplicably bound up with sex, that men "do" and women "receive," thus perpetuating existing gendered relations. While Mulvey went on to refine her early ideas, it was that initial critique of film *per se* that was so bold and controversial, which signaled a fundamental shift in the ways in which spectatorship would thereafter be researched, discussed, and theorized. Although hers was not the only voice at this time expressing such views – for example, John Berger (1977) also underlined the gendered power relations between the object (woman) and the subject (man) as distinctive ways of seeing – hers was perhaps the most trenchant.

Much subsequent scholarship has challenged Mulvey's overdetermined and rather inflexible framing of the various subject positions that she allocates to the constituent parties to the film experience, and her overdependence on psychoanalytic theory (see Gaines 1988; Gledhill 1988). These scholarly variations have often sought to problematize exactly that which Mulvey's early work tended to homogenize, in that they explore how women audiences find pleasure in female (and male) characters, and perhaps even desire those characters, as well as to distinguish other forms of identification between spectator and text/star, such as race, ethnicity, and sexuality. More contemporary scholarship takes into account the counter-narratives produced by women filmmakers, authors, and creative artists who themselves embody distinctive identity markers that manifest in their work, as well as identifying moments of textual rupture in classical film (see Brunsdon 1986; Penley 1988; Grosz 1995; Jayamanne 1995; Thornham 1999): some specific examples of such counter-narratives are provided in Chapter 5.

The Female Monster and Other Stories

One of the key Hollywood myths of femininity is what Barbara Creed (1993) describes as the monstrous-feminine. On the first page of her eponymous book, she lists the various faces of the female monster, including the amoral primeval mother (*Aliens*, 1986), the vampire (*The Hunger*, 1983), the witch (*Carrie*, 1976), woman as bleeding wound (*Dressed to Kill*, 1980), and woman as possessed (*The Exorcist*, 1973). To this list could be added any number of more contemporary horror movies with a female monster lead, such as *Species* (1995), *An American Vampire Story* (1997), the *Terminator* series, and *Alien Resurrection* (1997). For Creed, describing women in horror as monstrous-feminine rather than simply female monsters is a conscious act to signify the importance of gender (as a constructed category) in the reading of the female character as monstrous. In other words, women's sexuality is the reason why she horrifies.

If these are the ways in which women were represented historically in film, how have they been represented in more contemporary popular culture? Space precludes a full discussion, so we are restricting ourselves to a brief discussion of those genres that have attracted most scholarly attention, namely soaps, crime, action, and fantasy. We consider both film and TV shows together since what we are interested in exploring is the ways in which women are characterized in these cultural products rather than the particular medium through which they are circulated.

Considering Soaps

The soap opera, an enduring cross-generational and cross-cultural art form, has traditionally been regarded as the "woman's genre" par excellence, not simply because of its original location in the broadcast schedule, at a time when "mothers" would be at home and thus a captive audience, but because the melodramatic narrative style and structure, its preference for dialogue over action, and its focus on intimate family and community relations are regarded as particularly popular with women (McQuail 1994). In addition, the soap opera lends itself particularly well to the incorporation of familiar cultural themes and storylines. For this reason, soaps have commanded significant attention from feminist media scholars cross-culturally, with a number of important early studies setting the critical context for contemporary analyses, looking at both content and consumption (see particularly Ang 1985; Brown 1990; Hobson 1990; Geraghty 1991; Mankekar 1999). What those studies made clear was that soap opera as a genre had an important place in the lives of their women viewers, and that a significant part of the mainstream academy's disdain for the genre was rooted in both its gendered inflection and its functioning as a low-brow entertainment. Despite the clear popularity of soaps, which consistently top the ratings charts in both Western and non-Western nations, Charlotte Brunsdon (2000) is still compelled to argue, in her analysis of feminist scholarly engagements with the academic study of soaps, that there is a requirement for all of us engaged in work on popular culture to constantly defend our interests against claims of trivial pursuits.

The more popular British, American, and Australian soaps are very different in their framing of women and women's concerns, with the American serials often having rather glamorous, mostly affluent, and well-groomed actors, while Australians are a bit more homely but still mostly attractive, and British soaps are more avowedly rooted in working-class culture. However, they nonetheless narrate remarkably similar storylines about the human condition. While, as Geraghty (1991) points out, soaps do not homogenize women's experience, nor do they allow for overly transgressive renditions of femininity. The diversity of small-screen soap women and their life choices allow multiple identifications by the audience as we empathize with and rail against their good fortune and bad luck, their choice of partner, and their poor judgment. Crucially, soap characters (women and men) are portrayed as abidingly flawed individuals, who are never wholly good or bad but, rather, struggle with the complexities of their impossible lives.

The paradox of soaps, then, is that women viewers are encouraged to empathize with soap characters who are rarely allowed to live a transgressive life outside the normative expectations of patriarchy. In the end, soap women seek fulfillment by achieving success in their personal lives, retreating into the private realm as their proper space and place. This is not to say that soaps have not dealt with important social issues or that soap women don't work outside the home, because they have and they do, but soap writers are seldom brave enough to seek structural answers to personal problems. Soap storylines *do* deal with incest, rape, racism, sexuality, teenage pregnancy, drug abuse, domestic violence, and so on, but the characters who work out these storylines are forced to solve their "problems" themselves, provoking a community response that is pathologized within the private sphere. Too often, the final resolution of, say, a whispering campaign about lesbian lovers ends with their departure from the soap rather than a straightforward confrontation with the issues, with a more informed outcome.

In India, Purnima Mankekar (1999) examined soap operas and popular Hindi-language films, as well as female viewers' responses to these, prior to the early 1990s, when commercial cable stations began to supplant state-sponsored programming under the government system, Doordarshan. Mankekar found that "like the audiences of American soaps, those of Indian serials deeply identified with characters on the screen" (p. 7). Mankekar said there was a kind of "metalanguage" in the types of sets, dialogue, costumes, and music used, and viewers formed relationships with the characters depicted in serialized stories (soaps). Representations of Indian womanhood as the embodiment of morality and tradition had been major sites of contention in colonial and anti-colonial discourses, and women often represented iconic portraits of these concepts. In addition, storylines emphasized new aspirations to what she calls "middle-classness" in a society in which "class and nation have been inextricably related from the outset" (ibid., p. 9). Middle-classness in this context refers especially to Western-style consumerism.

The Crime Genre

Other than TV soaps, perhaps the genre that has attracted most interest from feminist media scholars has been the crime genre, both film and TV, principally because this is one of the few formats that has regularly featured women in strong lead roles. With the exception of the hypermasculine figure of James Bond, whose female colleagues were rarely more than simply beautiful foils to his male hero (Lisanti & Paul 2002), any number of crime shows have featured women as either lead or strong support. James Chapman (2002) suggests that, in the context of popular British television of the 1960s, the quirky series, *The Avengers* (ITV, 1961–9), was seen by some to be the first to provide roles for women in which they were the equal of their male co-stars (Andrae 1996). The series, which originally cast two male leads, adopted a male–female pairing in the third series, most famously through the characters of Cathy Gale (Honor Blackman) and then Emma Peel (Diana Rigg). It was arguably Blackman's highly eroticized performance as a secret agent who wore "kinky" black leather that boosted the show's popularity, and generated the suggestion of a feminist hero who literally kicked ass in black stiletto-heeled, thigh-high boots. This particular narrative device (of sexual equality) was groundbreaking in the 1960s. However, this emancipatory nod was often undermined by lingering close-ups of Blackman's leather-clad curves – made to order for the male gaze.

Decades and several iterations of the female detective later, one of the most researched women characters has been DCI Jane Tennison (Helen Mirren), in the extremely successful mini-series, *Prime Suspect* (ITV, 1991–2003). Although British-made, the series has been syndicated and broadcast in many other countries. Although placing strong women characters in male occupations and in the macho world of crime-solving has been quite an advance, producers have rarely done much to challenge sexism or politi-cize unequal gender relations through narrative development. Indeed, even while *Prime Suspect*'s Jane Tennison and (Christine) Cagney and (Mary Beth) Lacey display a number of hypermasculine traits, such as heavy drinking, smoking, and swearing, these behaviors only appear to subvert more traditional versions of acceptable femininity. In addition, the hetero-sexuality of the female hero in crime dramas is enforced from the first episode to the last, denying any space for sexual ambiguity or a lesbian identity. It is precisely these lost opportunities that have exercised a number of critics, where a series explicitly focused on sex discrimination with a potentially feminist address instead becomes just another tabloid show, rather than a vehicle for transformation (Brunsdon 1998).

The increasing visibility of women in lead roles in crime fiction shows has altered forever the terrain of the crime genre; if not quite arrest-ing its macho image, then at least confounding some of the normative assumptions of women's place in society and showing, discursively, the ways in which women negotiate a particular kind of male space (Nunn & Biressi 2003). In the interstices of these confusions and contradictions lie precisely the possibilities and practicalities of women's diverse lives and experiences.

Women and Action Movies

The cinematic parallel of the TV crime show that features strong women is the action movie, where the number of "tough girl" lead roles has risen exponentially over the past two or three decades (see Gough-Yates & Osgerby 2001), and with each generation, the toughness of the girls has increased. Although toughness has particularly permeated women's roles in Western films, we shall also see permutations on the theme in certain contemporary Asian films featuring female martial artists. An example of the Western tough girl is Sarah Connor (*Terminator*), who is more able to withstand physical and psychological difficulties than any of Charlie's Angels. Similarly, Xena is tougher than the Bionic Woman (Inness 1999). Yvonne Tasker (1993) argues that during the 1970s, film and TV companies responded to feminism's demands for less stereotypical images of women with films such as *Klute* (1971) and *Julia* (1977), made as vehicles for strong, independent women, in both cases the role being taken up by Jane Fonda.

On television, US-produced (and globally distributed) shows such as *Charlie's Angels* (ABC, 1976–81), *Policewoman* (NBC, 1974–8), and *Wonder Woman* (ABC/CBS, 1976–9), did showcase women in lead roles, although the women actors still conformed in very obvious ways to the stereotypes of normative femininity, being beautiful, slender, and white. While most critics who look at the moment of *Charlie's Angels* see the show as part of a misogynistic, anti-feminist backlash during the 1970s, others are a little more circumspect in their condemnation. Susan Douglas (1994: 215) probably speaks for many women growing up in the 1970s who saw Farah Fawcett and her crew as suitable role models for any number of "good" reasons, "It was watching . . . women working together to solve a problem and capture, and sometimes kill really awful, sadistic men, while having great hairdos and clothes – that engaged our desire." What Douglas signals is the reality of a reading position that is intuitive rather than "feminist," but nonetheless meaningful in its own terms, speaking to the kinds of contradictory responses that many of us (women) feel when viewing images of women who are both assertive but also icons of male fantasy.

It is interesting to note that the two film versions of the TV show which came out recently, *Charlie's Angels* (2000) and *Charlie's Angels: Full Throttle* (2003), rework the original (white) lead actors into an ethnically diverse trio in the shape of Cameron Diaz, Lucy Liu, and Drew Barrymore. Unquestionably a marketing strategy, this move nonetheless also signals Hollywood's need to respond to a growing multicultural, global audience. The centrality of women of color in global culture has not escaped the notice of feminist postcolonial scholars such as Radhika Parameswaran (2002). She has critiqued what she calls the hegemonic packaging of ethnic culture for profit, particularly the "celebration of racial diversity as the discovery of unusual consumer experiences" (ibid., p. 229). Looking particularly at Malaysian actress Michelle Yeoh, star of the celebrated martial arts film *Crouching Tiger, Hidden Dragon* (2000), Parameswaran sees Yeoh's character as an orientalist construct – displaying fearless, athletic grace as a warrior woman while at the same time "subtly cocooned by the vestiges of patriarchal [Western] femininity" (ibid., p. 296).

So women's strength and their performance as tough women in the contemporary action genre cannot be read off simply as progress, art reflecting life. Rather, such performances may connote a deep ambivalence about the limitations of women's flight to equality. The tough woman is testament to a still male-dominant society's own contradictory responses to women's demands for equal treatment, equal pay, and equal status (see Inness 1999). In these examples, the tough girl is nearly always stripped down (often literally) to what lies at her core, her essential, biological womanliness, her essential subordinate position to man.

Women and the Fantasy Genre

Where women often feature as leads or sidekicks to the principal hero in action genres, the circumstances in which the woman is equal to her male co-stars (heroes or villains) are mostly those where she is either an enhanced human being such as the Bionic Woman, gifted with mystical powers, or else located in the future and therefore offering no threat to the here-and-now status quo. This isn't always and everywhere the case, but those contradictions and ambivalences are common enough to constitute a pattern of representation worthy of comment. There have been any number of women in sci-fi movies, and we are too limited by space to consider these characterizations in detail, but a brief discussion of the film and the character credited with producing the first significant action hero within the science fiction genre, Ellen Ripley (Sigourney Weaver) in the *Alien* tetrology, is probably worthwhile. The aspect of Ripley's character in these films that has fascinated critics is the destabilizing effect of casting a woman hero within this particular genre, who is allowed autonomy, intelligence, and a strong survival instinct (Clover 1992) but who nonetheless performs a familiar ambiguity. Despite her considerable abilities to outwit the enemy and keep herself safe, Ripley is still made available for a voyeuristic gaze; she is still commodified as a sexual object. Discussing Ripley's role in the original *Alien* (1979), Ros Jennings (1995) articulates precisely the contradictions and tensions that are provoked by so many female hero figures, where the positive aspects of their characterizations are too easily undermined by the retreat into normative femininity. By showing Ripley's undressed body to the audience, her heroic status is neutralized:

> By rendering her available to male voyeurism, [Ridley] Scott's control of filming in the final scene ensures that in addition to the "so-called" masculine traits of bravery, technical ability and so on – all of which we have seen her demonstrate so well up to this point – she now signifies a wholly intelligible form of femininity. (Jennings 1995: 197)

Contemporary manifestations of the fantasy queen, such as *Buffy the Vampire Slayer* (Twentieth Century Fox, 1997–2003) are, physically at least, little different to their earlier 1960s sisters. The character of Buffy (Sarah Michelle Gellar) is a knowing and playful young woman, who combines the domesticated femininity of girl/witch with the kick-ass assertiveness of the action hero (Owen 1999). But Buffy provokes paradoxical readings. Her blonde, physical attractiveness and youth resonate well with male Lolita fantasies, while her skills in taking care of herself and always defeating the bad guy offer women audiences the prospect of differently powered gender relations. But is the kind of empowerment traded by Buffy merely another saleable commodity – girl-power as the latest must-have (see also Riordan 2002)? As Rachel Fudge (2001) points out, at the height of her popularity, Buffy merchandise was available from any number of US retail outlets and *Glamour* magazine did a feature on how to emulate Sarah Michelle's toned bottom.

Possibly the most discussed female figure in contemporary fantasy fiction is *Xena: Warrior Princess* (MCA Television Entertainment, 1996–

2001), who actually stands out in both the performance of her fantasy heroism as well as in her ability and expressed desire to live her life and engage in adventures without depending on men. Indeed, as Sherrie Inness (1999) points out, Xena (Lucy Lawless) has more attachment to her horse and certainly to Gabrielle (Renee O'Connor), than to any man who she encounters. The show was a spin-off from the adventures of the male hero Hercules, and one of *Xena*'s producers, Liz Friedman, makes clear the debt owed to Hercules but also the hope embodied by Xena: "Hercules is the hero we hope is out there. Xena is the hero we hope is inside us" (quoted in Weisbrot 1998: 161). But what is attractive about Xena-as-hero is her inherently flawed character: she is dark, selfish, and venally bloodthirsty. Even if the narrative insists that her triumphs are always over evil, so that she is always the force for good, there is also a clear moral ambiguity in her dealings with the world because of the way in which she arrogantly revels in parading her power and strength.

The so-called lesbian sub-text, which is often so overt as to constitute a main text (Gwenllian Jones 2000), also sets Xena apart from other fantasy heroes and adds an interesting dimension to her already complex character. But Xena is scarcely a feminist icon since, despite her clear ability to force a serious reconsideration of what a hero could and should be – that is, not necessarily *male* – she is still an immensely attractive white woman who performs arduous and dangerous feats without breaking sweat or disturbing her fringe. Her lack of need of a man is, perhaps, a step forward on the road to independence for women warriors, but she still draws the eye with her leather boots and brass bra. While one show cannot be expected to carry the burden of all women's expectations, it is precisely the scarcity of positive images of women that makes many women viewers continue to want exactly such a representation.

Beyond Straight White Lines

A careful analysis of the representation of women in the media, in both fiction and factual genres, reveals significant differences in the ways in which the object "woman" is constructed along highly codified lines in terms of ethnicity, age, sexuality, and disability. While the kinds of genre analyses in which we engage above might signal the various personal identifiers of, say, Buffy or Ripley or Sue Ellen, what a discussion of those characters does not necessarily also demonstrate is the *absence* of so many women – women of color, lesbians, disabled women, older women. This is not to say that they do not feature in the popular media landscape, but it is to argue that they are often absent in circumstances when they would be present in real life (and soaps are a good example of realist genres that almost willfully refuse to include a realistic diversity of women – see Bourne 1998). Where they *do* feature, they often bear the burden of multiple stereotyping.

Comes in other colors

In response to the failure of mainstream feminism to address the interrelated themes of race and gender in representation, a number of feminist media researchers of color have worked hard to bring to light, in every sense of the word, the numerous (and different) ways in which the race–gender–culture nexus functions in film and television (see Bobo 1988; hooks 1991, 1992, 1996; Mankekar 1999; Malik 2002; Parameswaran 2002). In Lola Young's astutely titled book on this subject, *Fear of the Dark* (1996), she traces the provenance of contemporary African Caribbean women characters found in British cinema back to the much earlier slave period and the circulation of racist and sexist images of African Caribbean women. Those images have since informed the contemporary popular characterization of African Caribbean women as prostitutes, feckless single mothers, nurses, and other public-sector workers. As an actor, Young recalls being persistently typecast:

> After having several years experience as a professional actor in a children's television series, I was asked to play a bus conductor, a prostitute, a nurse. Later ... I was asked to play a witch in Macbeth: I wanted to play Shakespeare, so I did. Eventually, I didn't enjoy these limited roles so I stopped acting. (1996: 1)

Through her work on race in mainstream (white-framed) texts, Young identifies the continued circulation and promotion of racist and sexist myths of African Caribbean women as manifest in "Empire" films such as *Sanders of the River* (1935) and their contemporary resonances in films such as *Mona Lisa* (1986). Carmen Gillespie (1999) undertakes a similar archaeological task when she maps Hattie McDaniels's portrayal of Mammy in *Gone With The Wind* (1939) against the contemporary figuring of Molly Abrams (Gina Ravera) in the soft-core porn movie, *Showgirls* (1995). For

Young (1996), such stereotypes (past and present) speak to the historical period in which they are elaborated, and African Caribbean women characters are often appropriated as mechanisms through which racialized differences between competing masculinities are played out, ciphers in the struggle for control (see also Manatu 2002; Smith-Shomade 2002). The shifting shape of African Caribbean characterizations can therefore be seen as indicators of a given society's feelings of ease about itself and a product of specific global sociopolitical moments and ideological positions in relation to notions of "us" and "them" (Malik 2002). Indeed, the African Caribbean or exoticized female "other" provides a benchmark against which white femininity under patriarchy can be better understood and the normative nature of whiteness itself, as an ethnic category rendered visible and problematized (Negra 2001).

However, in discussing the ways in which the cinematic representation of African Caribbean women have been inadequate, Young and others (see Ross 1996, 1997a) caution against the suggestion that "negative" stereotypes can be substituted with more positive ones that would have a wider currency amongst the communities from which such characterizations are drawn. Is it even possible to represent the "real" African Caribbean experience, even if everyone involved in any given production is part of that same community? Such questions of authenticity are always present when race is present, but that concern is more overt when screenplays are based on material written by minority ethnic authors. For example, there was considerable criticism generated against Steven Spielberg's screen adaptation of Alice Walker's novel, *The Color Purple*, made in 1985, and again when Terry McMillan's novel, *Waiting to Exhale*, was made into a film (1996).

A significant aspect of the critique of such films has been focused around how "real" they are in their depictions of African American life (Carstarphen 1999), even as such films often receive an enthusiastic reception by many members of African American communities. Once again, these different takes on the same text demonstrate how the possession of the gaze and the "reading off" of texts is highly personal and entirely subjective. This is not to say that individual analyses are not worth doing, but it is to offer a reminder that critiquing a text for its impact on real people, looking for a cause–effect outcome, is not as fixed or immutable as some commentators might suggest.

The great majority of studies that are published in English and undertaken on the image of women in entertainment media focus on women in Western cultures, and while problematizing the gender relations that often attend plotlines, especially where women are lead characters, the category "woman" is often homogenized even though she is nearly always white. Such issues have been taken up by a number of postcolonial scholars such as Radhika Parameswaran (2002), who reveal the complex ways in which women's representation has been influenced by culture, class, colonial, and national processes. They are also concerned with showing how the oppression of men under colonial domination makes it essential to examine depictions of both male and female gender roles.

However, for balance, we should also include an example of a more positive response to a screen adaptation of a African American novel, in this case, *The Women of Brewster Place*, which was a two-part adaptation of Gloria Naylor's novel, first aired on ABC in 1989. It tells the story of a group of women living in a run-down neighborhood through their relationships with each other. It attained a certain amount of publicity partly because its primary character and executive producer was Oprah Winfrey, who used her own celebrity to urge ABC to broadcast the serial (Bobo & Seiter 1991). It was also the first time that a woman (Donna Deitch) had been hired to undertake a film adaptation of work by a black woman novelist. Although, as Bobo and Seiter argue, the serial contained the routine elements of melodrama and soap, it also discussed less common themes, such as the community to be found between African American women, the importance of their peer support, and issues around violence, racism, sexism, and homophobia. While a (small) screen adaptation of an important novel rarely does justice to the complexities and nuances of the latter, *The Women of Brewster Place* tried to remain faithful to the original book. The show symbolizes the enormous possibilities for honest, interesting representations of women in media when women are in control of scripts and production.

The brief discussion above looks at the critiques of the images of women of color in mainstream, Western entertainment media, but what about the representation of other women, other identities, other geographies? Sheena Malhotra and Everett Rogers's work (2000) shifts the Anglocentric gaze eastward in a study that explores the rapid development of private satellite television in India that occurred during the 1990s, analyzing the shifts in the representation of women which that technology ushered in. For these authors, new media developments transformed the routine and traditional image of woman as housewife and mother to images of women who existed as sexual beings, had adopted Western lifestyles, and often worked outside the home. However, as we have seen elsewhere, women's newly found empowerment is severely compromised by their mediated construction within the boundaries of existing patriarchal relations. Thus the progressive potential of more modern images is too often defeated by a lack of progress in the real world.

Portrait of a lesbian

Issues of race and gender have received critical analysis in large part because of the efforts of feminist scholars of color insisting on identifying a clear politics of difference within mainstream feminist activity. Lesbian representation in fictional media has received rather less attention, although there is a growing literature on the topic. The inclusion of lesbian characters in soaps and drama has been a rather hit-and-miss affair, with efforts often foundering because storylines focus exclusively on sexuality rather than character development. Darlene Hantzis and Valerie Lehr (1994) suggest that early attempts to signal lesbian and gay sexuality in mainstream entertainment media often resulted in what they describe as one-off "featured" characters; that is, they featured *because* they were lesbian or gay, often introducing some kind of camp element into an otherwise mainstream comedy show, or a more murderous or psychotic element in many police dramas and mainstream films (Croteau & Hoynes 1997). As Young (1996) and others have identified, a very typical role for an African Caribbean female actor to play is as a prostitute, especially one who gets killed, and Cathy Tyson's portrayal of the African Caribbean lesbian prostitute, Simone, in *Mona Lisa* (1986) manages to score several stereotypical hits with one character. While the film attracted considerable acclaim, with some critics even suggesting that the teaming of Tyson and [Bob] Hoskins was "inspired" (Bourne 1998: 184), others were less positive. The film critic Louis Heaton comments that:

> Cathy Tyson's Simone, though competently acted, lacks both credibility and character. Despite their obvious best intentions, the filmmakers have given us yet another stereotyped "hard"; black woman whose hatred of men manifests itself in lesbianism. (Heaton, quoted in Bourne 1998: 186)

By the late 1980s, there was a small but visible push toward the inclusion of lesbian and gay characters as part of ensemble casts in serial dramas, as the hitherto taboo subject of homosexuality had been recognized for its commercial potential (Moritz 1994). In 1988, in the United States, ABC began to broadcast a new show, *Heartbeat,* set in a women's medical center and featuring Marilyn McGrath (Gail Strickland) as a nurse practitioner who also happened to be a mother and lesbian. However, it folded after less than a season because of poor ratings (Moritz 1994). Another early example of a US mainstream show's efforts (which also ultimately failed) to incorporate a lesbian character is *L.A. Law.* The show had a bisexual female character in the early 1990s in the shape of C. J. Lamb (Amanda Donohoe) but she only appeared in season five and by the end of season six she had been erased from the show. The show has since attracted a lesbian cult following, despite the infrequent appearances of C. J., but such is the desire to identify with her amongst lesbian audiences that infrequency was still better than invisibility:

> Given the fact that so few lesbian and gay characters appear on television, it could be argued that *any* portrayals of lesbians and gays that are not clearly negative should be valued. (Hantzis & Lehr 1994: 118 – original emphasis)

When Jeanette Winterson's novel *Oranges Are Not the Only Fruit* was adapted for television and screened in the United Kingdom in 1990, it was scheduled in what Hilary Hinds describes as the controversy slot, a prime-time evening slot reserved for risky and adult material, most usually portraying sex scenes (Hinds 1992). With *Oranges,* the explicit sexual nature of the narrative was even riskier than usual, since scenes of lesbian sex were (and are still) rare on mainstream TV. However, Hinds argues that despite the author's explicit intention to subvert the normative assumptions around home, church, and sexuality in the piece, most critics' positive reception of the work was because they saw it as an allegory of the human condition – we are all seeking love – not because they understood the lesbian love story at its core. In particular, given the relatively circumscribed nature of lesbian characters in most mainstream shows, one-off screenings such as *Oranges* or the more overtly erotic *Tipping the Velvet* (BBC, 2002, adapted from the novel by Sarah Waters), provide more credible and complex characterizations than the 2-D women we more usually see, devoid of passion, tortured, dependent, passive.

While lesbian and gay characters can be safely domesticated and their potency neutralized by their framing as figures of (albeit witty) fun, as in the US programs *Will and Grace* (KoMut Entertainment, 1998–) or *Queer as Folk* (Channel 4, 2002–), or even the eponymous *Graham Norton* (So Television, 2001–), when the reality of sexual passion is played out in the living room, there are often vociferous complaints. On Christmas Eve 1993, the UK's Channel 4 soap, *Brookside* (Mersey Television, 1982–2003), featured the first lesbian kiss on TV between Beth (Anna Friel) and Margaret (Nicola Stevenson), prompting a deluge of complaints from offended viewers. However, when Channel 4 cut the scene from the omnibus version screened later that week, there were corresponding complaints about their crass decision:[1] in 2002, "the kiss" featured at 59th place in Channel 4's viewer-determined top 100 sexiest moments.[2] Similarly, Larry Gross (1994) points to the furore surrounding the character of C. J. Lamb in *L.A. Law*, when she kissed another woman attorney in one episode in 1991.

On the face of it, all these efforts to include lesbians in the media landscape are laudable but, sadly, they have nearly always been extremely short-lived: lesbians come and go with unseemly haste. The fanfare that heralded Della and Binnie's arrival in *EastEnders* (BBC, 1985–) was quickly muted when they left to start a "new life" in Ibiza less than 12 months later. Clearly, there is a structural dynamic within soaps that requires regular upheaval and controversy, but the problem with lesbian characters is that they are never firmly integrated within the fabric of a particular soap or drama: once storylines focused on their sexuality have been exhausted, they are written out of the narrative rather than allowed to play an "ordinary" part in the life of their particular community.

Program-makers are mostly unwilling to "represent women's desires because [they are] unwilling to threaten heterosexuality and the heterosexist male role of definer and center of female relationships" (Hantzis & Lehr 1994: 119). However, the more routine lesbian characters that now occasionally populate US mainstream series such as *ER* (Warner Bros, 1994–), and even *Buffy the Vampire Slayer* (UPN, 1997–), suggest that lesbian lifestyles might eventually be "normalized" within the fictional worlds of entertainment media. And there continue to be "firsts" in television's relationship with sexuality: in October 2000, the long-running US soap, *All My Children* (ABC, 1970–) took a bold step when 16-year-old Bianca Montgomery (Eden Reigel) came out as lesbian and did so in a lesbian bar. As C. Lee Harrington (2003) remarks, both the outing and the venue were remarkable for their never-before-in-daytime-soap novelty.

However, there remains a tentativeness about *really* dealing with sexuality, so that even in the relatively progressive characterization of Bianca, she is not part of a lesbian group, her love affairs mostly take place off camera, and the community around her shows total and unrealistically unconditional support (Harrington 2003). Nonetheless, the more-rounded lesbian characters exemplified by Bianca or Willow (*Buffy*) or Kerry Weaver (*ER*) are unarguably more appealing and more credible than the badly drawn psychopaths who populated the media landscape in the 1970s and 1980s. Part of this shift is due in no small part to the cynical recognition on the part of film- and program-makers, that the pink pound has considerable purchasing power (Becker 1998). The production appeal to the affluent middle-class, well-educated white lesbian does of course prompt concern over the simple substitution of one set of stereotypes for another, since many TV genres rely heavily on their audience's implicit understanding and recognition of particular stereotypes.

Conclusion

What we have attempted to show in this chapter are the various ways in which the subject "woman" has been portrayed in popular television and film, principally over the past 30 years. There is no doubt that the landscape for women has changed considerably over that period, and that images and plotlines that are now routine would simply have been inconceivable 30 years ago. To a large extent, this really is a case of art following life, since women's progress must eventually be mirrored on the large and small screen. Since at least 2000, *Law & Order* (Universal, 1990–) has had a woman chief, strong women have lead roles in the most popular soaps, lesbian doctors feature in *ER*, and Jessica Fletcher (Angela Lansbury) enjoyed repeat success on BBC in 2004 as the pensioner detective in *Murder She Wrote* (CBS, 1984–96). In other words, women's representation today is certainly "better," in many ways, than ever before. Sometimes, this has come about through women film- and program-makers subverting routine, stereotypical, and normative versions of their lives, by taking control of the camera and producing their own material. Sometimes, it has come about through working with men in alternative and mainstream production. But as women still experience actual prejudice and discrimination in terms of unequal treatment, unequal pay, and unequal value in real life, then so too do these themes continue to occur in media portraits. We hope that we have shown some of these contradictory impulses and the uneven nature of women's progress on both the large and small screens. We argue for women's greater control over the representations of their and our lives, so that the wonderful diversity of all our experiences becomes incorporated in the popular media landscape.

Notes

1 See www.bbc.co.uk/drama/tipping/article_1.shtml (accessed September 23, 2004).

2 See www.channel4.com/film/newsfeatures/microsites/S/sexy/nominees_b4.html (accessed September 23, 2004).

3

Images of Women in News and Magazines

What I find amazing is that, when a man is designated as prime minister, nobody asks the French if they think it is a good thing that it is a man.

Edith Cresson, 1995[1]

In the early years of the twenty-first century, the representation of women in news and other fact-based media presents a complex and mixed picture of women as subjects and actors in society. Women still face many of the same problems that were evident several decades ago, when feminists first raised their critiques of women's marginality and misrepresentation. On the other hand, news and feature articles about women's experiences have increased in range and scope over the past three decades. But there are worrying trends, especially in the commodification of women's bodies, where we are actually being reduced to less than the sum of our body parts. A number of studies show that this description, which appears in a proliferation of advertising that dominates the space of magazines and newspapers in much of the world, is quite literally apt: many of today's adverts display women's bodies in parts, "as buttocks, thighs, legs, breasts, facial skin" (Carter & Weaver 2003: 122), primed and ready to be fetishized (Caputi 1999; Kilbourne 1999). Despite the hyper-unreality of many of these mostly male-ordered constructions, the persistence and regularity of their (re)production provides easy passage into everyday discourse, subtly defining the contours and limits of the "proper" ways of looking and being female, thus maintaining gender inequalities without even being seen to do so (Smith 1990).

In spite of a global women's movement that has lasted more than three decades and made substantial gains on both legal and cultural fronts in most nations of the world, there has been a stoic stability in sexist media representations everywhere. This is certainly not to argue that such imagery has gone unchallenged by feminist scholars, by pressure groups, by women media workers, and by ordinary women themselves. In the 1970s, feminists in Europe and the United States held annual Take Back the Night marches in major cities to demand an end to depictions of rape, battering, and sadistic portraits of women in film and other media. Since then, however, the underground nature of pornography industries has leached into the mainstream of many nations, with violent videos (featuring abuse and denigration of women) now available in the corner video store and numerous advertisements parading nude and near-nude figures of both women and men. Television programming in some nations – particularly in the late-night zone – features overtly sexual content, including graphic sexual assaults. Print and television news are similarly problematic, especially as they have shifted toward celebrity and lighter content.

Again, women have not stood idly by but, rather, have acted in a number of ways to improve coverage or to produce alternative news and other media structures. In addition, women working in media professions have made some gains through the years in terms of their own advancement in creative and decision-making ranks, as well as in increasing the amount of content about women.

This chapter, then, considers these issues as documented through the work of feminist media scholars who have examined media content over the past few decades in order to expose the patriarchal ideology lying beneath, looking specifically at images of women in news discourse, and exploring the key tropes associated with women's subject positions in relation to news narratives, as well as the ways in which women's voices, both elites and publics, are allowed (or not) to speak. The chapter then moves to a consideration of women and/in advertising, focusing in particular on women's magazines. Given the considerable volume of scholarship that has explored and critiqued the representation of women in both fiction- and fact-based media, this chapter can barely scratch the surface of that body of work. Instead, we aim here to provide an overview of some of the recurring themes that have emerged from a canon of work that spans several decades.

Objectifying Women in News Discourse

Although it is possible to think that the ways in which women are constructed and represented in entertainment genres is mere fantasy and doesn't necessarily say much about women's place in the real world, the same comforting thought cannot be brought into play when considering women and/in news discourse. While program- and filmmakers might insist that they must be free to follow their creative muse wherever it takes them, even if that's into politically incorrect waters (see Ross 1996), news media workers on the other hand, insist that what they show us is indeed the real world. The lie of authenticity that sits behind this facile and pompous claim has been constantly challenged by any number of studies that seek to understand how news *really* works, how decisions about content are made, how sources are identified and used, who owns the media, and so on (Tunstall 1977; Jones 1996; Franklin 1997; Croteau & Hoynes 2001; Manning 2001; Sanders 2003; Cottle 2004). That news programs prescribe their own routinized functions and protocols in the same way that fictional formats have *their* own internal logics – for example, soaps need dramatic tension, changing relationships, disasters, and so on – is often not appreciated by the audiences for news. There is never any acknowledgment that what we see, read, and listen to in the news is the result of myriad selection decisions that follow journalistic conventions in terms of what constitutes a "good" news story (see Allan 1999).

But news programs are deeply contradictory in nature: on the one hand, they provide a regular update, at the macro-level, on the social, political, economic, and cultural order of the day (Bennett 1997). Thus the news performs an affirmatory and confirmatory function in (re)articulating the rules of the game to which we are all supposed to subscribe. But then, on the other hand, the news comes to us, the audience, in small, discrete units that are often free-floating in a contextual vacuum, lacking background and thus unable to offer us precisely the explanatory coherence that would enable sense to be made of the particular news event in question (Iyengar 1991). News stories are everything and nothing at once, providing "information" about the social world but often without the necessary context that would make the events described fully meaningful.

As Pippa Norris (1997a) argues, to understand news it is first necessary to understand the various "frames" within which news narratives are contextualized (see also Entman 1989). These frames provide an interpretive structure that enables a particular story to be described, but they are not value-free. They are, rather, ritualized ways to understand the world, of presenting a reality that excludes/includes, and that emphasizes/plays down certain facts. News frames constitute highly orchestrated ways of understanding social (including gendered) relations that encourage a commitment to share a particular interpretation of and ways of seeing the world that are entirely partial and that preserve the male-ordered status quo.

The ways in which women are represented in news media send important messages to the viewing, listening, and reading publics about women's place, women's role, and women's lives. The media, and in particular television with its huge audience share, are arguably the primary definers and shapers of the news agenda and perform a crucial cultural function in their gendered framing of public issues and in the gendered discourses that they persistently promote. If news media fail to report the views of women judges, women parliamentarians, or women business leaders, but *always* report on violent crimes against women, then it is hardly surprising that the public fail to realize that women do in fact occupy significant roles in society or, equally, that men are much more likely to be victims of serious crime than women.

If it has become something of a homily to say that the media, both news and entertainment, perform an important affirmatory role in reinforcing dominant gendered norms, it is no less true for the repeating. The extreme sadness and frustration is that after decades of feminist media analysis of media and marginalization, so little progress has been made. This is absolutely not to undermine the efforts of women (and men) over the past decades who have worked assiduously toward the goal of greater equality, some of whose stories are captured in the following chapters. But it *is* to argue that the stereotypes of women that emerged from work such as Gaye Tuchman et al.'s foundational work on images of women in mass media (1978) or Jane Root's (1986) work on women and television are almost exactly the same ones that feminist media scholarship identifies in the contemporary context of the early twenty-first century.

Over the past decade, successive studies have attempted to map and analyze the ways in which women are portrayed in factual media, and that *her*story is not especially positive, showing as it does a pattern of marginal presence on the one hand and stereotyping on the other. For example, in 1995, the Global Media Monitoring Project (GMMP) organized a simultaneous monitoring of news media on one day across 71 countries, in order to explore patterns of gender representation in news. In that study, it was discovered that, globally, 19 per cent of individuals featured in news stories were women and that the most popular roles that they occupied were as victims, mothers, and wives (Media Watch 1995). Five years later, a second monitoring exercise, undertaken with more or less the same number of countries and over 50,000 separate news items, found that the focus of women-oriented stories was almost identical to the previous study and that the proportion of women featured in news stories had actually gone down by 1 percent (World Association for Christian Communication 2000). Once again, the "woman-as-victim" trope was the most popular. In both of those studies, radio, television, and the press were monitored nationally, regionally, and locally, but there were few points of departure across these different parts of the news landscape.

Looking at the European scene, the European Commission (1999) conducted a pan-European analysis of gender and news representation, and the rather negative conclusion of the report cites the low volume of women's appearances in the media across all genres, and argues that women are overrepresented as victims, usually of violence and often sexual in nature. Women are also often subject to overly sensational reporting (Michielsens 1991; NOS Gender Portrayal Department 1995) and later studies provide yet further corroboration (see Carter & Weaver 2003; Kitzinger 2004) of this trend. The Commission's study also found that "old" forms of gender stereotype have recently been introduced as a consequence of political and economic upheaval, so that in the case of Germany, reunification has resulted in a new emphasis on women as mothers and housewives. In former Eastern European countries, demands for "Western" goods and services, including easy sex, have encouraged the reemergence of women as sex objects in popular media discourse in those already ravaged and now ravished countries (Lemish 2004). The Commission's gloomy conclusion was that "the most that can be said is that change in gender images is hesitant and contingent" (European Commission 1999: 13).

Elsewhere, a Southern African study was undertaken in 2003 using the GMMP model – the Gender and Media Baseline Study – and covering 12 countries.[2] That study found that women are "grossly under-represented and misrepresented both in the newsrooms and editorial content of Southern Africa [and that] there are still cases of blatantly sexist reporting that portrays women as objects and temptresses" (www.genderlinks.org.za). In her work on Israeli media's portrayal of Russian women immigrants, Dafna Lemish (2000) comes to similar conclusions, arguing that the "whore" motif was the one most frequently brought into play. In India, Shree Venkatram (c.2002) conducted a 50-year longitudinal analysis of Hindi and English-language newspapers to determine how they had covered political, health, and other issues of interest to women, and how women had figured in that coverage. She found that English dailies had increased woman-related news from 3.6 percent to 13 percent over those five decades, and Hindi dailies' coverage had increased from 5 percent to 11 percent. In photographs, she found women's representation to be falling in both language dailies. She summed up the biases: failure to take note of women's concerns, negating women's achievements, and a disproportionate emphasis on women's beauty and how they should properly behave and dress.

Of course, there are always exceptions to every rule and a surprising example of this is to be found in Shahira Fahmy's analysis of Associated Press photographs in the period during and after the Taliban regime in Afghanistan (2004). In her work, Fahmy suggests that although there were enduring frames of women's subordination, most women in the sample studies were portrayed as more interactive, more involved, and symbolically equal to the viewer when considering photographic features such as point of view, social distance, and imaginary contact. She concludes that AP photographers appear to be reflecting the realities of a more complex set of social relations, as women wearing burquas nonetheless perform liberation in the context of a deeply traditional society.

Women as Victim: The Trope of Fear

As discussed above, one of the most frequent frames of women in news discourse is as victim, and the media's fascination with the fragile female form and her vulnerability to violation probably bears a little further scrutiny, since it says something very powerful about women's agency and women's role in society. Several studies that have used qualitative approaches to women and news have looked at the media's treatment of women and violence and, in particular, at the media's reporting of sex crimes (Soothill & Walby 1991; Kitzinger 1992, 2004; Lees 1995; Cuklanz 1996). Women who are the target of male violence are routinely described as "victims," placing them as eternally passive and dependent, their lives entirely circumscribed by the whim of men. Identikit pictures of assailants are captioned with "sex monster," "crazed animal," or "fiend" labels, which distance these men from the ordinary variety, implying that normal men do not do these things, only beasts and maniacs. In the United Kingdom, the law was changed in 1993 in order for a young man under the age of 14 to be convicted of rape, and the media carried reports that suggested that "the public" was concerned at legislation that would criminalize children, as if adolescents are not capable of criminal and violent acts.

The framing of sexual assaults as "unusual occurrences" carried out by "unnatural men" encourages the view that such crimes are both rare and the result of individual pathology that requires a law-and-order response, rather than constituting a serious social problem that requires a social reform solution. And the fast turnaround for news in the contemporary just-in-time newsroom environment, as well as a lack of interest in providing context for any story, means that each time a rape case is reported, it is as if for the first time. This results, once again, in the framing of such items as isolated and random events rather than the consequence of patriarchal power relations that structure all personal relations, including sexual ones (Myers 1997; Berns 1999; Cuklanz 2000). But using the frame of rapist-as-sex-fiend flies in the face of the considerable evidence from even a cursory look at sex crime statistics all over the world, that the majority of convicted rapists are friends or acquaintances of the (mostly) women they attack. So why does the orientation and language of most news reports on sexual violence still perpetuate the "sex beast" or "stranger-danger" myths despite the facts relating to intimately acquainted violence? Is it because to acknowledge that hard and shocking reality is to acknowledge the thin and perhaps imaginary line that separates the thought from the act, the shouting from the slapping, the tongue from the knife?

Helen Benedict's (1992) study of sex crime reporting found that women were often blamed for their "provocative" behavior but that not all victims were framed in exactly the same way. White, middle-class women tended to get more favorable coverage than either black women or working-class women. Thus, as with other kinds of crime reporting, issues of gender are further complicated by issues of race. Exactly the same kinds of value judgments are, of course, also made about the perpetrator, so that the good husband must have been provoked but the social isolate is truly monstrous. Mostly, the media message is clear: men just can't help their biological urges and women must dress modestly if they are to avoid provoking a sexual assault. It is thus women who have to bear the burden, in every sense of the word, of men's inadequacies, women who must modify and change their behaviors, women who are the guilty ones.

Women thus appear to be at their most interesting when they are in most pain, when they experience most suffering. Lisa Vetten (1998: 8), at the Center for the Study of Violence and Reconciliation in South Africa, argues that "... as a general point, of course men accused of rape are entitled to present their version of events, as are the women concerned. But when women are not given this opportunity, then coverage of rape rapidly degenerates into a media trial by innuendo and speculation." But the ways in which rape cases are dealt with by the media are not always the same, and the contradictory rhetorics surrounding particular incidents could as easily encourage as discourage more women to come forward to report a sexual assault. Using the example of Nombonis Gasa, who was raped in 1997 on Robben Island, Lisa Vetten (1998: 5) suggests that:

> The assault was widely and schizophrenically reported on, with Ms Gasa being portrayed at various times as a liar, a survivor/heroine, an indulged government favorite, or MP Raymond Suttner's wife. One Afrikaans newspaper, along with some members of the SAPS [South African Police Service] denounced Ms Gasa as a liar who concocted a false rape allegation; simultaneously, *Femina* [a woman's] magazine, honored her as a woman of courage.

The contradictory approaches that journalists use to report on sex crimes continue to inform the tense debate over the precise role that the media plays in, on the one hand, trivializing sexual violence against women and routinely discrediting women's testimony and, on the other, helping to highlight what has become an almost endemic problem and thus encouraging more women to report such crimes to the police. Of course, as Vetten (1998) and others have pointed out, the media probably does both simultaneously.

News Media and Women Decision-Makers

While women-as-victim stories are by far the most frequent type of gender framing in mainstream news, the slow but steady progress of women decision-makers, as parliamentarians, local council members, and occasionally CEOs or other senior professional women, has prompted an interest in studying the ways in which such elite women, especially politicians, are portrayed in news media (Fowler 1991; Liran-Alper 1994; Kahn & Goldenberg 1997; Norris 1997a,b; Lemish & Drob 2002). In an extended study of the relationship between women, politics, and media across continents, Karen Ross has looked at both content issues (1995a), as well as how women politicians themselves think about their media-ted image (2002, 2004c). In all of these studies, Ross (and others) argue that women parliamentarians are rarely treated by the media in the same way as their male counterparts, they are always rather less than the sum of their body parts. They are persistently trivialized by media speculation over their private lives, domestic arrangements, and sartorial style: they might be allowed to speak about policy, but their potency as change agents or even as serious politicians is casually undermined by the media's use of extraneous detail such as their age, their shoes, or their latest haircut.

Journalists' differential treatment of women and men politicians is thrown into particularly sharp relief in studies that make direct comparisons between the sexes. For example, in a study undertaken by the British Women in Journalism group (1996), the media's treatment of two political "defectors," Emma Nicholson and Alan Howarth, both Conservative MPs who joined other parties, was compared. A selection of quotes from the newspapers at the time of their defections (adapted from Women in Journalism 1996: 15) illustrates well the differences in reporting style and language.

On Nicholson:

[P]rostitutes her views around the House for some months (John Carlisle MP, in *The Observer*)

She and her husband, who was married to someone else at the time, "fell in love at a lunch party (*The Daily Mail*)

[H]as been known for years in right-wing Tory circles as the Wicked Witch of the West (an anonymous Tory MP, quoted in *The Observer*)

Emma Nicholson is an admirable woman but not a serious politician. Her defection is a dramatic gesture, gratifying to her personal opinions and fulfilling a psychic need but it will have the opposite effect from the one she wants to make. (*The Guardian*)

On Howarth:

[U]nquestionably one of the most thoughtful, intelligent and independent-minded people in the whole House (*The Observer*)

The Howarth testament insinuates itself into the party bloodstream and will dominate its body politic at Blackpool. (*The Guardian*)

[D]isillusioned (*The Daily Mail*)

[A]n extraordinary man in extraordinary times (*The Guardian*)

This kind of negative–positive framing when matching women and men across story types was also very clear in another comparative study, in which Karen Ross explored the ways in which the press reported on the main contenders for the Labour Party leadership in 1994. In that coverage, Tony Blair was framed as upstanding family man, whilst the only woman in the contest, Margaret Beckett, was described in universally unflattering and grossly personal terms (Ross 1995a: 502):

> Mr Blair is a man of rare ability. Rarer still in modern politics, he has an unblemished reputation for honesty and integrity that commands the respect even of his most committed opponents . . . he is happily married to fellow-barrister Cherie Booth . . . and they have three children . . . Blair is a devoted and active father . . . committed to family values. (*Daily Mail*, May 13, 1994)

> Deputy leader Margaret Beckett, 51, has the task of leading Labour through the European elections [although] most Labour MPs admit she has been a disaster . . . and has even been ridiculed for her lack of fashion sense . . . Smith didn't look like the man to lead Britain . . . particularly with that gargoyle Margaret Beckett in tow . . . (*The Sun*, May 13, 1994)

Confounding the limits of "normal" female aspirations and role-types carries with it specific penalties that speak in the register of hysteria and aberration. The women politicians interviewed in Karen Ross's more recent work (2002: 98) identified a number of language strategies that were routinely employed by the media to describe themselves and their activities. Carmen Lawrence (Labor, Australia), commenting on the time when she was Premier of Western Australia, suggests that, as Australia's first ever female State Premier, the media were constantly finding new ways in which to signal her gender and her novelty, mostly because they simply didn't know how to cover this unique situation. She is well aware of the ways in which the use of first names is always a mixed blessing.

If some of the more powerful women in any given society have problems with being taken seriously by their nation's news media, there is little reason to be hopeful for the rest of us, although this generally dismal picture of women's struggle to voice is occasionally ruptured by studies that show less negative tendencies. For example, in Francis Lee's (2004) study of women officials in the Hong Kong press, he found that they were mostly portrayed positively and indeed were often constructed as the "perfect" woman, embodying the best of feminine and masculine traits and enjoying successful careers. However, even here, the construction of the perfect women masks the difficulties that those women will almost certainly have faced as they progressed through their careers, rendering work–life balance issues entirely invisible. In this way, gender inequalities in society can actually be seen to be reproduced by such "positive" reports, since, by implication, if some women can make it, then all women can, and if they don't, then it's their own fault.

The Gendered Source

When challenged, journalists will often say that they don't cover stories focused on women politicians because there are relatively few women in positions of authority, either in government or in opposition parties. Although this is becoming less true, it is nonetheless seen as a legitimate excuse for marginalizing women's voices. However, what is less excusable is the ways in which journalists, either through laziness or tight deadlines, or any other of the reasons they put forward, tend to use the same (non-political) sources as expert commentators. Given what has become conventional wisdom about sourcing more generally – that is, that journalists will tend to use people like themselves who share the same opinions and will not select quotes with which they disagree in their own reports (Manning 2001) – source selection (meaning, choosing men) begins to become a little more explicable. As most journalists are men and most politicians and/or leaders and/or senior executives are also men, then a male-ordered circle is repeated endlessly in this buddy–buddy world. The journalistic predilection for using mostly "official" sources means that the kind of news that we then receive is the sanitized and official version (Gans 1980). How journalists gather news, who they use as sources, and then which quotes from those sources they actually incorporate into their stories all combine to produce a constructed version of "reality," both of the particular story or event in question but, more broadly, of a type of society.

Feminist media research focusing specifically on the use of women and men as sources for news reports provides predictable but still disheartening conclusions (Leibler & Smith 1997; Zoch & VanSlyke Turk 1998). In the latter study, the researchers set out to explore, among other things, the gender variable in sourcing, analyzing a sample of stories over the decade from 1986 to 1996. Of the 1,126 stories that were coded, the researchers found that only 20 percent of named sources were women. Similarly, in a large-scale study of women and television in Europe in the mid-1980s (25 channels in 10 countries), 1,236 news stories were analyzed over a composite week, and of the individuals interviewed in all those items, a mere 16 percent were women (Gallagher 1988). Venkatram (c.2002) found that Indian dailies (both English and Hindi-language) seldom quoted women and included very few letters by women in the "letters to the editor" sections. Little progress appears to have been made, then, over the past decade. In Lynn Zoch and Judy VanSlyke Turk's study, they also found that articles featuring women tended to be shorter overall, and that the length of the female source's actual attribution was also significantly shorter than for male commentators:

> Since length is one cue journalists give to importance in a story (longer is more important), it appears, then, that men were quoted more frequently in the longer, more important stories, and were more trusted than women to give the longer, more in-depth quote. (Zoch & VanSlyke Turk 1998: 769–70)

Listening to "Ordinary" Jane (and Joe) Public

If there are relatively few women nuclear scientists and the current news debate is around nuclear testing, mostly sourcing men as experts has a logic, but what about when the views of the ordinary woman and man on the street are being canvassed? Surely here there is absolutely no reason why similar numbers of women and men should not be asked to comment on an issue of the day, especially at times when opinion poll results are constantly quoted in the media, such as during general elections. In studies that focus specifically on the incorporation of the public into news and political discourse, those that look at the gender dimension of who is asked to speak show that men are much more likely to be invited than women (Hernandez 1995; Ross 1995c). In a study of the radio phone-in show, *Election Call*, in 2001, around one-third of the callers were women (Ross 2004a) and a much larger study of British citizens and public access programming showed an even lower percentage of women contributing to such shows (McNair et al. 2003). However, it should be said that overall, the views of "ordinary" people are not routinely sought in news reports: in a study of "the public's voice" during the 1997 UK General Election (Ross 1997b), only 18 out of the 136 news items studied during the monitoring period (13 percent) used vox pops at all.

Magazines and the Same Old Story

If women are vulnerable to gender stereotyping across all media, nowhere is this more obvious than in the shaping of an entirely unreal construction of passive female beauty in women's magazines, women whose broad characteristics are (mostly) white-skinned,[3] thin, and young, and which is manifested every day in every way, from advertising billboards for the Wonder Bra, to Jennifer Aniston's girlie lunches, to the manicured women who read the news. Over the past three decades, feminist media scholarship has shown, incontrovertibly, that advertising addresses us along clear gender lines (see Wolf 1992; Williamson 1994; Kilbourne 1999) and, within the category "woman," in ever narrower definitions. But the circulation of images of those perfect women with their perfect teeth and their perfect lives is nothing new. While most work on women's and teen magazines has focused on materials produced over the past 30 years or so, magazines, periodicals, and journals aimed at female audiences have been in circulation for more than 200 years (Waller-Zuckerman 1998) and were particularly abundant in the Victorian era (Damon-Moore 1994; Beetham 2001). In Erin Mackie's (1997) study of fashion and commodity in two magazines – *The Tatler* and *The Spectator* – she suggests that the eighteenth-century reader in England would have learnt about changing tastes and the latest fashion through such lifestyle magazines. But those publications also provided class-based analyses of taste hierarchies and, through their editorials and content, translated style into prescription. Mackie argues that these publications promoted more than just a lifestyle but, rather, functioned as key definers of women's lives more generally, fixing their place firmly within the realm of the private.

Exactly the same point is made by Jennifer Phegley (2004), commenting on Victorian family magazines in which the woman reader was encouraged into thinking and doing things "properly." But Amy Beth Aronson (2002) has a much more positive take on eighteenth-century magazines published in the United States, which were more often described as "periodical miscellany," and which were driven much more overtly by the contributions and perspectives of their readers rather than their editors. She suggests that these magazines were able to accommodate diverse views and opinions, and in fact encouraged lively debate within the pages of the publications so that (educated) women who read and contributed to such magazines were afforded an unique opportunity for open debate and discussion.

Of course, political–economic concerns and particular ideologies are usually found together when commodification and exploitation are constituent of particular cultural products such as magazines and indeed other popular media. Over the span of the twentieth century, and into the opening years of this current one, it would seem that women's and girls' magazines are still pushing the same agenda. The fundamental difference between then and now is that the straitjacketing of women's lives and aspirations now masquerades as girl power. As much as the rhetoric of empowerment gives women so-called control, the question is, of what? How empowering is it, really, for a woman to wear a French Connection T-shirt with the legend, "Fit Chick, Unbelievable Knockers" written across her breasts? Or to mimic the bad-boy behaviors of her male counterparts, such as excessive drinking, fighting, and swearing, and rationalize it as sexual equality?

It is ironic that, in the early years of the twenty-first century, amid frantic debates over the global (for which read "Western") problem of obesity, women in advertising are getting skinnier, if only through the expert use of image management software. And for many girls and women, the impossible bodies that ripple through their favorite magazines provoke anxiety and disgust with their own "imperfect" legs, arms, buttocks, and thighs (Edut 1998; Edut & Walker 2000; Arnold 2001). The potential influence of magazine-reading on the development of women's sense of self has thus preoccupied any number of researchers, because women's and teen magazines have long been seen as exemplars of hyperfeminized images that provide highly satisfactory sites for the mining of meaning (see Wykes & Gunter 2004). An important component of the feminist media project has been to understand the development of the genre and the role that magazines play in "defining" woman and femininity.

What successive studies of women's and teen magazines (McRobbie 1978, 2000; Winship 1980, 1987, 1990; Ballaster et al. 1991; McCracken 1992; Kilbourne 1999; Gough-Yates 2002) have shown are patterns of stereotypical gender images that have been remarkably consistent over the past three decades, promoting highly restricted (for which read patriarchal) versions of "acceptable" femininity, of what women are, and what they could and should be. As Meenakshi Gigi Durham (1998) argues, girls' magazines are involved in the circulation of a dominant and patriarchal ideology that privileges the male subject as an authority icon, whose desires are realized by the beautiful but subordinate female. By ensuring a regular diet of bad hair days, zit control, slimming tips, and helpful articles on catching and keeping a boyfriend, a heterosexual and self-obsessed lifestyle is blithely passed on as "normal," so that the maintenance of hegemony is achieved without even a hint of coercion (McRobbie 1991).

While many magazine studies have concentrated on semiotic analyses of the fashion pages and sometimes on the responses of readers to those airbrushed and digitally enhanced images, a handful of studies have looked at other content, in an attempt to identify what other messages are being conveyed about the social world and women's place in it. In a study spanning 40 years of women's magazines, Kathryn Keller (1994) charts the changing justifications that those magazines promoted for the maintenance of a gendered division of labor, both in the home and in the workplace. Similarly, looking at the very popular magazine aimed at adolescent women, *Seventeen*, Kelley Massoni (2004) argues that the broad social landscape mapped in the magazine promotes a highly gender-stratified world in which men are routinely assigned the role of "worker" and wield all the power, whereas women, when they are given license to work, are encouraged to consider the entertainment industry as a good place to be. Importantly, in an arguably self-serving process of professional "grooming," Massoni argues that her analysis shows that fashion work, especially modeling, is promoted as the occupation of choice, the pinnacle of a women's career aspirations.

Some commentators, including workers in the magazine industry itself (see Milkie 2002), suggest that teen magazines are "just" entertainment and should be regarded as dream-schemes rather than reality-based artifacts, but that is surely a naïve and disingenuous reading. Teen magazines are structured in ways that actively encourage their audiences to identity with content, giving advice about real problems allegedly sent in by readers, tips on make-up and various kinds of sartorial advice, and of course endless articles on how to find the perfect man: this is not the stuff of dreams but of teen readers' real concerns, no matter how unrealistic.

Maybe It's Not All Bad . . .

While women's magazines are routinely and roundly criticized for their perpetuation of normative and impossible renditions of perfect femininity, occasionally, as is the case with Kazue Sakamoto's work on Japanese women's magazines (1999), they are applauded for their groundbreaking and different approach. In her work, three magazines aimed variously at teenagers and the twenty-something market, and published in the 1970s, were scrutinized for content. Sakamoto argues that these magazines – *An'an, Non'no*, and *More!* – constituted transgressive vehicles for the circulation of extremely subversive ideas, such as finding ways to avoid parental surveillance (the first two) and strategies for avoiding a traditional life centered around husband and children (*More!*). Importantly, what these magazines promised was not an impossible fantasy, but real knowledge and information about how to obtain this different life. Sadly, the counter-culture signaled by these magazines did not develop into a full-blown assault on traditional (and thus patriarchal) values within Japanese society, and as Catherine Luther and Nancy Nentl (2001) show in their work on young contemporary Japanese women, the desire to be married is still a dominant aspiration. Nonetheless, the hopeful moment of the 1970s did seem to provide a catalyst for change, however short-lived, and even the global product *Cosmopolitan* has been vaunted as championing sexual and economic freedom in its content during that decade (Ouellette 1999).

The promise shown by the magazines considered in Sakamoto's work is further advanced by David Gauntlett (n.d.) in his analysis of some of the newer British young women's magazines such as *More!* He suggests that such magazines promote a girl-power message that is strong, assertive, and insists that women can do whatever they want, dress how they want, and be whoever they want to be.Whilst he acknowledges the overt heteronormativity of the magazine, and that the magazine has mostly replaced men behaving badly with their female counterparts, and that the advertising perpetuates the same thin white models as the rest of the industry, he nonetheless feels able to conclude that this is still acceptable. The ex-journalist Brian McNair (2002) makes a very similar, anything-goes, point, arguing that the pervasive use of sex and sexual imagery throughout popular media should be seen as the democratization of desire and a positive expression of postwar liberalism rather than as a decline in social morality. Elsewhere, evaluations of the impact of the erotic in advertising have received a rather more critical treatment (see Reichert & Lambiase 2003). But Gauntlett (2002) still insists that contemporary teen women's magazines are so varied that they should not be condemned *en masse* for peddling the same stereotyped message, but his very identification of their shared and largely negative (for women readers, at any rate) characteristics somewhat undermines his diversity argument.

To be sure, the content of many women's magazines *is* varied, but is often also contradictory, and it is precisely these kinds of mixed messages that can create such problems for readers (McCracken 1992). For every article on girl power and career planning, there's another one on attracting a boyfriend and honeymoon destinations. For every agony aunt who insists that the reader should be happy with herself, there's a real-life story of finding love with Weight Watchers. As Laura Compton (2001) notes wryly, whilst *Bridget Jones's Diary* was an instant success for its American writer, Helen Fielding, because of "ordinary" women's easy identification with the eponymous hero, when the film was released, the only aspect that critics wanted to discuss was Renée Zellweger's decision to gain 20 pounds to play the lead role more convincingly.[4] It is precisely this issue of weight and body image, and the promotion of the thin white fashion model, that continues to cause considerable concern, especially the possible cause–effect relationship between teen readers, magazines, and the prevalence of eating disorders (Bordo 1995; Hesse-Biber 1997).

Worryingly, the staff who work on teen magazines are only too aware of the fantasies being peddled through their own endeavors. In Melissa Milkie's (2002) interview-based work with editors of two teen magazines aimed at young women, her respondents express ambivalence toward the demands by audiences and researchers that magazines should portray "real" women within their covers and their own ambivalent feelings about the contradictions that they face in their daily lives. Milkie suggests that although editors mostly agree with the repeated criticism from teen readers (and others) that they rarely use "real" women in their content, they offered two kinds of reason for maintaining the status quo. One set of reasons related to exogenous factors such as not wanting to challenge photographers' choices of models, as they had a better sense of the right kind of aesthetic, being at the mercy of the advertisers who wanted gorgeous models to sell their products, or simply the requirement to reflect the wider media landscape, which valued youth and beauty. The other set of reasons related to readers' misunderstanding of the content of the magazine, including that they didn't know how to "read" the images as fantasy, that they wouldn't *really* want to see real people, since reality was synonymous with fat and ugly, and that readers should look beyond one or two images and understand that the total message of girls' magazines is about empowerment. The outcome of both forms of rhetorical strategy is to de-legitimize young women's demands for more authentic representations of themselves and instead contribute to the maintenance of a tightly controlled rendition of correct femininity via editors' cultural gate-keeping role.

Efforts to try to challenge the damaging and stereotypical images that teen and women's magazines persistently circulate through both their texts and their images have been at the center of much practical feminist work, including through self-help books, films, and media literacy programs. In Mary-Lou Galician's exploration of the themes of sex, love, and romance in popular culture (2003), she offers not only a critique but also a set of media literacy strategies to empower readers to challenge the myths of romance. The work of filmmakers such as Jean Kilbourne has also helped to provide accessible analyses of advertising and the beauty myth through documentaries such as *Slim Hopes: Advertising and the Obsession with Thinness* (1995) and her Killing Us Softly series – see *Killing Us Softly 3: Advertising's Image of Women* (2000) – and also written texts such as *Can't Buy My Love: How Advertising Changes the Way We Think and Feel* (2000).

Conclusion

What a discussion of feminist media analyses of women's representation in news and magazines demonstrates, incontrovertibly, is that the media's framing (in every sense of the word) of women in highly restricted and mostly negative ways is not simply the consequence of the idiosyncrasies of this newspaper, that TV channel, or that radio station but, rather, is a *global* phenomenon that has endured over time and media form, and continues to do so. The fruits of all the various research studies briefly discussed above have interesting but ultimately depressing things to say about women's role and function in modern societies, not least that the most common way for women to feature as subjects for news stories is as victim, especially of sex crimes. The news media are primary contributors to public debate on violence and play a crucial cultural function in their use of explicitly gendered frames in news reportage. As Allan points out, "reports of male violence being perpetrated against women have appeared in the news on a routine basis since the emergence of popular newspapers in the nineteenth century" (Allan 1999: 149). And the way in which the media continue to contribute to this circulation of passive and victimized femininity is through the repetitive framing of woman as victim, woman as object, woman as body. This particular frame is routinized and normalized, endlessly recycled to protect the status quo – men on top, again, and women underneath, in every sense. Women remain always less than the sum of their body parts. The blatant sexism of some of the tabloid press – for example, the British tabloid *Sunday Sport's* regular pull-out of almost-nude women with its attendant slogan "Ave it!" – provides an apposite comment on the place of women in the news: we are there to be *had*.

Furthermore, as any number of studies show, the scene is remarkably similar across developed and developing nations. Venkatram (c.2002) found that Indian newspapers in the 1970s gave more attention to women's serious participation as leaders and doers when there was a vibrant women's movement. By contrast, today, she said:

And then, emerged the global stereotype. Beautiful and sexy, in a world of her own where nothing matters except good clothes and make-up, five star food and exercises in the gym. Propelled by the advertisers, the media trained its lenses on this creature, making her into an icon, and lost sight of the carriage carrying the real women. (p. 62)

However, we would be remiss if we did not acknowledge – as we will throughout the book – that change happens alongside recalcitrance, as feminists address media bias, discrimination, and exclusion in systematic ways and push the agenda forward. For example, as a consequence of the publication of the Gender and Media Baseline Study in 2003, the South African News Editors' Forum (SANEF) agreed, at their AGM that same year, that they would make renewed efforts to improve the representation of women in their media, and thus far, workshops and discussions have taken place in several key newsrooms across South Africa.[5] The impact of the news industry itself waking up to its responsibilities will not be felt for some years to come but, as we stated at the beginning of this chapter, part of the purpose of feminist media scholarship is to be in for the long haul, to monitor the media closely, and to provide longitudinal findings against which the rhetoric of the industry can be measured, challenged, and hopefully made more real.

Notes

1   Edith Cresson interviewed by Laura Liswood (1995: 65).
2   See www.genderlinks.org.za
3   Although there are a few nods toward the global village through the industry's use of minority ethnic models such as Naomi Campbell or Iman, few nonwhite women (with the exception of Campbell) have been able to sustain a commercially viable presence in the sector when compared to women such as Kate Moss, Claudia Schiffer, or Christie Brinkley.
4   On the British release of the sequel, *Bridget Jones: The Edge of Reason*, in 2004, these comments resurfaced.
5   Interview with Judy Sandison, SABC, June 8, 2003; email correspondence with Judy Sandison, May 10, 2004.

4

Women as Audience[1]

*With women it's "pardon me while I bake a cake or have a child," they're pulled
60 ways from Sunday. It's hard to know what's woman and what's custom. I
find a woman's point of view much grander and finer than a man's.*
Katharine Hepburn, *Newsweek*, January 10, 1969

The ways in which an audience interacts with a text have been the object
of much feminist media research over the past decades. While the concept
of "the audience" has itself moved through an arc from passive to active to
interactive, so the embodied audience has become fragmented as the media
industry tries to deliver niche audiences to particular advertisers. It is of
interest, then, to try to understand the contours of particular audiences,
including women, for different cultural products, including film, television,
radio, print media, and, more recently, new technologies.

While there remains a relatively modest literature on women as audiences – in general, there are significantly more text-based than audience-
based studies, largely for reasons of cost – much of the research that does
exist concerns women's relationship with popular genres such as television
soap opera. It is for this reason that the chapter begins with a sustained
discussion of feminist media scholarship on women audiences for soaps,
before moving on to consider research on other aspects of women's audiencehood, including film-going, crime genres, news, and magazines. To
date, most of this work has taken a cultural studies approach; therefore,
this will be the main literature that we cover. However, because feminist
political economists have raised important structural critiques of the

media–audience relationship, we will also highlight that debate and its work. The history of feminist engagement with the female audience is, in some ways, exemplified by the overdetermination of research studies on soaps which, as we will see later, is itself a product of feminist scholars' recognition of what women watched and enjoyed. The last section of the chapter concentrates on women's use of and relationship to new technologies; the rise of the Internet, in particular, is forcing a new (re)consideration of the ways in which we function as an audience. Importantly, the level of interactivity that is enabled by technologies such as the Internet or digital television means that the viewer really can exert influence over how she watches, listens to, and reads popular media: finally, there is a reality to the rhetoric of audience power.

Soap Opera as the Ultimate Female Genre

Research on the gendered audience spans more than half a century, although even 50 years ago there were contradictory views on what kind of women were consuming popular cultural products such as soap opera. For example, while some studies (Arnheim 1944; Warner & Henry 1948) identified the "typical" consumer of radio soaps as working-class women with little education and limited possibilities for advancement, others in the same period (Herzog 1944) suggested that women across *all* social classes enjoyed soaps. However, there was a little more agreement about some of the other (imagined) characteristics of the typical female audience, including that she was usually married and between the ages of 18 and 35, with some education (Brown 1994). Herzog's analysis of soap consumers was more "positive" than other studies because she argued that audiences used soap opera to learn about aspirational middle-class values and behaviors. Later studies (see, e.g., Compesi 1980) began to conceptualize soap audiences as being more educated than previous studies had suggested, but still characterized them (women) as being socially lacking or isolated, watching soaps to escape the tedium of their dull lives.

By the 1980s, much "mainstream" work on soap audiences still maintained that there was a correlation between social interaction and sociability in the real world and the extent of soap-watching (Rubin 1985). This reinforced the idea that soaps function as a surrogate friend for social inadequates. But what was often absent from these somewhat positivist and generally harsh analyses of the soap audience was any real sense of the discursive and pleasurable possibilities for social interaction based on a shared enthusiasm for particular shows. This analytic gap was puzzling, since there was often an acknowledgment running through such studies that viewers *did* talk about shows with other people, and that they derived pleasure both from individual consumption and the post-broadcast discussion with friends, family, and/or workmates.

However, one study that finally identified the social glue of soap-watching that held groups of people, or more precisely groups of women, together was the groundbreaking work of Dorothy Hobson (1982) on the British soap *Crossroads* (see below). Arguably, it was the interest of (women) researchers who wanted to explore the genre of soap as a specifically gendered practice, aimed at women and enjoyed by women, that marked a shift in the way in which the audience for soaps began to be perceived during the late 1970s and early 1980s (see Brunsdon 1981; Geraghty 1981; Hobson 1982; Ang 1985). It thus became possible and even desirable to think about "popular" texts as foci for serious scholarly analysis, and with that shift came an understanding of the significance of popular culture in the lives of "ordinary" people. It is ironic that up until that point, mass communication theorists had mostly concentrated on researching those genres.

Dorothy Hobson's (1982) ethnographic research on the British series *Crossroads* made a significant departure from the more usual research mode. Hobson went to women's homes and recorded the conversations that she had with them about their viewing experiences of and responses to the show. A significant component of the research was the relationship of the researcher to the research community: in this case, Hobson specifically aligned herself with her participants as a sister *fan*, and was thus able to provoke candid discussions as a consequence of a shared and knowing interest. What Hobson found were viewers who enjoyed the show but were often embarrassed to admit that they watched, or defensive about their guilty pleasure, expressing an internalized disdain for the series, which they had "learned" from cultural critics. Her more recent theorizing on the value of soaps to women's lives has lost none of its potency:

> The use of events within fiction to explore experiences which were too personal, too painful, to talk about . . . is beneficial and a creative way of extending the value of the soap into their own lives. (Hobson 2002: 183–4)

Focusing on the same genre but using a different approach, Ien Ang's important study (1985) of the US program *Dallas* found, rather surprisingly, that most viewers who participated in her study believed the show to be "realistic" and congruent with their own lives and experiences. Ang sought to give credibility to a show and a genre, which, at least in her home country of the Netherlands, was often dismissed as low-grade entertainment, despite its huge global popularity and, she would argue, its social and cultural importance. The moment of *Dallas* crystallized feelings, especially among the European cultural elite, about the dangers of the global American trash aesthetic invading national (and therefore better) culture and degrading it forever (Ang 1985). While *Dallas* was a conventional soap opera in terms of its genre mechanics, it wasn't intended to be a show that appealed exclusively to women. Still, Ang's work made very clear that women and men derived different pleasures from their watching and were interested in different aspects of the narrative.

Given that Ang's informants were Dutch women who had responded to her request, in *Viva* magazine, to write to her with their reactions to the show, the likely mismatch between viewers' own lives in mainstream Dutch society and the glamorous lifestyles of the *Dallas* families was likely to provoke interesting responses. How then could Ang account for audience perceptions of realism and experiential congruence in those narratives? While the female audiences for other soaps, such as Hobson's *Crossroads* viewers, also comment on the realistic storylines and identify with the personal problems and predicaments of characters, such forms of identification in *Crossroads* were more understandable, since viewers and characters could conceivably share a similar social milieu. With the *Dallas* viewers, though, this was clearly not the case. Ang's answer to this apparent conundrum was to theorize a notion of "emotional realism," so that the pleasures of affect for audiences were derived from a shared sense of personal tragedy, allowing them to empathize at an emotional level with the pain associated with familiar renditions of domestic dysfunction.

As with much earlier examples of gendered representation discussed in Chapter 2, the ways in which soap "problems" are resolved is often through an appeal to familiar renditions of "acceptable" (read "traditional") behavior. The pregnant schoolgirl, or the woman who leaves her cheating partner, or the daughter who kills her abusive father are not celebrated in soap texts but, rather, become the focus for a hegemonic discourse that inevitably positions them as deviant. Although some soap texts have taken a rather more considered approach in their elaboration of less "conventional" lifestyles and choices, such as gay relationships or teenage motherhood, there remains an underlying normative subtext that relegates those subject positions to the very limits of "acceptability." In part, this is a consequence of the conventions of the genre itself, with its need for twists and turns and poor decisions, but it is also partly a product of moral convention. As Dorothy Hobson (2002) makes clear, the success of soaps is in large part due to their enviable ability to make the mundane interesting, to make the domestic dramatic – to make us, the viewers, believe in the characters even as we sometimes ridicule the storylines:

> The characters in soap operas are the key to why audiences watch the programs. The chemistry of a soap opera and its audience is one which involves a considerable commitment on the part of the viewers. (Hobson 2002: 105)

Recognizing these paradoxes is a significant aspect of better understanding the ways in which women find both pleasure but also create resistance to soap texts. Indeed, in Vicki Mayer's work with Mexican American women in Texas and their use of telenovelas,[2] she found that her participants believe that the narratives and storylines of their favorite telenovelas reflect "*some* of the national, ethnic, gender and class tensions"(2003: 479 – our emphasis) that shape their identities as young, working-class Mexican American women. Thomas Tufte's work (2000) on the same genre, but with audiences in Brazil, makes similar observations, including the suggestion that telenovelas make explicit social commentary on the culture and society of Brazil, made more overt by the title of his book, *Living with the Rubbish Queen*, which is also the name of a popular Brazilian telenovela.

Contemporary work on women and soaps has thus both continued the ethnographic turn as well as reviving more structured research modes. As with earlier studies, researchers have been keen to credit audiences with sophisticated deconstruction and interpretive skills, trying to understand their viewing behaviors and pleasures as forms of active engagement rather than passive dislocation. In her work on women soap opera audiences, Mary Ellen Brown (1994) insists that fan networks have the potential (and reality) of providing sites of resistance for women to engage in critical discourses about sex-role stereotyping and expectations. By doing this, she further develops Hobson's argument that the process of discussing plotlines and character development in their favorite soap can actually enable women to use those narrative themes as a springboard for much wider debates about their own lives and those of other women they know. The potential of a safe rehearsal of one's own life choices through the discussion of soap characters' circumstances is an important function for audiences, where the shared experience of bad luck or poor outcome provides strong identifications between audience and character. Viewers thus "use television's narratives to comment upon and come to understand events in their lives, thereby providing themselves with a certain pleasure and perhaps relief ..." (Wilson 1993: 86).

Lyn Thomas (2002) detects a layering of pleasure in taste, this time viewers' identification with a high-end as opposed to a trash show. Thomas shows that viewers and listeners of "quality" programs, such as the British productions *Inspector Morse* (ITV, 1987–2000) or *The Archers* (BBC Radio 4, 1950–), will often identify precisely with the values in such a way that the texts become part of audiences' own personal narratives. She argues that in this postmodern era, it is possible for women viewers to display conventional feminine attitudes toward the heroic male lead – "I *love* Morse" – while at the same time espousing a feminist politics. This apparent paradox is enabled because of the "distancing powers of ironic humor and camp exaggeration" (2002: 174) to be found in such texts. In this way, it is acceptable to find pleasure in viewing superficially traditional renditions of masculinity and femininity, because they have an inherent "quality," which means that consuming them is an acceptable cultural practice.

It is the narrative produced by audiences that constitutes the primary site of resistance, not the primary text itself, which is more usually encoded in line with the dominant conventions of a patriarchal status quo. However, some scholars have argued that soap opera itself is a subversive genre, since its staple ingredients of broken marriages, casual sex, unintended pregnancies, domestic violence, and petty crime are directly antithetical to the socially acceptable norms of romantic love contained within the domesticated marriage arrangement (Lovell 1981) and good citizenship. Martha Nochimson (1992: 121) suggests that at a very fundamental level, soap's interest in and thus portrayal of women's lives, because of the assumed female audience, provides useful gender role correctives to the more normative renditions of femininity and masculinity found in the archetypal Hollywood film: "There is good reason to believe that daytime serial audiences ... respond to soap opera with joy and devotion because they are relieved to have an alternative to the dominance–subordination film narratives." Similarly, they might be relieved to see, in the case of strong female characters who also happen to be lesbian or old or black, a reflection of their own reality rarely glimpsed on TV, and thus grateful for the opportunity for identification, no matter how flawed the character may be (see also Bobo 1988).

C. Lee Harrington and Denise Bielby (1995) suggest that, unlike viewers who attempt to subvert mainstream narratives through, say, writing alternative storylines, the women in their soap study derived genuine pleasures from the original texts as they were broadcast. Far from wanting to construct alternative stories and characters in order to subvert sex-role stereotyping, soap fans' principal enjoyment was precisely in experiencing the affect and emotion provoked by the storylines. Crucially, Harrington and Bielby's work with women audiences reveals the importance of personal agency and autonomy. It allows that women do not necessarily watch their favorite shows in guilty disgrace, but in fact that they derive an additional enjoyment from the act of watching itself, a time-out-of-time when they *should* be doing any number of *other* things, but they *choose* to watch TV.

Perhaps we need to follow Julie D'Acci's (1994) advice, which is for feminist scholars to be a little less certain about soaps' aspirations and effects, given the highly contradictory ways in which the industry's figuring of women works both with and against real women's understanding of themselves and their representation in popular entertainment genres. In the end, according to Ang, soaps "do not function as role models but are symbolic realizations of feminine subject positions with which viewers can identify *in fantasy*" (see Ang 1990: 86 – original emphasis).

On the matter of resistance, feminist (and other) political economists have found it difficult to connect audience agency to any real democratic participation by women from that audience in their own behalf to either form or reform policies and practices. Lisa McLaughlin (2002: 38–9) cites Radway and others who contend that reader (audience) agency "often acts on a different terrain" than traditional politics, allowing women to resist something in their personal life rather than at the social level. McLaughlin expresses her skepticism, looking to Ang's assessment that ethnographic approaches to audience study (which have given us the notion of audience resistance through texts) perhaps only "promise to offer us vocabularies that can rob television audiencehood of its static muteness" (Ang 1991: 104). In fact, some international studies using a feminist political economy approach have found similar results to those framed within the cultural studies paradigm. Divya McMillin's (2003: 509–10) research with women factory workers in Bangalore, India, for example, found that women were able to critically assess the messages in television soap operas and the adverts they contained, and to make rational decisions about buying products and other aspects of their lives. She said that "these laborers achieved critical agency through their economic productivity" and their ability to use television soaps (and adverts) as useful information. However, she acknowledges the reality of power structures that limit these women's autonomy – the low safety standards that they experience on the job, low wages, and the high cost of living. She advocates for media literacy workshops to help them develop a critical consciousness for "long-lasting policy and social action" (p. 510).

Women and Film

The principal focus for much academic study of women and film has been textual analysis (see Modleski 1982; Kaplan 1983; Kuhn 1984; Brunsdon 1986). Part of the development of "seeing" film through a gendered frame has pushed some feminist media scholars to look beyond the text and their own interpretation and toward the views of the audiences (see, e.g., Gamman & Marshment 1988; Pribham 1988). Helen Taylor's (1989) work in the late 1980s sought precisely to rupture the firm hold that "the text" had on film researchers, and the dangers inherent in theories that irrevocably situate women and men in fixed subject positions based on identifiable sex characteristics. In her work with women viewers of the 1930s film, *Gone With The Wind* (dir. Victor Fleming, 1939), she showed the multiplicity of readings that audiences could bring to a single cultural product, let alone a genre in terms of the "woman's film." She also identified the importance of historical specificity in understanding changing responses to texts, since the women who she interviewed in the late 1980s had seen the film when it was first made and brought a critical distance of at least 40 years to their readings of the film, then and now.

Similarly, Jacqueline Bobo (1988) set out to explicitly problematize the position of women and men as audience by focusing on black women's reactions to Steven Spielberg's (1985) adaptation of Alice Walker's novel, *The Color Purple*. In her work, she found that, contrary to the mostly critical tenor of (white) feminist analyses of the film, many black women found pleasures in the film. This was not only because Walker's narrative was an authentic and resonant one for them, but because they really wanted to identify with strong black women characters and such opportunities for positive identification were rare.

Such studies, although relatively infrequent, have been significant. They have placed the female spectator at the center of the analysis in ways that have given her importance in her own right, as possessing agency, rather than being simply "positioned" by the text. Jackie Stacey's (1994) work also has a women-watching-women focus. In her research, she analyzed hundreds of letters and questionnaire responses from British women who had been regular cinema-goers during World War II and in the postwar period (the late 1940s and the 1950s). She was able to identify the pleasures that her subjects derived from Hollywood films of that era, particularly the pleasures that women experienced in looking at female actors who were intended to appeal to male viewers.

Women Watching Crime and Violence

One of the genres that we discussed in Chapter 2 as a vehicle for gendered representations was crime, and given the popularity of TV shows and films on this theme, the female audience for such material has become of interest to feminist researchers. In her work on horror movies, Carol Clover (1992) found more than she expected when she discovered the diversity of audiences for this particular genre both in class and gender terms, and the various pleasures that viewers derive from horror texts:

> One of the surprises of this project has been the number of what I once thought of as unlikely people – middle-aged, middle-class people of both sexes – who have "come out" to me about their secrete appetite for so-called exploitation horror, and I have developed a great respect . . . for the variety and richness of people's relationship to such texts. (Clover 1992: 7)

Through her work, Clover (1992) provides a gentle challenge to Laura Mulvey's insistence on the male voyeuristic gaze being always and everywhere dominant and directed toward the female figure in a fetishized and misogynistic appeal. Instead, Clover suggests that when looking at a genre that is well known for portraying women victims – the horror or rape–revenge movie – the viewer is often invited to identify with the female victim-turned-victor rather than with the male perpetrator objectifying the victim. Moreover, given the mostly male audience for these films, Clover makes the very postmodern suggestion that much in the genre encourages male identification with the female victim–protagonist–hero, which is an aspect of cinematic pleasure that is rarely discussed.

This way of seeing different things, and especially of giving value to what is considered a "trash" form of entertainment, is part of how audiences justify their "low-grade" viewing behaviors. For example, an appreciation of the fighting skills of the martial artist is a seductive pull for some of the participants in Tiina Vares's (2002) study of women and "killer women films," giving them an "acceptable" reason to enjoy watching what would otherwise simply be a kick-ass movie. As the audience intellectualizes aspects of the content, the text is transformed into an object of aesthetic appreciation, giving the viewer a high-culture "defense" for her enjoyment. Such are the ways in which women's position and "required" behavior in society is constrained by prescribed norms of femininity, it is little wonder that women have had to invent strategies that allow them to breathe. In her study of women audiences for so-called "new brutalist" films, Annette Hill (2001: 146) found that women said they liked the ways in which films such as *Reservoir Dogs* (1992) and *Pulp Fiction* (1994) were "more" than just violent movies, because their focus on narrative complexity and character-ization made them into "good" films:

> Female fans challenged the traditional perception of women as either non-viewers or squeamish views of violent cinema and in the process, tested personal, social and cultural boundaries. For this community of moviegoers, women enjoyed watching violent movies on their own terms.

Hill's discovery reflects, to some extent, Janice Radway's (1984) work on women readers of romantic novels, where she recuperates the importance of a familiar women's cultural activity. Radway's ethnographic work with women readers, discussed earlier, suggests that although women's consump-tion of romantic fiction could be seen as an internalization of patriarchal norms, it is the act of reading *itself* that is a resistant practice. It is precisely the time spent indulging in romance reading instead of doing chores that allows women the thrill of doing something for themselves rather than something for other people. Thus, Radway concludes, whether it's watching soaps, reading novels, or watching action films, women's engagement in these kinds of trivial pursuit are undertaken both for their own intrinsic pleasure but also, for some women at least, as acts of subversion.

The Gendered Audience for News

If soaps are regarded as the archetypal "women's" genre, then news and current affairs are seen as of almost exclusive interest to men. It is often taken almost as read that women are not interested in news and that, as a genre, it is very much the domain of men. Consequently, although there have been any number of studies that have focused on how audiences understand news discourse, both print and broadcast, few of those studies disaggregate findings in terms of gender. However, in one early British study that did describe findings in gender terms (Wober 1981), women appeared to be less interested in national news programs than men, but more interested in local news. Also, in that same study, women and men were asked to describe women and men in real life and, perhaps not surprisingly, women were more likely to say that they and other women were more interested in careers and politics than men thought they were.

Women's actual interest in politics is rarely reflected in their on-screen characterizations or as a thematic in either fiction or fact-based programs, which ignore the very real interest that "ordinary" women have in the political process and the policies that affect all our lives. However, we would argue that women's views about news media have rarely been specifically canvassed and that when they are, they demonstrate at least as much interest in the world outside their own direct experience as men, but more often they believe that their interests and enthusiasms are not reflected in the diet provided by mainstream news media. In a country such as South Africa, with high rates of illiteracy, it is not surprising to find that the consumption of news media by women is far lower than that for men, and in at least one recent study – the 1992 *All Media Products Survey* – men are twice as likely to read a daily newspaper than women (Gillwald 1994). But this does not demonstrate that women are less interested in regional, national, and international events than male counterparts, since it could just as easily be interpreted as the news media's failure to engage with the agenda of more than half of its potential audience.

Karen Ross (1995c), one of only a few feminist scholars to conduct empirical research on women and news, was specifically interested in exploring the ways in which British women viewers engage with the images of themselves that are routinely portrayed in news media, and the extent to which they negotiate or challenge traditional gender orthodoxies (see Hall 1980; Morley 1980). Ross's participants fully understood the existence of specific slants and foci in news reporting. Sometimes the issue was political – for example, that programs are too politically biased – and sometimes the concern was expressed as news being too male-oriented. Yet other women suggested that news stories simply don't talk about women enough. Some viewers suggested that the news reflected different opinions and priorities to their own, and that too much content has nothing to do with their everyday lives and concerns. Some opinions directly contradicted others: the opinion that there was not enough local news was matched by another opinion that suggested that the news was too wrapped up in parochial issues, and a number of women suggested that the news was not international enough, and was biased in favor of Western European concerns. Elsewhere, the style of news coverage was criticized for being too oppositional or involving too many word battles between politicians. Indeed, one response could have been culled directly from a media textbook: "Television quickly loses interest in subjects and 'drops' them with no follow-up. News coverage is concentrated on certain aspects of society and certain countries" (anonymous respondent, quoted in Ross 1995c: 12). What that study showed very clearly was that, contrary to popular opinion, women *do* watch news and current affairs programs, and when asked specifically about their consumption, the great majority of respondents reported that they always watched or listened to at least one news program every day and most read a newspaper regularly.

Women and Magazines

The ways in which advertising influences girls' and women's sense of self-worth through the representation of women and women's bodies in magazines have received considerable and enduring scrutiny over the past few decades in a number of nations. Some studies with magazine readers have produced ambivalent findings that cause us to question the uniformity of textual analyses. For example, Joke Hermes's (1995) study of women and men magazine readers in the Netherlands explored the ways in which readers comprehend the media product through their own interpretive frameworks. She found that readers used women's magazines as a recreational activity to while away time, but quickly discarded them when more pressing demands arose.

While much audience research is situated within a white Western paradigm, a number of important studies look beyond the Anglophone world. Some of these studies show that, irrespective of the traditional norms of "sanctioned" femininity associated with a particular country, young women may still aspire to the version of white bodily perfection promoted by global (fashion) advertising: they still want to be the wispy Kate Moss. For example, although the young Japanese women in Catherine Luther and Nancy Nentl's (2001) study felt that it was important to have a career, they also wanted to be married. But what they craved above all else was social approval, looking outward rather than inward, and judging attractiveness to be important both for a successful career but also in order to perform the homemaker role. For these young readers, a belief that ugly women (that is, women who don't fit the mold) don't find partners and, therefore, are not "successful" was the ultimate disgrace.

In an interesting cross-cultural study of fashion advertising, Prabu David et al. (2002) interviewed women about how images of black and white women in advertising affected themselves and other people. Their study found that although all the participants thought that women who shared the same ethnic marker as the model would be more highly influenced by a particular "look," they had different views about their own likelihood of being influenced. While black women identified closely with black models, white women did not display the same affinity and the researchers suggest that this might be because black women were more likely to promote positive, community-based, self-esteem than their white sisters.

Erynn Masi de Casanova's (2004) interviews with young Ecuadoran women sought to determine the extent to which they "bought in" to Western norms of beauty. The researcher argues that although young women did adhere to Eurocentric beauty ideals, they also identified with an idealized Latina beauty image, suggesting that some young women have a more sophisticated, multicultural understanding of the concept of beauty than is usually appreciated.

One study emphatically in support of women's magazines – at least, teen magazines such as the UK-distributed *More!* (aimed at teens and twenty-something women) – is that conducted by David Gauntlett.[3] Gauntlett insists that these magazines encourage women to take control of their lives, to become sexually ambitious (although still avowedly heterosexual), and that such empowerment messages constitute a feminist progress. He justifies his claim by suggesting that research with the target audience, undertaken via online discussions, found that young women like the content of teen magazines, as they feel that discussions about sex and condoms, say, constitute contemporary rejections of the stuffy morality of previous decades.

The Interactive Woman

The vast majority of feminist media scholarship on women as audience has tended to focus on women's appreciation and understanding of particular "female-oriented" texts, what they mean to them and their lives, and how they work with content both on their own and with others. However, these studies have generally assumed the audience as passive, in the sense of simply "watching" or "reading" material. More recently, though, the rapid developments in information and communication technologies mean that we have to rethink what it means to be an audience and consider the (potential, at least) shifts in power between the audience and the artifact. In 2005, if women like watching *Xena: Warrior Princess* but want to see Xena and Gabrielle in a more explicit embrace, they can watch or even create alternative storylines on any number of Xena fan sites. If women want to read news that resonates with their own interests and lifestyle, they can access any number of online newspapers and magazines on both mainstream and women-focused websites (see Harcourt 1999). If women want to watch a film but don't want to go to the cinema on their own, they can rent a DVD and watch it at home, including star interviews and outtakes.

The more active, discerning audience has not escaped the notice of media owners and advertisers, who now recognize the active audience in new ways as they seek to keep their attention and loyalty. For example, the producers of reality TV shows such as *Big Brother* (Bazal/Endemol, USA 2000– /UK 2001–) let audiences play an active part in how the show develops over a period of weeks by voting off contestants. The relative power of the audience seems to have grown, and although these innovations impact on women as well as men, how women and men actually experience being interactive is often quite different. These differences (and similarities) offer new sites for interrogation for feminist cultural studies scholars keen to understand these new practices of audiencehood, and to identify the extent to which traditional discriminations are being maintained or challenged in this brave new world. Feminist political economists are also interested in questions about whether these new interactive arrangements between women audience members really change either women's relationship to the media industries or their social status. Meehan's (2002) work, which considers gender in the commodity audience, offers a foundation. Among other things, she asks whether one can understand women's true power as a commodity audience without also examining women's economic status, their wages, and their ability to render meaningful institutional decisions made within media industries.

To be sure, for some time now, the emancipatory potential of a technology such as the Internet *has* been both celebrated and challenged by feminist and other scholars. In particular, there has been anxiety not to over-romanticize the Internet as always and everywhere a force for "good." Early supporters of the Web celebrated its facility to offer not only a quasi-community in which to affirm membership but also a safe space in which to "try out" different identities (see Spender 1995; Turkle 1995). But other scholars (e.g., Scodari 1998; Sterne & Stabile 2003) have been much more cautious about the Web's allure. In particular, the overt and covert "rules" that limit and delimit user involvement continue to cause concern, as does the increasing availability of pornographic material and images (Arnaldo 2001; Taylor & Quayle 2003).

Interestingly, the same gender skews that exist in relation to audience involvement and participation in older forms of media are also found in new technologies. In other words, "old" forms of differential access based on personal characteristics such as gender and age, as well as geography (the North–South divide) are replicated in this new medium, as any number of studies on the "digital divide" have found (Norris 2001; Katz & Rice 2002; Warschauer 2003). For example, Liesbet van Zoonen (2001) argues that, with the exception of the United States, many more men than women use the Internet, and that women are more usually conceptualized as consumers (i.e., online shoppers) rather than active users, further reinforcing traditional dichotomies of woman-passive and man-active. The male-dominated development of new technologies is thus conceptualized as being yet another way in which to entrench gender divisions. Several studies in both the developing world (Misu Na in Korea, 2001; Priya Kurian and Debashish Munshi in India, 2003) and the developed world (Gillian Youngs 2001; Mei-Po Kwan 2003; Michelle Rodino 2003) show that women's use of the Internet is often squeezed in between discharging their other domestic and family responsibilities. In their work with rural women in India, Kurian and Munshi (2003: 353) precisely demonstrate the hollow reality of the gender/empowerment/technology discourse:

> In a conversation with some rural women in an "e-village" in southern India, a complex picture emerged where although they "ran" the village computer centre, the actual directives on the "who, what, when, where and how" of the data downloaded came from an urban-based administrative structure that was not only overwhelmingly male, but highly bureaucratized as well.

Most gender-focused work on ICTs has tended to look at the ways in which women audiences and users are marginalized and even excluded from the marvels of the World Wide Web. However, a few more recent studies have explored the active relationship that women have as consumers and users of new technologies, both in general terms (see Lee 1999; Lægran & Stewart 2003; van Zoonen 2002; Wakeford 2003) and also in terms of sites aimed specifically at them as niche audiences.

For example, in her work on webcams, Michelle White (2003) considers the ways in which women's webcams differ from those produced by men, arguing that the traditional figuration of the gaze as exclusively male is being challenged by women's use and production of webcams. Similarly, in Frances Cresser et al.'s study of e-zines (2001), the authors found that women writing for and producing e-zines believe that they are doing something useful in their work for women consumers, including the establishment of online networks to enable like-minded women to communicate. However, the authors argue that what became clear in their work was that the Internet neither marginalizes nor liberates traditionally underrepresented groups such as women, but rather replicates the unequal social relations that exist in real time.

From Liesbet van Zoonen's (2002) interview-based work with young couples in the Netherlands, she suggests that whilst there was a sense in which the home-based PC (and Internet use) was regarded by both women and men as constituting an extension to male territory, women didn't necessarily feel excluded from the technology. Rather, van Zoonen suggests that instead of thinking of technology as inherently gendered, its use or status is much more situation-specific. But given that women are less likely to be using new technologies than men, an interesting and innovative national response to this problem (both of representation and consumption) has been the development, by Norwegian designers, to produce CD-ROMs and Web services that appeal to girls and young women, in order to improve their ICT skills and make them more employable (Spilker & Sørensen 2000). When designing those technologies, aspects such as architecture, navigation, and learning styles have been important considerations.

Looking at the ways in which women and men use the Internet differently, Supriya Singh (2001) suggests that, contrary to the view of women as consummate gossips who are only interested in being entertained, their use of the Internet is much more deterministic and oriented toward information-gathering, where they regard the Internet as a useful tool rather than a technology to be "mastered." There are also class-based dimensions to Internet activities, and in his study of users in Switzerland, Heinz Bonfadelli (2002) found that highly educated users tended to use the

Internet more actively to seek out information, whereas less-educated consumers were more likely to use the Internet for entertainment. The parallels
with Singh's gender-based work are interesting, and at the very least suggest
that audience-based studies of Internet use must take account of a range
of different demographic factors if such research is to be able to say anything meaningful. Even where women appear to confound gender expectations in relation to technology, as in the case of adolescent girls and young
women enjoying so-called "male" computer games, they are quickly put
back in their sex-box. Heather Gilmour (2004 [1999]) argues that Nintendo
insisted that girls only enjoyed playing *Tetris* – a game without characters[4]
– because they like to bring order to the world.

A fast-moving technology such as the Internet forces a regular reconsideration of how technology advantages and disadvantages certain communities or groups, and as notions of the digital divide become more
complex (see Selwyn 2004), so the debate moves beyond the simple binary
of North–South[5] into a more sophisticated and layered analysis of exactly
who does have access, and where and in what ways, how use differs, and so
on. Even in the prosperous North, the divide between those who do and
those who do not have access to the Internet is widening in some countries,
as Heinz Bonfadelli's work in Switzerland discovered (2002). And if Africa
and Asia now boast tens of millions of users, prompting the claim that there
is no digital divide, the differential take-up by women and men nonetheless
mirrors not only the social relations that characterize different African and
Asian countries but also the gendered bias of the technology itself, *pace*
the Norwegian example above. Melinda Robins's (2002) work on African
women and online services makes an important point about the fiscal realities of ICT development. She makes clear that as governments and NGOs
establish ICT-based projects throughout the developing world, there are
any number of strings attached to their progress and process because of
the involvement, both overtly and covertly, of private investors. Where the
users fit into this model is often not as comfortably or equally as the
proponents of the Internet suggest, with compromise being a much more
common outcome than needs-led provision.

However, the Internet *can* be a force for change in developing areas (and
elsewhere), as Priya Kapoor (2003) shows in her exploration of a specific
site, the Global Reproductive Health Forum South Asia. This site emerged
in the mid-1990s, facilitated by Harvard University and managed and
maintained by the Centre for Women's Development Studies (New Delhi)
and the SNDT Women's University (Mumbai). Kapoor suggests that the

GRHF South Asia site is "inclusive of multiple perspectives, well managed, and participatory in that it shows coordination and collaboration with many different institutions within South Asia" (Kapoor 2003: 370). Because of its prominent position – unlike many activist websites, GRHF is often included in search engine hits – the site disseminates information that is otherwise very difficult to access, providing a counter-narrative to the state-sponsored rhetoric that is otherwise the only source of "information." Similarly, Ananda Mitra's (2004) study of a woman-focused website, SAWnet (South Asian Women's Network),[6] suggests that some of the strategies that women adopt in SAWnet, such as distancing authorship (where personal stories are posted but authorship remains invisible), could show a different future trajectory for the Internet. For Mitra, the "voicing" of women without sourcing of those voices encourages trust and authenticity, subverting power dynamics and leading to a "hypervoice" being created by the website itself. However, there are always different perspectives in play with any artifact, and Radhika Gajjala (2002) describes the ways in which her own effort to construct an ethnographic account of SAWnet were thwarted as debates about whether the group should be studied at all overtook their initial agreement to allow her access.

Conclusion

What we have tried to show in this chapter are the different ways in which women use, make sense of, understand, and interact with media products such as television, films, magazines, and the Internet. What seems clear is that the academic pursuit of the interrelationship between women audiences and the "text" is the ultimate unfinished story, and that in order to understand the phenomenon of *EastEnders* or *Xena: Warrior Princess*, or the online version of *The New York Times*, we need to explore both the particular historical moments that produced those artifacts and also the time in which they continue to exist in their contemporary manifestations. It is through the exploration of social context and women's lived experience, and the tensions between the two, that we can better comprehend how women negotiate their position as audience against the reality of their own lives. At the same time, we have tried to introduce the critiques of feminist political economists who have challenged the notion that one can study women's relationship to the text without also examining women's relationship to the deeper structures that produce those texts. These scholars also question the matter of women's ability to act in any kind of oppositional way to resist patriarchy simply in the act of "reading" the text, without entering into some form of democratic (political) action.

Crucially, we want to insist that it is not possible to position "woman" as a part of an archetypal female audience but, rather, that women bring their own particular *her*stories, experiences, and lifestyles to the viewing, listening, watching, and interactive context. This is not to say that members of audiences do not sometimes think of themselves as sharing something in common with others, such as women fans of particular soaps, but it *is* to argue that being in an audience can be both an individual and a group activity, and can mean different things for different people. Women audiences use cultural products for particular gratifications and pleasures, including being unruly in their viewing behaviors by watching trash when they "should" be doing something more "useful." Their media habits are therefore hard to generalize, which suggests that future research should continue to examine trends and shifts in female audience attitudes and behaviors.

Notes

1   Some material in this chapter has been reprinted from Karen Ross and Virginia Nightingale (2003, ch. 6), with the kind permission of the Open University Press/McGraw-Hill Publishing Company.
2   The more popular description for Latin American soaps.
3   See http://theoryhead.com/gender/more.htm
4   In the sex-typed world of computer games, girls are supposed to like games that have lots of characters and relationships, whereas boys are alleged to prefer games that have fast action.
5   However, this discourse of inequality is still a crucially important one in the context of a global knowledge economy that increasingly relies on involvement in the wired world.
6   See www.umiacs.umd.edu/users/sawweb/SAWNET/

5

Women and Production: Gender and the Political Economy of Media Industries[1]

> *In the name of freedom of speech, the media claim the right to represent women as they wish.*
>
> Margaret Gallagher, *Gender Setting* (2001: 18)

The ways in which media represent the female subject and the experiences of women working in media organizations themselves are the product of a world system of patriarchal capitalism whose globalizing tentacles currently threaten to strangle the fragile flower of change. This chapter, then, is concerned with exploring the ways in which the relationship between women and media industries is played out. We begin by looking at the highly problematic issue of media ownership and, in particular, the implications of a global industry controlled by increasingly fewer (male) players. We then discuss the location of women, as media workers, within different parts of the media industry, looking at patterns of women's employment over time. We go on to consider the experiences that women have had and continue to face in the media workplace, including issues such as acculturation in an avowedly male-ordered newsroom, the "normalization" of routines that are actually male-defined, harassment, and the denial of promotion to decision-making jobs, otherwise known as the "glass ceiling." The second part of the chapter looks at the strategies that women have employed to bring about change, including the production of alternative magazines and women's filmmaking practices. The chapter concludes with a discussion on moving from theory to action, and calls for a synergy between feminist media scholars and feminist media activists to push the change agenda.

The Problem with Media Ownership

Most analyses of the increasingly conglomeratized nature of the media industry have considered the phenomenon largely through a gender-neutral lens, making it difficult to see how women and women's interests are implicated in this trend. Carolyn M. Byerly (1998, 2004b) has argued, somewhat despairingly, that what has been missing from these critiques has been a sustained critical political economic analysis of women's position in media industries themselves, which recognizes the relationship between who owns media organizations and what is produced by them. Large commercial news companies today are more or less inseparable from entertainment, educational, and other media enterprises, which, since the mid-1980s, have merged into six huge multinational corporations – AOL Time Warner, Disney, Viacom, News Corporation, Bertelsmann, and Vivendi, the first three of which are headquartered in the United States. These corporations own the majority of newspapers; network and cable television and radio stations; both conventional and cellular telephone companies; and Internet news sites that form the backbone of today's capitalist global economy, both in terms of the massive resources that they command and the essential functions that they perform. Media conglomerates have been increasingly influential in economic, political, and cultural forums that constitute the public sphere and, if for no other reason, we must better understand how they work.

Issues of gender are a deeply embedded but invisible aspect of the restructuring that has been taking place in news and other media industries in today's global media scene. Canadian communications scholar Michèle Martin (2002) reasons that contemporary media systems serve as the instruments through which modern capitalism both produces and reproduces wealth, with the owners of those systems having greater control and access to revenues than ever before (p. 53). Theorizing women's location in this process requires that we consider how women are implicated in the macro-, meso-, and micro-level realms of media conglomerates.[2] The macro-level is associated with finance and investment, and the meso-level with relations of production, including the day-to-day decision-making concerned with policy-making and creation of products.[3] The micro-level is associated with media content, particularly the representation of women as subjects and the coverage of issues relevant to women's lives. Ellen Riordan (2002) has challenged feminist scholars to venture into studies of media economics in order to examine how matters of resources, labor, and content are never gender-neutral. Riordan's own recent work on interrogating a so-called "woman-positive" text (*Crouching Tiger, Hidden Dragon*, dir. Ang Lee, 2000) for its cynical capitalist intent, makes precisely this kind of intervention (Riordan 2004). Similarly, Alison Beale and Annette van den Bosch (1998), Carolyn M. Byerly (2001), and Sumati Nagrath (2001) agree that feminist scholarship must begin to involve women more actively both in the analysis of media structures and in the development of media policy. They recognize that the structures of men's financial and political power have not been constructed accidentally or at random. Nagrath also emphasizes that alternatives must be found to funding news operations: until they are independent of commercial interests, she says, they will not have the autonomy to represent women. As will be clear from the discussions in Chapters 2 and 3, the work that has been undertaken on issues of representation paints a very gloomy picture. The extent to which that picture would be different if more women worked in the media is discussed later, where we make clear that an outcome of difference is by no means guaranteed.

Women in/and Media Industries

The tiny proportion of women working in senior positions in the media, including in film, satellite, and even new media, makes clear that the problem is not "just" with news media, but also with the media industry more generally. Although changes in media and communications technology and the increasingly global nature of mass media are forcing a reconsideration of the relationship of media to gender, it is nonetheless clear from those studies that focus on women's involvement in new media that "despite their egalitarian image, *new* media industries – like *old* media and other creative industries – are marred by the persistence of gender inequalities" (Pitt 2003: 378 – original emphasis).

During the 1990s, a number of studies from around the world attempted to map women's employment within media organizations. The trend revealed by such statistical analyses shows that in Western media generally, women experience the glass ceiling effect when they make steady progress as entrants into the sector but then do not go on to achieve senior positions. In Finland, for example, the number of women in media industries far outstrips men (Zilliacus-Tikkanen 1997), although their progression to decision-making positions continues to be blocked. In Margaret Lünenborg's (1996) study of nine European countries, women accounted for more than one-quarter of all reporter, sub-editor, and editor posts, but occupied a mere 12 percent of editorial executive positions. In the USA and Canada, the volume indicators are broadly the same (see Norris 1997a,b; Carter et al. 1998a; Robinson 2005).

When considering the status that women *do* achieve, it is clear that their involvement in the decision-making tier of media organizations has been extremely modest. At the turn of the twenty-first century in the USA, women comprised only 24 percent of television news directors and 20 percent of radio news directors, according to the 2001 Women and Minorities Survey conducted by the US-based Radio-Television News Directors Association and Foundation (cited in Lauer 2002). Similarly, a study published by the Annenberg Public Policy Center (2002) found that across telecommunications and electronic commerce (e-comm) industries, women make up only 13 percent of the top executives, and only 9 percent of individuals on boards of directors. Women make up only 26 percent of local TV news directors, 17 percent of local TV general managers, and 13 percent of the general managers at radio stations. Carolyn M. Byerly's (2004b) analysis of the six major media corporations revealed only seven women at board level and seven women occupying chief executive office positions. In her review of research on women in media decision-making from the 1970s to the 1990s, Ramona Rush (2001) found support for a phenomenon that she calls the "ratio of recurrent and reinforced residuum hypothesis," which predicts that the ratio of women to men in journalism and mass communication fields has remained more or less stable, moving slightly, from 1:4 to 1:3, over time.

On the creative side, Martha Lauzen (2002) suggests that 80 percent of situation comedies and dramas aired during the 2001–2 prime-team season on US network television were written by men: Lauzen also found that, overall, women comprised 23 percent of all creators – that is, executive producers, producers, directors, writers, editors, and directors of photography – in the same season. This percentage has remained almost unchanged for the past three seasons. However, the numbers of women writers hired to shows has declined, dipping dramatically from 27 percent in 2000–1 to 19 percent in 2001–2, although the reasons are unclear.

Unmasking the "Macho" Newsroom

The incorporation of women journalists into a traditionally male profession has the effect of "normalizing" what are essentially male-identified concerns and a male-directed agenda. Thus, acceptance of journalistic practice and convention made on the basis of routinization allows male perspectives to be constructed as unproblematic, uncontested, and – most importantly – to appear as value-free (Komter 1991). In work undertaken with women working on metropolitan newspapers in South Africa, Alison Gillwald found that "few journalists, even those dissatisfied with discriminatory allocation of news stories, were aware of the 'male-centricity' of what they saw as standard journalistic practice – newsworthiness, readability, public interest" (1994: 27). Some women in Gillwald's study were not only apparently gender blind, but used the convenient example of their own success as a means by which to refute the suggestion of sexism in the industry. This strategy of self-deception – or, at best, a refusal to empathize with the real experiences of other women – was mirrored in the responses of some of the women journalists who took part in Karen Ross's (2001) study, responses that neatly exemplify an internalized sexism that places the blame for women's subordination squarely back in their own hands.

Newsroom culture that masquerades as a neutral "professional journalism ethos" is, for all practical (and ideological) purposes, actually organized around a man-as-norm and woman-as-interloper structure. And what feminist scholarship shows, when applied to a range of national contexts, is that these structures are remarkably similar and remarkably stable over temporal and geographical dimensions, as ample empirical and anecdotal evidence shows. For example, the experiences of women journalists in Aida Opoku-Mensah's (2004) study of African newsrooms was broadly comparable to those discussed in Ammu Joseph's (2004d) study of women in Indian newsrooms, and those examined in Louise C. North's (2004) critique of the newsroom in Tasmania (Australia). The consequences for women who choose to work in the male-ordered domain, which is the newsroom, are to develop strategies that involve either beating the boys at their own game or else developing alternative ways of practicing journalism. This latter is often achieved by working in concert with other professionals who are also on the "outside" of the "inner" circle by dint of the same or different reasons for exclusion; for example, journalists of color, self-identified gay and lesbian journalists, and so on (see also Byerly 2004a).[4] How women deal with the "typical" newsroom culture will of course depend on any number of personal, professional, and experiential factors, and such strategies can include (following Margareta Melin-Higgins & Monika Djerf-Pierre 1998): *incorporation* (one of the boys), which requires women to take on so-called masculine styles, values, and reporting behaviors such as "objectivity";

feminist, where journalists make a conscious decision to provide an alternative voice – for example, writing on health in order to expose child abuse
and rape; and *retreat*, where women choose to work as freelancers rather
than continue to fight battles in the workplace. Interestingly, although
Melin-Higgins and Djerf-Pierre regard women's exit from mainstream
media as a "retreat," many women media workers see their decision to quit
as assertive and empowering, as will be clear from the narratives contained
in subsequent chapters. For these women, stepping into the light of alternative media production is an exciting and liberating escape, even though the
uncertain future of such work provokes a range of different anxieties.

The macho newsroom remains the focus of considerable feminist
critique, as well as a site of political activism the world over, as Chapter 8
explores in considerable depth through the experiences of those engaged
in efforts to make newsrooms and the news more egalitarian. These struggles are often quite public, as demonstrated, for example, in early 2005,
when feminist lawyer Susan Estrich took *The Los Angeles Times* editor
Michael Kinsey to task for *The Times*'s decidedly male-oriented editorial
pages. Her argument gave rise to a series of articles, letters to editors, and
editorials in the nation's media, calling into question the persistent lack of
women journalists in US newspapers' editorial pages and, in some cases,
the pigeonholing of women editorial writers into narrow topics typically
thought of as "women's issues." In a letter to the editor of *The Washington
Post*, political consultant Kirsten A. Powers (2005) asked why women
shouldn't be able to comment on all matters of public importance, and
then pointed out the obvious issue:

> It is 2005, not 1905. Seeking more than 10 to 20 percent representation on
> the nation's top opinion pages shouldn't be considered a radical feminist
> agenda. (p. A13)

Harassment in the Media Workplace

The few studies that have focused specifically on overt sexist and discriminatory behavior have found overwhelming evidence of both subtle and
overt harassment against women staff. Research by David Weaver (1992)
in the USA revealed that between 40 and 60 percent of female journalists
who took part in his study had had direct experience of harassment. More
than half the women and just over a quarter of men who took part in

Mary-Ann Sieghart & Georgina Henry's study of British journalists said that they had either experienced and/or witnessed discrimination against women, with newspaper environments being more likely to produce discriminatory behaviors than magazine publishing (Sieghart & Henry 1998). In yet another study, 60 out of 227 participating journalists believe that sexual harassment is a problem for women in the industry, with 10 percent also stating that they had personal experience of harassment (Walsh Childers et al. 1996). The kinds of harassment described in that study varied from degrading comments to sexual assault, and approximately 17 percent of the study's participants reported having experienced physical sexual harassment at least "sometimes." Byerly and Warren's (1996) study cites the experience of one woman reporter who was considered to have an aggressive reporting style, and who was given a jock strap as a leaving present by her male colleagues, with the words "sniff this for luck" written on the band. In a study of women journalists undertaken by Karen Ross (2001), a majority of her informants reported experiencing discrimination in the newsroom, viewing such behaviors as the price they had to pay to work in a male-ordered environment.

More subtle but equally pernicious examples of harassment are not hard to find. In interviews that we carried out with women journalists in South Africa for the cross-cultural study reported in this book, there were clear anxieties about how women's internal promotion would be viewed by their colleagues, precisely because a woman's advancement was routinely characterized as the fruits of her sexual labors:

> You find that if a woman gets a job they will say, something else was going on. They don't even look at your work, the first thing that comes to their mind is no, there has to be something else like you've been sleeping with somebody, you're involved in one way or another with somebody and sometimes you really feel, well, OK, I'll do this [go for promotion] but what is going to be the perception of other people? Will they think that I got this because of my own work or will they start talking around and saying all the nasty things that they can say. (Thandazo[5])

But women newsworkers have fought back against unfair practices in the newsroom, especially in the USA, where a number of high-profile court cases have served to keep the disgrace of gender discrimination in the public arena. One of the best-known cases involved Christine Craft, who fought a long drawn out campaign against her employer, the Kansas City television station KMBC.[6] In the end, Craft lost, but her successor at the station, Brenda Williams, also filed a discrimination case against the station and settled for $100,000. One of the largest ever suits was won by Janet Peckinpaugh ($8.3 million), against WFSB-TV in Hartford, Connecticut, but as Deborah Chambers, Linda Steiner, and Carole Fleming (2004) point out, such wins have served as little deterrent for stations that continue to fire women staff once they reach their thirties.

Activism in the Newsroom

Despite the gloominess of much feminist media scholarship, which documents the unfair practices that occur within media industries, the abidingly macho culture of too many newsrooms, and women's struggles to achieve decision-making positions, there is a long history to women's efforts to change the picture, both for themselves and for other women. In their work on women and journalism, Chambers et al. (2004) discuss the development of such efforts, from the first wave of suffrage publications in the early part of the twentieth century to the second and third waves, which mapped onto the political "waves" of feminism throughout the past century. As the authors point out, although this early history has been almost entirely neglected by historians, "reform and activist groups invested heavily in periodicals to disseminate their ideas, especially when access to existing mainstream publications was blocked" (ibid., p.168). During the 1970s and 1980s, hundreds of feminist publications were published in the United Kingdom and the United States, albeit that many were very short-lived and addressed a highly specialized audience (Chambers et al. 2004). Similarly, one directory listing lesbian and gay periodicals published over the entire twentieth century cites 2,678 publications (Miller 1991). In particular, one immediate impact of the Stonewall Riots in New York City in 1969, an event that ushered in the gay liberation movement, was the blossoming of a number of local and regional publications aimed at lesbian and gay audiences, with titles such as *Amazon*, *Dyke*, and *Lesbian Feminists* (Chambers et al. 2004).

One magazine that enjoyed a relatively long shelf-life for an alternative publication was the British *Spare Rib*, set up in 1972 and enjoying 21 years of often controversial but never dull publication until its final liquidation in 1993. As with many magazines produced by collectives, *Spare Rib* was often beset by internal struggles over ideology and meaning, and what was legitimate content for a feminist magazine. A newer magazine that exploits the significant developments in e-zine publishing is *Bitch!*, founded in 1996

> ... on the impulse to give a voice to the vast numbers of us who know in our hearts that these images are false, and want something to replace them. We want to see images of women as smart and capable as we know we are. We want to find those women out there who are articulating with things like writing, film, art, music, and feminist t-shirt businesses, the experiences that Hollywood and Madison Avenue refuse to admit exist. (*Bitch!*, premiere issue 1, vol. 1, Winter[7])

Fightback in the Movie Industry

In the same way that feminist media scholarship is rediscovering the history of women's involvement in alternative print media production, there is a similarly long history of women working creatively behind the camera. Although the concept of women's cinema is a relatively new one (see below) and women filmmakers are seen as a rather contemporary phenomenon, women have been producing and directing films for over 100 years. Alice Guy is credited as being the first woman director of a fiction film in 1896, and she directed hundreds of films during her long career, as well as owning and running a film studio, Solax (Butler 2002). And Alice Guy kept company with a number of other women who emerged in the silent film era (Slide 1996), although by the beginning of the "talkies," women's involvement in film had all but disappeared. It is not entirely clear why this happened, although possibly the expense involved in converting from silent to sound might have resulted in financial stringencies that adversely affected women's employment. Whilst women continued to direct in the early decades of the twentieth century, the numbers were not great and only two women – Dorothy Arzner and Ida Lupino – are credited with significant bodies of work (Butler 2002).

Although not as prolific or as popular as mainstream cinema, feminist filmmaking arguably began in the late 1960s as part of second-wave feminism; early examples of this "genre" were documentaries such as *The Life and Times of Rosie the Riveter* and *Not a Love Story*. In her exploration of the provenance of the genre of the feminist documentary film, Julie Lesage (1984) suggests that feminist politics underpinned the desire to create alternative images of themselves by women, some of whom were professional filmmakers but many of whom were "ordinary," if politicized, women who were keen to contribute to history in the making. Assuming a primarily female audience for their work, pioneers such as Julia Reichert/ Jim Klein, Kate Millet, and Donna Deitch made films with relatively simple aesthetics and structures, where the audience was intimately engaged through direct-to-camera dialogue in an effort to privilege women's own versions of their own stories. As Lesage (1984: 21) argues, the use of a realist structure in these early films was the consequence of both aesthetic and political decisions, since women were motivated to press their creative outputs into the service of awareness-raising, film as both art and education: in the act of hearing women's experiences, and their thoughts on how things could be, lies the material for political struggle.

Feminist film, like black or queer cinema, is an ambiguous and slippery term. Butler (2002) points out that this loose term is neither a genre nor a moment in film history; nor is it aligned with a particular aesthetic. In other words, it can be whatever we want it to be – everything and nothing. In their attempt to "refocus" the terrain of women's filmmaking, Jacqueline Levitin, Judith Plessis, and Valerie Raoul (2003) alert us to fundamental questions of representation, appropriation, and authority that continue to inflect women's cinema. The contributors to the 1999 conference[8] that produced their anthology reveal "different trends, either towards or away from the mainstream, and varying levels of commitment to or rejection of the label 'feminist'" (p. 10). But those different voices are gathered together under the broad term "women filmmakers," implying that despite the differences within their practice, there are enough similarities to be considered as a particular form of praxis. At the very least, as Levitin et al. point out, women acknowledge that their experiences of filmmaking *as women* have influenced their practice, even if those experiences do not always find their way into politicizing their creative outputs.

Arguably, feminist filmmaking (as opposed to films made by women without a feminist political agenda) emerged as a concept during the late 1960s and early 1970s, as part of the wider debates brought about by second-wave feminism but, like feminism itself, the concept became a battleground of contestation, with two clear sight-lines emerging. One was film culture as political feminist project, countering gender stereotypes with alternative figurations and providing a vehicle for self-expression, while the other focused on deconstructing the medium itself in order to expose the ideological (patriarchal) apparatus beneath (de Lauretis 1987).

In several books on film theory and analysis from feminist perspectives –
for example, Charlotte Brunsdon's collection of essays, *Films for Women*
(1986), Constance Penley's edited collection, *Feminism and Film Theory*
(1988), and E. Ann Kaplan's anthology, *Feminism and Film* (2000) – editorial decisions that were made about criteria for inclusion of articles were
rooted in personal political standpoints. In Brunsdon's introduction, she
suggests that she had chosen articles and sequenced them in ways that made
sense to her but would not necessarily be endorsed by the authors of the
texts and, in addition, that she chose to focus on films tht seemed to her
to address a female audience, even if the filmmaker was male. In Penley's
text, she has a specifically political project in mind and a desire to make
available texts with a similar intent in terms of their relationship with
formal film theory, so that essays

> . . . were chosen because they represent one distinct and insistently polemical
> strain of feminist film criticism, one that directly takes up the major issues
> of film theory as they were formulated in the theoretical ferment of the
> 1970s, generated and sustained by the interest in semiology, psychoanalysis,
> textual analysis and theories of ideology. (1988: 1)

In the preface to Kaplan's compilation, she states that choosing which
articles to include from the "abundance of excellent essays" (2000: v) was
difficult, but in the end, she decided, in similar fashion to Penley, to focus
on texts that responded to – in one or another, either challenging or
confirming – Laura Mulvey's critical perspectives elaborated in her essay
"Visual pleasure and narrative cinema" (1975). Kaplan made this decision
on the basis that Mulvey's contribution to the field of feminist media
enquiry has been so profound (and still continues) that it was worth trying
to bring together a set of essays that debated this theme. We make this point
about editorial orientation here to signal the importance of understanding
different feminisms and different ways of viewing and looking, and the
particular idiosyncrasies of individual authors.

Black and Ethnic Minority Women Filmmakers

While the provenance of racist and sexist stereotypes cannot be unlearned,
black women filmmakers have been mounting a challenge to the repetitive
circulation of their mirrored image since they found their filmmaking voice.

As more women secured a toehold in the highly competitive film industry, it became possible to think and write about an emerging genre of filmmaking that was determinedly political and overtly feminist and, importantly, was created from *within* an Anglocentric geopolitics but *outside* the dominant hegemony. Although the moment of black women's mainstream debut was probably in the early 1990s, Sarita Malik (1994) points out that a black and Asian filmmaking culture had existed in the UK since at least the 1970s (for example, Horace Ove's *Pressure* (1975) has become a cult classic), but the outputs from most minority filmmakers (women and men) had been largely ignored or relegated to small theaters with very modest distribution runs. Even today, filmmakers of color are still considered to be "minority artists" (Malik 2002). But in the early 1980s UK, the trumpeted launch of the Channel 4 TV station in 1981 and the Workshop Declaration signed in the same year, which pledged funding for the nascent independent film and video industry, heralded – in principle, at least – a new vibrancy to filmmaking in the UK, but that particular funding was only available for the production of noncommercial films (Ross 1996). Companies therefore had to work extremely hard to establish themselves as serious players before bigger studios would finance larger and more mainstream projects.

For black British women filmmakers, then, the late 1980s was a turning point for their creative enterprises, a time when some of them, including Martine Attile, Maureen Blackwood, and Ngozi Unwurah, struck out on their own and became solo filmmakers. As Karen Alexander (1993) argues, film had been particularly resistant to black women's participation, but with the establishment of "third cinema," one-off productions such as *Dreaming Rivers* (dir. Martine Attile, 1988), *A Perfect Image?* (dir. Maureen Blackwood, 1988), *Coffee-Coloured Children* (dir. Ngozi Unwurah, 1988), and *I'm British But . . .* (dir. Gurinder Chadha, 1989) finally pushed their directors onto the art-house circuit, if not quite into the mainstream. For all these women, filmmaking was both a political as well as a creative pursuit, where content continually challenged the particular circumstances of their lives as women living and working in the UK but experiencing a very different place to their white neighbors. For many black and minority ethnic women filmmakers, issues around cultural identity are often in flux, deterritorialized by colonialism and migration, by patriarchal marginalization, and by the unreflexive incorporation of their own lives and stories in an homogenized "women's cinema." Thus, much of the output of black women filmmakers in the 1980s was produced as oppositional texts that countered both women's marginalization from discourses of the postcolonial as well as feminism itself (Shohat 1997). What these films also brought into play were exciting blends of narrative and poetry, music, and rhythms, as well as a refusal to engage with the race relations dialectic of oppression and victimhood (Mercer 1988):

> What I've tried to do with all my work is to open up all that stuff – what it is to be British. What I'm doing is making a claim, as well as documenting a history of British Asian people . . . What I'm saying is that there is no such thing as ours and theirs. There is no part of Britain or England that I can't lay claim to. (Chadha, quoted in Stuart 1994: 26)

But the real moment when it became possible to consider those few non-white, female-led interventions as an emerging genre was in the early 1990s, when women working predominantly in the USA and the UK achieved both art-house and mainstream success with films such as *Mississippi Masala* (dir. Mira Nair, 1991), *Daughters of the Dust* (dir. Julie Dash, 1992), *Bhaji on the Beach* (dir. Gurinder Chadha, 1993), and *Just Another Girl on the IRT* (dir. Leslie Harris, 1993).[9] What these early films did, in their treatment of human relations, was not simply to replace "negative" images with positive ones, but rather to develop and extend the more routinized stories about black people's lives, offering compelling alternative perspectives on both the familiar and the unknown. Of particular interest to filmmakers such as Mira Nair and Gurinder Chadha have been the ways in which diaspora communities make sense of living in an often hostile, so-called multicultural society.

The early work of African American women filmmakers was similarly varied, dealing with the problems of living an impoverished existence through to an exploration of a disappearing culture, subverting the tropes of crime and violence that characterized much of the output of African American men during the early 1990s, although women's films during this period did not enjoy the same level of commercial success. As filmmaker Mario Van Peebles pointed out at the time, "I hope to see black filmmakers move outta the 'hood and I think it's the sisters that will take us there" (Peebles, quoted in Ross 1993: 18). But Julie Dash's debut full-length feature film, *Daughters of the Dust* (1992), was 15 years in the making and, on completion, stayed in limbo for another 12 months waiting for a distributor. If it had incorporated the more saleable ingredients of sex, drugs, and violence, it would have had a ready market. As it is, the story, set at the turn of the twentieth century in the distinctive Gullah culture of the rural Sea

Islands off the South Carolina–Georgia coast, did not seem to be instantly commercial, but at a time when most "black" films focused on gangs, crime, and drugs, the textured portrait of a unique and largely unknown society found an interested audience (Turan 1992). British-based but Indian-born filmmaker Pratibha Parmar (2000 [1993]: 377–8) argues powerfully for a filmmaking practice that recognizes multiple negotiations and multiple positionalities:

> I do not speak from a position of marginalization but more crucially from the resistance to that marginalization . . . the reason I make the films and videos that I do is because they are the kinds of films and videos I would like to see; films and videos that engage with the creation of images of ourselves as women, as people of color and as lesbians and gays; images that evoke passionate stirrings and that enable us to construct ourselves in our complexities.[10]

In the years since that early black feminist filmmaking moment, South Asian feminist filmmakers such as Gurinder Chadha in the UK and Mira Nair in the USA have continued to find crossover success in their work, as they have attempted to remain true to their cultural identity and politics but to move debates around hybridity and belonging forward. In particular, both have been keen to enable white audiences to learn something new through a mainstream treatment of social issues such as racism, sexism, and homophobia, both within and between different communities. An excellent contemporary example of political filmmaking engaged with a specifically gendered and controversial subject is Deepa Mehta's film trilogy, *Fire* (1996), *Earth* (1998), and *Water*,[11] which looks at the historical and social position of women in Indian society. Each film is focused around events and themes, *Fire* looking at arranged marriage, *Earth* at sectarian violence against the background of partition, and *Water* at the plight of widows. The first two films met with considerable hostility and condemnation, especially amongst Hindu groups, when they were screened in India, including the vandalizing of cinemas and the burning of film posters. The day before filming for *Water* was due to begin in the holy city of Varanasi, 2,000 protesters stormed the area and destroyed the main film set, burning it and throwing it into the holy river. They also burnt effigies of Deepa Mehta and death threats began to circulate (Yuen Carrucan 2000). A spokesperson for one of the leading protest groups, the KSRSS (Kashi Sanskrit Raksha Sangharsh Samiti), a party formed overnight from the RSS

(Raksha Sangharsh Samiti) specifically to target the filmmaker, issued the following statement:

> Breaking up the sets was far too mild an act, the people involved with the film should have been beaten black and blue. They come with foreign money to make a film which shows India in poor light because that is what sells in the west. The west refuses to acknowledge our achievements in any sphere, but is only interested in our snake charmers and child brides. And people like Deepa Mehta pander to them. (*The Week*, February 13, 2000, cited in Yuen Carrucan 2000)

Sujata Moorti (2000) suggests that the response to Mehta's films can be understood as a clash between global modernity and local tradition, with some critics pointing to the films' lack of authenticity due to the expatriate status of Mehta (who lives in Canada).

Feminist Critiques of Women's Media Production

No genre is beyond criticism and feminist commentators must be able to bring a critical lens to works that are produced out of a feminist consciousness. For example, some of the early polemical works, which targeted issues such as pornography, as in Bonnie Klein's *Not a Love Story* (1983), have been the focus of considerable criticism. In B. Ruby Rich's (1986 [1983]) biting commentary on this film, whose subtitle is *A Film Against Pornography*, Rich's principal complaints are that the film focuses on the wrong thing, in the wrong way at the wrong time. Her criticism is not that pornography is acceptable but, rather, that the way in which it is discussed and analyzed in the film positions the audience as voyeur (albeit framed as repulsed), since the points-of-view shots in, say, the strip joint, are always from the spectator to the stage, thus continuing to objectify the woman on stage: how much more interesting it might have been for the camera to stand behind the stripper looking out into the audience, and how much more discomfiting. For Rich, the anti-porn movie becomes a licensed proxy for the real thing. But such criticism is a sign of the necessary debate over the politics of naming: there are, and must be allowed, different perspectives and different experiences of social phenomena such as definitions of feminism, or women's film, or even feminist filmmaking. Interestingly, the films and other expressions of artistic creation worked by women of color have been the subject of particular scrutiny, especially by women from the filmmaker's own cultural communities.

Jigna Desai (2004) explores the work of South Asian filmmakers such as Gurinder Chadha, Mira Nair, and Deepa Mehta, whose work focuses on difference within a diasporic framework that privileges the hybrid nature of the cross-cultural life, both British *and* Asian, both American *and* Chinese, both within and without. Through an extended exploration of these filmmakers and, in particular, the threads of gender and sexual politics that are woven into their narratives, she argues that part of the crossover appeal of films such as *Monsoon Wedding* (dir. Mira Nair, 2001) and *Bend It Like Beckham* (dir. Gurinder Chadha, 2002) is the explicit challenge that they raise in relation to women's agency, both sexual and cultural. Such a challenge resonates readily with a "liberal" audience keen to applaud efforts to subvert the stereotypes of women as passive victims of a fiercely patriarchal culture. However, the success of such subversion in these texts has been won at the cost of *not* dealing with more difficult and controversial issues such as "Asian queerness" (Desai 2004: 214); and, for Jigna at least, the disavowal of same-sex desire in, say, *Bend It Like Beckham*, if not a cop-out, is then certainly a deliberately missed opportunity, made in order to be more appealing to more people. While it is easy to argue the opposite politics – that surely it's better for more Westerners to understand Asian communities a little better through an entertaining mainstream film that subtly engages with prejudice than *not* to make such a film – there remains a niggling worry that the easier route has been taken rather too readily.

Part of the problem of representation, not just of women but of any group of peoples or communities, is the unbearable and impossible burden that we impose, as consumers of those images, for them to be representative of those wider bodies of humanity. As Jigna Desai (2004: 210) argues, there is an almost irresistible desire to identify the failure of "authentic" representation in South Asian diaspora films: "What I mean here is not the failure of inaccurate or negative representation, but the impossibility of completing or 'getting right' the project of representation at all . . ." What Jigna signals here is that even as we celebrate the emergence of more (rather than less) diverse images of women, we still scrutinize them in ways that necessarily result in dissatisfaction with what we see, because they can never be everything we want them to be because they cannot represent each and every "us." While supporters of Indian director Deepa Mehta's controversial films might defend her right to choose topics that show the difficulties of negotiating the global–local, traditional–modern dialectics, concern over the treatment of a particular politico-cultural identity – for example, her appropriation of lesbian sexuality in *Fire* (1996) for aesthetic rather than political purposes – is an inevitable and perhaps necessary criticism (Moorti 2000). What we see is never enough.

On the other hand, and equally problematic, representations of particular groups by members of those groups should not be sanctified or defended from criticism just because of their authorship or just because they purport to represent the authentic community from which they speak. Cultural works that put themselves into the public domain must expect to be critiqued, for their content, their aesthetic, their politics. For the black producer Keenan Wayans (producer of *In Living Color*, 1990s) to insist that he "knows" the boundaries of "bad taste" in, say, his parody of Nelson Mandela simply on grounds of *being* black is highly questionable:

> Now for the first time, you have black creators behind works that represent black people. So when it's coming from the source, you don't have to worry about the criticisms and uproars from the community. I know what's offensive. I know how far to go . . . I have the pulse of the folks that I'm having fun with. (Wayans, quoted in Rense 1991: 33)

From Theory to Action

Women's limited access to the public sphere, as newsworkers, filmmakers or e-zine producers, requires strategies for changing gender relations in ownership, control, and funding of media organizations. So, is part of the answer to recruit more women into the media? Well, not necessarily. As Jane Arthurs argues, "more women in the [televisual] industry is not enough: there need to be more women with a politicized understanding of the ways in which women's subordination is currently reproduced and with the will to change it" (1994: 100). And the logic of Arthurs's argument can be seen with a quick example. Let us consider what changes, if any, took place at the British tabloid, *The Sun*, after Rebekah Wade took over as editor in 2003. None were immediately apparent in terms of content, style, or orientation, and it certainly did not become more women- or family-friendly; nor was the notorious "page 3 girl" pensioned off. So Wade's sex is no guarantee of a different mode of being, thinking, working. This is not to say that women *never* make a difference and some studies that look at, say, the extent to which women journalists are more likely to seek out women sources for stories argue that women media practitioners can have this positive effect in terms of extending the range of voices that are heard (see, e.g., Liebler & Smith 1997; Zoch & VanSlyke Turk 1998; Lavie & Lehman-Wilzig 2003) and the breadth of stories told. Women *are* working to change the picture, both from inside mainstream media as well as through the establishment of alternatives, both by their own practice and through active campaigning.

For example, in late March 2002, more than 60 feminists demonstrated outside the offices of the Federal Communications Commission, in Washington, DC, to protest the further dismantling of regulations against media mergers and acquisitions in the cable and television industries. The demonstration was organized by a grassroots coalition that included Jennifer Pozner, a long-time US media activist who recently formed Women In Media and News (WIMN); members of Media Tank and American Resurrection, and Terry O'Neill, vice president of the National Organization for Women (NOW). The coalition intends to grow its membership by including human rights advocates, feminist organizations, and other groups pushing social justice agendas. O'Neill regards the media as more than just a business, but rather as an entity with "a responsibility to serve the public interest and ensure that all voices are heard" (Bennett 2002: 13; Byerly 2004b: 258).

In the UK, the Women in Journalism group, which was formed in 1997, grew out of a bottom-up demand for women to be more effectively represented at senior level in newspapers and magazines, and has since evolved into a forum for women journalists at all levels across all media. Since it began, its regular seminars and meetings have offered opportunities for women to discuss career issues with their peers, as well as providing occasions for networking, and have become major events in the media calendar. Seminar topics have included "Making a Difference (How Words Can Change Lives)," "Writing the Big Book," "The Internet for Journalists," and "The Art of the Real Life Interview."[12]

In India, the Network of Women in Media in India held its second national conference in January 2004 in Mumbai (Joseph 2004b), and one of the issues that members discussed was the necessity of networking among themselves, both in local chapters and nationally. Out of that conference came a series of recommendations for action, including the setting up of an NWMI listserv/Egroup to facilitate communication across the country, supplementing the role of the existing website. The suggestion of a printed newsletter for the benefit of those with limited access to the Internet was also considered and a decision taken to explore the idea further, starting with a one-off publication providing information about the network(s), which could be translated into different languages by local groups.

Feminist engagement with media reform in the USA has been slowly emerging alongside a media reform movement begun in the 1980s. Led mostly by progressive men from groups including Fairness and Accuracy in Reporting (FAIR), the Institute for Public Accuracy, the Media Access Group and, more recently, the Media Education Foundation, the movement proposes both broad and specific goals. These include applying existing anti-monopoly laws to the media; passing new laws curtailing ownership; conducting research; holding public hearings; establishing low-power, non-commercial radio and television stations; and reinvigorating the existing public broadcasting system to eliminate commercial pressures. In addition, the movement proposes economic changes that include taxpayer credits for donations to media, eliminating political candidate adverts as a condition of broadcast licensing; reducing or eliminating TV advertising targeted at children under 12; and adopting regulations that require local TV stations to grant journalists an hour of commercial-free news each day (McChesney & Nichols 2002). All of these proposals would serve to de-commercialize and broaden the democratic potential of the media, and women would clearly benefit from them, as would all citizens. But the absence of gender-specific language and specifically gendered concerns signals an underlying problem in the "traditional" media reform movement, and provides a compelling reason for a parallel feminist movement to articulate what women need from a more democratic media system.

Conclusion

This chapter makes clear some of the obstacles that women face in advancing their careers within media industries, and provides some examples of the kinds of strategizing that women are using to take control of their professional lives, including finding strength in solidarity and working for change. But even as women are achieving very senior positions within media organizations, their skills and abilities are still routinely undermined, if sometimes unintentionally. When BBC Radio 4 was named as Station of the Year in the Sony Radio Awards 2004, *The Independent* newspaper ran a serious interview with the station controller, Helen Boaden. Boaden has had a career of "firsts," having been the first ever woman to be appointed as Head of Current Affairs at the BBC (in 1998) and the first woman controller at BBC Radio 4 (in 2000) since Monica Sims in 1978. Given her experience, why then is the otherwise serious interview headlined "Radio's golden girl" (Burrell 2004)? Perhaps the copy-editor was simply casting around for a suitably celebratory phrase, and inadvertently slipped into cliché, but then again, perhaps not.

There is already a theoretical and political base on which feminists are building local, national, and international challenges to media conglomeratization and to persistent patterns of exclusion and misrepresentation. As early as 1968, US feminist economist and civil rights activist Donna Allen was raising the alarm about the dangers of conglomeratized media systems. She argued that the level of concentrated media ownership constituted not a free press but, rather, a press controlled by a handful of very wealthy individuals. Until her death in 1999, Allen articulated a vision of journalism that would provide essential news for and about women with regard to health and safety, economics, politics, global issues, and the media (cited in Nagrath 2001). Similarly, women in India, various nations of Latin America, and elsewhere are beginning to question structural sexism and to develop strategies for change. The problem, then, is not a lack of vision but about finding ways to join feminist media scholarship and popular political activism in order for it to be realized.

In succeeding chapters, we examine the experiences of women on the front lines of making changes to media, including their assessment of what has been accomplished. In addition, we revisit many of the endeavors briefly touched upon in the preceding discussion. We conceptualize feminist challenges to media as "women's media activism" and we examine its myriad forms within the framework that we have named the Model of Women's Media Action. We believe that women's efforts to gain greater access to media represent much more than a disconnected group of events, strung out over several decades and continents. Rather, we will show how these nonlinear, nonchronological, seemingly disconnected events can be viewed as aspects of a unified phenomenon that symbolizes women's struggle to speak and act within both local and global contexts. The phenomenon has had a shared purpose, shared tenets, and shared strategies, which we have identified as paths.

Notes

1   Some material in this chapter has been reprinted from Karen Ross (2005), with the kind permission of the Open University Press/McGraw-Hill Publishing Company.

2   The essays in Eileen R. Meehan and Ellen Riordan's (2002) book, *Sex and Money: Feminism and Political Economy in the Media*, begin to provide precisely these kinds of analyses.

3   For longer discussions of women's location in these levels of production, see Diane Elson (1994), Carolyn M. Byerly (2004b), and Ellen Riordan (2002).

4   For explorations of women newsworkers' experiences in different national contexts and the kinds of strategies that they adopt to cope, see Marjan de Bruin and Karen Ross (2004).

5   Personal telephone interview with Thandazo (not her real name), a black woman journalist who works for a major newspaper, June 18, 2003.

6   Craft was hired by the station in 1981, and within six months she was reassigned away from news on the grounds that focus group research on her performance suggested that she was "too old, too unattractive, and not sufficiently deferential to men" (cited in Chambers et al. 2004: 140). Craft took out an action, and although the trial jury awarded her $500,000 on the basis that there had been sex discrimination and hiring fraud, an appellate judge reversed the decision. Despite numerous further efforts to have the case re-heard, Craft was ultimately unsuccessful.

7   See www.bitchmagazine.com (accessed October 11, 2004).

8   Women Filmmakers: Refocusing conference, Vancouver, March 1999.

9   For an extended discussion of these films, see Karen Ross (1996).

10 Space and focus preclude any longer discussion of a specifically queer filmmaking practice, but for a useful edited collection on this topic, see Michele Aaron (2004).

11 At the time of writing, December 2004, this film remains unfinished.

12 See www.leisurejobs.net/wij/index.cfm (accessed February 13, 2004).

PART II

*Women, Media,
and the Public Sphere:
Shifting the Agenda*

6

Toward a Model of Women's Media Action

[E]verything thought to be the most difficult to say, everything forbidden, rooted in the personal, private sphere, becomes, once confessed, public, political, and knowable. Feminism . . . contributes to this movement of exposure to and transparency in the public sphere but equally in the broadening of democracy . . .
Nilufer Gole (1997)

Previous chapters have surveyed women's relationship to media industries and the products that they create, revealing that progress has often taken its place uneasily alongside persistent problems of omission, stereotyping, and trivialization of women's lives in media content. Such problems have historically contributed to women's invisibility and lack of access to social spaces where ideas are posed, exchanged, and debated, and where agendas for cultural and public policy changes take shape. In the modern world, it's commonly understood that participation in such spaces – often referred to as the public sphere – is a prerequisite for social advancement and power. Communication scholars recognize that participation in the public sphere occurs increasingly through the news and other communications media, including those representing entertainment genres. But what is the public sphere, and what is women's relationship to it? More important, how has women's relationship to media affected their participation, and what have they done to utilize media to increase their participation?

Here, we shift the focus from women's problems with (and scholarly critiques of) the media to the realm of action. Our concern in the remaining chapters is with how women have worked against constraints to try to gain greater access to and reform mainstream industries, as well as transcend the structural limitations of large industries by using a range of other media forms in order to speak publicly, both among themselves and to broader publics.

This and succeeding chapters are based on research that we conducted in 2003 and 2004 in order to learn more about the varied ways in which women had entered into media activism across the world during the years of global feminism, roughly from the 1970s to the present. The findings from this research enabled us to see patterns in women's media activism and to discern the role of such activism in women's larger struggle for social advancement. The new Model of Women's Media Action that we propose here, which is based on this research, serves as an analytic framework for interpreting the responses of those in our study, as well as explaining the role of that activism in feminist political work. The model illustrates how women manifested their agency in creating both a feminist public sphere and a feminist component within the dominant public sphere in which men are still ceded the greater authority. Subsequent chapters explore aspects of women's media activism through the patterned paths that participants in our study followed in their creation of that sphere. We argue that their work contributed to the political task of the women's movement and can be understood as instrumental to women's advancement. These chapters, which draw extensively from the responses of the 90 women from 20 different nations in our study, also reveal more about the nature of gendered struggle cross-culturally through the self-determination women have shown to speak publicly through various forms of media in order to participate meaningfully in their societies.

Women's Media Activism

Women's media activism has been the vehicle through which women's agency has worked to create both a feminist public sphere and a feminist component within the dominant public sphere – concepts that we will explore at length in the next section of this chapter. As explained at length in Chapter 1, the term "feminism" (and its derivative "feminist") is used in reference to social movements through which women in various times and places have sought not only to obtain their equal rights with men, but also the ability to enter into public deliberation, institution-building, and other processes associated with citizenship in their societies. Women's media activism, which has been integrally linked to feminist movements, may be defined as any organized effort on women's part to make changes in established media enterprises or to create new media structures with the goal of expanding women's voice in society and enabling their social advancement. Examples might include: increasing the number of women hired and promoted; making media content (e.g., programs, news stories, films, etc.) more representative of women's highly diverse experiences; eliminating media stereotypes of women; changing public policy governing media operations; increasing the amount and/or quality of news coverage or other media about women; establishing women-owned (or controlled) media; and organizing women (and men) to take some kind of action in relation to the above issues.

Also included in women's media activism is women's establishment of their own media enterprises, such as broadcast production companies, news agencies, film companies, or book publishing firms. In still other cases, women's media activism has been carried out through media monitoring projects or through advocacy campaigns to address specific media issues, such as sexist advertisements. Media interventions such as these will be explored in subsequent chapters. Women have also sometimes used the legal system to challenge media policies, and have lobbied elected officials to adopt new laws to assure that media will represent women's interests. Feminist media scholarship, which examines and critiques media practices, has also been integral to women's media activism through research and analyses that have produced useful data and other information for use in women's grassroots media campaigns. What binds these varied activities together into one collectivity – or, in academic terms, a social phenomenon – is their shared goal of advancing women's status through public, mediated communication.

Women's media activism is rooted in early women's rights campaigns in the nineteenth century in Europe, the United States, Latin America, and other parts of the world. However, it may be best understood as a modern phenomenon that grew out of women's liberation movements that emerged throughout the world during the 1960s and 1970s. The phenomenon of women's media activism is not only modern but it must be recognized as a cross-cultural phenomenon by virtue of its place both within individual nations and as a global feminist movement that sought an expanded communications infrastructure for the routine sharing of ideas, the mobilization of new members, and the dissemination of information about advancements that women were beginning to achieve (see Gallagher 1981; Boulding 1992; Byerly 1995). We believe that these activities are both under-investigated and under-theorized in feminist and media scholarship.

The Need for Theory

Feminist communication scholarship has developed along two main lines. The most common has been the adaptation or extension of existing critical or cultural studies in ways that allow women's experience or concerns to be addressed within existing theoretical frameworks. This approach has fused feminist analysis to a range of theoretical approaches, including Marxism, political economy, race, cultural studies, and postcolonial theory, reworking these theories with a feminist inflection. For example, Eileen Meehan and Ellen Riordan (2002), H. Leslie Steeves and Janet Wasko (2002), and Lisa McLaughlin (2002) are among those who extend general political economy theory into a theory of feminist political economy to enable structural analyses of women's relationship and media and other communication processes. Riordan (2002) identifies her own specific goal as being to produce a feminist political economy that "looks to the meso- and macro-levels of capitalism as they shape women's day-to-day inter-actions" (p. 8). Divya McMillin (2003) fuses postcolonial analysis with feminist political economy theory to examine the ways in which female factory workers in Bangalore, India, interpret and use messages from tele-vision advertisements.

A second and less common line for feminist communication scholars has been the building – and naming – of new theories to enable some spe-cific communication phenomenon associated with women's experience to be analyzed. This building of new theory has been pursued by scholars such as Cheris Kramarae (1981), whose muted group theory identifies women's (and other subordinate groups') lesser power than that of men (or other dominant groups) to control language and speech-making in society. Nancy Hartsock's (1983) standpoint theory, which emerged from the political science discipline, provides a feminist theory of historical materi-alism that has been used by a number of feminist communication scholars around the world, including Sandra Berkowitz (2003) in her examination of the Women in Black movement in Israel, Patrice M. Buzzanell (2003) in her analysis of women's discourse about maternity leave, and Sharmila Rege (2004) in her effort to create an emancipatory position for Dalit women in Indian society. Sara Mills's (1999) discourse competence theory enabled her to identify and describe speech that is both assertive (i.e., con-cerned with speaker needs) and cooperative (i.e., concerned with group needs). Mills developed this theory in order to examine strong women's speech outside a system of masculine–feminine opposition in the UK, but the theory has broad cross-cultural appeal.

While feminist scholars have long recognized women's media activism, very few have viewed the various activities collectively as a communicative phenomenon, or begun to theorize them in terms of function, structure, or contributions to popular feminist movements in the social change process. Nor has women's agency in media activism been conceptualized and examined. Like Sara Mills, who wanted to recognize and theorize the phenomenon of strong women's speech by getting inside her subjects' daily interactions, we wanted to recognize and theorize modern feminists' determined struggles to communicate publicly using media by getting inside their motives and practices. Our research sought to discover whether there existed patterns in their goals; their strategies and activities; their perceived accomplishments; and what they believe remains to be done. We were informed by the substantial research that had already problematized and documented women's invisibility, misrepresentation, and lack of employment in media industries – research summarized in previous chapters. Similarly, we were aware that women's efforts to remedy these problems had produced varying levels of progress alongside well-entrenched status quo practices – a situation that characterizes any dialectical process (see Byerly 1999). But we saw little scholarly effort to understand the nature of women's communicative struggles as a distinct part of the self-determination process that would lead to greater participation in society.

Where earlier feminist media scholarship focused disproportionately on women's problems with the media and, to a lesser extent, on the ways in which the larger-scale media have changed, we wanted to focus on the process of communicative struggle itself, considering the work of change agents (i.e., feminist media activists) and the activities that they conducted on multiple fronts where they worked, not only in traditional mainstream media, but also in community organizations, nongovernmental organizations, and a range of independent women's media enterprises. The 1970s and 1980s had seen a blossoming of feminist political activity throughout the world, inspired by events that included both grassroots mobilization among women in many nations as well as the establishment of governmental, nongovernmental, and cultural working relationships cross-culturally.

Women had been involved in national independence movements in India, a number of African nations, and elsewhere, between the early 1900s and the 1970s, thereby freeing their voices and giving them political experience. In addition, women's increased participation in international gatherings gave growing numbers of educated women a larger vision of the world and their role in it. *The United Nations and the Advancement of Women 1945–1995* (United Nations 1995) chronicles the ways in which the UN body provided an international space for women's rights to be advanced over a course of decades. In 1946, the UN Commission on the Status of Women was established, with its original 15 (now 45) members reporting to the Economic and Social Council to the General Assembly (p. 13). In more recent decades, the General Assembly has adopted dozens of conventions, treaties, and declarations; passed resolutions; and commissioned hundreds of studies that resulted in reports about women's status. However, Boulding (c.1980) said that it was the face-to-face contact that women were beginning to have at events such as the International Year of Cooperation (1965) and the Conference on the Environment in Stockholm (1972) that suggested there should be a sustained dialogue focused specifically on women's advancement:

> Each time they came in larger numbers, and with better documentation to show how the conference subject impinged on women. Each time they also saw how blind most of their male colleagues were to the importance of women's roles in economic production and social welfare. (Boulding c.1980: 27)

International Women's Year in 1975 and the Decade for Women that would follow (from 1976 to 1985) were born out of this mounting frustration. To be sure, women's problems and status varied considerably from nation to nation, and women were stratified by economics, religion, and other factors in many nations, even within their own gender. However, many women also recognized that they shared a *de facto* secondary status in relation to men, and that they would benefit through cooperation in their universal desire for equality and full participation (*World Plan of Action*, quoted in Boulding c.1980: 29–30).

Regional preparatory meetings in Africa, the Middle East, North America, Latin America, Europe, and other areas preceding the IWY meetings in Mexico City allowed participants to identify the barriers to women's advancement in the respective geographical areas and set forth goals to address them. Media concerns arose immediately in every region, emphasizing women's invisibility, misrepresentation and stereotyping in major media, as well as their inability to enter and advance in media professions. The official UN (i.e., governmental) Conferences, held in Mexico City (1975), Copenhagen (1980), and Nairobi (1985), served to build working relationships among women of diverse language, national, religious, and other backgrounds, and helped to spawn agendas for women's advancement. Formal documents, such as the *World Plan of Action*, adopted by UN Conference delegates, subsequently became road maps for women to use in advocating for national-level policy both internationally and within individual nations. Of equal importance were the nongovernmental forums that met at the same time (and in the same cities) as the UN Conferences, and which attracted thousands of women from around the world. The forum gatherings allowed women working in a range of independent organizations around the world to hold open exchanges with each other in order to identify distinct problems within nations, but also commonalities and shared visions around issues. High on the list was a desire to expand women's communication through media. Women's media activism had taken center stage in global feminism.

Women-and-media dialogues that erupted and became central to both the UN and NGO meetings in the 1970s and 1980s manifested themselves in many concrete ways. Jane Cottingham (1989) tells of how in 1976, after receiving poor news coverage of a Tribunal on Crimes Against Women, in Brussels, Belgium – an event that had been planned by Cottingham and others during the NGO forum in Mexico City the previous year – a small number of feminists launched a women's international newspaper called the *Isis International Bulletin*. The Tribunal, attended by more than 1,500 women from 40 nations, had made a space for women to share their stories of discrimination and abuse that they had suffered from men. After the organizers voted (by a narrow margin) to exclude male reporters from entry, Cottingham said, many major news organizations withdrew their correspondents altogether. Cottingham said that this experience "emphasized more than ever how much women needed their own vehicles, where they could talk about their own realities" (p. 239). *Isis International Bulletin*, initially headquartered in Geneva, Switzerland, and Rome, Italy, published 29 issues in four languages – English, Italian, French, and Spanish – over the next seven years, each focused on a theme of concern to women; for example, health, prostitution, migration, religion, feminist theory, motherhood, and peace. In order to further what it calls "South–South cooperation and South–North linkages," Isis relocated from Europe to Manila, Philippines, in 1991, with additional (independent) offices in Kampala, Uganda, and Santiago, Chile. Today, the organization carries on a range of media (and other) advocacy and education.[1]

Fempress/mujer magazine and news service, headquartered in Mexico City (and later Santiago, Chile), *Media Report to Women* bulletin, headquartered in Washington DC, and Agence Femmes Information (AFI), based in France, are additional examples of new feminist print media established in the mid-1970s that specifically sought an international women's audience (Allen 1989; Cottingham 1989). Feminists in India, Jamaica, and many other nations were also launching publications for their national women's audiences, with many of these in the local vernacular. Examples include *Manushi* (in English and Hindi), *Feminist Network* (English), *Baiza* (Marathi), *Ahalya, Sabala Sachetana, Pratibadi Chetana* (Bengali), *Women's Voice* (English), and *Stree Sangharsh* (Hindi) magazines, in India; and *Woman Speak!*, published by the Women and Development (WAND) unit of the University of West Indies, in Jamaica (Cuthbert 1989: 157; I. Sen 2004: 197).

It might be argued that, together, these publications, along with their counterparts in radio and film, formed both regional and global feminist communications infrastructures that functioned initially and over the years to shape a feminist public sphere both within and across nations. Although the nature and purpose of that sphere will be explored at greater length momentarily, we note that its presence is evidenced today by the extensive and global reach of women's media. The *Directory of Women's Media* (Martha Leslie Allen 2002), compiled by the Women's Institute for Freedom of the Press, in Washington, DC, identifies 250 print periodicals, more than 50 Internet periodicals, more than 40 publishing houses, 50 media organizations (which support and advocate for women's advancement in media professions), five women's news services, 12 women's film and video groups, and nearly 20 women's music groups and websites, in 48 different nations. This list, which is surely incomplete, is impressive. Still, it represents only part of the story. The feminist communication infrastructure, which played a vital and central role in creating a feminist public sphere, was not just composed of women-initiated and/or -owned enterprises designed for a women's audience. Indeed, a range of additional media were involved in reaching mainstream audiences with feminist-oriented information. Included here are media that we believe have contributed to the formation of a feminist public sphere that overlaps significantly with that larger public sphere in which men's voices and power still prevail. Women do belong to the larger social and political world in any given society, of course, and in nations where women vote and serve in elective office, they are afforded meaningful opportunity to represent women's interests in policy-making. Yet, research shows that men dominate in government and other social institutions in all nations, as well as in the decision-making structures of mainstream media (whether commercial or noncommercial). Historically, therefore, women have found mediated ways of communicating among themselves; that is, of forming their own public sphere, which has functioned to circulate new ideas about and by women, to allow women to speak to broader issues and broader audiences, and to embed feminist values in the mainstream social fabric. These forms of media have included published feminist academic research on women, feminist news agencies with mainstream distribution, book publishing houses, radio and television production companies, feminist magazines and newspapers, and, more recently, Internet websites, databases, and listservs. Feminists working on the inside of mainstream industries have also contributed to the greater circulation of feminist-oriented content, thereby amplifying women's presence and diverse voices amongst the general public comprising the dominant public sphere.

Our research allowed us to move toward a theory that would begin to explain the structure and function of such women's media activism in women's social participation and advancement. We have called this a Model of Women's Media Action. While close to a theory, which functions to understand or explain a phenomenon, a model serves more as a general structural representation of different sets of elements that work together to constitute a greater whole. O'Sullivan et al. (1994: 185) note that a model is less stable than a theory, and therefore not fully reliable as an overarching explanation for a phenomenon. Therefore, we offer the Model of Women's Media Action as an intermediate step toward a more fully defined theory on the subject that we or other scholars might elaborate at some future point.

Before we take up an explication of the concepts and tenets central to the Model of Women's Media Action, we will review the study on which this model is based.

Cross-Cultural Study on Women's Media Activism

Research goals and questions

The goals of the research were to document, analyze, and begin to theorize media activism that had been conducted by women in different nations between the 1970s and 2004 – years that coincide with the global feminist movement. We were interested in learning about participants' own: (1) roles in media activism; (2) personal (and/or organizational goals); (3) views of what had been accomplished through their own work (or generally by media activism collectively); (4) current involvement (if any) in media activism; (5) views of what remained to be done; and (6) advice for other women engaged in media activism.

Method

We sought participants with a feminist orientation and who understood their work regarding media as being activist (i.e., social-change oriented). A feminist[2] can be understood as someone who takes an active part in social movements through which women in various times and places seek not only to obtain their equal rights with men, but also the ability to enter into public deliberation, institution-building, and other processes associated with citizenship. We selected participants who were well known for their media activism as well as those who were newer to their work, or who had operated out of the public spotlight using a screening process to assure that they met these criteria. Most of the participants contacted us in response to a "call for participation" that we circulated on several international feminist listservs; others came to us by way of contacts we had through our previous international research. Since our sample was intentionally constructed, it can be characterized as purposive. A full list of participants and their affiliations by nation appears in the Appendix; they may be summarized geographically as follows:

Table 6.1   Participation by geographical region.

Region	Number of participants
Africa	15
Cameroon 1, Ghana 1, South Africa 10, Sudan 2, Zambia 1	
Americas	30
Canada 2, Colombia 1, the Dominican Republic 1, Jamaica 4, the United States 22	
Europe	11
Belgium 1, France 2, Germany 1, the Netherlands 2, the United Kingdom 5	
South Asia, Middle East, and Australia	34
Australia 1, India 29, Iran 1, Israel 1, Malaysia 1, Philippines 1	
TOTAL	90

We conducted approximately half of the interviews online, and the remainder face-to-face in India, South Africa, the USA, and the UK, and a few by telephone. In all instances, participants were first provided with a statement explaining the goals of the research and their rights as research subjects. This statement told them of our intent to publish their names and organizations in any publications resulting from the study. Ultimately, we obtained permission to quote from all 90 interviewees, although a few requested that we use a pseudonym when quoting them, to which we agreed. Both in-person and telephone interviews were transcribed. Transcriptions and written responses were then subjected to both qualitative and systematic quantitative analysis. The latter entailed use of a coding tool designed to derive descriptive statistical data about participants' roles, goals, perceived contributions of their work, and other topical areas suggested by the questions.

Quantitative findings

As Table 6.1 shows, informants came from nearly all regions of the world, with relatively more participation from the nations of India, the USA, and South Africa. India and the USA have experienced extremely active feminist movements since the 1970s, including women's media activism. South Africa has experienced these developments since the end of apartheid in the late 1980s, with the emergence of a newly democratic South Africa. We aggregated data in order to discern trends across nations. Greater detail about the specific work undertaken by women media activists in their individual nations emerges more clearly within the chapters, where we cite these frequencies again but in relation to qualitative data and excerpts from interviews.

While we did not ask informants to specify their ages or to provide other personal details, many did so voluntarily in the course of their interviews. Thus, we were able to abstract a profile of them. All participants appeared to be college educated, with many holding postgraduate degrees. About a third referred to their backgrounds as "privileged," in relation to socioeconomic class and the educational and other advantages that this had brought them. Many, including those specifying privileged backgrounds, said that their involvement in feminist and other social justice work was the result of having grown up in progressive, politically active families. Others came to their activism through varying routes, such as gaining a better analysis of women's status through something they had encountered at work, or through events that had convinced them to get politically involved. Since social class specifically emerged time and time again in the course of interviews as a motivating factor in women's media activism, we have explored this facet in more detail throughout the chapters. Women freely offered a variety of personal details about themselves. In terms of religion, participants included those of Jewish, Protestant, Catholic, and Muslim backgrounds. In terms of sexuality, they included both heterosexual and lesbian women. Political philosophies that participants expressed ranged from what has been called liberal (i.e., reformist) to Marxist or other radical-leftist (i.e., interested in major structural transformations). We draw clearer similarities and differences among participants in greater depth in the chapters, making efforts, where possible, to situate their media activism within the national and cultural contexts in which the work took place.

Forms and goals of media activism

Two-thirds of the respondents indicated that their media activism involved using print or broadcast media in some way. Print media included both traditional (mainstream, commercial) and nontraditional (audience-specific, often nonprofit) newspapers, magazines, and journals. Broadcast media included radio and television, both within traditional enterprises and in alternative ones. The remaining third of respondents was split between those who were engaged with film, video, Internet, and book publishing, and those who were involved in some other form of media activism, such as media monitoring and advocacy. About one-quarter (26 percent) of the respondents identified their first goal to be increasing information about women in the media. Sixteen percent said that their main goal was to inform women about their rights or to stop media stereotypes of women. Another 15 percent said that they wanted to inform women about their legal rights or about some issue specifically related to women's status and well-being. A smaller number (11 percent) said that they wanted to use their media activism to help connect feminist issues to other broader concerns (e.g., housing, war, health, environment). The most frequently mentioned secondary goals were to mobilize activism around women's issues (26 percent) and increasing coverage about women (22 percent). Very few (10 percent) cited some form of personal satisfaction as either a primary or secondary goal for engaging in women's media activism. Preceding chapters show how responses to the matter of goals relate to activists' paths, cultural contexts, and other variables.

Current involvement

Because the timeframe that we were considering in the study involved a three-decade period, it was useful to inquire about what participants were currently doing. Among other things, this allowed us to determine whether those who had made contributions in the 1970s and 1980s were still involved in some way. Nearly all participants indicated they are still active (though not necessarily in the same way that marked their earlier years). For example, just over a quarter (27 percent) said that they remain active through their professions in the media, with many being print or broadcast journalists who are able to find ways of incorporating a gender angle into their stories, or undertake longer investigative stories about women on a regular basis. Others said that they work as feminist media advocates (17 percent), teach or train others to be media activists (17 percent), or serve on media monitoring projects (10 percent). The remaining 29 percent said that they engage in some other activity; for example, working for women's advancement in media through unions, participating in nongovernmental organizations, working through traditional political activities with the aim of expanding women's voice in the media, developing Internet websites, or running a women's book publishing house, among others.

Perceived accomplishments and future work

From their vantage point as activists, the women who we interviewed saw a range of outcomes from their (and in many cases, their organizations') work. A third (33 percent) said that there is more women-focused content in the media today because of women's media activism. A fifth (20 percent) said that they believe there exists a stronger public consciousness about feminism because of their media activism. Slightly fewer participants believed that women's media activism has enabled women's ability to enter and advance in media professions (18 percent), to mobilize followers into women's rights work (12 percent), or to improve the image of women in mainstream media (less than 10 percent). The remainder believed that their work had contributed to changing legislation relating to media or shifting public policies, or had served to legitimize feminism among broader audiences. Participants believed that the need for women's media activism was far from over. The most frequently mentioned challenges were the need to secure greater coverage of women's lives and concerns in the news media (25 percent) and continuing to advance women into decision-making roles within media industries (25 percent). Some participants believed that feminists needed to build political alliances with other political movements to engage in media activism together (13 percent). Still others (12 percent) believed that sexist or inaccurate portrayals of women in advertising, television, news, and other mainstream media remain compelling problems to be addressed. The remainder said that women's media activism should focus on lobbying for better public policies governing media content, or developing and circulating updated feminist critiques of media.

Advice for other women on media activism

A third (32 percent) of the respondents would encourage other women to engage in women's media activism as a way of spreading and reinforcing feminist goals and values. Another fifth (19 percent) said that women's media activism was needed to amplify women voices. Fewer numbers wanted women media activists in media careers to strive for excellence so that they could advance and do more for coverage of women's lives (14 percent) or to continue monitoring changes in the media, thereby tracking progress from their efforts or to spot new problems requiring feminist attention (less than 10 percent). Several veteran activists of many years wanted younger women engaged in media activism to remember who had helped to lay the groundwork for them.

Limitations of the quantitative data

The study was designed within a critical and interpretive theoretical framework that made use of the ethnographic method of interviews and narrative reports, rather than social science methods; for example, the survey questionnaire. Therefore, the quantitative data summarized here should be understood as descriptive of this particular sample of 90 participants, but not necessarily generalizable to all women media activists. We hope that the study, and the Model of Women's Media Action derived from it, will encourage others to extend and refine both our qualitative and quantitative work in order to develop clearer understandings of the role of women's media activism in social change both within and across nations.

Women's Right to Communicate

The principle of women's right to communicate is embedded in their media activism, and in turn in the Model of Women's Media Action that we pose here. Although the use of media has been central to social change movements since the nineteenth century (see, e.g., Kielbowicz & Scherer 1986), the discourse about the centrality of communication to citizenship (and the social participation that flows from it) was not debated until the twentieth century. The right to communicate was officially established as a basic human right in Article 19 of the Universal Declaration of Human Rights, which was adopted by the United Nations General Assembly in 1948 and is celebrated annually around the world on December 1 (the date of passage). That article asserts that:

> Everyone has the right to freedom of opinion and expression; this right includes freedom to hold opinions without interference and to seek, receive and impart information and ideas through any media and regardless of frontiers. (United Nations 1948)

Although not binding by the member states that adopt it – as are UN conventions – the Declaration's various articles have served as guideposts for human rights advocates in years since. Women gave a gender-specific designation to the "right to communicate" concept in 1975, during the first UN-sponsored International Women's Year meeting in Mexico City, when delegates adopted a *World Plan of Action* that included provisions recognizing the mass media's power to shape popular perceptions of the role of women in society and establishing specific programs that would strengthen women's access to those media (Byerly 1995; United Nations 1995: 36). Although these official governmental documents did not contain an analysis of women's historic denial to the channels of communication across the world, UN-funded research that emerged through implementation of the *World Plan of Action* laid a foundation of both academic and independent research documenting women's relationship to media industries, and calling for greater and fairer representation and participation in the production aspects of media messages and images. Some UN funds were also directed toward establishing women's alternative media, such as several women's feature services, in the developing regions of Africa, the Caribbean, Latin America, and the Middle East (Gallagher 1981; Byerly 1995). The era of women's media activism dates from this period of the 1970s, when women in larger numbers at the local community level, as well as at national and international levels, sought to circulate new ideas about women's condition, status, and contributions. Global feminism, as represented both by the UN Decade for Women, as well as a proliferation of nongovernmental organizations, placed mass and specialized media central to women's advancement (Boulding c.1980; Byerly 1990).

Women's right to communicate was dealt with more specifically in the Beijing Declaration and Platform for Action in 1995. Delegates who attended the official UN meeting, which met to assess what had happened in the 10 years since the UN Decade for Women ended, set as their goal the removal of "all obstacles to women's active participation in all spheres of public and private life through a full and equal share in economic, social, cultural and political decision-making."[3] Leslie Regan Shade (1999) notes that the platform focused most of its attention on women and media in addressing women's right to communicate. For example, Strategic Objective J.1 sought specifically to increase "the participation and access of women to expression and decision-making in and through the media and new technologies of communication." In 2002, gender and communication burst forth again as a global concern in Pôrto Alegre, Brazil, at the World Social Forum conference. Under the banner of "Communication and Citizenship," participants representing a range of nongovernmental organizations located barriers to open and free communication within the power structures of corporate-dominated media systems the world over (Burch 2002). The significance of this event for feminists is that women's right to communicate had now become formally raised by a broadly based constituency composed of both men and women working in concert on a range of international issues. The WSF was designed to provide a new democratic framework for those from labor, indigenous, environmental, human rights, feminist, and other groups to organize against what they saw to be corporate hegemony manifested through globalization (see J. Sen et al. 2004). A seminar on communication and citizenship at the Pôrto Alegre event identified a central barrier to communication in the form of megacorporations controlled by a small elite of predominantly white, Northern, and male entrepreneurs. Instead, participants said that they favored:

> . . . building an information society built on the principles of transparency, diversity, participation and solidarity inspired by equitable gender, cultural and regional perspectives, a democratic information society, in which all people can exercise the right to communicate, to be full actors in the public arena. (quoted in Burch 2002)

In 2002, feminists took their demands for women's right to communicate to international governmental forums through what they called a Campaign for Communication Rights in the Information Society (CRIS). Representatives of CRIS participated in the UN-sponsored World Summits on the Information Society, in Geneva, Switzerland, in 2003, and in Tunis, Tunisia, in November 2005. Women working in grassroots movements around the world have joined in solidarity with those pushing media rights in the WSIS. For example, participants at the World Social Forum in Pôrto Alegre, Brazil, in 2005, adopted a statement calling on social movements to work on building an international communication rights movement from the bottom up. Communications was a core theme at the 2005 World Social Forum, calling attention to what participants called "the growing communications divide between one third of the world's population with the power to communicate globally, instantaneously and the other two thirds who barely have access to electricity and for whom the Internet is an unknown world."[4]

Women's media activism, manifested in these and other ways, represents women's sustained efforts to exercise their right to communicate in order to participate in public life. The gendered struggle for control over the making and distribution of messages and images, intended for varied audiences, has occurred both within a feminist public sphere, as well as the dominant public sphere. Message- and image-making occur at such sites of production, with the struggle aimed at changing the balance of power in relations between men and women in society. Even women's initiatives to establish their own media enterprises must be viewed within the framework of struggle, since the goal of women's initiatives has been to communicate their experience in their own voices within public spaces, or spheres. The underlying concerns with power relations, structures that produce them, and social change (i.e., emancipation) places the Model of Women's Media Action most obviously within the critical theoretical paradigm. Critical theories assume the goal of enabling social change – in this case, women's advancement through the use of media. The MWMA follows the structure of a critical theory: it problematizes and then situates a phenomenon historically, reveals the structures of power (in this case, in gendered social relations) inherent in the phenomenon, and poses alternatives for change (i.e., employment of media to create a women's public sphere, etc.). However, the MWMA also incorporates elements of the interpretive paradigm through its goal to understand the ways that women have gone about engaging in their activism. We pursued the research through the intersubjective (interpretive) method of interviewing, in which we asked participants to tell us about their experiences, how they had come to their activism, and what they had learned. Interviews revealed that women had pursued their work along four main paths, or strategies, each embodying similar goals and methods. These will be revealed in succeeding chapters.

The Public Sphere and Communicative Action

Central to the Model of Women's Media Action is the concept of a women's public sphere, which may be defined as a feminist communicative space in which women articulate their experiences in their own voices, critique gender inequality, advocate for women's advancement, and identify related social concerns that are often inseparable from gender (e.g., race, class, and ethnic) inequality. Our use of the term "feminist public sphere" follows from Rita Felski's (1989: 9) conceptualization of a "feminist counter-public sphere" as "an oppositional discursive arena within the society of late capitalism, structured around an ideal of a communal gendered identity." A feminist public sphere is also a space within which women bring their perspectives to issues and problems of the day – issues and problems that are not necessarily identified as "women's issues." We agree with Felski (1989) that such a sphere should also allow for tensions and contradictions within women's move- ments to be addressed. Therefore, it should not be assumed that by partici- pating in the creation of a feminist public sphere, women are acting as a unified interpretive community governed by a single set of norms and values (p. 10). In fact, a feminist public sphere is ideally one that honors and encourages diversity of thinking in the creation of social policies. The notion of a feminist public sphere also assumes that this sphere will take on its own national and regional identity as women from nation to nation use media and public gatherings to identify the specific things that they care about.

The importance of media to the construction of feminist spaces has long been understood. Journalism historian Linda Steiner (1983) found that nineteenth-century suffrage newspapers helped US women's rights advo- cates achieve a sense of community and common purpose, even while they actively disagreed in those same pages about approaches to obtaining the vote and other issues. A similar example can be found in South Africa's alternative presses during the early twentieth century, when feminists such as *The Guardian*'s Ruth First used her journalism to try to build an identity for African women during mobilization against the government's expanded use of passes for black citizens outside their own townships (Pinnock 1997: 318). In 1975, women's rights leaders from around the world recognized the key role of both mass media and specialized women-controlled media.

The mass media, they said, could "exercise a significant influence in helping to remove prejudices and stereotypes, accelerating the acceptance of women's new and expanding roles in society" (*World Plan of Action* 1975, paras 161–2, cited in United Nations 1976). The recognition of mass media's centrality to women's advancement was reaffirmed in the platform of the UN's Fourth Conference on Women, held in Beijing, China, in 1995, in which delegates called again for the "increased participation and access of women to expression and decision-making in and through the media and new technologies of communication" and laid out more than a dozen specific recommendations to governments to enable such access.

So far, we have referred to Jürgen Habermas's (1984, 1987, 1993) concept of an ideal public sphere without a full explanation of it, or of the problems that it has posed for feminists. Habermas's notion of an ideal public sphere – an imagined space separate from the state or the economic marketplace, where citizens could deliberate their common affairs – was derived from the historical context of British, French, and German developments in the eighteenth and early nineteenth centuries (Habermas 1993: 422–3). In Habermas's original formulation, participants in the emerging public sphere were part of a new educated elite (i.e., a bourgeoisie) who would mediate between society and governmental, economic, and other structures. He saw the bourgeoisie's role as crucial in the evolution of modern democratic processes. Habermas's (1987) ideal public sphere concept is part of his theory of communicative action, which he set forth in two volumes whose content ranges from critiques of previous theoretical understandings of the roles of communication in social evolution to a positing of new theory for the way in which society progresses. Of particular relevance to our own discussion is his treatment of media, which he saw serving as a "coordinating mechanism for reaching understanding" (p. 390) among participants in the public sphere. Especially appealing to critical theorists has been his recognition that mass media permeate our modern world and daily life, and these media serve generally to reinforce existing hierarchies. He said, "there is a counterweight of emancipatory potential built into communication structures themselves . . . abstracted and clustered as they are, these communications cannot be reliably shielded from the possibility of opposition by responsible actors" (Habermas 1987: 390).

Feminist scholars have debated Habermas's value for their own work, criticizing him for not addressing gender, race, and class more explicitly in the original formulation of the ideal public sphere. Nancy Fraser (1993) recognized that the general idea of a public sphere is indispensable to critical social theory and democratic political practice, but she has been among the most vocal in calling Habermas's lack of a gender and class consciousness into question (pp. 112–18). Lisa McLaughlin (1993) agrees that the emancipatory nature of the public sphere is attractive to feminists. Citing Mary Ryan (1992), McLaughlin points out that despite exclusion from the dominant public sphere historically, women across classes and ethnicities did (and do) gain access to public life and public arenas. Habermas has responded to feminists (and other critics) by making a number of revisions to his original theory. Among these is a recognition that some aspects of his original formulation were too simplistic and, from the beginning, that the early democracies were characterized by competing (counter) publics. Regarding this last point, he has said:

> An analysis of the exclusionary aspects of established public spheres is particularly revealing in the respect, the critique of that which has been excluded from the public sphere and from my analysis of it too: gender, ethnicity, class, popular culture. (Habermas 1993: 466)

This understanding has led to a general acceptance of the existence of multiple public spheres, also referred to as counter spheres (Habermas's own term). Envisioning a multiplicity of public spheres offers a clearer picture of communicative practices in the real world, and it allows for an explanation of how ideas move from the private sphere of personal life and home into public discourse. The notion of a feminist public sphere that intersects others, including the dominant sphere – in which men's power prevails – allows for a clearer explanation of how women have articulated personal and political views and concerns both among themselves and within a wider public forum. What Habermas called the dominant public sphere – and which we refer to as the dominant masculine public sphere from time to time – has also been called the "official public sphere," designating it as the place where power elites shape discourse that leads to official policy (see Lisa McLaughlin 1993: 602). Key here is that there appears to be consensus among scholars today, including the originator of the concept and theory surrounding it, that there are multiple public spheres competing with a dominant one in a dialectical process over time – and, we would add, space.

In showing one way in which women in recent times negotiated that dominant sphere, Nancy Fraser (1993: 123) noted that "feminist women have invented new terms for describing social reality, including 'sexism', 'the double shift', 'sexual harassment', and 'marital, date and acquaintance rape', thereby reducing, although not eliminating, the extent of our disadvantage in official public spheres." Fraser's useful example shows how feminists' articulation of a language of experience moved first from the private sphere to a feminist-created women's public sphere, and then on into the dominant sphere and presumably also other counter public spheres. The new language and analysis associated with violence against women initially circulated through feminist publications in the 1970s, but through the force of public speak-outs (which mainstream news often covered), and strategic public relations (carried on by women's organizations such as the National Organization for Women in the USA and Isis International, based in Europe), the terms gradually reached audiences occupying other public spheres.[5] Both mass and alternative media provided the means for circulating these terms (and the ideas that they embodied), both within and among the respective public spheres (Byerly 1994, 1999).

Jean L. Cohen (1995: 81) argues that Habermas's later work on, for example, facticity and validity, which further corrected for his earlier gender blindness, makes his theory an extremely important contribution to the "equality/difference" debate, animating feminist legal theory in the USA. She argues that these advancements, together with his elaborations on social theory on the civil society, make Habermas's work indispensable to feminists. We would agree with Cohen's assessment. We see substantial potential for subaltern (following Spivak 1988) theories deriving from feminist, intercultural, lesbian and gay, and postcolonial scholarship to expand on the ways in which marginalized groups entered into a dialectical process through their use of media. Our own task here is to consider feminists' experience in this regard.

The notion that multiple public spheres operate and that women have a relationship to them has caught feminist imaginations around the world. Feminist scholars, writing from diverse national and cultural perspectives, have added complexity to an understanding of the public sphere by showing how factors such as race, ethnicity, social class, and nationality are involved. Nilufer Gole (1997) recognized the inherent gendered nature of the public sphere, and she considered the ways in which feminist leaders have helped to place women's issues related to culture and religion central to modern political debate in Muslim countries such as Turkey. Amanda Kemp, Nozizwe Madlala, Asha Moodley, and Elaine Salo (1995) demonstrated the extent to which an understanding of the public sphere has been reformulated in talking about the dramatic growth of gender consciousness in South Africa since 1990. Women's efforts to constitute themselves as participants in the emerging pluralistic South African society, they said, have shaped their movement's understanding that "ideologies of woman- hood had as much to do with race as they do with sex" (p. 133). These authors also factored in concerns about national development, which femi- nists in developing nations have long recognized to be bound up with women's advancement and hence their work as social activists. Thus, in articulating a politics of equality and advancement for women, black South African feminists, they said, also must raise issues such as access to clean water and housing – things not specifically defined as "feminist" (ibid.).

At the conceptual level, we can imagine that these spheres exist as indi- vidual communicative spaces, as well as interlocking spaces, in the form of a Venn diagram (see Figure 6.1). The salient question now is: How have media been utilized in this negotiation process? McLaughlin (1993: 600) found that "feminist work on the Habermasian public sphere gives the media scant attention, despite the necessity to account for the feminist movement's

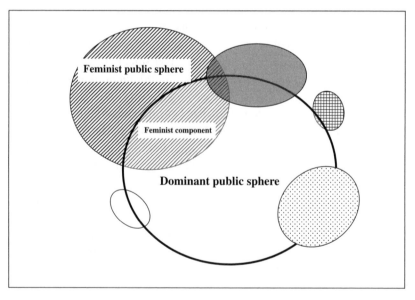

Figure 6.1   The relationship of the feminist public sphere to the dominant public sphere. Conceptualizations of multiple public spheres recognize that marginal groups vie for influence with a dominant public sphere. In this model, the feminist public sphere exists as its own entity, as well as being a formation within the domi- nant public sphere.

publicist orientation." She argued that a theory of the public sphere "demands a sustained consideration of publicity and media's role in it," something she admitted is "no simple task, since reconceptualization need address feminists' production of hegemonic discourses, feminist discourse's insinuation with hegemonic discourse, and feminism's marginalization, cooptation and dilution by media institutions" (McLaughlin 1993: 612).

Emerging feminist scholarship is considering ways in which women are engaging hegemonic discourse through media activism. One example emerges from a study by Ananda Mitra (2004), who examined the ways in which women in South Asia are beginning to use the Internet to express shared concerns about their roles and marginalization, and to discuss ways of taking action. Mitra observes that historically, women in South Asia have used protests – rallies, strikes, and demonstrations – to voice their concerns. This began to change in the 1980s, as women in India worked to get socially conscious programming about gender onto the state-owned television network Doordarshan. Today, South Asian women are using Internet resources such as the website and listserv of SAWnet – the South Asian Women's Network. Mitra argues that SAWnet provides authority and legitimacy to the participants who are in the process of creating a South Asian women's public sphere.

As we move toward creating a Model of Women's Media Action, we will adopt these basic understandings of what public spheres are and how they function in democratic processes. More specifically, we will show how feminists have used a range of media in order to construct both a feminist public sphere as well as open entryways for women to the dominant masculine public sphere, thereby bringing women more fully into democratic participation in their societies.

Structural Constraints and Feminist Interventions

An essential starting point considering the relationship of media to women's and dominant public spheres is the question of who controls media. Lance Bennett et al. (2004) acknowledge that Habermas can be read as both an indictment of modern media as instruments of elite control and as a collection of gate-keepers who manage interactions among elites and broader publics. Making a specific connection between gender and media ownership, feminist historian Linda Kerber (1997) reminded us that the characteristic site of the emerging public sphere in eighteenth-century Europe was the political newspaper, which served as a mediator of public discussion. While men controlled the press and used it "to explain to each other how good republicans could retain their manhood while eschewing the patriarchal order," Kerber recognized that women of that time and place actively sought the means to achieve a "female public sphere" and participate in institution-building (1997: 189). Women's involvement at decision-making levels of larger media enterprises has always been miniscule in nearly every society, and ample research shows that such lack of access and control help to explain the dominance of men's values and interests, and women's enduring problems of invisibility and misrepresentation in media content the world over (Gallagher 1995; Byerly 2004b).

There has never been a time when ownership and control of large media organizations were more significant to democracy – or to women. As noted in Chapter 5, six enormous mixed conglomerates control the majority of publishing, film, and music companies, cable stations, television and radio networks, and other telecommunication industries in the world. Byerly (2004b) has observed that women have almost no place in either the ownership or top management levels of these corporations or their individual enterprises. The global reach of these media conglomerates means that audiences the world over can watch more ESPN sports, CNN and Fox/Sky news, and Hollywood movies than they can access in their own language and culture. They can also see advertisements for everything from luxury cars and perfumes to household cleansers. All media products emanating from "big" media have been accused of carrying a particular ideology – hyper-commercial, strongly Western and male, as earlier chapters explain at greater length. How should this highly significant gendered structural problem in large media industries be conceptualized in the light of women and the public sphere, and our search for a Model of Women's Media Action?

Pilar Riaño (1994) put forward the argument that if the connections between the media and women's participation in public arenas are to be understood, feminist media scholarship must go beyond consideration of problems in the content and structures of mainstream industries and instead (or at least as well as) consider women-generated media. She said that:

> . . . excessive emphasis placed on issues of access and equity of representation has silenced a more central structural question regarding the absence of voice of subordinated groups in the media. Participatory practices of media production have placed this issue at the center, defining themselves as spaces for grassroots communication, for the building of representations that foster communication of the others (of women, ethnic immigrants, minorities, and

homosexuals). These practices, therefore, challenge dominant representations and forms of communication. (Riaño 1994: 122)

Riaño's work is located within a small but significant literature emerging from Latin American and other feminist activists who make a case for women-created media as a means of giving women a voice and creating a feminist public sphere. Marta Lamas (1992) explains the ways in which the Mexican magazine *Debate Feminista* (Feminist Debate) connects feminist activists with the development of feminist theory in academia. Zoila Hernandez (1992) identifies the feminist strategy of gaining placement of feminist magazine supplements in large circulating mainstream dailies. Typically published monthly, these supplements are variously named *Mujer y Sociedad* (Peru), *La Doble Jornada* (Mexico), and *Nosotras* and *Lawray* (Bolivia). In India, Shabnam Virmani (2001) recounts the efforts of the Drishti Media Collective, of which she is a member, to use video as a networking tool so that women in small Indian villages can learn to use the technology to speak to each other, share experiences, and form self-help groups to deal with discrimination and other daily problems.

Another approach to women's media activism has been for women to establish their own media enterprises that are designed to increase women's access to the dominant public sphere. Byerly (1995) examined one such feminist-controlled media enterprise, the Women's Feature Service (WFS), based in New Delhi, pointing out the service's goals of increasing news flow from a progressive women's perspective in mainstream magazines, newspapers, and other media. WFS follows the format of development journalism by reporting on women's problems in developing nations within an historical context, foregrounding the solutions that women have developed to address those problems, and allowing both elite (educated, official) and nonelite (working-class, rural) women the space to voice their views and experiences.

Since the 1970s, women have undertaken a range of other activities intended to expand women's access to mainstream media, or to encourage women-controlled media programs. Among these is a range of evaluative activities aimed at revealing the way in which mainstream media represent women's experiences and concerns. These include projects sponsored by nongovernmental organizations such as the Global Media Monitoring Project, sponsored by the progressive group the World Association for Christian Communication. The WACC launched the GMMP in 1995, with the goal of monitoring and changing media around the world to improve gender representation (Ross 2004b). Published reports provide women media activists with the data that they need to lobby for changes in public and media industry policy, as well as to work with media managers who are open to improving their gender coverage (Gallagher 2001).

A Model of Women's Media Action

While the contours and objective details of women's media activism can be described by the literature reviewed above, we sought to obtain a subjective history of that activism through the work of those who engaged in it, so as to begin to analyze and theorize it. The Model of Women's Media Action (MWMA) posed here takes us a step closer to a well-developed theory of how this particular form of women's agency has functioned to advance feminist principles in effecting social change. The model, which begins to consider the range and purpose of these activities in an organized way, is based on the research that we described earlier. In analyzing the interviews and written answers of respondents in our study, we found that their activities had followed four distinct patterns that we have called paths. The metaphor of the path suits the present research on women's media activism well. A path connotes direction, purpose, and movement. It embodies the notion of a journey that begins in one place and ends in another. These characteristics reflect all or major parts of what participants in the study told us about their experiences, knowledge, and lessons from working as feminist media activists.

Four paths – described below – suggest the organizing mechanism for women's media activism. These allow us to show how specific kind of activities helped women to gain access to the mainstream media or to reach smaller groups of other like-minded women over a period of some three decades. These activities, collectively, we argue, formed feminist public spheres both within and across nations that can be understood as extending women's democratic participation. Although the four paths are distinct one from another, as the discussion will show, it is important to keep several things in mind. The first is that while most women in our study indicated that they followed a particular path more than another, those who engaged in media activism for many years tended to have followed several. We categorized them by the path that they most emphasized in their information to us. Second, we have designated paths as first, second, third, and fourth arbitrarily, to denote one from another rather than to suggest a linear development, or a hierarchy of importance. We assume that all are of equal and complementary importance in advancing women's ability to communicate publicly. Third, nor is any chronology of development suggested among the four paths. In fact, all appear to have operated simultaneously over several decades of time.

The first path – which we call "politics to media" – is represented by feminists' decision to begin to use media as some part of their feminist political work. In other words, these women moved from simply being "feminist activists" to producing media products of some kind. Motivation to learn how to "do media" included a desire to publicly articulate a stand on a specific woman-related issue, to help other women to speak, or to mobilize a constituency (women or both women and men). For still others, it was a desire to celebrate or reinforce women's experience and culture. Women following the first path were not trained as media professionals, but they acquired skills that enabled them to publish newsletters, produce radio or television programs, construct Internet websites, or "do" some other form of media. Some who pursued this path were working with feminist groups as well as other politically oriented groups whose goals they saw to intersect with those of feminism.

For example, peacemaking motivated several respondents to obtain media skills. In the Netherlands, Janne Poort-van Eeden serves as the education officer for a pilot program, Women Peacemakers and the Media, at the International Fellowship of Reconciliation, an inter-faith organization. Poort-Van Eeden[6] has produced several video films for the project, depicting women in India, Hungary, Zimbabwe, and elsewhere engaged in peacemaking activities expressing their views about society and goals for peace. In Colombia, Angela Cuevas de Dolmetsch, an attorney and a member of Consensus of Women of the Peace Boat, wanted to bring women formally into negotiations between the government and guerrillas toward ending the two-decade-old Colombian civil war. Cuevas decided to host a weekly women's public affairs television and radio program called *Looking at the World through Women's Eyes*, to help break the silence about women's reality and to help women enter public life. She also encourages women journalists to "show gender solidarity to other women" so that women's opinions can begin to change society through the media.

The second path – "media profession to politics" – describes the strategy followed by women employed in media industries who decided to use their vantage point as insiders to expand women-related content, or to reform the industry's policies to improve women's professional status. Women who followed this path are media professionals. They were formally trained in a media profession – in news reporting, radio or television production, film or video production, or some other kind of media work. At some point in their career paths, they developed a strong identity (and perhaps involvement) with feminism and began to explore ways of increasing information about women in media content. Some also sought ways of making company policies more egalitarian. For example, Lubna Yousif Ali, in Sudan, who has been a newspaper and magazine journalist since 1978, said that her goals are "always to keep women informed about their rights." As the editor of a women's page for many years, and later a writer for the *Azza* monthly women's magazine, she has published articles on voting laws (enacted in the 1970s), women's illiteracy and educational programs to meet them, female genital mutilation, divorce, economics, and what other women in the world are doing politically. Yousif Ali is active in two journalism unions (one of them for women) and the Arabs Union. She also takes on independent projects to expand women's understanding of media, such as coordinating a major media workshop for women in December 2003.

Women who follow the third path – "advocate change agent" – used a strategy of pressuring media to improve treatment of women in one or more ways. The outside advocate's path often entails research and analysis about women and media, including publication of reports or articles, or it may mobilize a constituency to write letters or take some other action. For at least 20 years, Margaret Gallagher, an independent media researcher based in Paris and London, said that she has been "driven by two broad preoccupations" as an outside advocate. She identified the first as the growing commercialization in the media and its subsequent influence on audiences. For this, she has tried to bring about changes in national and international policy that expand citizens' (including women's) rights to communicate. She identified the second preoccupation as an unequal distribution of resources (economic, political, and informational) among social groups, including women. She sees the unequal gender balance of power as "primordial – something embedded in all other inequalities (e.g., ethnic and political)." Gallagher's media activist work is too extensive to chronicle here, but it can be exemplified by her recent work overseeing the third round of the Global Media Monitoring Project (described earlier), in 2005. Gallagher's role is to compile the data as it comes in from all over the world and publish it for use by women in their efforts to make changes in media. Another woman who follows the third path is Colleen Lowe Morna, director of Gender Links, a nongovernmental organization in South Africa, that conducted the first Gender and Media Baseline Study in her nation in 2003. The study revealed (among other things) that black women journalists were substantially underrepresented in the profession, while white females had done well. Lowe Morna's group now works through mainstream editors and journalists' groups to raise hiring and representational issues. The group has also begun to conduct trainings on race and gender issues for media organizations' (still mostly) white male members.

The fourth path – "women's media enterprises" – allows women the maximum control over message production and distribution. Enterprises illustrated by this path include book and magazine publishing, syndicated radio programming, women's news agencies, and independent film and video companies. In India, for example, Shree Venkatram left a high-ranking editorial position with an English daily newspaper in 1996 after she became weary of what she saw to be a drift toward celebrity and superficiality in news. With funds from the USA-based MacArthur Foundation, she established Unnati Features, a women's news agency specializing in stories on environment, health, development, nutrition, and other stories of interest to women. Venkatram says that she and her pool of writers share the goal of serving the popular press with these stories, thereby reaching mainstream audiences. Believing that all journalists should understand how to see gender in their assignments, Unnati Features also sponsors an annual competition on a gender-related news theme for high-school-aged students, encouraging both boys and girls to enter. By contrast, Women's eNews, a nonprofit Internet-based international news service headquartered in the USA, sees women as its main audience. Veteran journalist Rita Henley Jensen created the service in 2000, under sponsorship of the National Organization for Women. Two years later, she went independent and remains the company's president, editor-in-chief, and publisher. The service operates by using feminist news correspondents around the world. Jensen says that Women's eNews was born out of her realization that women could no longer rely on newspapers to report on women's success, that "we had to measure our success by our own performance." She believes that "the white male hierarchy has to be told – in no uncertain terms – that their gender and race bias is destroying the institution they love [because these] fail to promote and retain women and do not include women in their news columns; they ignore issues of concern to women and that is reflected in low readership among women." She adds that this same hierarchy fails to see that "black and Latino Americans, as well as other people of color, know full well how they treat minority employees and therefore have little to no confidence in the accuracy of the news published. And, if they do not reach women and minorities, they will eventually go out of business."

Jensen's words are a fitting transition to the succeeding chapters and a fuller exploration of these four paths and the experiences of those who follow them. Women's media activism has typically not operated narrowly as only a gendered project but, rather, as one that embraces a comprehensive sense of liberation. In the real world, gender is always aligned with other signifiers of power, and media activism carried on by the women who we interviewed illustrated this time and time again.

Notes

1 See the Isis International website (www.isiswomen.org/advocacy/media/index. html).

2 For a longer discussion of the meaning of "feminism" and "feminist," see Chapter 1.

3 See www.un.org/womenwatch/daw/beijing/platform/, (accessed August 18, 2004).

4 See www.reclaimthemedia.org/stories.php?story=05/02/01/8735312 (accessed April 1, 2005).

5 A number of feminist scholars have examined the communicative routes by which a new language (and analysis) of violence against women emerged and traveled. See, for example, Patricia L. N. Donat and John D'Emilio's "A feminist redefinition of rape" (1992); Carolyn M. Byerly's "An agenda for teaching the news coverage of rape" (1994), and Diana E. H. Russell and Roberta A. Harmes's edited volume, *Femicide in Global Perspective* (2001).

6 The women media activists quoted in this and other chapters participated in our study between March 2003 and June 2004.

7

First Path: Politics to Media

This has largely been my work, which is to show my and other people's films. We have worked a lot with films by women, for women, trying to create the women's space . . . We also work with Dalits[1] and tribal communities. In India, all three need that creation of space.

Gargi Sen,[2] Magic Lantern Foundation, New Delhi, India

All women who engage in media activism are politically motivated; that is, they want their work to contribute to a world in which women's influence shapes everything from culture to social policy. How activists go about securing a larger space for women's voices using media depends on the strategy (i.e., approach) that they adopt in their work. As discussed in Chapter 6, we have conceptualized these strategies as "paths." In this and succeeding chapters, we use a system of four paths to organize the findings from our study, whose goal was to reveal the nature of women's media activism through the experiences of those who have practiced it. The Model of Women's Media Action, comprising feminist tenets associated with women's right to communicate and participate in their societies, enables us to analyze one form of women's agency in social transformation.

As described at the end of Chapter 6, we discerned four main paths in the information provided to us by women who participated in the study. We have numbered these paths for easier reference; however, we reiterate that no hierarchy of importance is intended. Nor do the paths' numbers signify a linear order in their evolution. Indeed, all four paths have coexisted and served to mutually reinforce each other during the three decades under consideration, from the 1970s to 2004. In addition, a number of feminists whom we interviewed indicated that they had pursued more than one path, particularly in cases where their media activism took place over a continuous period of time and/or if they moved from one organization to another. In analyzing the various forms of activism that our participants pursued, we have situated each woman (and her work) on the path that she most emphasized in responses to our research questions. While this will not provide a comprehensive picture of a given woman's work, it should provide a clearer analysis of one trajectory of that work and allow her work to be compared and contrasted with that of others who pursued the same path.

The goals of this chapter and the three that follow are, therefore, to explicate these four paths – "politics to media," "media profession to politics," "advocate change agent," and "women's media enterprises" – through an analysis of the work of those who have traveled them. Throughout the chapters, we use participants' own descriptions of their work to reveal how they contributed to the construction of a feminist public sphere and/or to the construction of a feminist component in the dominant public sphere. We attempt to locate participants' media activism in the historical, national, and cultural contexts in which it occurred. The literature on global feminism has shown that feminists share many of the same goals, regardless of national contexts, because many categorical problems – for example, secondary legal status, poverty, rape and incest, wife beating, and lack of access to education and health care – are experienced by women everywhere. The particular ways in which these problems manifest themselves, however, may differ considerably depending on local customs, religious beliefs, family relationships, socioeconomic (class) relations, historical, and other factors. Women's political responses to their problems, and the media activism growing out of those responses, have also varied accordingly.

Characteristics of the First Path

This chapter is concerned with what we call the first path: "politics to media." This path is has been followed by women who were not trained as media professionals but who learned how to "do" some kind of media in order to communicate about specific issues related to women. Women following the first path acquired the skills to write news stories, publish newsletters, produce radio or television programs, make films, construct Internet websites, or "do" some other form of media. There are a number of other shared characteristics among the 18 women from eight different nations in our study associated with this path. First, as mentioned, their media skills were self-taught or gained through other informal means, rather than through formal training in media professions. Second, their motivation to engage in media activism was a specific outgrowth of their feminist political work, which they believed needed a wider audience. Specific motivation differed from woman to woman. In some cases, this was a desire to help women (themselves and others) talk publicly about a specific issue; in other cases, motivation was in wanting to use media as an organizing tool; for example, reflecting back upon women's political gains in order to mobilize for additional ones. For still others, it was a desire to celebrate or reinforce women's identity and culture. Third, in most cases, women following this path carried on their media activism through independent or alternative (i.e., noncommercial, nonmainstream) media.

Fourth, all 18 of the women we interviewed described doing media activism as only one component of a larger collection of feminist-oriented activities that they carried on in their lives. In other words, they also continued work such as lobbying for new laws, raising money for services or facilities beneficial to women, or organizing public events to educate others about women's issues. Most women following the first path whom we interviewed, from both developed and developing nations, said that they tried in their media activism to show how women's oppression related to other oppressions, such as poverty and class, race, war (and the making of peace), or gay and lesbian identity. We found the goal of using media to generate a more complex understanding of overlapping oppressions to be shared by all our women informants (as each chapter will show), particularly with respect to shaping a feminist component in the dominant public sphere. In fact, the ability to bring overlapping concerns into a common discourse was often made possible through women holding membership in more than one organization, or through conducting their feminist media activism within the context of a multi-issue organization, some including both male and female members.

In other ways, women following the first path varied considerably in characteristics. They reported using a range of media – film, radio, television, the Internet, newspapers – in their work. They were multi-generational, ranging in age from the early twenties to the sixties, and they came from all over the globe (as indicated by the eight nations that these 18 women represent). Some women had conducted their media activism through women-only organizations, while others conducted it in organizations that included both women and men. Women who worked in collaboration with male colleagues reported doing their work in multiple-issue organizations that integrated an analysis of sexism with other forms of oppression. Quantitative data from the study showed that women who followed the first path had the widest range of goals for their work.

The following 18 women (listed alphabetically) followed the first path, "politics to media":

Red Chidgey, UK

Angela Cuevas de Dolmetsch, Colombia

Dorothy Dean, USA

Deepa Dhanraj, India

Jay Hartling, Canada

Ulrike Helwerth, Germany

Katherine (K. T.) Jarmul, USA

Jill Lawrence, USA

Anne Lewis, USA

Anjali Mathur, India

Laxmi Murthy, India

Janne Poort-van Eeden, the Netherlands

Moira Rankin, USA

Chelsia Rice, USA

Boden Sandstrom, USA

Sanjana, India

Gargi Sen, India

Claudia Wulz, Belgium

Women who followed the first path emerged from feminist political circles that were instrumental in defining new issues in women's lives, or that were bringing a new perspective to an issue that had been around for years. These include issues particularly seeking a dialogue – perhaps even a debate – among women. Study participants described their work as wanting to reach women with their message, and some sought media specifically targeting a female audience. These kinds of statements reveal the central role of media activism in creating a space for women to share, analyze, and otherwise address their everyday experiences. In some cases, the goals would be information sharing and the building of community; in others, some kind of action. Women following the first path stated the widest divergence of goals for their work. In other words, they were fairly evenly distributed around purposes such as increasing media content about women, mobilizing feminist activism, helping to connect feminist issues to others, and informing women about their rights. By contrast, they were strongly united in their belief that their work had helped to expand media content around women's lives and feminist issues. There was also strong agreement that their media activism had helped to raise public consciousness about women, from a feminist perspective.

Starting Women's Media[3]

As feminism emerged in the United States in the early 1970s – a period that has been called second-wave feminism[4] – **Dorothy Dean**[5] was one of many feminist media activists using small-scale publications and women's music as organizing tools. Dean worked initially with the Milwaukee (Wisconsin) Women's Coalition, to publish the newsletter *Amazon*, which told women how to do things for themselves (such as take care of their own cars). The newsletter published sporadically as members found the money, and it ended when they could no longer afford it, Dean said. She and her friend Debbie St. Charles then started a women's music production company, bringing in feminist singers such as Chris Williamson, Margie Adam, and Meg Christian to give concerts in the Milwaukee area. They did all of the work required to put on the concerts: scheduling the groups, publicizing the appearances, and managing the sound systems and lights during performances. Dorothy Dean saw a central role for women's music in helping women to gain a feminist conscience and to bond politically. Olivia Records, a national feminist recording company, was forming, and Dean wanted to help promote it. The list of women's musicians that she began to compile expanded into a magazine called *Paid My Dues*, which Dean composed using an IBM typewriter and an old-fashioned waxer. She said the magazine published "as many interviews as I could get" with women musicians and other others who had something to say to a feminist audience. In 1973, Dean met and suggested to a founder of the Daughters Press that it would be useful to call a conference on feminist publishing. At that event, Dean had a flash of insight:

> It struck me that there were two major categories into which just about everyone there fit. For some, feminist publishing was a way to come out as a feminist or as a feminist lesbian. The other group was women who were publishing out of a need to communicate. I fell into the second category.

Dorothy Dean left women's media activism a few years later to enter electoral politics and today is the Milwaukee County Treasurer; but she assesses the media activism carried on by herself and others in early second-wave feminism as essential to creating "a climate that legitimized and helped open doors – not for ourselves because we were too radical, but for other women to get into the media."

Feminist media activist Donna Allen, who founded Women's Institute for Freedom of the Press in Washington, DC, in 1972, wrote extensively about the role of grassroots women's media – such as that in which Dean and possibly thousands of other women engaged during the 1970s in the USA – in women's liberation before her death in 1999. "A radical feminist analysis of mass media," a treatise written by Donna Allen and her daughter Dana Densmore (reprinted 2002), locates women's ability to mobilize politically in having their own media. The authors argue that women's media are the only mechanisms by which women can speak to their own interests, arouse righteous anger in other women, and mobilize them to action. In addition, they offered one of the earliest feminist political economy critiques of mass media, pointing out that men's ownership and control had cut women's lives and experiences out of important dialogues necessary for women to enter into their own self-governance. The establishment of larger-scale women-owned media enterprises as a response to the limits of male-owned mainstream media will be explored in depth in Chapter 10; here we emphasize the important parallel role played by the small-scale publications such as Dean and her allies created to develop feminist dialogues among women, and that women today continue to use in varied settings.

For example, **Chelsia Rice**,[6] chair of the Women's Resource Center at Portland Community College, in Portland, Oregon, USA, said that in 2002, she launched a newsletter called *The F-Word* to write about water conservation and other current issues from a feminist perspective. Rice believes that "the voice of feminist media needs to be amplified" because women's rights the world over are being lost." Rice has a clear vision for the role of feminist media activism, and she sees its connection to other liberation movements.

Clearly, media activism has perpetuated many of the rights that women have today, including the right to choose [i.e., abortion rights], which is in such jeopardy today ... Feminist media activism ties in closely with the civil rights movement [for racial equality] and the human rights agenda.

Taking Women's Movements into News

Rice's commitment to the politics of women's media activism finds its counterpart in other nations. **Ulrike Helwerth**,[7] in Berlin, Germany, today an information officer for the National Council of German Women's Organizations and chair of a German network of women journalists, said she is a "sociologist who became a journalist by chance" when she was in Latin America studying some years ago. Becoming involved with Latin American feminists, she found herself writing about her activities for German media. "I felt a clear mission," she said. "I wanted to give women and their discrimination and suffering a voice and a platform, but also articulate their demands, successes, and power." Helwerth says that media activism (her own and others') helped to get former taboo subjects into the mainstream, especially domestic and sexual violence, and homosexuality. She sees the increased public visibility for these issues, created by media activism, as something that has contributed to better laws; for example, against marital rape. Another impact of women's media activism for women in Germany, she believes, has been women's advancement in the journalistic workforce, where today women are nearly at par (45 percent) with men. Helwerth recognizes that there's more to do: demand a bigger space in the news, an end to stereotypic portrayals that persist, and more women in decision-making roles in media industries. The League of Women Journalists, which she chairs, has tackled some of these, moving toward the goal of what she calls greater "gender democracy." The League sponsors a training program on gender issues for young journalists, a mentoring project that pairs entry-level and veteran female journalists, and an annual award that goes to young journalists for gender-sensitive reporting.

Working in the genres of both print journalism and documentary film, a number of Indian feminists since the 1970s have sought to use their work in the service of social change.[8] Their work exemplifies a shared commitment to connect gender oppression to other signifiers of power, including social class, race, ethnicity, and sexual identity, and to use their journalism and films to raise consciousness, promote public dialogues, and organize constituencies to demand new social policies or other changes. **Anjali Mathur**,[9] in New Mumbai, and **Laxmi Murthy**,[10] in New Delhi, both sought writing careers in response to their political activism. Mathur says that she became a militant feminist in the mid-1970s, after she joined the Communist Party of India, a party that follows a Marxist–Leninist philosophy.

In that capacity, she set up organizations of working women in Bombay and of Dalit women in nearby Pune. When Mathur was facing arrest in 1976, after Prime Minister Indira Gandhi declared a state of emergency – one aspect being to curtail leftist activities – she went underground and assumed a new identity. When she reemerged a few years later, she decided to pursue journalism, working first as a freelancer for *The Indian Express*, a national mainstream daily, where she moved up into editorial positions.

In 1983, Mathur became part of a core group of feminist journalists in Bombay to form the Women and Media Group in order to discuss issues relating to gender in the profession, and, later, to act as a political pressure group. Mathur and her colleagues – many of whose stories are told in the course of this book[11] – had a range of successes, including getting a television program called "It's a Women's World" withdrawn from the government channel Doordarshan, after protests and letters led by Women in Media argued that the prime-time program reinforced stereotypes of women. Mathur and the remnants of Women and Media would reemerge in 2002 to form the national activist organization Network of Women in Media in India (NWMI), a group composed of 13 chapters that address labor issues related to women (e.g., wages, the shift to contract employment working conditions) but also larger concerns such as the adverse impact of globalization processes on women. With funds from UNESCO,[12] Mathur's own contribution has been to establish a website for the organization (www.nwmindia.org), and she has been successful in knitting the network together, reaching out to a wide international audience, and providing a resource for women journalists. A similar initiative was undertaken a few years ago by Mathur and her journalist husband, Kiron Kasbekar, who formed an online media organization, the Information Company, Ltd., to promote issues and groups that they have spent their lives advancing.

Laxmi Murthy was working as a full time volunteer at the Women's Centre, in Mumbai, in the mid-1980s, assisting women in crisis, when she became involved with campaigns to protest what she calls "obscene representations of women in advertising." She and her colleagues painted "Women Not for Sale" slogans over objectionable posters or tore them down. This work continued with the group Saheli after she moved to Delhi a few years later through similar campaigns against "indecent representations of women." Saheli members explored and debated various understandings for obscenity and indecency,[13] focusing particularly on beauty pageants and other ways in which women's bodies were exploited (typically for the financial gain of men's industries) – topics still under discussion by

Saheli members, she said. Murthy began to write about these and other feminist issues as a freelancer in the late 1980s, and in 2000 she joined the Women's Feature Service, an international women-owned news agency in New Delhi, as an editor. The WFS, which is discussed at greater length in Chapter 8, gave Murthy a chance to promote the circulation of women's issues to mainstream media. Today, Murthy writes for several groups and media, including the activist India Resource Centre and www.infochangeindia.org, an online daily news outlet that specializes in development news.

Generating Dialogue through Film: An Indian Story

Deepa Dhanraj,[14] **Gargi Sen,**[15] and **Sanjana,**[16] whose stories are recounted here, have all worked in male–female film collectives with strong political orientations. They represent three generations of women with a common purpose in their use of film. All came from educated, privileged backgrounds, have traveled, speak several languages, and have chosen lives that seek to benefit those in lower classes or across classes. India has a distinctive, complex class system, the legacy of a caste system that was legally abolished in the 1950s, but which continues informally through kinship and entrenched customary practices, especially in rural India. Feminists once again became involved in the public debate about the plight of the former untouchable caste members (who had assumed the name Dalit, meaning "oppressed") and other lower classes reemerged in public debate in 1989 after a government decision to provide a "reservation system" of representation in government for "backward classes." Anupama Rao (2003: 5), who has chronicled women's relationship to the caste system, reminds us that "the symbolic economies of gender and sexuality and the material reality of the economic dispossession of dalit women" need to be viewed together in order to understand the complexities of today's Indian society. Evidence of this complexity in women's narratives included a strong self-consciousness of class-belonging, together with a desire to transcend class and be useful in the advancement of less advantaged groups.

Bangalore-based filmmaker Deepa Dhanraj can't talk about her own work in feminist media activism without placing it strategically inside Indian history. The 1970s have been characterized as a watershed in the history of the women's movement in India (I. Sen 2004). Women's disillusion with government policies that had failed – failed to bring greater

equality to women in employment, family and other institutions; to address
family violence, women's health, and sexuality; or to distribute resources
more equitably for rural women – was further fueled by environmental
destruction (especially deforestation) and abuse of women by authorities
(as described below). Deforestation had mobilized women in what became
known as the Chipko Movement – the term "chipko" derived from the
Hindi word for tree-hugging, which formed the central strategy that women
employed *en masse* in order to prevent indiscriminate forest felling by commercial interests (I. Sen 2004: 193–5). However, the autonomous Indian
women's movement[17] would be ignited by two high-profile rape cases in
the late 1970s, one in Mathura and the other in Maya Tyagi, where women
were raped by police while in custody.[18] These became what Dhanraj called
"flash points" for her and many others. Deepa Dhanraj had completed
studies in English literature and become interested in the possibilities of
using film to document the feminist movements that were erupting around
her. Teaching herself the fundamentals of using projectors, cutting, and
editing, Dhanraj, her husband Navroze Contractor, and two female friends,
Abha Bhaiya and Meera Rao, formed a small production collective that they
called Yugantan. They turned their cameras toward the labor organizing
that was occurring among women domestic workers, in the tobacco industry and elsewhere, with the support of women from more privileged backgrounds. She said:

> The idea was to capture this stuff on film and demonstrate really what made
> it happen. What was women's agency about in those situations? These films
> could then feed back into the movement as tools for further mobilization,
> organization or discussion. We saw our role in '79 and '80 really as hand-
> maidens to the movement, if you like. We were going to be the communica-
> tion foot soldiers.

They made a series of five documentaries in various local Indian languages,
using funds from a German donor. Today, Dhanraj particularly remembers
the tobacco workers' film, *Tambaku Chakila Oob Aali* (whose title refers to
the spontaneous combustion that occurs when heat builds up in stacked
leaves), in which women in the factory assisted in the filmmaking process.
She describes the working conditions that these laborers experienced as
"hellholes," as there were no regulations on safety, hours, or wages. Thousands of women each day pounded dirty, pesticide-covered tobacco leaves
by hand, with dust rising in thick clouds that they breathed in. When a

worker was hired, she was given unlimited amounts of free chewing tobacco to develop her immunity to nicotine. In addition, some managers demanded sexual favors in return for employment. Finally, ill health and anger, fueled by consciousness-raising sessions, convinced the women tobacco workers to unionize and demand contracts that specified better wages and a better working environment. Dhanraj's film captured the story in stark detail, in the voices of the women themselves. Once the film was finished, she and her collaborators held a screening one night for the tobacco workers in order to show them their own history:

> When we brought it back, we had to hold the screening on the highway, because 3,500 women showed up. We took that 16 mm projector and showed it, as women sat all around the screen. It was fantastic.

Several things were accomplished in this and similar projects, she believes. First, was the ability of those involved (and other audiences later) to see the process of their unionization struggle. Second, was the "business of [affirming] women saying no" to abuse, to sexual favors, to exploitation. Third, women were able to see a different role for themselves as citizens. "What the union activity did was give them a whole different persona, a whole different identity, a political identity, really."

In the years since, Dhanraj has created a series of training films, under government contract, to promote girls' education and other aspects of women's status. One far-reaching project has encouraged Indian women's emerging role in local government. The state of Karnataka had initiated legal reforms in the 1980s, and then adopted a "reservation" system whereby 25 percent of the local council (panchayat) seats were set aside for women. The Indian Parliament expanded that reservation to 33 percent for all of India's local councils with passage of the Panchayat Raj Act in 1993 (Jain 1996). The "reservation system," as it is described, had brought 330,000 women into office by January 1994, and millions more since then. Feminist scholar Devaki Jain (1996) found that the sheer number of women involved in these councils has begun to transform local governance. Slower to emerge, however, has been a feminist consciousness among most of these newly elected officials, few of whom have had previous political experience.[19] Dhanraj's film *Taking Office* tells the stories of five women looking back after their first term in office and assessing how the experience changed their lives. These and other training films have recently been used in conjunctions with high-tech, multimedia sessions beamed via satellite from studios out into villages to hundreds of women at a time. Sessions combine a screening followed by a studio panel comprising government, political, and feminist leaders, who receive phone-in questions from village audiences. The questions that women ask are pointed and probing, and the experience has energized women's interest in government:

> The response from the women was so electric . . . I started to think that this was a more efficient way to work because you know who your target groups are. You're working with a very particular agenda. At the end of that time, you know [nearly] a thousand women have seen it.

Gargi Sen and two friends formed the Magic Lantern Foundation in 1989 to promote cultural diversity and human rights through films. Based in New Delhi, the Foundation's work encompasses the production of their members' own films (including Sen's), as well as films from their network and the distribution of films by other Indian filmmakers. Produced in English, Hindi, and other Indian languages, films take up subjects aimed at provoking public dialogue about rights, gender, sexuality, and a range of other issues. The quote that opens this chapter, drawn from Sen's interview, captures the clarity of understanding that she (and her colleagues) are contributing to public discourse through their work The Foundation specifically connects women's experience within larger campaigns for human rights, particularly in indigenous communities; for example, the forest rights movement in the Himalayan region of Saharanpur, in the state of Uttar Pradesh; and the Dalit movement for an end to discrimination against the former untouchable caste. Working in documentary format, the Foundation's members initially produced one film each year, showing them all over India in conjunction with discussions about the issues involved:

> We are very serious at Magic Lantern that you don't just show a film. You make a dossier of information which you must have in order to reply to questions. You introduce the films and present the context [for their issues]. Otherwise film has no meaning and is just like television.

Sen reflects on her personal breakthroughs that led her to political work through media activism. It all began with her dissatisfaction with the options:

> In India, we live a life, traditionally, from the upper castes and upper classes which teaches us that we are superior and there are inferior beings. For

instance, most of us have servants at home who do not eat on the same plates, on the same tables, don't use the same space. It has always bothered me, even in my own home.

Though privileged, her liberal mother and socialist father had also been politically active and provided a model for her own drive to transcend class and be "useful." She went "idealistically" into rural villages through service organizations and began to understand the problems of rural India through its people who, to her surprise, accepted her – her smoking, her manner of dressing, even her upper-class background. "That's India," she says, "Everyone knows the caste you come from. The names give it all away." Sen began to incorporate the issues and lessons learned from India's rural poor into her films:

> You really have to look at diversities, what are the different voices, what are our strengths . . . As feminists we've talked a lot about creating spaces. We create spaces [with our films] . . . The next challenge is what do we do with the space?

Particularly "in the women's sphere some very interesting things have happened," she says. Indian feminist documentary filmmakers, whose work Magic Lantern Foundation now distributes, include politically taboo subjects, such as the rights of women sex workers to organize. *Tales of the Nightfairies*, by Shohini Ghosh, treats their organizing as a human rights issue, confronting issues of morality around sex work. Sen says:

> This film is a celebration of life. These women talk about pleasure. This is the first time I was confronted with the discourse of pleasure. These women [sex workers] refuse to be victims. They said they have fun and enjoy sex. They said, "Okay, my mother used to sleep with one man and he took care of the family. I sleep with many and I take care of my family." The filmmaker is very much a part of the film, the way she's constructed it.

Sanjana belongs to a media collective called Pedestrian Pictures, a group of women and men in their twenties, with membership ranging between five to seven individuals at any given time. Based in Bangalore, the group formed in 2001 in response to several national and international crises, including the religious-based rioting in the state of Gujarat (India), the US invasion of Iraq, the continued impact of economic and cultural globalization on India, India's emerging alliance with Israel, and an increase in the numbers of acid attacks on women. She and her colleagues had several goals. First, they wanted to expand cross-gender public dialogues, through which men could speak to women's issues and women could speak to economic and political issues: "There is a consciousness of women's issues that is important, but there is a very limited consciousness that women also have things to say about globalization, for example. Their views are no less inferior to men's." Second, they wanted to use media to let women and indigenous groups working in political and human rights campaigns speak publicly for themselves. Lastly, they wanted to begin to connect the issues and actors among movements. For example:

> We went into about 16 villages in the north of Karnataka [State] with our projection equipment and films. The idea was really to start to get women to acknowledge that violence is an everyday part of their lives. And we saw the impact that made . . . More recently, we've being using film media to connect movements. We screened films about the Adivasi[20] movements [around different parts of India]. We felt they were able to catch on, that language wasn't an issue. They were able to say yes . . . here is a movement, which is very similar to ours, and we need to network. Networking is something that we never expected to be this positive or this strong. So, that is something Pedestrian Pictures has been able to do.

Short documentaries on specific issues "let the people talk for themselves": "There is a key person in the movement who articulates the positions well, and that interview forms the backbone of the film. A lot of the content is also developing understanding about what the group is doing." Like the community "screenings" that Deepa Dhanraj and Gargi Sen described for their respective groups, Sanjana and her colleagues show a film and then stay to hold discussions with the audience. Sanjana received what she calls a "crash course" in a college program in mass media, but her skills in digital videography have been honed through her work with Pedestrian Pictures. She and her colleagues rent out their equipment to other community groups for a small fee, but most of their activities are funded through their own income from full- or part-time jobs.

In summer 2004, the documentary *Burnt but not Destroyed*, directed by Sanjana and her colleague Deepu, was completed and screened around India in order to mobilize public response to the failure of government to respond to acid attacks against women. The film focuses on the strength of acid attack survivors who want their assailants brought to justice. The film was developed in collaboration with the Campaign and Struggle Against Acid Attacks on Women (CSAAAW), a Bangalore-based group, which has petitioned the state of Karnataka's Minister for Women and Child Development for action (see *The Hindu* 2003). In addition, this and other groups are seeking greater regulation of corrosive acid to limit its availability.[21]

Leading Peace and Social Justice

Moving across continents, peace activist and educator **Janne Poort-van Eeden**,[22] based in Alkmaar in the Netherlands, both produces videos on women and peace and trains women in developing nations to create their own media in the service of peace-action, through her work with the International Fellowship of Reconciliation (IFOR). Poort-van Eeden, a former teacher, learned to produce radio programs as a freelancer when her children were young. Several organizations and grants later, she found herself producing materials and radio programs for children on consumer boycotts targeted at nations at war or committing human rights violations (e.g., the apartheid government of South Africa, the Angola government). She turned her freelance work toward global issues and peace education before joining IFOR in 1997 as the education officer for the Women Peacemakers Program. A self-taught videographer, Poort-van Eeeden's 20-minute, English-language videos emphasize the work that women are doing to build peace in Europe, Asia, and Africa through nonviolence education. For example, her 60-minute documentary *Asian Women Speak Out* shows the ways in which women in Sri Lanka, Bangladesh, India, and Nepal are confronting violence against women. The 20-minute documentary *Building the Decade for a Culture of Peace and Nonviolence* allows participants in the Asian Girls Peace Camp, in Nepal, to talk about peace. And, most recently, she completed work on *Nonviolence for the Brave*, a half-hour educational video on how to organize what she calls a "gender-sensitive training program." In addition, Poort-van Eeden gives workshops to teach women the basics of developing their own grassroots training materials on nonviolence, as well as how to gain greater access to mainstream media with their messages.

Poort-van Eeden believes that media activism helps to circulate "values often considered to be female, like caring, nonviolence, being of service, loving" to counter prevalent values focused on gaining power, economic strength, and saving face. She advocates developing "indicators for a culture of nonviolence and promoting those through the media."

Several themes related to women and social justice have occupied the work of award-winning independent documentary filmmaker **Anne Lewis**,[23] of Austin, Texas (USA). During her two-decade long association with the Appalshop arts and educational center in Whitesburg, Kentucky, Lewis says that she tried to make films that "respect the dignity and power of women." Lewis's films show complex relationships between gender and issues of violence, labor, economics, and environmental degradation, as well as the social movements that address these. They have been shown on the PBS program *Point of View* (POV), and are used in college classrooms to educate, and by labor unions and community organizations throughout the USA to mobilize citizen action. The 1991 film *Fast Food Women* looked at women's struggles to raise families on minimum wage jobs with no benefits. *Belinda* (1992) was a story about an AIDS advocate who advocated a collective response to the disease unfettered by homophobia, racism, fear, or ignorance. Lewis's years of living in the coal-mining regions of Kentucky and Southwest Virginia enabled her to develop working relationships with local residents and to tell their stories in her films. The 1995 feature-length film *Justice in the Coal Fields* explored the impact on the local community of the United Mine Workers's strike against the Pittston Coal Company, and *Evelyn Williams* (1995) related the story of a coal-miner's daughter and wife, mother of nine children, domestic worker and community organizer, whose awareness of race and class oppression led her to a lifetime of activism. Lewis's recent 60-minute film *Shelter* tells the story of the US women's shelter movement against domestic violence through the experiences of five families who sought safety and new lives in their local women's shelter.

Presently a lecturer at the University of Texas, Lewis belongs to a local labor union and, in her creative life, is affiliated with the Women's Film Association, Reel Women, and the Austin Film Society. The last of these was her sponsor for two recent Texas-based films, *Ya Basta,* about Texas women's labor history, and *High Stakes,* about the high stakes testing of elementary-school children. Lewis says that she turned to documentary filmmaking in order to "tell the truth" about social justice in relation to class, race, gender, the environment, health, education, and other issues. She sees a long future for women's media activism to expand funding and distribution of independent media, open more doors for women in media, and try to improve what she calls the "truly pitiful" coverage of working-class, African American, and Latino women.

Feminists' use of independent documentary film is complemented by their media activism in radio. British feminist media scholar Caroline Mitchell (2004: 158) describes radio as a "medium that is particularly accessible and pertinent to women," as it has long been a companion to them in their work at home, driving in their cars, and other daily routines. In addition, she says, women who have worked in radio have long been aware that it is a more sympathetic medium because it allows the voice (rather than the appearance) to dominate. Thus, Mitchell chronicles the long list of ways in which feminists since the 1960s have formed relationships with radio – on the air, as producers, as writers, and even as owners – in order to take feminism onto the public airwaves and, ironically, back into women's private sphere of the personal (Mitchell 2004: 161). Citing Lisa McLaughlin (1993), she calls for women-made media to be grounded in a feminist theory of the public sphere, including the introduction of oppositional discourses.

The research on which this book is based has shown that feminists' affinity for radio has been international. These next examples show various ways in which several generations of feminists in their respective nations of Colombia, Canada, Belgium, and the USA have used radio to advance women's culture and political visions. In the process, they have tried to stir public awareness and discourse not only about gender, but also race, culture, lesbianism, and other issues.

War is a form of violence that has moved women to media activism, as we saw earlier in the example of Janne Poort-van Eeden's work in video. Using community radio (and television) to bring women into peace negotiations has also motivated **Angela Cuevas de Dolmetsch**,[24] an attorney and peace activist in Cali, Colombia. Cuevas was president of the International Federation of Women Lawyers from 1990 to 1992, during which time she began to publish and edit the *Abogada Newsletter* (*A Women Lawyer's Newsletter*) in order to raise legal issues related to women's lives. She has stayed on as editor of the newsletter since her presidency ended, and she has also made forays into broadcast journalism. In 1995, she began to produce *Looking at the World through Women's Eyes*, a public affairs program broadcast daily on radio and weekly on television, in order to "make women's voices heard" in civic affairs. Cuevas uses an interview format to "discuss subjects with a gender perspective," and she tries to project a positive image of women in the very media that she believes otherwise treat women as sex objects, or leave them silent and invisible. Cuevas sees the potential for media to reshape society, but her most immediate goal is to empower women first to speak up, then to run for public office. Women in office would "bring a maternal way of thinking, an ethic of care, up to now neglected in western patriarchal societies." Otherwise, "We will continue to elect governments whose main platform is to engage in wars."

Cuevas's involvement with the international, nongovernmental Peace Boat has also motivated her media activism. One aspect of that work has been trying to bring women into peace negotiations aimed at convincing "the government and the guerrilla that dialogue should be the best way out of the conflict" that has plagued Colombia internally since the 1960s. The violence, spawned by a complex civil war that has pitted the nation's security forces and army-backed paramilitaries against guerrilla groups in a struggle for territory and economic resources, has also been particularly brutal toward women. In 2004, Amnesty International reported that the armed actors, in order to terrorize particular communities, or to inflict humiliation on the enemy, routinely target women with rape, mutilation, torture, kidnapping, murder, and disappearance. In 2003, more than 220 women were killed for sociopolitical "reasons" outside combat, and more than 20 "disappeared" (see Amnesty International 2004). Cuevas also advocates legislation prohibiting the "exploitation of a woman's body as a sex symbol," which might include fines for advertisers, newspapers, and other publications that violate this standard. In 2002, the Colombian military dropped thousands of calendars from a helicopter over guerrilla-occupied land. The calendars contained a sexual photograph of a woman with a message for combatants to rejoin civil life: protests by women's groups forced the government to stop these practices.

Shaping Multiple Public Spheres

Canadian feminist **Jay Hartling**[25] has been involved with a Vancouver-based (British Columbia) cooperative radio station since 1995, serving in various roles as board member, membership and outreach worker, and, presently, producer and host of *America Latina Al Dia* (ALAD, translated as *Latin America Today*). Hartling's station is made up of a broad, multicultural, multilingual coalition of people and organizations working to open up a radio space to political discussion, poetry, music, panel discussions, live drama, and other content. The ALAD collective also participates in Latin American festivals and community events to promote the use of alternative media. *Americana Latina Al Dia* has an overriding political goal of encouraging Latin American and Canadian groups to work together:

> ...to build solidarity with communities of other alternative media in the South, to provide critical analysis of stories that either don't get covered in mainstream media...or are manipulated by corporate-controlled media. This includes a feminist perspective – all our producers are women! We ensure that female voices are heard.

For example, one recent program focused on women's poverty and education in towns along the Mexican border. But distant Mexican populations aren't her group's only concern. Hartling and her colleagues carry on important grassroots work in a city that has undergone rapid, dramatic demographic changes since the 1980s. Recent census figures show that Latin Americans, who number around 30,000, constitute the smallest "visible minority" in Vancouver, an increasingly ethnically diverse city of 1.2 million. People of Chinese heritage number nearly half a million, and those of South Asian, Filipino, Japanese, Southeast Asian, Arab, Korean, Native American, and African make up another quarter of a million, in addition to the dominant European-based population of 1.2 million (GVRD 1998). University of British Columbia anthropologist Pilar Riaño found Latin American immigrant women living in Vancouver to be particularly disadvantaged by low incomes, poor health, and lack of access to basic services (see Pilar Riaño-Alcalá, Marta Colorado, & Berta Alicia Perez 2001). Thus, the ALAD program brings an informational resource to raise public awareness of gender and other concerns in the community, and it serves as a bridge between the Latino and dominant (white) populations. Hartling sees herself doing community radio in some form or another "for the rest of my life." After all, there is so much more to be done to provide a voice for women – something she believes mainstream radio is lagging behind in: "If women control the agenda, the image and the level of participation will change."

K. T. Jarmul[26] has used radio and other alternative media to put into circulation what Caroline Mitchell (2004) has referred to as oppositional discourses about women. Jarmul came to women's media activism by way of the punk-rock scene in California, where she grew up. She first learned to express her ideas about life and punk-rock music through zines,[27] because these offered a nonhierarchical way of publishing. When she enrolled at the University of California – Santa Barbara in 2001, she turned to the campus radio station KCSB-FM, where she was "one of only two womyn (sic) playing my type of music – hardcore, metal, punk rock" – and artists such as Sleater-Kinney, The Butchies, Wage of Sin, 7-year Bitch, and singer–songwriters Ani DiFranco, Tori Amos, and Michelle Shocked. She says she met other womyn-identified womyn at the station and gained the confidence to state her feminist beliefs on her own program, which emphasized womyn artists and ideas. By her second year, Jarmul says she had moved into news, striving to give coverage to those less visible on campus:

> I have attempted to continue a focus on underrepresented groups and on womyn's issues in our news coverage. I have done this by trying to make formal relationships with some of the amazing groups (Mujer, the Hispanic womyn group; womyn's commission; queer commission; black student union; and many others).

Jarmul's goals are to "create a tomorrow that is drastically different from today." Included in this is the making of connections between feminism and racism, homophobia, and related oppression. But she also wants to help other young people and womyn to "form their own channels of power and to feel their voices *are* valid." She does not believe media need to mimic "hierarchical male designs," or be "testosterone-driven," but that they can be egalitarian in approach.

Affirming Lesbian Experiences

Building their own work on values and goals similar to those of K. T. Jarmul, **Claudia Wulz**[28] and two female colleagues founded their own lesbian-feminist radio program on a community radio station in Brussels, Belgium, in 2001. Their two-hour weekly program, which they finance themselves, follows a mixed format of news, information, and interviews. The content is lesbian-feminist in its orientation, which challenges the heterosexual male standard for "normality." Wulz and her colleagues invite guests onto the program who can talk about lesbian-feminist events and issues in Belgium and the surrounding European nations. In addition, they have presented three-day practical workshops for other lesbian-feminists to learn how to use digital and other new technology in radio production. Wulz wonders why only her own and one other program are produced by women at the noncommercial station where she's affiliated. At least in Belgium, she does not believe that much has happened to change the gender imbalance in radio over the past 20 years, in spite of a growing feminist movement.

The use of radio to circulate feminist and lesbian-feminist issues, information, and music to a mainstream audience began in 1972 for the Sophie's Parlor Radio Collective, in Washington, DC. **Jill Lawrence**,[29] **Moira Rankin**, and **Boden Sandstrom** were three among a group of about 10 women calling themselves the Feminist Radio Network, who would launch Sophie's Parlor as a weekly program on WGTB-FM, at Georgetown University[30] during the heady days of second-wave feminism. The group's members ranged in political perspectives – Marxist–Leninist, Socialist Worker, lesbian-feminist, radical feminist, and liberal feminist – and all were self-taught in their broadcast and journalism skills. The program was overtly political, featuring news, interviews, and poetry, with a main core of recorded music by women musicians such as Meg Christian, Chris Williamson, Margie Adam, and other lesbian singers and songwriters involved in founding Olivia Records in the mid-1970s.

Lawrence, who today runs her own consulting business, says she believed that "every woman who had put her heart and soul into writing a lyric or playing a song ought to be heard, and we shouldn't let our own tastes interfere . . . we were there to showcase these women for the world." In spite of its radical orientation, however, Rankin says that Sophie's was aimed at a general audience:

> I was very interested in getting information to a general audience about radical feminist ideas, and radio was a really inexpensive way to do that. One of the things that I really loved was when strangers called up the studio and wanted to talk about something. I was thrilled that we could be out [as lesbians] on the air.

Sophie's Parlor, which became a model for other feminist radio programs across the country, was born in the nation's capital at a time when feminist political life and culture were converging. Sandstrom, today a university lecturer in ethnomusicology, remembers:

> We had an amazing network, and it all related to media in some way. We had Lamas Bookstore, *Quest* (feminist quarterly magazine), Rising Women's Coffee House, *off our backs* (feminist newspaper), women's concerts. And,

then I started Women's Sound (concert sound systems). We all fed each other, and once the concerts started, we promoted them on Sophie's Parlor.

Rankin, today the executive producer of a public radio series called Soundprint, emphasizes that the program also brought feminist perspectives to mainstream current events, such as an increasingly unpopular war in Vietnam, the Watergate scandal, and Richard Nixon's resignation in 1974. The listening audience was responsive and the program developed a following. Although the women who have produced Sophie's Parlor have come and gone through the years and the character of the programming has changed, Sophie's Parlor continues to broadcast regularly on WGTB. Rankin, Sandstrom, and Lawrence view this as a feminist legacy. Rankin muses that the show also influenced the men with whom they interacted at the station. Sophie's encouraged everyone to find a women's angle in news, music, and other programming. At first, some of the men thought it was a joke, Rankin says, but after a while, they began to take the approach seriously, incorporating feminist principles into their own work and lives.

Creating a Virtual Feminist Public Sphere

Red Chidgey,[31] in Essex, England, has also used media activism to move women's sexuality and a range of mainstream issues from a feminist perspective into the public sphere, this time through the Internet. Chidgey, a postgraduate student and activist, says that her principal contribution has been to establish "a distribution network of young women's feminist, personal, political and artistic zines, pamphlets and books." The name of her website, which advertises the availability of low-cost zines on different topics, is FingerBang distro – a reference to female masturbation. Examples of zine titles include "Radical menstruation and healthcare," "Sex and sexuality," "Naming and overcoming racism," and "Environmental awareness," among others. Located online at www.geocities.com/fingerbangdistro, FingerBang distro also advertises Ladyfests, or women's film festivals, and films of Ladyfest gatherings. Chidgey's venture demonstrates a convergence of media forms (printed material, musical performances, commentary) through a single communication technology, employed in the service of feminism. Such an enterprise represents a contemporary means of achieving what Sophie's Parlor managed, in developing a close-knit network of feminists working in similar varied media forms in Washington, DC, some 30 years earlier.

Feminist scholar Gillian Youngs (2004) refers to the kind of work that Chidgey is doing as cyberfeminism, or the use of virtual space by women who want a low-budget, high-visibility means of communicating with other women. Youngs notes that feminist scholars have studied the Internet as a mechanism that transgresses both patriarchal boundaries (that work through social institutions to silence and limit women) and national/international boundaries. She says that:

> [V]irtual space has particular significance for women and feminist work. The transgressive potential of the Internet with regard to these boundaries and their significance in maintaining different forms of patriarchal power and social structure, has implications for women's capacities both to relate to one another, and to make political, economic and cultural contributions to their own and other societies and to local, national and international issues and processes, as individuals or collectively. (Youngs 2004: 189)

Nor should Chidgey's (and Jarmul's) commitment to zine culture as a form of media activism be underestimated. Chidgey says that the goal of zine-making is "about empowerment, dialogue, creativity and taboo-breaking," a way to "speak in public" about her own survival of domestic violence and sexual abuse and other "secrets that pass in the mail, pass between strangers and friends . . . affecting you in incendiary ways." Chidgey looks to the radical feminist magazines of her generation with respect – *Bitch!* and *Bust*, for example – which came out of zine culture. Zines, published in quantities of 200–300 copies, would be easily lost in time, but Chidgey voices "a commitment to preserving the histories of women's activism, art, and politics by contributing to national zine archives at feminist libraries."

Conclusion

Pilar Riaño (1994) has recognized the range of ways in which women working in various forms of grassroots communication around the world contribute to social change. Her "Typology of women, participation and communication" identifies these types as "development, participatory, alternative, and feminist, each with related goals of mobilizing citizen action toward some kind of particular development-oriented change"

(Riaño 1994: 6–7). The last of these is specifically concerned with advancing women's leadership in and control over media in order to articulate public dialogues on gender, race, and class. Marita Mata (1994: 196–7) cites the work of Peruvian scholar R. Alfaro (1988), who has recognized that "private speech is social silence, and liberation demands" that women convert the lessons of their daily lived experience into "social speech," an act that Mata believes takes women into the "territory of new speech."

In this chapter, we have reported and analyzed the work of women media activists who pursued similar political goals following the first path in our own communications model, which has taken them from radical political activity into media work. In various ways, their agency, commitment, and enthusiasm helped to place (and keep) gender-specific issues of violence against women (sexual harassment, rape, torture, disappearance), sexuality (health care, prostitution, reproductive rights, lesbian identity), and labor exploitation (low wages, dangerous workplace conditions) on the public and political agenda. In addition, their support for women-oriented cultural product such as film, video, poetry and music, through women-focused distribution channels such as radio and film cooperatives, provides public airings for such creative endeavors, expanding audience exposure and understanding. The various enterprises discussed in this chapter, women's narratives of their own experiences and their own goals for their practice, should give us considerable hope for the future of women's media-making and the sustained nature of women's interventions in the public, political, and cultural spheres of contemporary society. The next chapter considers women who conducted their media activism within the context of their careers as trained media professionals, thereby helping to give women a public voice in the news of 10 different nations.

Notes

1 Dalit, which means "oppressed," is the name assumed by members of the former untouchables caste. Dalit communities include feminists working to advance the awareness and status of Dalit women; in addition, a number of non-Dalit feminists have also worked actively to promote the rights of Dalit people. For a longer discussion, see Anupama Rao (2003) and Sharmila Rege (2004).

2 Gargi Sen and other women's media activists quoted in this chapter participated in the study in 2003 or 2004, via interviews or in writing.

3   Names of informants who participated in the study are bold faced.

4   US feminist historians refer to "first-wave feminism" as synonymous with the nineteenth-century women's rights movement, dated from the Seneca Falls Convention in July 1848. First-wave feminism focused primarily on gaining suffrage, with secondary campaigns for women's right to own property, adopt anti-alcohol laws (temperance), reform divorce laws, create educational access, and so on. Second-wave feminism, which many date from the founding of National Organization for Women in 1966, focused on securing abortion rights; prohibiting discrimination in employment, education and other institutions; and reforming (or introducing) laws on rape, incest, battering, and other violence against women, among other things. For a comprehensive analysis of US women's history, see Linda K. Kerber and Jane Sherron De Hart (2000).

5   Dorothy Dean submitted answers on August 20, 2003.

6   Chelsia Rice submitted answers on October 7, 2003.

7   Ulrike Helwerth submitted answers on October 14, 2003.

8   The information that we introduce here about Indian society and the desire of middle- and upper-class Indian women filmmakers to work in politically radical ways (through media activism) to address a wide range of oppressions experienced by women and those of lower classes will be applicable to the stories of Indian women that we speak about throughout the book.

9   Anjali Mathur submitted answers on March 20, 2004.

10 Laxmi Murthy submitted answers on March 14, 2004.

11 See the stories of Preeti Mehra in the Introduction and Chapter 8, as well as those of Ammu Joseph and Kalpana Sharma in Chapter 8.

12 UNESCO stands for United Nations Educational, Scientific and Cultural Organization, an agency that promotes international cooperation on matters identified by the parts of its name. Various UNESCO programs provide seed money and other grants to promote communications, particularly in developing nations.

13 As we saw in Chapter 5, disagreements within feminist organizations and amongst feminist activists, over what is a legitimate target for action, or legitimate content for a feminist publication, is a necessary part of feminisms' engagement with itself, even though it can be painful to negotiate at the time.

14 Deepa Dhanraj was interviewed on January 8, 2004, in Bangalore, India.

15 Gargi Sen was interviewed on January 6, 2004, in New Delhi, India.

16 Sanjana was interviewed on January 11, 2004, in Bangalore, India.

17 The designation "autonomous women's movement" distinguishes modern grassroots women's liberation from women's rights activities carried on by Gandhi and his followers both during the Indian independence movement

and in the new state after independence in 1947. For an overview of Indian feminism, see Maitrayee Chaudhuri (2004).

18 For an account of the importance of these rape cases to modern Indian feminism, see Ilina Sen (2004).

19 Several women from India interviewed in our study mentioned focusing their media activism on promotion of feminist consciousness among women in the panchayat system, and among women who might consider standing election. For example, see quotes from Nupur Basu and Preehi Mehra in Chapter 8.

20 The Adivasi are indigenous tribal peoples. Adivasi throughout India have been dislocated by government decisions to allow the building of dams (thereby displacing them from their ancestral villages), the granting of permits for commercial forest harvesting, and so on. Adivasi have responded by protesting and seeking legal intervention. Their campaigns have drawn support from middle- and upper-class political activists, including some of the women interviewed for this study.

21 Human rights groups have reported that hundreds of women have been attacked in India, Bangladesh, and Pakistan, many hundreds of those attacks resulting in death. Incidence in those countries appears to be increasing by 40–50 percent per year. While there are no comparable figures for India, anecdotal evidence suggests that the most populous nation of South Asia also has a high prevalence (see Ammu Joseph 2004a).

22 Janne Poort-van Eeden submitted answers on November 1, 2003.

23 Anne Lewis submitted answers on October 31, 2003.

24 Angela Cuevas de Dolmetsch submitted answers on October 6, 2003.

25 Jay Hartling submitted answers on October 5, 2003.

26 K. T. Jarmul submitted answers on September 28, 2003.

27 A "zine" is a noncommercial, self-published pamphlet, newsletter, or other small-scale publication intended for a particular audience, often a subculture. The concept of zines is most closely associated with the punk-rock movement in the United Kingdom and the United States in the 1970s. Today, e-zines (on the Internet) circulate zine material electronically.

28 Claudia Wulz submitted answers on March 23, 2004.

29 Jill Lawrence, Moira Rankin, and Boden Sandstrom were interviewed in Hyattsville, Maryland, on July 8, 2003.

30 Georgetown University, a Jesuit institution in downtown Washington, DC, gave its station manager and self-taught volunteer producers free reign to develop programming of interest to both college and community listeners. Rankin, Lawrence, and Sandstrom said that Sophie's Parlor was one of several leftist politically oriented programs, but the only one specifically feminist in the early 1970s. WGTB is a noncommercial, community-supported station.

31 Red Chidgey submitted answers on March 31, 2004.

8

Second Path:
Media Profession to Politics

*I want women's lives to be made real, as opposed to the plastic celebrity con-
sciousness in so much of the media . . . Feminism did influence many of the
pieces I did, for example, two long radio pieces in 1989 on the Michigan
Women's music festival – possibly one of the first times the L-word [lesbian] got
mentioned on public radio.*

Margot Adler,[1] reporter, National Public Radio (USA)

The chapters comprising Part I of this book paint less than a rosy picture of
the media's treatment of women around the world. As we have observed
elsewhere, one could look at this situation and come away with a sense that
women either don't work in these industries, or that they do work there but
have succeeded little in turning around the persistent patterns of sexism
(Byerly 2004a). Neither assumption would be accurate, of course. In fact,
women inside media enterprises have been the torchbearers of feminist-
oriented changes that have come about within both mainstream commercial and noncommercial media enterprises the world over during the past
three decades. Women with a feminist consciousness, sometimes assisted by
enlightened male supervisors and allies, have worked both individually and
through unions or other pressure groups to reverse patterns of workplace
discrimination, to train both women and men in the industries to be more
gender sensitive in their work, to expand content about women – and feminism – in both news and entertainment, and to otherwise put media in the
greater service of women. In the process, women have sometimes risked
(and lost) their jobs. Some have been threatened physically or in other ways,

and many have been stigmatized by labels or shunned by their colleagues. Some of the most overt cases have resulted in legal complaints that challenged unfair practices, and many of these challenges have been successful. Informants in our cross-cultural research shared these problematic experiences with us, but they also gave examples that might be characterized as positive steps forward for women through their media careers.

It will be important in the ensuing discussion to bring out the full range of experiences and actions in which women have been involved when trying to bring feminist-oriented content into public discourse through their work as media professionals. We should keep in mind that while the feminist public sphere (and the feminist component in the dominant sphere) is formed through the circulation of ideas and information, women in media professions have frequently had to first confront or negotiate the structural constraints in their own newsrooms that prevented the development and circulation of such content. Overall, advances for women in media professions have been incremental rather than quantum, and the level, number, and kind of advances have varied from nation to nation and situation to situation. Similarly, the number and kinds of stories, films, and other products that they were able to create reflect these internal organizational dynamics.

The goal of this chapter is to examine the work of women's media activism within professional media settings through the experiences of women professionals who have served as agents of change. Thirty-eight (41 percent) of the 90 respondents in our cross-cultural study have followed what we have called the second path. In the early stages of our research, when we sought participants in the study, it was media professionals who emerged first and most frequently to talk about their activist work. Like those who followed the other paths, they were eager to share the ways in which they had developed a feminist consciousness, their problems and victories in making a wider space for women in news or newsrooms, and their opinions of what remained to be done. Women following the second path represent 12 different nations, located in all regions of the world. While certainly not a complete picture, the findings here provide something of a global snapshot of the leadership exerted by women within media professions to bring women and feminism into the public sphere through their work. As in Chapters 7, 9, and 10, we note that the goal here is not to evaluate the success of these efforts – such evaluation is needed, but it is the work of empirical researchers who can hopefully discern useful cues from our work for their own investigations. Instead, the intent here is to better understand the nature, structure, and process of women's media activism, conducted within mostly conventional (male) media environments, which sought to secure women's right to communicate. We demonstrate in this chapter, as throughout the book, the ways in which women's agency has created a feminist public sphere and a feminist component in the dominant public sphere, by carrying feminist thinking about women into society via the media – a vehicle that Habermas and many others have recognized as the major communicative force in creating contemporary public spheres in which issues are constructed and addressed, and where citizens otherwise engage in the democratic process.

Characteristics of the Second Path

Women following the second path – "media profession to politics" – have employed an activist agenda as part of their professional careers in media. They were formally trained in one or more media fields such as print or broadcast journalism, or documentary film or video production. They came to their activist path sometime during their chosen careers, typically through a particular experience (or an accumulation of experiences) that heightened their understanding of gender imbalance, discrimination, or marginalization. Such experiences may have included denial of a job or a promotion, experience of sexual harassment by a colleague or supervisor, being denied the more substantial story assignments (reserved for men), or witnessing these events committed against other women. Sometimes it was witnessing the exclusion of women's views and voices from routine news coverage by male supervisors – exclusion that was both routine and normalized, as well as targeted because women's angles were deemed unimportant. For many of these women, a feminist consciousness was further honed by the daily barrage of sexist portrayals of women in advertising, films, and magazine photographs. Gaining a feminist political consciousness came to have specific consequences for their work, as they began to view their profession as an opportunity to advance women's views and status. A number of women also expressed their motivation as a feeling of responsibility toward other women. In some cases, getting women's stories or issues into the news (or other media content) occurred quietly as they went about their tasks, typically as journalists going out on assignment. In other cases, they would have to develop elaborate strategies to convince a male supervisor that such a story was worth covering.

The logic of examining the experiences of women media professionals in more depth and across nations was suggested by an emergence of first-person books in the 1980s and 1990s by women who had come through traditional media careers and, in the process, found themselves as advocates for gender-related changes in the media. US broadcast journalists Marlene Sanders and Marcia Rock's *Waiting for Prime Time: The Women of Television News* (1988) reported their insider stories of negotiating with producers to cover second-wave feminism, as well as bringing a feminist frame to political stories. Day-to-day struggles like those in which Sanders and Rock engaged fall into what Diane Elson (1994) has described as the meso-level of economic relations in social institutions. Their (and certainly many other women media professionals) experiences of challenging the norms of news definitions, assignments, and production codes suggest the basis for a gender analysis in this realm of production. Similarly, Nan Robertson's *The Girls in the Balcony: Women, Men and The New York Times* (1992) chronicles the events associated with the decision by members of the Women's Caucus to file a sex-discrimination suit against their powerful employer in 1974, which resulted in a number of changes including promotional policies and pay increases for female journalists, and more enlightened coverage of rape and other women's experiences. Robertson says that there were also other lessons:

> First, from beginning to end, it was the women of the *Times* that pushed and prodded the paper and its most powerful editors to account and insisted upon action. They received their staunchest support from younger male staff members ... and Anna Quindlen's emerging voice on the Op-Ed page is unmistakably the voice of a woman. (Robertson 1992: 245–6)

Indian journalists Ammu Joseph and Kalpana Sharma's *Whose News: The Media and Women's Issues* (1994) similarly snapped into focus both their own and their women colleagues' struggles to bring widespread but largely ignored problems of dowry deaths, rape, female feticide, and sati (widow-burning) into front-page news coverage, beginning in the 1970s and 1980s. These authors' collaborative work to break this and other ground in their field is discussed at length later in this chapter. Here we preview it with this reminder, from the preface to their book, of why women's leadership in the field has mattered:

> The advent of women reporters and the presence of some senior women journalists in positions of responsibility have made a significant, if limited,

difference to the coverage of women's issues by the press. The most important factor, perhaps, is the opening up of communication channels between the press and women's groups. This has come about through the involvement of journalists (including a few male) in the women's movement as participants or sympathizers. (Joseph & Sharma 1994: 20)

Joseph and Sharma acknowledge that women's groups in India had not experienced the kind of media silence, hostility, or overt sexism, racism, and pornography evident in British tabloids. Instead, Indian women journalists faced the challenge of finding ways to rise above the superficial coverage paid to women and to overcome the sense that women are "the other" as far as the press is concerned (Joseph & Sharma 1994: 21).

The agency of women's media activists who followed the second path helped to redefine news organizations' policies, news definitions, and other aspects of news production, and through their stories and other media products, they placed women's experiences and social analyses into public discourse. We have conceptualized this process as one of shaping a feminist public sphere that intersected the dominant public sphere in significant ways. The Model of Women's Media Action, which provides the analytic framework throughout the discussion of study findings, suggests that this (second) and other paths that women media activists followed served as the foundation for women's greater public presence and political influence.

Informants (listed alphabetically) who followed the second path include:

Margot Adler, USA	Patricia Gaston, USA
Virginie Barré, France	Nomusa Gaxa, South Africa
Nupur Basu, India	Vasanthi Hariprakash, India
Suzanne Francis Brown, Jamaica	Natacha Henry, France
Jo Campbell, USA	Ammu Joseph, India
Agenda Collective, South Africa	Sonal Kellogg, India
Stacey Cone, USA	Trella Laughlin, USA
Patience (Patti) Dapaah, Ghana	Dalia Liran-Alper, Israel
Rajashri Dasgupta, India	Preeti Mehra, India
Nombuso Dlamini, South Africa	Madeleine Memb, Cameroon
Tanushree Gangpadhyay, India	Kristie Miller, USA

Continued

Mildred Mulenga, Zambia	Gretchen Luchsinger Sidhu, USA
Sakuntala Narasimhan, India	Surekha Sule, India
Louise North, Australia	Sandhya Taksale, India
Crystal Oderson, South Africa	Thandazo, South Africa
Radhika M., India	Sue Valentine, South Africa
Howedia Saleem, Sudan	Sylvia Vollenhoven, South Africa
Judy Sandison, South Africa	Lubna Yousif Ali, Sudan
Geeta Seshu, India	
Kalpana Sharma, India	

Considering Context

Women's media activism that leads to greater egalitarianism in commercial and noncommercial media always occurs within a larger social context. One interesting example can be seen in Israel, where, in the early 1990s, Israeli feminism was mobilizing at the same time as the Israeli telecommunications industry was undergoing a major restructuring that would result in a shift from state-run television to cable and commercial networks. **Dalia Liran-Alper,**[2] a broadcast journalist who chaired the Women's Status Committee of the Israeli Broadcasting Authority from 1993 to 1998, said that the committee strived to disseminate feminist values by increasing women's visibility in broadcast media, limiting sexist portrayals, and expanding the number of women in the profession. The committee, a governmental body composed of representatives from the media, women's organizations, and the academy, undertook a number of specific campaigns to bring these about, with mixed success. The latter brought cable television (including foreign programming), an event that she said drew a "thick and stormy communication map . . . into the blue skies of Israel, which until the '90s had been dominated indisputably by the Public Broadcasting Authority." She said that women's organizations of the period, even those that had previously served a social function, made their focus sociopolitical issues that affected women, such as unemployment, discrimination, sexual harassment in the workplace, family violence, and strategies for helping women's way into politics (e.g., setting aside seats for women).

In the same era, Israeli universities were introducing programs to train women for management and other leadership positions, and women's studies programs were emerging. In spite of a strong feminist atmosphere, the committee that Liran-Alper chaired met resistance to its initiatives. The first of these aimed to replace the image of a bikini-clad woman, contained in the introductory clip used each week to open the popular public affairs program *Yoman* on Channel One, with an image of a professional woman. Demands by the committee and other women's groups put the station managers on the defensive, and while the station took seven years to make the replacement, feigning financial restrictions, the process also opened up a dialogue between management and feminists. Another committee initiative aimed to encourage original programming to reflect contemporary Israeli women's interests and real-life experiences. The legal advisor to the Israeli Broadcasting Authority responded that "Drama cannot be recruited, drama is art," and he rejected the notion that women viewers would identify with women in nontraditional roles, such as judges.

The committee persisted, developing a data bank of women experts in different fields who could serve as news sources, drafting a statement of equality between the sexes for use by stations in both hiring and representation in content, and an "Equalizing Language" recommendation to overcome differential references to males and females. Although the committee based its recommendations on sound research, Liran-Alper argues that some of them resulted in "harsh disputes" between members of the committee and station managers, and a refusal by stations to adopt some of the recommendations. In addition, Liran-Alper observed that the number of women employed by the Israeli Broadcasting Authority during the 1990s was very low; for example, only 20 percent in senior roles. While wage levels for journalists were at parity between the sexes, women earned substantially less than male colleagues in management posts. Israeli feminist scholar Dafna Lemish (2004) cites a growing body of research – including her own – that shows a persistent exclusion and marginality of women in the Israeli media, as well as the widespread use of traditional stereotypes such as the virgin, the good mother (or caretaker), the victim (especially of war), and the bad girl (whore). Some research has shown the tendency of Israeli television to treat young, pretty women as decoration, dressing up news coverage of political campaigns or other events (Lemish 2004).

The timetable for similar challenges to media treatment of women has varied between nations. Journalism historians Deborah Chambers, Linda Steiner, and Carole Fleming (2004) note that Britain adopted the Sex Disqualification (Removal) Act in 1919, which prohibited discrimination on the basis of sex or marital status in employment, but it wasn't until the Sex Discrimination Act of 1975 that women had a sound statutory basis for mounting legal challenges against employers for lower pay, unfair dismissal, and sexual harassment (p. 134). The authors suggest that British citizens in general are less litigious than those in the USA, and even now, women in British media are less inclined to take up such challenges. Margaret Gallagher's (1995) report on gender patterns in media employment around the world showed that women accounted for only 34 per cent of the British journalistic workforce in 1990, and still only around 41 percent of the entire media workforce by 1995. Moreover, women's image in advertising and other media became increasingly violent and sexualized during the 1990s, as participants in our study indicated when recounting their challenges to these images (see quotes by Rakoff, Drew, and Lewis in Chapter 9).

In the United States, feminists mobilized against the media in various ways, beginning in the early 1970s. US journalism historians Maureen Beasley and Sheila Gibbons (2003) note that the passage of Title VII in 1972, modifying the 1964 Civil Rights Act to include sex as a category forbidden in employment discrimination, provided women media professionals with their basis for litigation. And file lawsuits they did! The 1970s, 1980s, and even 1990s are replete with cases, brought by groups of women at large agenda-setting American media enterprises, as well as smaller ones. A number of these, filed jointly by female and black employees, were won with the support of unions and feminist and civil rights groups. For example, a landmark 10-year discrimination case against Associated Press news service, finally settled in 1983, brought equal assignments and salary to women and minorities on a par with their white colleagues, as well as back pay and other compensation (p. 187). A similar case against *The Washington Post*, brought by women, had been settled in 1974, requiring the newspaper to improve its record in hiring and promoting women (Beasley & Gibbons 2003: 188). Recent data, however, show minimal advancement for women within the field, either at management or worker levels. For example, women across telecommunication industries comprise only 13 percent of the top executives, 9 percent of boards of directors, and 26 percent of local TV directors (Annenberg Public Policy Center 2002).

US feminists also challenged media content in a number of ways. Elayne Rapping (1994) argues that feminism placed violence against women issues on the nation's public – and policy – agendas through made-for-TV films such as *Something About Amelia* (incest), the *Burning Bed* (wife battering), and *When He's Not a Stranger* (date rape). Anti-pornography campaigns, beginning in the 1970s, helped to emphasize connections between graphic images of sexual violence and the real-life experiences of so many women. In relation to news, feminists protested (and eventually stopped) the segregation of classified job listings by "women's" and "men's" categories, the designation of women's marital status through the use of "Miss" and "Mrs." in news stories, and the use of "he" as the standard pronoun (regardless of the sex of the person being referred to). With varying success, they also campaigned against stereotypical portrayals and omissions of women from serious media content in the 1970s and 1980s. Byerly and Warren's (1996) study – quoted more extensively in earlier chapters – also showed that feminist activism remained alive and busy even during the conservative (Reagan and Bush presidential) years of the 1980s through women's caucuses that found many male allies.

Stucture and Agency: Making Change

However, it was the years *before* such challenges began that print journalist **Jo Campbell**[3] remembers. She said that it was hard to think of herself as a feminist in the early 1970s, when she entered one federal agency press conference and was given a badge identifying her as a "Newsman." In the mid-1970s, one assignment editor refused to send her to cover the first international UN Decade for Women meetings in Mexico City, because, he said, as a "known feminist" she would be biased in her reporting. On her own time and money, Campbell covered one of the preparatory conferences for the Mexico City meetings, held at Harvard University, and her editor used some of her stories, because "they quoted such powerful women in their own countries that my news agency did not dare ignore them." Today, Campbell is editor of the online magazine *Ecotopics International News Service* (www.ecotopics.com), where she integrates feminist concerns with those of the environment, human rights, and international affairs.

Historical shifts relating to women's professional standing can also be seen in the US broadcasting scene. **Margot Adler**,[4] a broadcast journalist and author of *Drawing Down the Moon*,[5] characterizes her long-time workplace, National Public Radio, as a gender-friendly place to work. Indeed, its celebrated political reporters include Nina Tottenberg, Cokie Roberts, Linda Wertheimer, and others whose journalism has dominated the station for at least two decades. But in the early 1970s, US radio was a different scene. One East Coast radio program director told Adler that women "didn't do news" because their voices were "too high." At the same time, he was playing footsie with her under the table. At another station, she escaped being fondled by a male colleague one night by running from the building.

Today, NPR creates the space for Adler's feminist approach to reporting, including interviews with high-profile feminist leaders such as Gloria Steinem; stories that include a feminist angle, such as one on ways in which drug laws oppress poor women; and those stories on the Michigan Women's Music Festival, described in the opening quote to this chapter.

Radio has also been a shifting scene for women in Ghana, where broadcast journalist **Patience (Patti) Dapaah**[6] became producer of her own radio program in 1994. Dapaah said that that the government's monopoly was giving way to private entrepreneurship in the early 1990s, and she wanted to find ways to raise women's interests in relation to the national budget, economics, religion, and other issues that were seen as men's preserve. In 1997, she became the first woman among 13 men at the commercial FM station Kapital Radio, where she continued to expand the station's gender content. She noted that "as a matter of interest, Kapital Radio was, and still is, headed by a woman CEO, the first in the country." Dapaah's contribution has been not only to expand gender in content but also women's place in journalism. She is presently working through a not-for-profit organization to develop the structure for a women's radio station and a women's weekly newspaper in her nation.

In nearby Cameroon, **Madeleine Memb**[7] – whose male colleagues call her "the feminist" – began producing women's television programs in the same timeframe of the mid-1990s. *Au Nom de la Femme* (In the Name of the Woman), which broadcasts weekly in French over the parastatal station Cameroon Radio-Television, has been advocating for women and giving them a voice since 1995. Like Dapaah, Memb also takes her media activism into the community. Through involvement in the International Association of Women in Radio and Television, she has organized one regional meeting, "Empowering Women through Rural and Community Radio," and participated in a regional seminar in Guinea on how to increase women's participation in media, particularly at decision-making levels.

Consciousness-Raising as Change Agent

Informants who followed the second path frequently said that entering feminist activism in the media followed a consciousness-raising that grew out of discrimination – both others' and their own. For **Trella Laughlin**,[8] the journey began early in life, by shaking off what she calls her family's "fundamentalist white racist indoctrination." Laughlin, who worked both for newspapers and as a freelancer for a number of media, found journalism a way to do that. For example, in 1980, she began her 18-year running weekly public-access television program *Let the People Speak!* in Austin, Texas, as a forum for white people to speak out against racism. The program, which won numerous awards, integrated feminist perspectives into its format.

Founded in 1987, in South Africa, the magazine *Agenda* focuses specifically on issues of women and the media. Published by a diverse group of feminist activists, the **Agenda Magazine Collective**[9] wanted to overcome perceptions that the journal was predominantly white and too academic in its orientation. Project manager Amanda Trotter and other collective members said that they "began to push for ways to let black women's voices shine through." During the 1990s, the group initiated writing workshops, broadened the magazine's call for submissions, and matched inexperienced writers with mentors to gradually increase its articles by both black and young writers. In 2003, Agenda worked with 26 local community radio stations across South Africa, providing copy in the form of five or six articles at a time, for journalists to use in broadcasts. Most recently, the collective has sought a way to open up channels for men with a feminist consciousness to speak out.

After writing for *Femina*, a prominent women's magazine in India, **Sakuntala Narasimhan**,[10] of Bangalore, said she was invited by the *Deccan Herald* newspaper to write a column "On women, for women." The column, which ran for 21 years, gave her a voice for the feminist consciousness that she was building through her involvement in the women's movement. In those years, she also pursued a doctoral degree, a three-decade-long process that she eventually wrote about in one column. She said that a particular piece that she wrote provoked a flood of calls and letters from middle-aged women saying that she had given them the courage to enroll for degrees, despite their "housewife" roles. Narasimhan began covering women's rights marches and conferences, as well as women's court cases and experiences with police officers in the 1980s. These experiences made her feel the need to shift toward greater activism in her journalism, something she insists has brought greater public awareness about the discriminatory practices that are ingrained into society. The royalties from her book *Born Unfree*, a compilation from her *Deccan Herald* column, on policies and practices affecting women in India, including legal, medical, social, and cultural issues, go to a women's activist group called Vimochana, in Bangalore. The group helps to fight dowry harassment cases.

Stacey Cone,[11] a former producer for CNN, the all-news cable TV network based in Atlanta, Georgia, in the late 1980s and early 1990s, had her consciousness raised by enduring what she terms a "highly sexist environment" that included a period of sexual harassment by a male colleague. As a result, Cone became "quietly pro-active," pushing for more coverage of women's and minorities' issues and volunteering for projects that focused on the treatment of women. One project investigated a secret government experiment performed on impoverished pregnant women in Tennessee, where it was discovered that, decades earlier, scientists had injected the women with plutonium to see what would happen to their unborn children. There were also documentaries about women's issues such as the glass ceiling and overpopulation (associated with gender inequality), as well as a five-part series on women who go to prison for killing their abusive partners. In this last project, Cone followed the court case of a woman on trial for murdering her abusive common-law husband in his sleep. The camera captured the woman's testimony on the stand and the subsequent jury acquittal. Cone said that the number of phone calls she received after the show aired indicated that the program had raised public awareness of – and empathy for – the psychological impact that long-term abuse has on victims.

But these projects, some of which won awards, were few and far between, and many had to be developed on "shoe-string budgets." Getting approval took careful planning before the pitch to management, and still only about one story out of five had any direct relevance to women or minorities. Cone argues that among the painful lessons was learning that women co-workers weren't necessarily her allies. "They will sometimes but not always, speak out against harassment or discrimination they see others endure," and many still find it easier to go along with rules of a male-dominated workplace because "it's easier," she said.

Negotiating Complicity

Stacey Cone's experience with unsupportive female colleagues who reinforce male norms (and power) in the work environment demonstrates women's complicity in patriarchy, something that can be a major stumbling block to those trying to challenge androcentric practices. The effect of such complicity is the perpetuation of women's secondary status in the journalism field and, by extension, in society through the content that flows from such gendered relations of production. This problem, which is by no means confined to a single nation or workplace, arose in a number of our interviews with women media professionals. As we explore some of their situations to illustrate the problem, we want to suggest that complicity may be best understood within the framework of masculine hegemony.

Italian intellectual Antonio Gramsci's (1971) employment of the concept *hegemony* was fairly sketchy, but in the 1970s, British cultural studies scholars frequently used it to mean noncoercive ways by which the dominant class obtained the consent of the less powerful. They placed the media and other cultural products central to the manufacture of consent. Making specific application to gender relations, Sonya Andermahr, Terry Lovell, and Karol Wolkowitz (2000) observe that a dominant ideology of gender is passed down through culture and carries with it certain punishments and rewards for adherence (or not) to that ideology. Their explanation of hegemony is useful here as we try to bring an analysis to the question: Why would one woman not stand up for another? In addition, we hope to reveal, where possible, how informants in our study negotiated women's complicity as they sought to bring feminist principles to their reporting and other newsroom behavior.

Australian print journalist **Louise North**[12] said that she was nine years into her 15-year career when she enrolled in gender studies courses at the University of Tasmania. There she found "the tools to articulate what I saw in practice every day and to allow myself to believe I could be part of a process for change for women." As a sub-editor, North had had certain advantages of promotion and status, but she saw that for most women in journalism, the glass ceiling was firmly intact. The masculine newsroom, as she calls it, was characterized by men who never talked about needing to increase coverage of women, and who reminisced about the old days before women intruded on their turf. Women who complained were singled out as "whingers," and their "whinging" resulted in a failure to win the support of (male) section editors who directly influenced women's career advancement. North found that younger women coming up through the ranks were not generally helped by seniors who may have feared that their jobs would be taken by these junior female colleagues. She added:

> But surely if those women had a politicized understanding of the ways in which women's subordination is currently and historically reproduced and have the will to change, then some shifts could occur.

North negotiated this situation indirectly by trying to bring feminist content to news where she could, such as writing book reviews for her (Tasmania's only) metropolitan daily. In 2001, she initiated the annual Women Tasmania Media Award to encourage progressive reporting on women, and she gives workshops to women's nongovernmental organizations on how to gain access to news media.

Women's complicity in sexist practices can be subtle, as **Preeti Mehra**,[13] a print journalist in New Delhi whose feminist media activism was profiled in the Introduction to this book, has been troubled by a tendency in her junior female colleagues to accept media employers' shifts from permanent employment to that of contract labor. A trend in the last decade, contracts often bring better benefits and higher wages, but without the job security that Mehra's generation fought for. She believes that a lack of gender and class consciousness is involved here, as "a lot of newspapers began taking people who were more from the upper classes or people who they gauged would not be so political," as her own generation had been. Mehra recognizes that women are particularly vulnerable to contract agreements, but she argues that these "take away their voice completely." She adds, "You can't freely be involved in movements or things you would like to because you are being watched somewhere," and she fears that journalists are losing their social change missions.

Veteran print journalist **Tanushree Gangopadhyay**,[14] in Bangalore, India, also wonders whether gender inequality can be addressed when some female colleagues exploit their femininity to "go up the ladder." Like Preeti Mehra, she agreed that younger women in the profession are less likely to challenge inequality than women of her own generation. Gangopadhyay, who entered the field in 1976, has spent her career challenging sexism and unfair practices on the job, including what she believed was unfair termination. Backed by her union, Gangopadhyay's challenge to that termination would go on for 13 years. The minute she went to court, she said, her employer approached her about going through conciliation. "I said 'No, I can find a job tomorrow if you don't take me back,' but the interesting thing is that as journalists we are not aware of our rights."

Sonal Kellogg,[15] who works for Gujarati-language newspapers in the northwest Indian state of Gujarat, strives to put a women's voice in all of her stories, but sometimes that has been difficult. The women she has sought to include in stories have not always understood the benefits of such coverage and some have turned on her. When Kellogg was covering the Gujarat riots of 2002,[16] for example, she tried to interview Muslim women to get their response to seven shootings of Muslims by Indian police that day. The women refused and turned on her, resulting in drawing attention from nearby male police officers. Kellogg and a male journalist colleague retreated after they were pursued and beaten by those police officers. She has persisted in other ways, seeking out angles that highlight gender and, when interviewing a male politician, always asking him how he is going to address women's concerns so she can report his answers. Kellogg believes that both men and women need to be sensitized to ways in which they can promote gender angles in stories; for example, considering how women are affected by a policy, an issue, or an event.

Women's complicity in patriarchy is at the heart of women's lack of status in journalism, according to **Mildred Mulenga**,[17] bureau chief for the Southern Africa Pan African News Agency (PANA). Mulenga, who moved to South Africa from Zambia, believes that "women's traditional behavior is partly to blame for their marginalization in the newsroom," a place in which she has spent more than two decades. She said:

> Back home in Lusaka you find that the challenging [reporting] assignments are given to men, and the women are given the lesser assignments . . . I think that women must change their attitudes towards each other before they can be treated equally.

Mulenga observed that women sometimes buy into the myths of male superiority, and accept their marginalization. Like Sonal Kellogg in India, Mulenga has also encountered problems in dealing with female news sources, who sometimes denied her interviews because they said that "women should not be seen to be social agitators or commentators," on issues of human rights or politics – these roles "should be left to the menfolk." Mulenga has found that survival and advancement for a black feminist journalist such as herself have been aided by very hard work and by establishing supportive feminist professional networks, because "women must support each other." She has found such support through the International Women's Media Foundation, a group based in Washington, DC, that promotes women in media fields internationally and, through its annual Courage Awards, recognizes the substantial contributions that women make to political reporting around the world.

We found varied experiences on the question of whether and how race and ethnicity influences women's ability to support each other on the job. **Crystal Oderson**,[18] a broadcast journalist, said that she embarked on a study of black women's experiences at South African Broadcasting Corporation (SABC), where she believes black women have had to fight much harder than white women to gain advancement. White women colleagues could not be counted on as black women's allies, she suggests, as they have had the historical advantage of a better education and social position, which sometimes makes it hard for them to empathize with the experiences of black women. But even black female colleagues were encouraged to align with "the white camp" – something that was easier if they had lighter skin and straighter hair – if they wanted to progress. Over the past four years, a number of black women journalists have left mainstream broadcasting, including SABC. Although Oderson acknowledges that others have since come into the industry, "they have taken on a particular identity, having straight hair, speaking with a very English accent" – traits of assimilation into the dominant (white British) system, a legacy of colonialism and apartheid. The new kind of female journalist being sought, she believes, is one with a white consciousness who will not bring with her an opinionated black women's voice. When Oderson saw that she could not progress in that system – she has "quite curly hair" and offers her opinions – and after an argument with a male colleague over her lack of conformity in 2002, she said, "Hell no, I'm a reporter who can work as hard as you can." It was a turning point that took her into international reporting and to developing programs for women in journalism through Gender Links and Women's Media Watch, two advocacy groups for feminist journalists profiled in Chapter 9.

Similarly, **Sylvia Vollenhoven**,[19] a South African print journalist, has sometimes found support from colleagues hard to come by. Noting that she "came from a family of extremely strong black women who were very aware of their roots and own identity," Vollenhoven said that she has expected more than the chauvinism she sometimes experienced from her "black male comrades," and that "the kind of sisterhood and solidarity that women shared when they were fighting apartheid was a lot more intense than it is now." She believes that the limited numbers of top jobs in her profession cause greater competition, particularly for women.

Crystal Oderson's white colleague **Judy Sandison**[20] is the editor of new media for SABC news – a different division of the organization than the one in which Oderson worked. After Sandison became one of the first women regional editors in the anti-apartheid era of the early 1990s, Sandison said that she set about intentionally to become "an agent of change" in moving the newsroom toward a new, more professional kind of journalism and a better balance along gender and race lines. She was able to bring in more women, more professional journalists, and achieve a staff that was "around 80 percent Zuli-speaking or black journalists." Sandison's commitment to advance women and African journalists had been deepened while working for what she called the "old" (apartheid-era) SABC, which she characterizes as both sexist and racist, and which she had earlier sued for unfair labor practices. As she sought to make changes in that system, she said she "had a lot of support, especially from black journalists." Sandison believes that newsrooms need to have champions for equality, and that the equality in newsrooms is reflected in the information it provides to the outer world. In her view, the media are "the building block of our democracy," and as a white woman, she felt not only a responsibility but also in a position to do her part.

Professional Change Organizations

In order to open spaces in their stories or documentaries to women's voices and experiences, women media activists, as we have seen, often first had to confront entrenched organizational and journalistic practices. Such challenges occur in what feminist economist Diane Elson (1994: 40–1) calls the meso- and micro-levels of capitalist society that relies on its institutions for survival. In a neoclassical perspective of capitalism, meso-level refers to the realm in which norms and networks are needed for the economic system to carry on. Both commercial and public service institutions, argues Elson, are "bearers of gender." It is the norms that favor men (and also white authority, in some cases) that women media activists around the world have sought to change, and their networks have helped them to do that by providing the structural means to develop strategies and support systems. Making change at the macro-level enables changes to more easily occur at the micro-level, where day-to-day decisions are made with respect to the running of institutions. Elson said that gender has most often come into play at the micro-level within institutional structures. Indeed, most informants in our study talked about their routine, often individual, ways of negotiating sexist barriers to workplace practices. In this and the following section, we consider the interface between these two levels and the ways in which women's media activism fits into it. Along the way, we try to illustrate the ways in which the formulation and circulation of women's experience and ideas through media is always reliant on these forces.

Journalism historian Elizabeth V. Burt (2000: xxvii) found that whereas women's early press clubs in the USA had served to enlist women into the profession of journalism, those that sprang up after 1970 tended "to be fueled by the passions of strong leaders with the feminist goal of erasing continuing gender inequities." This also describes what we see when looking globally at the emerging phenomenon of women's journalistic organizations since 1970. We glimpse several of them here in order to demonstrate why these groups must be viewed as an essential component of a larger communicative infrastructure that enabled feminist discourse to emerge publicly. We begin in 1981, in France, where women journalists formed l'Association des Femmes Journalistes to promote women's status in the profession and to improve women's image in the media. **Virginie Barré**[21] and **Natacha Henry**,[22] who have been officers in that organization, said that the group has been particularly concerned about younger women in the field who are less confident in dealing with male bosses. With governmental grants and corporate sponsorship, AFJ awards annual prizes honoring outstanding journalism, books, documentary films, and public relations. AFJ also conducts and disseminates research, and produces reports and films on women in journalism fields. The last of these include Henry's short documentary *Où sont les femmes?* (*Where are the Women?*), in 2000, as well as a book on media sexism, written by Henry, Barré, and two other AFJ members.

The early 1980s also saw the formation of a particularly cohesive group of Indian feminist journalists, who have managed to create an enduring political, professional, and personal relationship lasting two decades. **Kalpana Sharma**,[23] **Ammu Joseph**,[24] **Anjali Mathur**,[25] and a number of others from various publications started the Women and Media Group (WMG) in Mumbai in 1984, which Sharma describes as "an informal group that met every fortnight." Initially a forum for discussing media portrayal, news coverage, and workplace conditions of/for women, the group made its first serious foray into media activism in 1985 by sending a four-member team to Ahmedabad, in the neighboring state of Gujarat, to cover the impact of the communal (caste-related) riots there on women. While members filed individual stories for their respective publications, they collaborated in publishing a joint report that included detailed accounts of some of the high-profile cases involving women – stories that had only been partially covered in the press, according to Joseph.[26] They found, for instance, that thousands of poor Muslim women (on whom the events had fallen the hardest) had protested on several occasions against police brutality and killings, and against extended curfews that prevented them from leaving their homes to buy food for their families.[27] WMG members increased their media activism by sponsoring public events (e.g., a festival of women's films) and by holding discussions with media professionals on gender issues in advertising and film. In 1987, when 17-year-old Roop Kanwar was burned alive on her husband's funeral pyre in Deorala, Rajasthan, WMG sent a team to investigate. Their stories and an analysis of the media coverage of this high-profile case of widow-burning, or sati, a practice outlawed more than a century ago, were published in the report *Trial by Fire.* The report, one of the first independent accounts, questioned the mainstream media's assertion that Kanwar had gone willingly to the funeral pyre. Basing its questions on eyewitness accounts of villagers, including many women, the report was a precursor of feminist monitoring of Indian media.

The formative role that these and other Indian women journalists played in shaping a public feminist discourse in India during the 1980s cannot be over-emphasized. Indian women were not only examining their own situation and history, but many were doing it within the complex circumstances formed by a colonial past. Issues involving traditional gender practices were central to these public discussions. Feminist scholar Lata Mani (1992) acknowledges the conflict that has existed around issues such as *sati*, primarily a high-caste practice in some parts of India of burning women on the funeral pyres of their husbands, something the British outlawed in the 1800s, but which Indian social reformers had also campaigned against. Even afterward, some Hindu fundamentalists continued to claim their right to the ritual, which was typically committed through force by first starving, drugging, or otherwise compelling women to death by burning. Contemporary Indian feminists wanted to reframe the emerging public debate after Roop Kanwar's death by focusing on the violence done to women, even though, as Mani acknowledged, "Indian feminists have always engaged the broader notions of women's self-negation and fidelity to husbands that are part and parcel of the ideology of *sati* though hardly restricted to it" (p. 406). Roop Kanwar had made *sati* a "live issue" for Indian feminists, she said, not only because of the violence but also because feminists had come to understand that colonial (and other Western) onlookers had romanticized the practice.

In 1988, WMG merged with the Women and Media Committee of the Bombay[28] Union of Journalists, but its members maintained their personal and collegial ties, and individually they continued to find ways to make women's issues public through their journalism. Still, women had hit the glass ceiling in Indian print journalism. In January 2002, Joseph, Sharma, Mathur, and others called 100 women in media professions across India to New Delhi for a three-day workshop. The event was an outgrowth of Joseph's book *Making News* (2000), which reported women's generally low status in media professions across India. After three days, participants gave birth to the Network of Women in Media in India (NWMI), a nonhierarchical collective of women in media fields who wanted to address a wide range of broad and specific issues in their profession. More than a dozen local chapters, covering all regions of India, would respond to local women's concerns within the broad framework of the charter, which identifies both structural problems (e.g., globalization of Indian media industries) and specific professional concerns (e.g., implementation of a Supreme Court directive that all media establish Complaint Committees to hear sexual harassment cases).

The mechanics of NWMI, as well as its substantive support for women media professionals, can be seen in the operation and work of its chapters. **Rajashri Dasgupta,**[29] a veteran print journalist in Kolkata, India, is a co-chair of the West Bengal chapter of Women in Media in India (NWMI). In February 2003, that chapter's members assumed an advocacy role for Rina Mukherjee, a reporter at *The Statesman* newspaper, who complained of sexual harassment by a senior editor. A letter from chapter members to the newspaper led to *The Statesman*'s notification to its employees of a committee to hear grievances in its Delhi and Kolkata offices. Rina Mukherjee's willingness to come forward "created a stir, a debate on the issue of sexual harassment, which became a talking point in media houses across the country," Dasgupta said.[30] A believer in collective action to change unfair practices, Dasgupta also served on the six-woman team that, in late 2003, conducted a study on media workplace policies, ethics, and the status of women journalists. The Press Institute of India sponsored the study, which was released in July 2004. Among other things, the report said that women journalists are pressing their workplaces to establish Complaint Committees to investigate cases of sexual harassment, something rampant in both English and regional-language dailies. Twenty-two percent of the study's 410 female respondents said that they had been sexually harassed at some point in time, but only 15 percent had filed complaints (quoted in Malvika Kaul 2004).

Dasgupta's colleague **Surekha Sule,**[31] a freelance print journalist and a member of the Mumbai chapter of NWMI, was a second team member on the Press Institute of India's survey. Sule was sent into the smaller towns in the west Indian states of Maharashtra, Gujarat, Rajasthan, and Goa, where regional languages (not English) dominate in journalism. Sule viewed this activity as a way of organizing rural women journalists, who have less confidence in themselves than their urban colleagues. Sule found no formal mechanisms in the smaller rural papers to "handle gender issues"; thus women who experience discrimination or harassment are left to pursue whatever informal procedures are available, if any. Sule encouraged her rural colleagues (who are in small numbers at their workplaces) to establish listservs in order to share problems that they experience and to seek ways of supporting each other to resolve them. Sule's experience organizing across the profession began in the 1980s, when she belonged to the Bombay Union of Journalists. Junior members of the Bangalore chapter of the NWMI, such as **Vasanthi Hariprakash** and **Radhika M.**,[32] said that they have come to feel more powerful through their involvement in the group. Interaction with older members has helped them to find the courage to speak up and make decisions about their careers, as well as the encouragement to pursue stories with a specific women's angle. For example, Radhika M. has written stories about dowry, sexual harassment at work, and women's health issues for her daily newspaper, while Hariprakash has emphasized women's longstanding leadership in music and other cultural forms.

Using the Power of Position

Feminist journalists we interviewed who had risen to take up decision-making roles in their news organizations explained ways in which they had helped to shape the content of reporting. Violence against women in its many forms was on the mind of **Patricia Gaston**[33] and her three male editorial colleagues at *The Dallas Morning News* when they hatched plans in 1992 to move women's human rights onto the front page of their newspaper. The series of stories, which would run from January through June 1993 and bring the editors and their reporting team a Pulitzer Prize for international reporting, had begun with a local problem, the rape of several Dallas women by on-duty policemen. Gaston said that she and her colleagues believed the story had a bigger context that was important to explore. The Bosnian war had recently revealed the systematic rape and torture of women, and stories about female genital mutilation, dowry deaths, and other forms of violence against women, which feminists had spent two decades putting on both national and international public agendas were routinely surfacing in the news. In addition, global feminist leaders had finally succeeded in getting the United Nations Conference on Human Rights, to be held in Geneva in June 1993, to add women's human rights to its conference agenda.

Gaston, a black woman, and her three white male colleagues, also believed that the story series offered them a chance to mentor veteran and junior reporters alike on how to reveal the universality of men's violence against women, as well as women's challenges to it. The series of more than a dozen stories would be striking in both its geographical reach and its diversity in subject matter. One story from Norway focused on government grants for women to buy door locks, mace, and other items in order to feel safer. A story from Kenya examined the effects of female circumcision on women. A story from Mexico probed the contradictions in a society in which women are symbolically esteemed but still often beaten by their husbands. A goal of the series was not just to show women's victimization, but also how they had organized to change laws, establish services, and demand that societies change. Gaston, today the national weekend editor at *The Washington Post* in Washington, DC, says that "doing a project of that magnitude really, really hits you deep, and you find ways of keeping the issues out there." She asks reporters to probe problems of violence in particular contexts, such as war.

Kristie Miller[34] has a rare perspective on being a woman serving at the top of the corporate news ladder. Miller was the lone female on the board of the Chicago-based Tribune Company[35] from 1981 to 2001, a time period during which she advocated for the recruitment of women into upper management – something she says "increased markedly" in those years. She also worked successfully to have gay and lesbian employees awarded domestic partner benefits and monitored the coverage of women in the media. She carried on the last of these informally, personally complimenting reporters who had done a good job. Today, Miller writes a weekly column on women and politics for her hometown newspaper in LaSalle, Illinois. But her years in US newsrooms and boardrooms have allowed her to see "dramatic changes" since the 1970s. She believes that:

> The work environment is less hostile, there are more opportunities for women in management and in boards, coverage is more extensive and less stereotyped ... [But] women are still vastly underrepresented on media

boards and in upper management of media companies, along with the rest of corporate America . . .

The last three decades – years in which feminism emerged as a social force globally – have brought changes to newsrooms in many nations. **Sandhya Taksale's**[36] present post as an editor at a weekly Marathi-language news magazine, *The Sukal Papers*, in Pune, India, allows her to build gender angles into news assignments and work with reporters to learn how to discern the gender dimension in their writing. It was her years working on women's magazines that let her understand the women's angle, she said, but she believes, "You have to say to people that it is not only a women's point of view but one that is socially important." For example, she asks that economic stories include the ways in which women will be affected, and she insists that women in sports be covered as well as men.

Confronting a Culture of Discrimination

Some nations have taken longer to see progress. While gender relations in African media remain an under-researched area, Aida Opoku-Mensah (2004: 106) has found anecdotal data that suggest women operate in a "culture of discrimination and bias, characterized by inequity and inequality in all aspects of media work." One small-scale study that Opoku-Mensah conducted verified the general perception within the journalism field that "women often work in hostile work environments," and many newsrooms have few or no women at all (p. 108). Women told her that they were confronted with patriarchal attitudes that assume women's inferiority to men. The lack of women-oriented reporting in Africa has led women practitioners to address these issues. For example, the Tanzania Media Women's Association (TAMWA) has produced radio programs for women that Opoku-Mensah said drew "instant popularity."

Women in the southern region have also formed the Gender and Media Network Southern Africa (GEMSA) to promote gender equity in the media through regional strategies that will address everything from election coverage to HIV/AIDS and other health issues. GEMSA grew out of a meeting in September 2004, in Johannesburg, where, interestingly, a third of the 184 participants were men – a possible sign that enlightened men are trying to address the gender gap. We saw earlier that journalists such as Patience

Dapaah and Madeleine Memb are among the African feminist journalists who use their vantage points on the inside of newsrooms and women's news advocacy groups to try to get women's experiences and gender analyses into the news. **Howedia Saleem,**[37] a reporter for the English-language *Khartoum Monitor*, in Sudan, looks for ways to bring a women's rights angle to many of her topics. She has written about many women's opposition to female genital mutilation, which is practiced in her nation, and about exercising women's right to select their own husbands. Saleem seeks support for her journalistic work through organizations such as the Tunisia-based Center for Arab Women's Training and Research (CAWTAR), which promotes women's economic and political advancement, and ENGED, which promotes information infrastructures for women.

Lubna Yousif Ali,[38] in Sudan, who has been a newspaper and magazine journalist since 1978, said her goals are "always to keep women informed about their rights." As the editor of a women's page for many years, and a writer for *Azza* monthly women's magazine in the 1990s, she has published articles on voting laws (enacted in the 1970s), women's illiteracy and educational programs to meet it, female genital mutilation, divorce, economics, and what other women in the world are doing politically. Yousif Ali notes that she feels supported through active participation in two journalism unions (one of them for women), as well as the Arabs Union. Today, she works for the Umma Party, Sudan's largest political party, as a media information officer, and she takes on independent projects to expand women's understanding of media, such as the media workshop that she coordinated for women in December 2003. She sees the difference that reporting on and about women has made in Sudan over these last decades. For example, women's rise to high places in government has been covered by the news, reinforcing the expansion of women into professions. But she laments the continued practice of female genital mutilation, which needs more news coverage. Though positive in her own experiences to open spaces for women in the news, Yousif Ali works in a larger context in which her female counterparts generally face great difficulties in their workplaces.

South African feminist journalists have been integral to bringing both gender and racial equality into the democratic changes that swept South Africa after 1991, when the nation transitioned from a white minority government to one ruled by Africans. **Thandazo,**[39] a Tanzanian who has worked in South African broadcasting for many years, sees part of her reporting job to be showing that "the role of women is not that traditional anymore." Women hold many of the same jobs as men and keep the same long hours, she said. She's had to struggle with male editors who wanted to change her stories because they didn't like her efforts to gender balance them, and she believes that there is some way to go before such challenges stop. **Nombuso Dlamini**,[40] a reporter for the program *Soul Beat Africa*, has had similar experiences with editors, particularly in "very white" newsrooms. Being black was a particular problem when working with Afrikaans-speaking people, who tended to run things by the "old rules" that propped up apartheid. With South Africa's new constitution that "enshrines" gender equality, she said that she sees newsrooms now moving in that direction. Broadcast journalist **Sue Valentine**[41] left mainstream reporting "as a principle of self-preservation," even though she found her work to be generally fulfilling. Valentine found it essential for women in the newsroom to support each other "in their work as women" as much as for their shared goals of black consciousness. But she also believes that "it shouldn't always be the woman arguing for women's issues [in news] – men can also be feminists – and for a more progressive and inclusive agenda, expecting the same for everyone across the board."

Refocusing the Routine Assignment

Following Elson's (1994) observation that the micro-level of institutions tends to be the most convenient – and common – realm for gender to surface and for women to challenge it, we may look to how the daily events and decisions, including production decisions, that govern and result in content, are located in this level of media institutions. Indeed, as we have seen throughout this chapter, it is in this realm in which the women activists whom we interviewed said they had often tried to have an impact. One common change was to expand the narrow definition of news, which typically covers the events and issues associated with institutions that involve men as central (news-making) figures.

Trained as a print journalist, **Nupur Basu**,[42] of Bangalore, turned to documentary film for television in the early 1990s when Indian television opened up to satellite broadcasts and commercially supported programming. Basu, presently employed by the NDTV all-news station, based in New Delhi, brought her specialty reporting on civil rights movements and environmental and women's rights issues with her. Her first television documentary examined the impact of government liquor sales on poor rural people, particularly women whose husbands squander their meager incomes on drink and then go home to abuse their wives and children. She argues that "A village with 200 people needs a potable drinking water source, not five liquor shops," which lead to addiction. Her film contributed to a short-lived ban on liquor sales in one state. Subsequent films have focused on problems common to poor Indian women, including malnourishment, lack of education, and even the relationship between global corporations and large urban slums. Basu puts 80 percent of her work in the category of "development" topics, because that is where her passion lies. She explained:

> You come from a privileged background, you've been to a good college, but that is because your circumstances were that. Once in the newspaper, you are going to be writing about people who can't even read that newspaper. Your whole agenda then is about social change, improving your country, strengthening your democracy, and insuring this beautiful document – the constitution – which we have in this country [is applied].

Basu's latest work has focused on acid attacks on women and other violence resulting in death. In Bangalore, 90 women die every month, many of these being dowry deaths. An acid attack, something on the rise in India and Bangladesh, can result in two dozen operations and permanent disfigurement. While bringing a feminist perspective, she insists that her work stays "firmly with the principles of journalism – fact checking and counter-checking – and true to ethics." But women are not the only victims of injustice: their stories, too, are the responsibility of reporters. She noted that:

> We in India would be judged for joining with the bold, the beautiful and the stock market while our poor farmers are committing suicide. Twenty-five thousand farmers have committed suicide in South India alone, many because their crops have failed, they have nothing to eat and cannot repay their loans. These are the stories that have to be told again and again.

Print journalists **Gretchen Luchsinger Sidhu**[43] and **Suzanne Francis Brown**[44] found that their mainstream media careers, together with interests in national development, turned into positions with the Women's Feature Service, a women-owned international news agency headquartered in New Delhi, India (the WFS is profiled in Chapter 10). Sidhu, who served initially as an editor for WFS in India, coordinated WFS operations for North America during the 1990s, and Brown for the Caribbean area, positions that allowed them to write stories about women and also to assign such coverage to others. Sidhu's experience transferred directly into her present freelance writing, based in New York, one part of which involves publishing a regular newsletter for the UN Children's Fund (UNICEF), which has 7,000 staff members in 150 nations. Sidhu said that bringing gender balance into stories now comes naturally to her. She also works for other forms of balance; for example, perspectives of workers from different geographical regions and occupations within the agency. Brown said that her training through WFS has enabled her to develop a curriculum on gender and development for the Caribbean Institute for Media and Development (CARIMAC) in Jamaica, where she teaches, and to represent development issues on the board of Women's Media Watch, a monitoring group (see Chapter 9).

Embedding Women in the Sphere

Women journalists the world over have led the way for women's experiences and perspectives to embed themselves in routine news reporting, both in print and broadcast media. This chapter has explored specific ways in which this has occurred through the work of 38 informants in a dozen different nations over these past 30 years. Their work, complemented by male journalists who have taken their lead, may be understood as women's agency in the creation of a feminist public sphere, which intersects dominant public spheres from nation to nation. Issues of women's legal rights, public leadership, and men's violence against women are among women's experiences that women media activists following the second path have helped to bring into public discussion through the media. Still, much remains to be done, particularly with regard to the last of these.

The under-reporting and incomplete reporting of violent crimes against women became the focus of a global feminist campaign called "16 Days of Activism Against Gender Violence" that began on November 25, 2004, in a lead-up to the annual celebration of Human Rights Day on December 10. At issue in the campaign are stories such as the following, which appeared in India's largest circulating daily newspaper, *The Times of India*, on January 4, 2004:

> **New Delhi:** A 25-year-old woman committed suicide by dousing herself with kerosene and then setting herself afire in the bathroom, at her Shahpur Jat residence on Tuesday. / The victim's husband, Rajesh, works with a private

company in Gurgaon. / The couple have a five-month-old daughter. / She was reportedly taken to Safdarjung Hospital but died before she could receive any medical aid. (*The Times of India* 2004)

Ammu Joseph (2004e) noted that incomplete stories are disturbing in their reminiscence of the news that was seen in the late 1970s, when, as discussed earlier, Indian feminists challenged reporting of such women's deaths as accidents rather than suicides or murders of young married women by their relatives. It was clear, Joseph said, that police accounts were being printed without a deeper questioning of the crime involved or an analysis of its frequency. In the 25 years since feminists in India and throughout the world opened the lid on domestic abuse, sexual assault, and other forms of violence against women, reporting in many nations remains little changed, particularly with regard to either the underlying causes of such violence or its consequences for women. Joseph notes that many world organizations have issued alerts. The World Health Organization has called violence against women a "global pandemic that needs urgent attention." Amnesty International identified violence against women as "the most pervasive human rights challenge in the world." The US National Advisory Council on Violence Against Women and the Violence Against Women Office call on "the responsible voice of the mass media" to refrain from glorifying or romanticizing such violence, and to show that such violence is unacceptable (quoted in Joseph 2004e).

The more specific ways in which feminist organizations have challenged media to take up these (and other concerns) are at the heart of Chapter 9, where we analyze the work of women media activists working as advocate change agents.

Notes

1   Margot Adler submitted answers on August 12, 2003.
2   Dalia Liran-Alper submitted answers on July 22, 2003.
3   Jo Campbell submitted answers on October 4, 2003.
4   Margot Adler submitted answers on August 12, 2003.
5   Margot Adler's *Drawing Down the Moon* (1979) is about paganism in America, with a particular focus on ancient women's and modern feminist spiritual rituals.
6   Patience Dapaah submitted answers on October 2, 2003.
7   Madeleine Memb submitted answers on September 29, 2003.

8   Trella Laughlin submitted answers on October 5, 2003.

9   The Agenda Magazine Collective was interviewed in Durban on September 10, 2003.

10 Sakuntala Narasimhan submitted answers on December 7, 2003.

11 Stacey Cone submitted answers on August 18, 2003.

12 Louise North submitted answers on July 7, 2003.

13 Preeti Mehra was interviewed in New Delhi, India, on January 6, 2004.

14 Tanushree Gangopadhyay was interviewed on January 11, 2004, in Bangalore, India.

15 Sonal Kellogg was interviewed on January 13, 2004, in Bandra, India.

16 A month's violence committed against Muslims in the state of Gujarat by Hindu fundamentalists, some of whom were policemen, occurred in February 2002. Muslim women were particularly singled out for mutilation and brutality, and the events brought an outpouring of feminist journalism and analysis. For a fuller account, see Martha C. Nussbaum (2003).

17 Mildred Mulenga was interviewed by telephone on July 31, 2003.

18 Crystal Oderson was interviewed by telephone on July 28, 2003.

19 Sylvia Vollenhoven was interviewed by telephone on October 17, 2003.

20 Judy Sandison was interviewed by telephone on July 27, 2003.

21 Virginie Barré submitted answers on April 2, 2004.

22 Natacha Henry submitted answers on August 26, 2003.

23 Kalpana Sharma submitted answers on March 9, 2004.

24 Ammu Joseph was interviewed in Arlington, Virginia, on March 23, 2003.

25 For additional information about Anjali Mathur's role in the Women in Media Group, see Chapter 7.

26 Ammu Joseph, personal communication, December 7, 2004.

27 For a fuller account of the WMG report, see Ammu Joseph and Kalpana Sharma (1994a).

28 The Indian government changed the name of Bombay to Mumbai in the mid-1990s.

29 Rajashri Dasgupta submitted answers on March 15, 2004, and comments on December 8, 2004.

30 The website of the Network of Women in Media in India, www.nwindia.org (accessed November 22, 2004).

31 Surekha Sule submitted answers on March 8, 2004, and comments on December 6, 2004.

32 Vasanthi Hariprekesh and Radhika M., both of Bangalore, were interviewed at the second NWMI meeting, in Bandra, India, on January 14, 2004.

33 Patricia Gaston was interviewed in College Park, Maryland, on August 4, 2003.

34 Kristie Miller submitted her answers on August 16, 2003.

35 The Tribune Company owns *The Chicago Tribune, The Los Angeles Times, The Baltimore Sun*, and nearly 50 other newspapers, television and radio stations, and online news services (including several in the Spanish language). See www.tribune.com.

36 Sandhya Taksale was interviewed at the NWMI meeting, in Bandra, India, on January 12, 2004.

37 Howedia Saleem submitted answers on July 2, 2003.

38 Lubna Yusif Ali submitted answers on July 12, 2003.

39 Thandazo (a pseudonym) was interviewed by telephone on July 29, 2003.

40 Nombuso Dlamini was interviewed by telephone on July 28, 2003.

41 Sue Valentine was interviewed in Cape Town, South Africa, on September 8, 2003.

42 Nupur Basu was interviewed in Bangalore, India, on January 10, 2004.

43 Gretchen Sidhu, of Jersey City, New Jersey, was interviewed in Hyattsville, Maryland, June 14, 2003.

44 Suzanne Francis Brown submitted answers on May 4, 2004.

9

Third Path: Advocate Change Agent

[M]ostly disadvantaged grassroots women who were the voiceless now have a voice. They have submitted articles that have been published in the mainstream media; they have helped us write policies, so they . . . know what the score is, and they can go back to their organizations and advocate, whether it is the Sexual Offenses Bill or the Anti-Terrorism Bill. Women can now go on the radio because the whole technology has been demystified. They can sit there in the studio and speak.

Judith Smith, Women's Media Watch, South Africa, 2003

Judith Smith's[1] words bring to life both the spirit and work of women activists engaged in change agency through nonprofit organizations that have specifically targeted media reform since the 1970s. Such work has been addressed by Margaret Gallagher (2001: 8–9) in her groundbreaking book *Gender Setting: New Agendas for Media Monitoring and Advocacy,* where she noted that while organizations of female media workers date back to the 1970s, it was not until the 1980s that networks and associations of media women really began to flourish in all regions of the world. Their shared concerns were to strengthen the position of women within media industries and to address what they saw to be inadequate representations of women in media content. Our cross-cultural research suggests two additional ways in which women's media advocacy groups, as well as independent advocates, have pursued change. One has been to open direct channels for women's voices to be heard both in mainstream and alternative media outlets. Another has been to bring about public policy changes (including regulatory mechanisms) that would make the media more egalitarian.

These concerns and goals are articulated in one or more ways by the women who followed the third path in our Model of Women's Media Action, that of the "advocate change agent." In the process of tracking and analyzing their work, this chapter both draws on and extends the recent work of Gallagher, whose own media research and advocacy over the past quarter of a century has done much to shape and spotlight feminist efforts to change women's structural relations to media industries throughout the world. Gallagher is one of 24 informants from 10 nations whose work as advocate change agents is examined in the discussion below.

The specific goals of this chapter are to reveal how women's agency has been organized in its aim to modify existing media structures, to create new baselines of knowledge through their research, and to develop strategies for mobilizing constituencies to further participate in this important work. We emphasize that advocate change agents have worked actively at both meso- and micro-levels to develop local, national, and international strategies and networks for media change. Such networking has been achieved through international meetings where they have met face-to-face, explored common interests and goals, and formalized collaborative working arrangements among themselves and their organizations. Networking has also been achieved more informally through regular electronic exchanges of information and correspondence. Significantly, such developments have been intentional and strategic, driven by the understanding that strong, concerted efforts were the best way to confront increasingly global male-dominated systems that continue to marginalize women and many others outside their halls of power.

Twenty-four of our 90 informants (27 percent), representing 10 different nations, followed the third path as advocate change agents (alphabetically):

Martha Leslie Allen, USA	Colleen Lowe Morna,
Sashwati Banerjee, India	South Africa
Libay Cantor, Philippines	Jeroo Mulla, India
Inja Coates, USA	Hilary Nicholson, Jamaica
Bishakha Datta, India	Seeta Peña Gangadharan, USA
Aliza Dichter, USA	Jennifer Pozner, USA
Margaret Gallagher, France/UK	Sasha Rakoff, UK
Abhilasha Kumari, India	Sandhya Rao, India
Margaret Lewis, UK	Joan Ross-Frankson, Jamaica/UK

Vicki Semler, USA	Patricia Solano, Dominican
Ramesh Sepehrrad, Iran/USA	Republic
Akhila Sivadas, India	A. E. Tijhoff, the Netherlands
Judith Smith, South Africa	

Characteristics of the Third Path

Women who followed the path of advocate change agent have used a range of strategies to expand women's communicative infrastructures, both within and across nations. Advocate change agents have typically carried on their work through organizations with specific goals of pressuring the media to improve the treatment of women in one or more ways, to disseminate information with a feminist perspective, and/or to expand direct access for women. In most cases, their activities have included conducting some kind of research on women and media, with those research findings then serving to advance their media advocacy work. In relation to the Model of Women's Media Action – the analytic framework for the present research – the third path holds particular potential to alter women's structural relations to both media and other social institutions. As an examination of the narratives of the 24 informants below will illustrate, those who follow this path engage in the creation of a feminist communicative infrastructure whose cumulative impact can be determined in a number of ways.

Such an infrastructure has been formed through both formal and informal networks of feminist individuals and organizations engaged in changing governmental policies, corporate media policies, production routines concerned with shaping content, and other structural aspects of the media in order to put them at the fuller service of women. In Chapter 8 we explored the importance of women's media activism at the meso-level, where norms and networks are needed for the capitalist system to survive: the micro-level is where day-to-day (routine) decisions are made with respect to the running of institutions. Because mass media around the world are increasingly commercial – thereby fitting squarely within the capitalist system to which Diane Elson (1994: 40–1) refers – we might view both meso-level and micro-level as strategically opportune points for feminist intervention. Elson reminds us that both of these levels of capitalist society are "the bearers of gender," thereby enabling us to situate the systematic work of advocate change agents within the realm of feminist political economy.

To strengthen our theoretical understanding of how change agents and their work have operated in relation to media systems, we might also look to the work of sociologist Anthony Giddens, whose structuration theory has had far-ranging effects on communication studies. Giddens laid out the components of his theory in a series of works during the 1970s and 1980s, explicating them as a whole in works such as *The Constitution of Society: Outline of the Theory of Structuration* (1984). Central to Giddens's theory is the concept of the *duality of structure*, something imagined as both medium and outcome of the practices that comprise social systems (p. 25). The duality of structure embraces the notion that action relies on agents' knowledge of their own social and cultural practices, and their relationship to these. Agents' self-knowledge is achieved through a process of *reflexivity*; that is, a self-assessment of one's biography within a political, economic, and social context.[2] Giddens's theory also emphasizes the importance of active agents working against structural constraints (e.g., outmoded rules and laws) in order to change systems and move societies forward. Of particular appeal to feminists is another of Giddens's concepts, the *dialectic of control*, where he argues that reflexive agents (e.g., women media activists) always have the capacity to make a difference. Applying Giddens's theory to the situation of powerful, androcentric media systems, we argue that women media activists must be understood as having acted in accordance with their knowledge of women's marginalized social status and the media's role in reinforcing and reproducing it. As the findings from our research illustrate, women media activists have undertaken a range of strategies and tasks with the shared goal of revealing and reducing these systems' tendency to reproduce the gendered status quo at policy, employment, and content levels of media.[3]

Change through Monitoring and Training

It might be said that advocate change agents (like other women media activists) proceed from the belief that mass media ought to serve the public interest – in this case, women's interest – by ensuring women's right to communicate, and to be represented appropriately in media content. "Public interest" has varying definitions, which generally coincide with that posed by mass media scholar Denis McQuail (1992: 3), as the complex "informational, cultural and social benefits to the wider society." Mass media industries, which are mostly commercial enterprises supported through advertising, exist first and foremost to generate profits for their (male) owners rather than to serve the (more pluralistic) public interest. Media monitoring has thus emerged as part of a process for making the media more accountable to the public. The media – and by this we refer to broadcasting, print, and electronic enterprises – may be monitored and assessed along a number of axes, including production/professional goals, content, audience reception, and even structural elements such as the background and composition of owners, boards, and employees. For media activists who have been monitoring media and publishing reports for several decades, the goal of transformation has inevitably come to include training, both for citizens and for those inside the industry.

The Global Media Monitoring Project (GMMP)

In 2001, there were feminist organizations with media monitoring projects in more than 20 nations (Gallagher 2001). The largest and most comprehensive program is the Global Media Monitoring Project (GMMP), which has been conducted in more than 70 countries every five years since 1995. The GMMP is sponsored and coordinated by the Women's Program Division of the World Association for Christian Communication, a progressive nongovernmental organization based in London, and administered by project consultant **Margaret Gallagher**,[4] who is based in the United Kingdom and France. Gallagher says that her personal goals are to "use research and analysis in the pursuit of practical change." These are also reflected in the goals and structure of the GMMP: a national coordinator in each participating nation collects the data from citizen researchers who have used a set of common tools to measure certain content, with respect to gender, in broadcast and print news stories on a given day. The idea behind the project, Gallagher says, "is to give people who are not necessarily trained researchers simple, reliable monitoring tools that can produce data useful in media advocacy and activism." Over time, the project has built up what Gallagher calls "the capacity of citizens' groups to critically analyze their media and to take action for change."

Several hundred women teachers, activists, community leaders, and trained researchers in 70 nations took part in the second round of the GMMP, which was held on February 2, 2000, and whose findings are reported in Gallagher's book *Gender Setting* (2001). Gallagher's work as an advocate change agent has spanned more than 20 years and has been driven by two preoccupations, she said:

First, is the increasing influence of the media on values and beliefs, in a situation of growing commercialization and concentration of media ownership. So, I believe that at the policy level, we must fight for the recognition and realization of communication rights worldwide. For instance, I am a member of the International Organizing Committee of the CRIS Campaign [Communication Rights in the Information Society]. Meanwhile, at the practical level, we need to build citizen awareness and give people the skills, tools and arguments with which to interact with media institutions, policy-makers and practitioners. The second preoccupation has to do with the unequal distribution of resources – whether economic, information, political – as between different social groups. And, of course, my particular concern is with gender imbalances within these spheres.

Gallagher regards the unequal gender balance of power and resources as "primordial, something that is embedded in all other inequalities (for example, ethnic, political)." She believes that policies must be put into place to assure that the media meet their responsibility to redress these imbalances. Gallagher's work has also included a more hands-on role with media enterprises striving to change. She conducts workshops in Europe and elsewhere to teach journalists and producers to examine their own practices in order to see how the choices they make both "reflect and reproduce patterns of inequality" in relation to gender, ethnicity, age, and so on.

Gender Links

Whereas Gallagher's work has focused on trying to effect change at both grassroots and global levels, the efforts of others have been regional and national. The 2002 Southern Africa Gender and Media Baseline Study, produced by members of Gender Links and the Media Institute for Southern Africa (MISA), was a regional monitoring and advocacy project that examined women's employment, as well as women's representation in media content, at print and broadcast media in the nations of Southern Africa. The study showed that women comprised only 17 percent of the sources in news stories (just under the 18 percent figure for all world news, as found in the GMMP), and their portrayals were typically limited to sex symbols or victims of violence.[5] Gender Links Director **Colleen Lowe Morna**[6] said that women in journalism had tried for years to get the South African News Editors' Forum (SANEF) to address women's marginalization in both newsrooms and news content. The data from the baseline survey, together with marketing research showing that women are the news media's largest market, convinced managing editors to pay attention. In 2003, the group devoted its entire annual general meeting to gender in the media, she said. Gender Links now provides training to both management and working journalists on how to address gender in their newsrooms and coverage, but she believes that this training can only work if the organization makes a deep commitment to change:

> You can take a journalist off to Stellenbosch and run a training course and they love it and they are all fired up, but then they go back into an institution that is not transformed: the managers and everybody else won't take them seriously . . . So, we have been trying to move towards a much more dynamic model which is, how do you link institutional change and transformation and training, and how do you do this holistically? Also, as we have been developing our training materials and testing them, we have been looking at how to take these into the micro-level so that you start to integrate gender in all areas of work.

In summer 2003, Gender Links launched four pilot projects at newspapers that had established internal transformation committees. Lowe Morna said that the project moves forward slowly, driven by four or five women in SANEF who are "strategically positioned and pushing the agenda." Gender Links is also expanding its resources to include a directory of women sources to assist reporters to locate such for their stories. She thus sees the process of transformation as an incremental one, not an avalanche:

> You build on successes. You find your entry points, very strategic. Get key people on board. Now we engage and engage and engage, and we've had a little success here and there.

Media Watch – South Africa and Jamaica

Judith Smith,[7] director of Women's Media Watch in South Africa – whose quote opened this chapter – said that her organization is hoping to set up Media Watches in each nation of the Southern Africa region to support the efforts of sister groups such as Gender Links. Smith said that she also has a general goal of bringing about awareness of the issues that women face on a daily basis, and the multiple roles they are required to play in their communities and at home. Awareness building is aimed at women's empowerment, she said, including the recognition that in the new South Africa they are guaranteed full rights by the Constitution. Media literacy training teaches women how to write press releases and how to develop and produce radio programs for broadcast on community stations (such as those referred to in the opening quote to this chapter). For example, media training with the Violence Against Women coalition led to a radio campaign in which women spoke out about the abuse they experienced from their husbands, something that brought wide public support. The group's training for journalists includes a focus on gender-sensitive language, something that has resulted in some participant-journalists helping WMW with their media training for other journalists. In addition, the monitoring of gender on television and other media has led to an annual report, which Media Watch members use as the basis for face-to-face dialogues with media managers and producers. Developing a nonconfrontational approach, Smith said, is a new direction for the organization and has been productive. Most recently, the organization has been able to suggest changes in media policy relating to public broadcasting, such as one calling for the elimination of racist content in advertising.

Similarly, Women's Media Watch – Jamaica was founded in 1987 by **Hilary Nicholson**[8] and a small group of other women who wanted to conduct public education around gender and media issues, including violence in the media. Over the years, Nicholson said, WMW has held symposia on gender and media; offered hundreds of workshops on how to conduct what she calls "gender-sensitive media analysis" for community groups, youth clubs, teachers, trainee journalists at the Caribbean Institute for Media and Communications (CARIMAC), and media professionals; and conducted media monitoring that has led to published reports. WMW's media monitoring has had both local and global foci, the second of these through their participation in the Global Media Monitoring Project (GMMP). Nicholson, WMW's program coordinator, emphasized the importance of her organization's collaboration with similar organizations, locally and internationally, including the Women and Development (WAND) organization in Barbados, the Women's Centre of Jamaica Foundation, the Caribbean Association for Feminist Research and Action (CAFRA), the United Nations Development Fund for Women (UNIFEM), the Caribbean Gender Equity Fund, and others.

Nicholson joins a growing chorus of women media activists who advocate for gender-specific policies and codes of ethics governing media operations, something they believe is essential if gender sensitivity is to be mainstreamed. Such policies, they say, are essential to free speech.

Challenging Media Norms

Among those making a connection between media regulations and women's free speech is **Martha Leslie Allen**,[9] who first became involved with free speech advocacy in connection with racial justice work in Louisville, Kentucky, in the late 1960s. In 1973, she incorporated gender justice into that work by founding and leading the Women's Media Project in Memphis, Tennessee. The group successfully negotiated with three local broadcasters for improved coverage of women, as well as expanding women's employment at all organizational levels. Allen has also advocated for local women's radio programs and the establishment of a women's cable TV channel. Allen's early work had a national context in the early 1970s, an era when the National Organization for Women (NOW) and other women's rights groups in the United States were pursuing a strategy of petitioning the Federal Communications Commission to deny broadcast licenses to television and radio stations that failed (1) to ascertain women's opinions on community issues, (2) to provide programming about women's issues, and (3) employ women. In the USA, broadcasting media are subject to federal regulation under the principle that the public owns the airwaves. However, the FCC has shown little inclination historically to insure that broadcasting truly serves the public interest. While the challenge to license renewals was rejected in a 1975 FCC opinion, there were a number of positive outcomes for women, the most lasting probably being the increased employment of women within the industry (Beasley & Gibbons 2003: 200–1).

Martha Allen would go on to form a working partnership with her mother, the late Donna Allen, who had founded the Women's Institute for Freedom of the Press, in Washington, DC (USA), in 1972, specifically to advocate for a more democratic media system. One stated goal of the Institute has been to "enable all people – rich and poor, male and female – to have the equal opportunity to speak directly to the whole public," on the basis that "access to the public constitutes political power in a democracy and must be equal." Such a right, the Institute asserts, "is a citizen right of democracy," not one "based on wealth" (Allen 2002: iv). Allen said that the Institute also challenges corporate mass media myths; for example, that journalists are "objective" and that the corporate media put out what the public wants. Allen argues that 1 percent of the population (the wealthy media barons) "do not speak for the rest of the people – women, the labor movement, people of color, children, anyone who's left out." In 2002, the

Institute joined in a protest against FCC rulings that further deregulated the rapidly consolidating broadcast industry.

Inja Coates,[10] of Media Tank, an advocacy group based in Philadelphia, Pennsylvania, said she is "heartened by the number of women who are involved in the emerging policy struggles and are challenging the old(boy) frameworks." Young women's involvement is particularly significant, she said, since they bring a different vision and model for change. Coates has been working on what she calls "democracy access issues" since 1997, through both alternative and mainstream groups. The latter includes the National Organization for Women, where she has helped to move communication policy issues onto the group's working platform.

Young media activists such as Coates are increasingly visible in the USA today. That protest targeting the FCC in 2002 was orchestrated by a small, savvy group of women from around the USA, mostly in their twenties and thirties, who were (and remain) determined to change public policy governing media operations. Among them are **Seeta Peña Gangadharan**[11] and **Aliza Dichter,**[12] co-founders of the Center for International Media Action (CIMA), in San Francisco, California, a nonprofit group that places changing federal policies on media ownership (and related reforms in the public interest) at the top of its agenda. In 2002, they joined with the National Organization for Women, the Women's Institute for Freedom of the Press, Women In Media and News, and other women's groups to mobilize opposition to FCC rules that further relaxed the number of media outlets that a single company could own. Peña Gangadharan wrote a reporter's guide to the media ownership debate, which was widely used by the independent press covering the debate at the time.

Not all of the women whom we interviewed believed that government policy aimed at gender inclusion in media was the most effective route in gaining access for women. **Abhilasha Kumari,**[13] a sociologist on the faculty of a New Delhi (India) university, specializes in women's involvement in political process. In her recent work, she has assisted women serving in panchayats (local governing councils), helping them to be more aware of gender issues and ways to address these through their elected roles.[14] Kumari has also been involved with media issues, both through her academic work and in feminist activism. She takes the position that control over broadcast media should lie with civil society, not governmental agencies. In India, she said that she has asked people what would happen if a right-wing government were elected: "Do you want those politics to determine what women should and should not do?" She added:

People tended to think they would always have a liberal government. But that's wrong. Things have changed to the extent that now women realize (as all minorities) that media should not be controlled by government – it should be in the hands of civil society to build pressure groups and raise issues with media people.

She believes that while corporations are firmly in control of media operations and content today, they realize that "they have to meet certain needs and requirements of their market – which is civil society." To that extent, she said, "they are responsive to the concerns of what people are saying, in some sense."

Genderizing Global Media Policy

As members of a younger generation, Aliza Dichter and Seeta Peña Gangadharan embody an emerging multicultural global network that is taking shape among feminist media activists. Dichter stresses CIMA's desire to connect gender concerns with those of other marginalized groups denied a voice through today's mainstream media. Thus, CIMA collaborates with youth groups such as ACME (Action Coalition for Media Education) and Y_FEN (the Youth Free Expression Network), as well as seniors, gay and lesbian, indigenous, and racial justice groups in order to organize a new generation of media activists. Peña Gangadharan also emphasizes her overlapping roles with CIMA and the World Forum on Communication Rights where, as the group's press officer, she helps to interface US-oriented reforms with international strategies for changing media policy.

Women media activists increasingly opt to push for greater media regulation in order to gain the communication rights of women and others at the social margins. Far from being a new thing, media regulation has long existed under all forms of government, the common purpose being to shape both the nature of media systems and the general guidelines for their operation within national boundaries. Conflicts have typically arisen around which kind of media models would exist: the market (commercial) model, the public interest model, the state-run model, or some combination of these. Celia Aldana (2004: 12), from the NGO Calandria, in Peru, who addressed a gathering in Piran, Slovenia, in April 2004, argues that the role of regulation is to establish the basic rules for communication so that democracy can function properly. Laws, she said, can promote the creation of channels of dialogue between media and their audiences. At the international level, the situation has been trickier, as was discovered in the 1970s and 1980s during the New World Information and Communication Order debates. Those debates grew out of discontent among many leaders in the nonaligned (developing) nations, who recognized a growing disparity between communication resources in their own nations as compared to those of the industrial world. Communication systems had by then become recognized as something central to both development and maintenance of modern societies. Thus, policies governing everything from the allocation of the electromagnetic spectrum to the treatment of reporters came under scrutiny in the decade-long course of the debates (Gerbner, Mowlana & Nordenstreng 1993).

Two aspects of these debates are relevant to the present discussion. The first is that the global media debates of earlier decades excluded women's participation almost entirely, as feminist scholars such as Colleen Roach (1990) have pointed out. Second, the problems of communication disparities between the more powerful and less powerful societies were unresolved during the 1970s and 1980s debates, and were thus destined to reappear in new forums and formats during the 1990s and since that time. As issues have indeed resurfaced, women media activists have sought to intervene, pushing gender to the forefront of discussions, and connecting it to related issues of social class, race, and ethnicity.

Libay (Olivia Linsangan) Cantor[15] found her route to Isis-Manila, the prominent international feminist media activist organization, through both professional media work and gay and lesbian media activism. For the first, Cantor said, she let her feminist consciousness guide her work in writing and editing, such as writing columns that critiqued the way in which media presented images of women, lesbians, and gay men. For the second, gay and lesbian activism, she engaged in letter-writing campaigns through Task Force Pride, a Manila-based network of lesbian–gay–bisexual–transgendered organizations in the Philippines, and, earlier, through the university-based Philippines Sappho Society. In her work at Isis, Cantor serves as a project team member on activities related to developing an international media network among and on behalf of women.

Isis International began in Rome and Geneva in 1974, but moved headquarters to Manila in 1991. Since then, independent Isis offices have also been established in Kampala and Santiago, reflecting what the organization calls "a commitment to South–South cooperation and South–North linkages" (www.isiswomen.org). Isis staff have actively participated in events associated with the first World Summit on the Information Society (WSIS) meeting, held in Geneva in December 2003, with plans to also participate in the second meeting scheduled for Tunis in November 2005. Isis's active involvement has included helping to define and advocate for the CRIS campaign (Communication Rights in the Information Society) and the WSIS Gender Caucus. The Gender Caucus emerged from WSIS preparatory meetings in Mali (Africa), in 2002, in order to better assure that women-specific language would be part of any recommendations for policy that might arise from the second WSIS process. The Gender Caucus's website (www.genderwsis.org) identifies additional goals as facilitating projects that will track women's access to and use of information communication technologies (ICTs), and to support campaigns that include a wide range of media, such as radio, television, computers, and others.

The International Women's Tribune Center ("the Tribune Center"), based in New York City, was also a participant in the WSIS Gender Caucus. Tribune Center Director **Vicki Semler**[16] emphasizes the importance of women at the community level gaining a stake in the outcome of the WSIS proceedings. Toward that end, she said, "we are trying to create an electronic toolkit which would support women at national and community levels in their ability to provide gender perspectives on the new media and information technology policies that are being formed." The greatest obstacle to women's involvement, she believes, is that "those in charge of structural power don't want to open their minds." The Tribune Center, which was established in 1976 to make feminist ideas available to women at the community level across the world, has played a major role developing and disseminating materials for use by community activists, particularly in low-income communities, both rural and urban. In addition, Semler and other Tribune Center staff try to represent the interests of those communities through extensive and global women's and other networks.

Global media activism has also affected women and social policy in other ways. **Joan Ross-Frankson**[17] is communications director for the Women's Environmental and Development Organization (WEDO), a nongovernmental organization founded by former US Congresswoman Bella Abzug and activist journalist Mim Kelber in 1992. Based in New York City, WEDO collaborates with women's organizations throughout the world to place women's concerns related to human rights, governance, social justice, economics, and sustainable development into recommendation sections of documents considered by the UN and other policy-making groups. Their influence is achieved by what Ross-Frankson calls the creation of the "shadow document" – an advance copy of proposed policy that bears the comments and suggestions made by WEDO based on suggestions from its partner feminist organizations.

WEDO has had substantial success using the shadow document strategy. At the Earth Summit in Rio de Janeiro in 1992, women's groups were able to get an entire chapter on women inserted into the document that was eventually adopted by delegates. Ross-Frankson said, "For the first time in global policy, we had them write in that women were central to the health of the planet and to poverty eradication. That is literally what WEDO does in this phase of implementation, building on the fact that we do have this network [whose membership] shifts and changes obviously." She also points to meetings of the UN Fund for Population Development, held in Cairo, and the UN Commission on Human Rights, held in Geneva, both in the 1990s, when WEDO played a similar coordinating role. A crucial follow-up aspect of WEDO's work is monitoring to see what all 192 member nations of the UN do to take action on those policies with gender conditions specified, and then publishing the findings in an annual report circulated to women's organizations and the world media. Joan Ross-Frankson's work at WEDO brings together her years of using video and other media in grassroots women's development, as well as her professional life as a broadcast journalist in Jamaica, her nation of origin.

Cultural Criticism as Advocacy

Using a different approach in advocating for responsible media policy, **Jennifer Pozner**[18] uses the power of her pen to engage public dialogue. Pozner is founder and executive director of WIMN (Women In Media and News), a nonprofit group, based in New York City, with a three-pronged vision for media reform that includes media analysis and critique, media education in the form of skills-building training for women's advocacy groups, and the creation of new resources for media professionals, such as a database of female news sources. Pozner said that she developed the skill of blending serious scholarly arguments and in-depth research with a sardonic writing voice while critiquing pop culture for the "Media Watch" column in the now defunct feminist newspaper *Sojourner* in the mid-1990s. She went on to head the Women's Desk at the media watchdog group FAIR (Fairness and Accuracy in Reporting), writing critiques of corporate media content as well as of women's unequal position in media industries, including in the boardroom. As a writer, Pozner said, she has tried to "explode and critique myths and inaccuracies, both ideological and factual, around gender in news and pop culture." Her most recent work, published by *Ms.* magazine and other outlets, has criticized the mainstream news media's trivialization of female political leaders, the misogynistic tendencies of "reality TV" shows, and the sidelining of women's perspectives in war news.

Campaigning to eradicate sexist media portrayals of women has served to mobilize women around the world, as earlier chapters have shown. Whereas earlier discussions have looked particularly at individual efforts, in this section we consider the work of advocacy groups whose media activism focuses primarily on those portrayals and, in some cases, on the real-life violence against women that is believed to be associated with them. Some of the informants who shared their experiences with us indicated that they wanted not just to stop media victimization of women, but also to replace these problematic images with more diverse ones. This suggests a complex advocacy approach involving multiple roles for feminist agents in bringing about intervention, dialogue, education, and finally change.

Several organizations in the UK have addressed a range of concerns about media sexism and what they see to be related real-life sexual exploitation of women. **Sasha Rakoff**[19] and **Jennifer Drew**,[20] co-chairs of the London-based group Object, use community education to develop what Rakoff calls "a groundswell of public support" to pressure decision-makers to end mainstream media's sexualization of women, as well as to address what Object believes is sexual exploitation by strip clubs. One principal campaign issue, for example, has been the use of images of naked women in advertisements on bus side panels and other public places, the long-standing practice of British tabloids to feature pictures of nude and semi-naked women on their pages,[21] and the recent proliferation of lap dancing clubs, which include both pole-dancing and women performing against men's bodies. On the last of these, Drew said she has conducted some research for Object to determine whether the behavior that takes place at strip clubs is related to an increase in reported incidents of rape in the small geographical area in which many of those clubs are situated. Object plans to make these findings known. Object also addresses other forms of media sexism, pursuing an interventionist approach by filing letters of complaint, for example, with television networks when programs stereotype women or omit them altogether. The group also has a concern that serious realities for women – the feminization of poverty, low pay, and racism experienced by nonwhite women – remain largely ignored by mainstream media. Public awareness that results in mobilizing others to complain, they say, is a major step in gaining media attention for women's real-life experience.

Jennifer Drew's own activism in relation to media sexism began in the 1990s with London3rdWave, another media advocacy organization that campaigns to remove sexually violent advertising featuring women's images from buses and other sites. One recent image featured the torso of a woman with very large breasts wearing a tight dress, with the caption "Weapons of Mass Destruction." Drew filed an official complaint on behalf of London3rdWave with the Advertising Standards Authority, asking that the advertisement's parent company be forced to remove the adverts. When the ASA refused to take action, saying that their members found it light-hearted, she appealed to an Independent Adjudicator. Although he upheld the ASA's determination, Drew said, London3rdWave members have continued to use this complaint process on other adverts, with more success. **Margaret Lewis's**[22] advocacy work with the Sheffield Women's Media Action Forum's Media Action Group closely parallels that of Object and London3rdWave in trying to get the ASA to be more responsive to advertising that sexualizes women. Lewis says that the group is in the process of finding alternative strategies to combat what they see to be the mainstreaming of soft-core pornography, both live and image-based (e.g., video games and music videos), targeted at young women and girls. Lewis believes that women should "feel comfortable about objecting" to soft-core pornographic imagery. To measure these attitudes and feelings, the Sheffield Forum is planning to conduct research among women about their views on soft-core pornography. Lewis believes that the strategic collaboration among the Sheffield Forum and sister organizations (such as Object and London3rdWave) in the UK will better enable them to be effective.

When socially sanctioned complaint processes either don't exist or seem unresponsive, women media activists have been known to take matters into their own hands. **A. E. Tijhoff**,[23] a university student in Groningen, the Netherlands, helped found a women's media action group called *de Natte Vinger* (The Wet Finger), which destroys images of women that they find objectionable. Members paint over bus advertisements, billboards, and other public images that they believe to be sexist. Like Margaret Lewis, Tijhoff said she believes that women are entitled to feel disturbed about sexist commercials and to "show the people that there is problem and that you can do something about it." She would advise people working in the media to consider what they are giving the public, to take responsibility for it, and to educate themselves about gender issues.

Generating Diversity in Content

In the Dominican Republic, **Patricia Solano**[24] has spent a decade trying to encourage media to portray what she calls "the diversity of women" and to put women's problems on the public agenda. She began her work in communications in the mid-1990s, at the nation's oldest nongovernmental organization for women, Centro de Investigación para la Acción Feminina (CIPAF). Eventually taking her feminist knowledge into full-time media work, Solano presently works as a television producer who strives to bring gender balance to news and other programming. Topics such as health, economics, violence, and inequality of opportunity are among these.

Although media monitoring and research have been companion activities for **Akhila Sivadas**[25] at the Centre for Advocacy and Research, in New Delhi, India, the trained social scientist and former journalist says that her real goal is to bring about change in media content. Television is particularly subject to influence, she believes. The market is challenged by the cultural kaleidoscope of India, but any group that wants to make a difference has to be "knowledgeable and understanding of the whole dynamics." The social groups that she helps seek a bigger voice in TV and other media are urban and rural poor women, young people, and disabled people (including those with HIV/AIDS). Although her political activism was inspired by the aftermath of India's liberation movement and her days as a student activist in the 1960s, Sivadas's attitudes about opening up the media were radicalized during a period of strict censorship imposed by President Indira Gandhi in the 1970s. Living through that era deeply affected her, producing a dedication to critical teaching that relies on a process of self-discovery – a process that she now tries to use with the community groups to whom she speaks about media. Sivadas brings views about media gathered in these grassroots encounters back to reporters and producers, with the goal of shaping news and program content. She also relies on research that she and her staff conduct about both social issues and media trends. Calling herself the old one in the organization, she takes heart that her young staff can carry on media advocacy for the next generation.

Little explored in media change work is the role of activist feminist college professors who intentionally train new generations of media professionals to put gender at the core of their work. In Mumbai, **Jeroo Mulla**[26] is head of the Social Communications Media Department at Sophia

Polytechnic, a women's college run by the nuns of the Order of the Sacred Heart. Mulla's professional background in television and documentary film prepared her to teach graduate courses in film appreciation, basic techniques of film and photography, and fundamentals of communication. In all of these, she builds in ways to help students to critique media treatment of women and to try to expand content on women once they enter the profession. Mulla said that her approach has the complete endorsement of her institution, which was established to educate women in order to empower them and make them economically independent through securing professional careers. This means that her work is "supported by the prevalent ideology of the institute."

For the past 24 years, Jeroo Mulla has sent students into both urban and rural areas to interview women in their everyday lives, to make documentary films and news stories on issues such as the state of the female child in India, women and cancer, rape, domestic violence, the portrayal of women in advertising, gender discrimination and property rights, women and health, domestic workers, girl street children, women and HIV/AIDS, and others. Mulla believes that the spread of information about the women's movement at all levels of college education has "made the students much more self aware, confident and not willing to be as passive as an earlier generation," and she believes that young women from elite backgrounds have particularly benefited from "discovering the inequities among those in other socio-economic groups and even in their own upper classes!"

Media Advocacy for Mobilization

Point of View

In 1997, the 50th year of India's independence, **Bishakha Datta**, **Sashwati (Sash) Banerjee**,[27] and several other women with professional media backgrounds questioned what independence had meant for the women of India. Their questions led to the formation of Point of View (POV), a nonprofit organization, and their first project, "Black and White," a photographic exhibition that "questioned the whole paradigm of independence and its meaning for the Indian woman." The exhibition, which traveled throughout India and to selected cities in the USA, featured the work of 42 world-class photographers who depicted women of varied backgrounds and social status, together with their statements about Indian society. Datta, a former journalist and documentary filmmaker, and Banerjee, an international advertising professional, said that POV's mission is to use media to promote the points of view of women and men from across India's social classes in such a way as to empower them.

In 2000, they saw opportunities for reaching a broad public through India's nascent television industry, and produced a 40-second public service announcement that breaks gender stereotypes and encourages girl children to pursue their dreams, whether traditional or nontraditional. The announcement begins with a young girl whose father has just bought her a doll, but the girl is already dreaming of becoming a pilot. She's next seen trying to make paper airplanes fly, but they keep falling down. Her father comes to help her fly them (a metaphor for giving her support). In the last frame, the adult woman is a pilot, stepping from the planes she has just landed. Her father comes up and gives her a hug. The announcement became part of "Color Your Dreams," a multimedia campaign sponsored by nine women's organizations that also included newspaper adverts, post-cards, and outdoor billboards. In a recent campaign designed to engage the most marginalized, the "Shootback" project teaches young women and men from slum communities to use a camera to document their daily lives for a photographic exhibition and book. The "Beyond the Cuckoo's Nest" campaign documents human rights abuses in mental institutions and emphasizes the need for respect – and hope – in treatment.

Datta said the idea is to use media to "widen the understanding of feminism," which is really about giving everyone choices and helping people to connect gender issues to broader concerns of human rights. POV's goals are to mainstream those concerns – for example, female feticide, violence, prostitution, agricultural labor, and mental health – and "reposition them in the public domain," said Data. Ultimately, the group wants to help marginalized groups to use media to represent themselves.

Hengasara Hakkina Sangha

The formation of a women's public sphere is strongly embedded in the work of a Bangalore-based women's organization named Hengasara Hakkina Sangha, which began in the mid-1990s to empower women to understand and use their legal rights. Founder and recently retired director **Sandhya Rao**[28] said that pamphlets and flyers are the primary media that the group uses to get the word out about what women should to do if sexually harassed at work, raped, or battered by a husband. Materials are written in both English and the local language, Kannada, using very simple vocabulary so that women of varied literacy levels and ethnicities can understand them. Rao said that women are encouraged to report abuse "even if it's not very violent," because "we're trying to encourage women that there can be a remedy in law." In a very long-term way, she said, "we are bringing about policy changes." Rao argues, "the time has come for us, even without being asked, to form policy. We need to get our act together and decide what vision we want reflected in the policies." To mobilize women at the community level to talk about such issues in order to participate in the political process, Rao has worked with Bangalore producer **Shamantha**[29] to develop a series of dramatic programs for radio that address issues of women's rights. The story format, she said, lends itself to a short discussion afterward. The idea, Rao said, is both to broadcast these programs and to obtain government funds for purchase of tapes of the programs. These could be circulated to women in villages, to listen to and afterward discuss the issues among themselves.

The Women's Forum Against Fundamentalism in Iran

Internet websites have recently enabled marginalized women separated geographically to find each other and develop dialogues, creating online feminist public spheres. Communication scholar Ananda Mitra (2004) studied the dialogues among members of one such group, SAWnet (the South Asian Women's Network).The website features places to post messages restricted to members, links to other websites, and a listserv. Mitra noted that SAWnet creators were among the first to bring issues relating to women of South Asia to cyberspace (p. 500). While Mitra's focus was on the communicative strategies, voice, and development of trust among SAWnet members, he recognized that the Internet has broad possibilities to serve the needs of the voiceless.

The diaspora of Iranian women living in the USA, Europe, and elsewhere in the world engage in their own dialogue and information-sharing through the website of the Women's Forum Against Fundamentalism in Iran – WFAFI (www.wfafi.org). As discussed in Chapter 1, WFAFI is a broad-based international group, headquartered in Boston, Massachusetts, that advocates for women's rights and religious pluralism in Iran and other nations with fundamentalist governments. The website houses up-to-date news about women's political situation in Iran, individual legal cases, and a range of other information, links to other groups, and contact information. In Fall 2004, the organization launched two new media services – a monthly electronic newsletter called *E-Zan* (the Farsi word for woman is *zan*), and a weekly Farsi-language radio program called *Voice of Women*. VOW, a 30-minute program on women's rights, broadcasts into Iran via shortwave radio on Saturday evenings, when women's listenership is at its highest. VOW broadcasts are produced in the USA and transmitted through a network of booster systems located in Europe. **Ramesh Sepehrrad**,[30] an active WFAFI member living in Washington, DC, first used websites to mobilize Iranian women through the National Committee of Women for a Democratic Iran, a group that merged with WFAFI in 2004. Sepehrrad's website for NCWDI posted articles containing details about women's imprisonment, hanging, and stoning to death from Farsi-language Iranian Internet sites, Amnesty International, and other reports, and informants living in Iran, in order to mobilize opposition to women's treatment but also "to make sure that the political voice of women was heard in the dialogue about democratization in Iran." The website also had the effect of drawing interest among women living inside Iran, who provided additional details of day-to-day life for women under the regime.

The Role of NGOs

Women who followed the third path of the Model of Women's Media Action, that of the advocate change agent, have typically worked through nonprofit, nongovernmental organizations (NGOs) to strengthen women's relationship to media industries, to stop sexist and inaccurate representations, to reshape media policies, or to amplify the voices of grassroots women through mediated communication. As the discussion has shown, they have used a range of techniques to accomplish these goals, including monitoring the media, training (or assisting) working journalists and other media professionals, developing alternative media forms, and striving to place gender-specific language in policy documents related to media operations. More recently, some women's organizations have used the Internet to mobilize constituencies through political websites containing news, activist campaigns, and other information. Because advocate change agents have understood the essential strength of well-organized, cohesive working relationships in opening new spaces for women to communicate, they have also established networks among themselves, both within and across nations. Such communicative spaces represent women's public sphere and the expansion of women's political participation.

Notes

1 Judith Smith was interviewed on September 9, 2003, in South Africa.
2 Giddens's explanation of reflexivity closely parallels Marx's original concept of consciousness. Feminists in the 1970s applied consciousness specifically in relation to gaining an understanding of gender oppression through a process of consciousness-raising. This process engaged women's dialogues in both private and public settings.
3 A particularly good digest of Giddens's structuration theory can be found in several chapters of Katherine Miller's *Communication Theories: Perspectives, Processes and Contexts* (2005).
4 Margaret Gallagher submitted answers on September 1, 2003.
5 A detailed report of the study can be found on the Gender Links website: www.genderlinks.org
6 Colleen Lowe Morna was interviewed on September 12, 2003.
7 Judith Smith was interviewed on September 8, 2003.
8 Hilary Nicholson submitted answers on April 5, 2004.
9 Martha Allen was interviewed in Washington, DC, on June 6, 2003.
10 Inja Coates submitted answers on March 31, 2004.
11 Seeta Peña Gangadharan submitted answers on May 6, 2004.
12 Aliza Dichter submitted answers on May 3, 2004.
13 Abhilasha Kumari was interviewed in New Delhi, India, on January 6, 2004.
14 For a discussion about the Panchayat Raj Act, which created the reservation system for women in local councils, see Chapter 6.
15 Libay Cantor submitted answers on March 19, 2004.
16 Vicki Semler was interviewed in New York City on April 22, 2004.
17 Joan Ross-Frankson was interviewed in New York City on April 23, 2004.
18 Jennifer Pozner was interviewed in New York City on April 22, 2004.
19 Sasha Rakoff submitted answers on September 25, 2003, and was later interviewed in London on December 29, 2003.
20 Jennifer Drew submitted answers on October 5, 2003, and was later interviewed in London on December 29, 2003.
21 *The Sun* newspaper is most strongly associated with the "page 3 girl," a feature that did not change when a woman, Rebekah Wade, took over as editor.
22 Margaret Lewis submitted answers on September 25, 2003.
23 A. E. Tijhoff submitted answers on March 15, 2004.
24 Patricia Solano submitted answers on September 29, 2003.

25 Akhila Sivadas was interviewed in New Delhi, India, on January 6, 2004.

26 Jeroo Mulla submitted answers on December 7, 2003, and was subsequently interviewed in Mumbai, India, on January 12, 2004.

27 Bishakha Datta and Sash Banerjee were interviewed in Bandra, India, on January 19, 2004.

28 Sandhya Rao was interviewed in Bangalore, India, on January 11, 2004.

29 Shamantha's work is examined in Chapter 10.

30 Ramesh Sepehrrad was interviewed on June 8, 2004, in Washington, DC. Note that Sepehrrad's work was also profiled in Chapter 1.

10

Fourth Path: Women's Media Enterprises

So it seems clear: We need a separate women's media. We need it because without it, women will never be able to speak for themselves in public discourse. We need it because without it, women's issues will continue to seem peripheral. We need it because in order to fight this inequality of the media, we must acknowledge that it is gendered and that therefore our strategies must also be based on gender. An independent women's media, dedicated to serving the needs of women that are not met by the mainstream press, is the ideal tool to equalize this gendered imbalance of power. Thus, we turn to women's media to rectify the injustice of the male-oriented mainstream press.

Joanne Lipson, Women's Institute for Freedom of the Press (2002)

In *A History of Their Own*, Bonnie S. Anderson and Judith P. Zinsser (1988) reported that women's newspapers and journals were among the ways in which feminists in Europe and the United States began to find each other in the 1960s and 1970s. Earlier chapters in this text have made similar observations about the critical connective role played by women-owned publications and electronic media in the formation of consciousness and the building of women's movements in India, South Africa, the USA, and elsewhere. In Chapter 6, we also noted that the broader structural implication of the proliferation of women's media has been the formation of both local and global feminist communication infrastructures. These publications, film and video, radio programs, and Internet sites connect women who share a vision for more egalitarian societies, allowing them to exchange ideas and information but also to develop strategies and working relationships. More explicitly, women's media include print and broadcast news, broadcast programming (both public affairs and dramatic), book publishing, journals and magazines, and film and video companies. The *Directory of Women's Media* (Allen & Densmore 2002), compiled by the Women's Institute for Freedom of the Press, in Washington, DC, identifies 250 print periodicals, more than 50 Internet periodicals, more than 40 publishing houses, 50 media organizations (which support and advocate for women's advancement in media professions), five women's news services, 12 women's film and video groups, and nearly 20 women's music groups and websites, in 48 different nations. These are miniscule numbers, of course, given the numbers of women-owned and -operated media enterprises worldwide, as a random search of the Internet will show.

Women's Global Reach

Women across the globe have clearly shown a determination to speak in their own voices, languages, and formats through media that they control. This chapter demonstrates that such determination is not only widespread but is also long-lived, spanning three decades of modern feminism. Thus, the following discussion examines the work and lessons of women media activists who followed the fourth path in our emergent Model of Women's Media Activism, that of establishing women's media enterprises. Included here is the work of 10 activists representing nine different women-operated (and nearly all women-owned) media enterprises in four different nations. Their enterprises include both national and international news services, film and video production and distribution companies, and radio and television production companies. Their narratives offer insight into a number of important facets of women's media activism. We see, for example, the intentional ways in which most of these enterprises have sought to move feminist ideas both to primary women's audiences as well as into mainstream discourse. These dual tendencies shaped the feminist public sphere that made a space for women's voices in the dominant public sphere where their access was otherwise limited. In addition, we glimpse the professional skill and considerable creativity that have been involved in establishing and maintaining women-owned media companies in the face of scarce resources and within societies whose prevailing gender values often guaranteed slow progress. What we identify as a women's communication system with global reach and highly important consequences is not an

original conceptualization. The late Donna Allen (1989: 64), who founded
the Women's Institute for Freedom of the Press, in Washington, DC, and
its primary communicative arm, the *Media Report to Women* bulletin, in
1972, was early to recognize that "for the first time in history women have
constructed an extensive and worldwide communication system through
which their contributions can now be heard." Allen, who traveled both
throughout the USA and internationally to discover (and report) the range
of women and media issues and activities, contended that a women's communication system began to develop in the 1970s, as women started to
establish newspapers, radio programs, film, video and book publishing
houses, and other media in response to mass media's exclusion of their lives
and ideas. Allen also saw women-owned media as a response to what she
called imposed periods of silence – for example, during and after wars, and
during years of conservative national leadership – when "huge problems
[arose] on which the public had received no information and thus could
not address." Among these problems were unequal educational systems,
workplaces, and the exclusion of women from positions of authority,
including dwindling numbers in elective office. "With mass media closed
to them and silent on these subjects, women sought new ways to bring their
needed information to the public" (ibid., p. 65).

Allen recognized that while these forms of women-controlled media
constitute the essential mechanisms for discussion and formulation of
ideas and positions on issues among themselves (what she deemed the "first
level" of communication), they also needed simultaneous outreach to the
broad general public (what she considered a "second level"). Allen's understanding of the role that women's media play in creating first and second
levels of communication parallels our own claim that women's media activism, more generally, has served to form a feminist public sphere and a
feminist component of the dominant public sphere.

Characteristics of the Fourth Path

Owning their own media has allowed women the maximum control over
content and image production and the distribution of media products.[1]
However, such ownership has also come with demands and responsibilities
with which those who followed the first three paths typically did not have
to grapple. Ownership, for example, requires financial skill, including the
location of sufficient initial capital to establish the organization and a

steady revenue stream to hire staff, install required technology, and maintain day-to-day operations. These economic considerations are ongoing and represent the greatest survival concern of the organization. In addition, there are the marketing issues – how to define the audience(s), package the materials to be sold, and physically get them into the hands of users. Management skill requirements are also considerable, including the ability to maintain a long-term vision and plan, to handle finances, to work with partners and collaborators, and to manage staff.

As Joanne Lipson's opening quote suggests, women who followed the fourth path of media ownership shared a common understanding that because the mainstream media were gendered in their composition and products, so would women's strategies for speaking have to be gendered: women would have to establish and run their own media. Those whose experiences we examine here did not go blithely down the fourth path – nearly all had worked in one or more professional capacities within the media beforehand and brought their professional skill and knowledge with them. As their narratives reveal, they have adapted to changing times and kept their enterprises intact. We have organized the chapter by media form.

The 10 women whom we interviewed comprise 11 percent of the 90 informants in our cross-cultural study on women's media activism. They are (alphabetically):

Anita Anand, India	Angana Parekh, India
Sheila Gibbons, USA	Grace Poore, Malaysia/USA
Rita Henley Jensen, USA	Shree Venkatram, India
Shamantha Mani, India	Frieda Werden, Canada
Ritu Menon, India	Debra Zimmerman, USA

Macro-Interventions: Women's News Agencies

The Women's Feature Service

The Women's Feature Service Project represented the first global strategy to expand news by and about women. The project emerged on the heels of the first UN Decade for Women meetings in Mexico City, in 1975, in response to feminist calls for more news and information on women's lives from the perspective of women's liberation movements (Byerly 1995). The project, which was funded by the UN Fund for Population and administered by the UN Educational, Scientific, and Cultural Organization (UNESCO), ran from 1978 to 1983, supporting Women's Feature Service programs in five regions of the world – Africa, the Caribbean, Latin America, the Middle East, and Asia. Each program was initially envisioned to be a sponsored operation – a completely woman-run project housed within an existing (male-run) regional development news organization – that would, after its first five years of UN funding, secure its own revenues to become independent. The vision for the original WFS project thus represented a macro-level structural intervention by feminists, one concerned with giving women eventual control over the financing, management, and production of their own news messages on a global scale.

While this was the goal, the project would only partially fulfill its potential. The politics and economics of different regions represented a significant barrier that these programs would encounter – and not the only one. Sexism and resistance from male colleagues and authorities marked the experiences of WFS correspondents for the Middle Eastern WFS project, based in Beirut, Lebanon. This same project experienced the effects of a civil war that included the bombing of its Beirut office. In addition, Western news organizations were resistant to supporting the WFS project, as some argued that it mirrored the anti-West, anti-capitalist, and anti-free-press tenets they saw wrapped up in developing nations' calls for a New International Economic Order and a New World Information and Communication Order (Byerly 1995: 112–13). Economics, along with the lack of political will on the part of those in donor agencies, however, also contributed to an untimely end for the project, according to some who watched its demise.[2] The Middle Eastern and Caribbean WFS programs would end with the termination of UNESCO funding in 1983, and a third, Depthnews Women's Service, in Manila, the Philippines, would continue only with minimal staffing at the Press Foundation of Asia (Byerly 1990, 1995).[3]

Lack of financial and other support also affected the WFS programs in Africa, as well as in Latin America,[4] both sponsored by Inter Press Service (IPS), a third world oriented news organization in Rome. IPS integrated the coverage of women's news under a single WFS coordinator at its Rome headquarters, but the service operated at minimal levels from 1983 to 1986, due to budget problems within the parent organization and the lack of staff. In 1986, IPS hired development consultant and writer **Anita Anand**,[5] an

Indian national, to oversee a regeneration of the WFS program under new funding. Anand says that she understood from the beginning that her job was one of establishing a strong internal structure for WFS so that it could "move away from IPS" to independence. Thus, she spent the next few years establishing a series of regional bureaus, training a new corps of bureau staff and correspondents, and identifying funding from a range of European development and other organizations. By the late 1980s, WFS was producing nearly 600 stories a year for worldwide distribution, with a solid use rate by both mainstream and women's publications. Stories, written in both English and Spanish, were translated into other local languages by many periodicals (Byerly 1990). As these changes occurred, IPS managers began to resist the departure of WFS, which had become a popular asset with IPS supporters.

Anand reflects today on the lessons learned from the painful conflict between herself and former IPS director Roberto Savio as she moved WFS to its new headquarters in New Delhi, India, in 1990. Among other things, she admits, she had not understood the extent to which IPS's own identity had become fused with that of WFS over the years, and the ways in which Savio and others who had supported the service might feel personally affected. Separating the mother from the child – a metaphor she used often in those days to explain the move toward independence – engendered hard feelings that would not be resolved for years to come. Anand began WFS in New Delhi with the promise of funding from a European development agency. She had an organization and 20 people (including correspondents around the world) to support, together with the cloud of separation from IPS hanging over the future success of the enterprise. Working initially from a desk at her sister's office, she asked her WFS colleagues to give her three months to get WFS on its feet. The staff who had followed her from Rome remained loyal – and on the job – and while the start-up funds that IPS had promised were never delivered, those from the European development agency came through as agreed: WFS had made a difficult transition and would survive.

The hallmarks of WFS stories under Anand's tenure (1986–2000) were the inclusion and reconceptualization of gender in development journalism. Believing that there is no such thing as a "woman's issue" – indeed, that all issues relevant to national development were women's issues – she set about bringing out gender politics in relation to national development; that is, the ways in which nations were addressing fundamental human concerns such as housing, adequate food, clean water and sanitation, education, security, war, and peace, among others. Development journalism is a genre dedicated to such coverage, presented in a news format that is issue- (rather than event-) oriented, and that situates problems central to the story in their historical, economic, and political contexts. In addition, development journalism focuses on the ways in which these issues affect people across socioeconomic lines, giving a voice to the least as well as the more powerful.[6] Looking back, Anand believes that WFS allowed women reporters, for the first time, to ask women and men across the spectrum – prime ministers, policy-makers, housewives, teachers, lawyers, teenagers – what they thought about issues that affected women. The agency, Anand says, also "analyzed the contribution of women to society by actually writing about what women do." Anand laughs as she emphasizes that "in truth, women keep the world going – from their reproductive function to their most productive functions they provide nutrition, love, care and families," and they enter into economic realms in so many ways, pointing to a 1995 UN figure that women's labor contributed some $11 trillion a year globally. She argues that women are not invisible, only under-reported, something that WFS has helped to change.

In Fall 2000, **Angana Parekh**,[7] a seasoned, traditional journalist, assumed the directorship of WFS, by then an established organization with a clientele primarily in South Asia – India, Sri Lanka, Nepal, Bangladesh, and the Philippines – but also the USA, parts of Europe, and, most recently, Afghanistan (Women's Feature Service 2003). Parekh's emphasis has been on mainstreaming the notion of women's news, seeking to reach an increasingly general audience and to train mainstream journalists to see the gender angle in *all* issues. The first has been accomplished in part through commissioned features, such as a 12-story, one-essay series on the work of the America–India Foundation support of earthquake-affected families in Kutch, India, in 2002. For the Population Council, WFS produced a series of 10 articles and a 30-minute radio program (the latter in Hindi) on adolescent reproductive and sexual health for mainstream English and local Indian-language media. One aspect of reaching mainstream audiences has been to develop stories in both print and electronic formats. The second activity, putting on journalists' workshops, has been accomplished through a series of day-and-a-half-long training workshops for 12–15 print and broadcasting professionals per session, on identifying the gender angle in development news (Women's Feature Service 2003). However, Parekh argues that "it's not enough just to sensitize journalists or women journalists –actually, it's editors and decision makers that need these insights." Nor is it enough, she says, "just to have a critical mass of women journalists – you have to have women journalists *in decision making positions.*"

Believing that the agency needs a more secure future, Parekh has expanded the organization's funding, thereby covering the salaries of WFS headquarters personnel and correspondents whose scope extends to more than 30 countries in a given year. She acknowledges that establishing a secure financial base is her biggest challenge.

Unnati Features

While WFS has sought an international mainstream audience, Unnati Features, also located in New Delhi, has aimed for a bilingual (English and Hindi) mainstream audience within the Indian market. Unnati Features emerged in 1996 after veteran journalist **Shree Venkatram** became disillusioned with the shift to soft news and celebrity that she saw occurring across mainstream Indian news media. Her career of some 15 years had taken her through various dailies over more than a decade in Mumbai, Bangalore and finally New Delhi, her home city. There, she had risen to the post of features editor of *The Pioneer,* one of India's oldest English-language dailies, and participated in conceptualizing and bringing to publication a Sunday section called *Pulse.* Venkatram said she felt good about her journalistic contributions, which she said, "had a strong woman focus." *Pulse* ran cover stories on women's sports – weightlifters, wrestlers, and marathon runners – and a range of other issues. It was in connection with the annual Children's Day event in the mid-1990s, when the advertising manager chastised her for running a cover story about a 10-year-old boy and his sister who picked through a garbage heap that she walked past every day on her way to work to help support their sick parents, that she decided it was time to move on. Unconcerned with the fact that she was trying to highlight child poverty, the manager wanted to know why his (middle- and upper-class) readers would want to see a picture of children on a garbage heap. She remembers:

> The hypocrisy of it all really sickened me. We did not mind living with the garbage or seeing the emaciated children all around us, but we did not want them on our paper for they would spoil the Sunday morning. It was at this time that I looked to move on, to do something else.

She applied for a fellowship from the MacArthur Foundation, which was investigating the issue of population and health, out of which she created

Unnati Features. *Unnati* is a Sanskrit word meaning progress – something she believed symbolized what she sought to do in producing stories on women's rights, gender equality, nutrition and health, population, and the environment in the popular media. Unnati Features works on the premise that the media are effective tools for social change, and Unnati, which is a not-for-profit organization, strives to help media achieve that by providing articles on gender and other issues. While Unnati uses a pool of women journalists and development specialists, Venkatram (like Angana Parekh) contends that men and women journalists both must commit themselves to finding gender angles in stories and then to write knowledgeably about them. The organization receives fees for specific services, and receives project funds from United Nations and other agencies for projects such as annual competition for high-school students, in which entrants submit stories on a gender-related news theme. Venkatram emphasizes that both boys and girls are encouraged to enter.

In 2000, the group added research to its services, with Venkatram conducting a 50-year systematic longitudinal study (1950–2000) of English and Hindi-language newspaper coverage of women's portrayal. That study, funded by UNIFEM and reported in *Women in Print* (Venkatram n.d.), revealed that women receive only 13 percent of space in English-language and only 11 percent in Hindi dailies in 2000 – figures that have risen by a tiny 1.35 percent and 2.3 percent, respectively, per decade since the 1950s. In both categories of newspapers, front pages were men's preserves, and when women *were* mentioned it was typically as victims of sensational crimes. The study found that women figured most prominently in crime news, fashion, and beauty news. Beauty queens, models, and actresses constituted the most visible image of women in both English and Hindi papers, in both news and photographs. The study ends with a call for concerted action to assure, among other things, that women dying in childbirth get the same coverage as men killed by speeding vehicles (both rampant problems in India) and for "the fact that 80 percent of Indian women are anemic will merit a banner headline on the front page" (Venkatram n.d.: 63).

Women's eNews

Women's eNews, based in New York City, shifted from its focus from national to international reporting after founder **Rita Henley Jensen**[8] realized that "international news was so compelling." Additionally, she said, "If the well-being of women across the globe was to ever improve, US women would most likely have to assume an important role." Jensen had created and launched the Internet-based news service in June 2000, under the sponsorship of the National Organization for Women's Legal Defense and Education Fund, based in Washington, DC. NOW saw mainstream news-papers as its major audience, and had the goal of changing the face of feminism and feminist issues in those papers. Jensen, an experienced print journalist and editor, decided to spin the service as an independent opera-tion in Fall 2001, after NOW found difficulty funding it. But there were also differences in goals, Jensen says. She believed that Women's eNews was its own medium (rather than a provider of information to other media) with a primary audience of women and men who wanted information about women.

Women's eNews (www.womensenews.org) circulates stories through the Internet daily to a list of subscribers who receive the service through a voluntary system of payment. Jensen, who as editor-in-chief, president, and publisher oversees every aspect of the business from story assignment and production to fundraising, has managed to keep the nonprofit organization solvent. Its writers are a mix of experienced journalists and feminist leaders, whose stories and commentaries examine current issues about women. A sample from late 2004 found:

- A story from Sofiya, Bulgaria, about the adoption of spouse abuse laws in a nation with changing gender mores.
- A story about what class-action discrimination lawsuits against large corporations have won for women in the USA with respect to back pay, compensation, advancement, and the setting of legal precedents.
- A story about a three-year interdisciplinary study at the University of Michigan, to understand why women of color are three times more likely than white women to die during pregnancy and why their children are twice as likely as white children to die before their first birthday.
- A story about the refusal of staff at women's shelters to surrender client information, in compliance with new federal reporting requirements for funding. Women's advocacy groups say turning over the information would place their clients at risk.

Women's eNews fills a gender gap in daily news. Jensen recognizes that while mainstream news has made some strides – for example, adopting more gender-neutral language, covering violence against women, and giving space to the occasional female newsmaker – she believes that newsrooms are still hostile to women's success, ideas, and concerns:

> The white male hierarchy has to be told – in no uncertain terms – that their gender and race bias is destroying the institution they love. That they fail to promote and retain women and do not include women in their news columns and ignore issues of concern to women is reflected in low readership among women. That black and Latino Americans, as well as other people of color, know full well how they treat minority employees and therefore have little to no confidence in the accuracy of the news published. And, if they cannot reach women and minority audiences, they will eventually go out of business.

Jensen points to enduring problems in mainstream news that many have challenged, analyzed, and sought to change. As noted earlier, Donna Allen was among those in the vanguard of that struggle.

Feminist Watchdog Journalism

Donna Allen understood that women would never be able to change their exclusion and misrepresentation by the media until they had a bigger window on media events. She established the watchdog periodical *Media Report to Women* in order to provide women with information about media issues, challenges, and other activities both in the USA and around the world. The periodical, which was published bimonthly until 1992 (when it became quarterly), emerged from Allen's conviction that women should be informed about media issues and activities that intersected women's interests. In addition, she advocated women's intervention in public policy that allowed men's control of media industries through concentrated ownership. In its early days, the pages of *Media Report* were crammed with news in 10-point type about everything from feminist media critiques to research findings on women and media, to announcements of new women's films and other media, to updates on discrimination lawsuits being filed (and won) by women at major media firms. *Media Report* was a activist tool that Donna Allen, her daughters, and her activist friends published from Allen's home office, even before the days of computers, to make sure that nothing media-related would escape the notice of the feminist US and global women's movements.

Since 1987, *Media Report* has continued under the editorial leadership of **Sheila Gibbons**,[9] a professional journalist with a background in reporting, editing, journalism education, and corporate communication, who says that gender imbalances in the news and stereotypical media depictions of women and girls first began to interest her in graduate school, when she turned her master's research to the subject. She incorporated those concerns into her journalism, editing a women's magazine for military families, co-authoring several books on women and media, and assuming editorship of *Media Report to Women*, beginning in 1987. Most recently, she has also begun writing a monthly column for the online news service Women's eNews. Gibbons believes that:

> Young journalists need to be mentored so they avoid making those mistakes [i.e., gender stereotyping and women's omission in news] as well. I don't think it's getting enough attention either in journalism school or at the newsroom orientation level.

Under Gibbons's direction, *Media Report* has taken on a contemporary look, with more graphics and a better balance of national and international stories, but stories still cover the range of research, analysis, and announcements characteristic of its early days. In 2003, *Media Report* began to publish full-length research papers on women and media, along with news of industry trends and commentaries. The *Media Report* website (www.mediareporttowomen.com) includes an archive, industry statistics, and other links.

Feminists Speaking through Radio

Throughout this cross-cultural study, we have seen various ways in which women media activists have used radio programming as a means of circulating feminist and lesbian-feminist ideas, analyses, music, poetry, and announcements of current events. Our own findings coincide with those of Caroline Mitchell (2004: 157), who found that all over the world, women "have used radio to campaign, entertain, inform, shock, and celebrate women's lives." She observes that radio is a particularly friendly medium for women because of its companionability and intimacy. She also argues that radio has been particularly accessible to women in terms of learning production and programming skills – something brought to life by a number of our own informants, including members of the Sophie's Parlor Radio Collective (USA), Jay Hartling (Canada), Ulrike Helwerth (Germany), K. T. Jarmul (USA), and others. The academic literature on women's radio since the 1970s forms a significant branch of feminist media studies, chronicling the advances that women throughout the world have used to place this particular medium in their service. Mitchell reminds us that underlying feminist radio practice is "the principle that women have a right to broadcast on their own terms: use their voices, articulate their concerns, and tell their stories in order to represent their lives, their struggles, and their achievements" (p. 176). She illustrates what we see to be a central tenet of the Model of Women's Media Action: women's right to communicate.

Frieda Werden[10] had been a media activist for 15 years when she and Katherine Davenport founded WINGS – Women's International News-gathering Service – in 1985. In the 1970s in Texas, she had organized with other feminists at a university press, been active in the small press movement, co-edited a feminist magazine, and produced syndicated radio projects (mainly about women). Moving to the East Coast, she worked on projects for National Public Radio but also volunteered for the women's departments at Pacifica community stations at WBAI and KPFK. She became operations manager for Western Public Radio, in San Francisco, in 1985, where she, Katherine Davenport, and others created WINGS – a project that would become independent a year later. Werden has relocated WINGS headquarters several times in the years since, remaining its administrative head and retaining the project's dedication to international women's activism and views on world events. The weekly half-hour current affairs and news programs are produced and distributed by Werden (now living in Vancouver, Canada), with the assistance of other women reporters, editors, and associate producers in the USA and around the world. Literally hundreds of such individuals have worked with WINGS during the two decades of its existence. Programs are available on CD, via satellite, and on the Internet. The University of South Florida Women's Studies Department has provided streaming audio of recent programs online (www.cas.usf.edu/womens_studies/wings.html).

WINGS is financed through a combination of station subscriptions, CD sales, and donations. Reporters and editors for WINGS are paid, but Werden volunteers most of her own time and works part-time for a campus radio station. She would like to see feminists becoming much more financially supportive of women's media, noting that other sources are "almost nil." Like FIRE and WATER (discussed below), WINGS has received much of its donations base over the years through the assistance of Genevieve Vaughan, founder of Feminists for the Gift Economy.

But the story of WINGS is only a portion of what the organization has allowed Werden and her collaborators to do in fulfilling WINGS's slogan, "Raising women's voices through radio worldwide." Space precludes a full accounting of these accomplishments, but a few of Werden's own include the following:

- Participating in laying the groundwork in 1991 for FIRE (the Feminist International Radio Endeavor), based in Costa Rica. Formerly a short-wave program, FIRE is now an Internet radio alternative that mixes audio, print, and pictures to cover women's human rights issues around the world.
- Providing training for women in using radio technology and doing production (e.g., for the Women's Access to Electronic Resources, WATER, in Texas, and for many WINGS correspondents).
- Pioneering sending audio files that cover women's events via the Internet.
- Advising Dorothy Abbott in creating the Women's Radio Fund (now administered by the Global Fund for Women).
- Being active in media diplomacy internationally; for example, serving as the North American representative to the Women's International Network of AMARC from 1997 to 2002, and on the board of the International Association of Women in Radio and Television since 2003, promoting the implementation of the media plank of the Beijing Platform for Action (adopted 1995), and of the women's right to freedom of expression as laid out in Article 19 of the Universal Declaration of Human Rights.

Politicizing Dramatic Broadcasts

The Saarathi Resource Center, in Bangalore, India, began to experiment with innovative formats for broadcast several years ago in order to better reach mainstream audiences with information about women's rights, human rights, health care, and other social issues. The word *saarathi*, which means guiding friend in the Kannada language, signifies the nongovernmental organization's objectives of working with mainstream media by serving as a documentation center on development issues; helping to create communication experts who are knowledgeable on issues of health, education, and human rights, water issues, and other health issues such as HIV and AIDS; and building a network of media professionals whose work can contribute to reshaping public policies on these issues (www.saarathi.org). **Shamantha,**[11] an experienced development journalist and consultant, has developed several series for radio that integrate basic information and critical questioning about women's lives into short dramatic programs using familiar Indian themes and stories. Some of these, profiled in Chapter 9 in connection with Sandhya Rao's advocacy center Hengasara Hakkina Sangha, lend themselves to a short structured discussion among listeners afterwards with the guidance of a local women's leader. The idea is to expand the use of the programs, recorded in the Kannada language, among poor women in both urban and rural areas of the state of Karnataka, for use as consciousness-raising tool by women's groups. One program series, concerned with the gross violation of human rights from women's points of view, was titled "Janaki," a Hindi word derived from Hindu mythology. She says while these were "gender programs with special emphasis on women," she wanted to break the stereotype of a women's program by including men as actors and narrators. Another program series featured interviews about gender-related government policies and their implementation.

The receipt of fellowships and grants from international groups such as Panos, the UK's Ford Foundation Project, and the Population Communication Institute of New York; regional groups such as the K. K. Birla Foundation (*Hindustan Times*, New Delhi) and the Karnataka Sahitya Academy; and contracts from All-India Radio, in Bangalore, have allowed her and others at Saarathi to develop both issue-related research and broadcast programming and seminars for media and governmental professionals since the mid-1980s. Her media activism through Saarathi and, more recently, as a consultant to the Karnataka State Women's Commission coincides with her personal life, she said. As a yoga practitioner and through constant interaction with marginalized people, Shamantha has become more philosophical and someone who wants "to be more simple and helpful." Her persistence as a media professional dedicated to women's advancement demonstrates that she also advocates all women standing up for themselves.

Through Women's Eyes: Feminist Films

The women's film organization Women Make Movies, based in New York, arose like a phoenix from the fires of Reaganomics in the early 1980s. The organization, which had trained women in independent filmmaking and distributed their films, had gone from a staff of six to none, and its operating space was reduced to one small room with no windows. When **Debra Zimmerman**[12] was hired as the director in 1983, she had to put on the answering machine to go to the bathroom. Zimmerman explains that the demise, under President Reagan, of various programs that had kept this and many other small community organizations afloat in earlier years, suddenly came to an end. Among these were the Comprehensive Employment and Training Act and segments of National Endowments for the Arts. After a series of community meetings, the board of directors decided to focus WMM's future on its income-generating activity: distribution. Since then, WMM's annual budget has grown from $30,000 to $1.4 million, and its employees have expanded from one to 15. Zimmerman emphasizes that a portion of the income from film sales and rentals is returned to the filmmakers who live around the world. Revenue also supports many other activities aimed at both promoting women's films and generating public dialogues – activities that are particularly relevant to our study of women's media activism.

WMM has two primary activities. The first is the renting and marketing of women's documentary and dramatic films, primarily to university libraries but also to museums, community groups, governmental offices, and schools. The second activity is production assistance to about 200 women, for whom WMM serves as an umbrella nonprofit sponsor through which filmmakers can fundraise. The organization also runs technical assistance seminars and workshops in marketing, production management, budgeting, and other activities associated with making and distributing their work. The list of notables is long and still growing, including the Academy award-winning film *Boys Don't Cry* (about transgender love and violence) by Kimberly Pearce, the nominated short *Asylum* (about female genital mutilation) by Natalie Reuss and Deborah Schaffer, and, most recently, the film *Maggie Growls* (about Maggie Kuhn, founder of the elder advocacy group Gray Panthers) by Barbara Attie and Janet Goldwater, which received the Henry Hampton Media Award for media activism. The organization often sponsors film festivals at international women's gatherings, but its local community activism is something that particularly satisfies Zimmerman. WMM, only a few blocks from the former World Trade Center, was deeply affected by the attacks of September 11, and the aftermath of anti-Muslim sentiments. Zimmerman said that:

> Muslim women in Brooklyn were afraid to go to the grocery store. Taxicab drivers were getting attacked. We realized that we had this extraordinary collection that was already in place at Women Make Movies, films that were by women from Egypt, Lebanon, Pakistan, Morocco, and elsewhere in the Islamic community.

WMM launched a campaign called "Response to Hate," offering all of the films in that collection without charge for three months to any group that wanted to use them for educational purposes. In wishing to ignite community dialogues, Zimmerman said WMM staff also wanted to give Muslim women a voice and presence. The campaign, advertised solely on the Internet, had more than 600 requests for films. Similarly, WMM has distributed the award-winning film by Lourdes Portillo, *Señorita Extraviada*, documenting the murder of hundreds of young women along the border in northern Mexico. Zimmerman says that the public response has been incredible, with the film grossing more than $100,000 in just over two years – highly unusual for an independent film.

As the largest distributor and promoter of women's films in North America, the work of Women Make Movies represents a structural intervention in institutional discrimination against women in the filmmaking business. Hollywood, Zimmerman says, represents the confluence of art and commerce (the second including financing), and a lot of money is required to make mainstream feature films: women are typically shut out from the big money. In addition, women often have diverse career profiles and have often moved through various creative positions (e.g., making commercials, B-grade films, and pornographic films) that can preclude them from getting the same breaks as men. Zimmerman cited research showing that Hollywood films with a woman producer are much more likely to have women in other key production positions; for example, as director, editor, cinematographer, and so on. However, once women do become filmmakers and raise sufficient funds to make their films, they often have difficulty gaining access to film festivals and other places where films are seen, judged, and awarded. Panels of judges are typically male,

Zimmerman argues, and they prefer to watch films by and about men: "So, the truth is that women do bring other women along." And WMM's production assistance program provides the infrastructure that women need to get experience, secure financing, gain visibility for their work, and then distribute it – both to specialized and mainstream audiences.

By now, we have seen a consistency of thinking behind the creation of women's media enterprises, most of which have sought both specialized and mainstream audiences as a deliberate strategy for circulating feminist ideas, and, often, related ideas concerned with broader issues of national development. We have also connected the search for both women-focused and mainstream audiences to the formation of both a feminist public sphere and a feminist component in the dominant (male) public sphere. By examining the work of women involved in the development of specifically women-oriented media enterprises, we have been able to track such developments in a number of nations over years since the 1970s. And, as these last two examples show, once again, the owners of women's media enterprises tend to bring a shared understanding to their activism that women's concerns span international boundaries.

The work of **Grace Poore**[13] and SHaKTI Productions aims to confront the invisibility of South Asian female victims of violence – and their perpetrators – living in South Asia and North America. Malaysian by background, Poore lives in Silver Spring, Maryland (near Washington, DC) and works with women from India, Sri Lanka, Malaysia, Indonesia, and other nations to provide what she calls a "South Asian perspective" on issues of rape, incest, and domestic violence. SHaKTI Productions develops documentary videos and accompanying training materials for use in workshops with agencies and organizations that serve South Asian female victims of violence and their perpetrators. Poore says she started this all-women independent video production and research team in 1989 to:

- document women's lives and struggles within and outside the USA;
- use art as advocacy to confront public and private violence against women; and
- challenge the power of hierarchies between image-makers and those who are "imaged."

Videos tell the stories of trauma victims, such as South Asian incest survivors and battered women who are lesbians, undocumented immigrants, disabled or deaf, prostitutes, or living with HIV/AIDS. This, she says, is

accomplished by screening the videos as part of workshops or events associated with sexual assault and domestic violence awareness. For example,
The Children We Sacrifice, released in 2000, is a 61-minute documentary
about incest in South Asian communities, which was shot in India, Sri
Lanka, Canada, and the USA. *Voices Heard, Sisters Unseen*, released in 1995,
is a 76-minute documentary about the victimization of battered women
living on the social margins.

Poore's work is driven by deeper political concerns that she believes need
improvement. One is discrimination against marginalized women by staff
in service and legal agencies. Another is the need to mobilize South Asian
women victimized by domestic and sexual abuse into support networks.
The first concern has been addressed through professional trainings, as
described above. The second has been addressed through community events
and the formation of a Network of South Asian Incest Interventionists in
the USA. The network sponsors dialogue sessions and training, with the
ultimate goal of early intervention and empowerment of victims. SHaKTI
Productions functions internationally, showing videos at gatherings such as
the 4th International NGO Forum for Women, held in Beijing in 1995.
Poore believes that media activism, such as her own, has increased the
visibility of women media professionals and the representation of women
in media production, both male-dominated areas. She recognizes that:

> Feminist influence and media activism have markedly increased the body of
> work by women that is available to the public – be it documentaries, news
> coverage, news commentary, political analysis, media theory, etc.

Like so many other informants, Poore laments the fact that funding
is still very limited for women – particularly women of color – to undertake media production. This is part of a larger problem associated with
women's lack of access to media. In almost all countries, she says, in both
government-controlled and mainstream (commercial) media, "the women's
voices that predominate are rarely feminist, and certainly not radical feminist." In the USA, in particular, even within alternative media, "precedence
is given to white feminist heterosexual perspectives," something that marginalizes "feminists of color across sexuality, culture and class." When
women of color are sought, she observes, it is typically "meant to fill in the
colored or cultural perspective to the white discourse." Young feminists
from a variety of political, racial, cultural, and racial backgrounds, she
believes, can address these through media activism.

Publishing Women: Kali and its Successors

Burgeoning intellectual developments among feminist Indian writers, academics, and community activists in the 1970s and 1980s were captured in books and disseminated by Kali for Women, a feminist book publisher founded by **Urvashi Butalia**[14] and **Ritu Menon**[15] in New Delhi, in 1984. Butalia and Menon had ideal backgrounds for founding what would become India's premier feminist press. They had both gained valuable professional experience by working for established mainstream publishing houses – Butalia with Oxford University Press in India and Zed Books in the United Kingdom, and Menon with Doubleday in the United States. Both also had solid ties with feminist movements, both in India and other nations. Butalia reflects that inspiration for starting Kali came in recognition that the women's movement in India was raising important issues that were not being represented in books. Mainstream Indian publishers at that time were unwilling to take books by and about women, and internationally, nearly all books referring to Indian feminism were being written by Western scholars who had limited experience in India. Menon believes that Kali's formula for success through the years has rested in its diverse offerings – the press has published theoretical and academic, fiction, biographies, memoirs, politics, and children's books, as well as posters and pamphlets. Butalia adds that Kali's growth was measured, expanding cautiously to assure stable revenues.

For more than two decades, Kali has provided a forum for Indian women's voices to be given legitimacy and to be given a supportive environment. The latter has come through Kali's continued close links with the women's movement, something Butalia says has enabled its survival. Kali's titles bristle with the issues that have formed central dialogues, political efforts, and academic research in Indian feminism, including works by Vandana Shiva, Radha Kumar, Anupama Rao, Brinda Bose, and Maitrayee Chaudhuri, among many others. Kali's publications retained a political edge, something Menon says "demonstrates that the personal is political." She argues that women's ownership of their own media is essential:

> One of the things that I think is critical to women's empowerment in the media is to control not just the message but also the medium. It is all very well to have a message, but if you don't have control over the medium, that message will go out of your hands.

Many women's presses have failed to succeed in recent years, allowing themselves to be bought by larger corporate conglomerates that have promised women some degree of autonomy. But Menon has observed that even sympathetic, progressive conglomerates may pull their support for feminist ideas if that women's enterprise fails to be profitable. The problem of corporate takeover of media on a grand scale, she says, is international, and one outcome, both in print and electronic media, has been the emergence of what she calls a pseudo-emancipated image of women: a portrayal of womanhood that has the superficial trappings of emancipation but that underneath has the conservative mindset of a traditional (dominated) woman.

While this situation has spelled an uncertain future for all women's publishing houses, Urvashi Butalia believes that feminist publishers have to be more forward-thinking. There are changing realities for feminist publishing, and she questions the value of taking the "pure" position and saying "we will never join hands with the biggies." There may be times to find ways to travel some of the distance with larger companies, and make other adjustments to maintain survival. By diversifying itself, she believes that Zubaan, the new publishing company that she heads, has reckoned with the realities of today's publishing world and created a model for other women's media.

During 2003 and 2004, Kali underwent a transformation when two new associate entities, Women Unlimited and Zubaan, were created, with Menon and Butalia as their respective heads. The new organizations, both established as nonprofit trusts, will continue to market Kali titles but will otherwise take new, independent directions. Women Unlimited (WU) is associated with a network called Women's World India, the South Asia chapter of Women's World International, which is a global free-speech organization. In addition to its publishing of women's books, WU will take on additional projects; for example, a study of violence against women in India, and workshops with adolescent girls. Zubaan, which means voice, speech language, in Hindustani, will continue to publish some 20 titles a year, including general academic, fiction, and other books with a focus on women, including some in Hindi. Zubaan also sponsors monthly conversations with women writers (with programs being taped for publication in a book), as well as workshops with young men and women and with school children, among other projects. Zubaan works closely with the NGO Pratham to produce books for children in numerous Indian languages, and has plans to co-sponsor an international conference in 2006 on gender and history.

Economics and Women's Media

Feminist economist Isabella Bakker (1994) has observed that the struggle to transform women's place in society has moved into the economic realm, with women of both the global South and North recognizing that global economic policies have affected men and women differently. The foregoing discussion of women's media enterprises finds its own context in this bigger picture, with most feminist media enterprises operating on thin financial ground and often on a small scale to hold their own. That the nine enterprises profiled here – and their counterparts around the world – *do* continue is of critical importance in the continuing battle for women to speak publicly in their own voices. As we have observed throughout this text, women's right to communicate is central to women's ability to enter into meaningful dialogues and deliberations in and across societies in order to address matters of concern to themselves and others. Women's media enterprises provide the strongest assurance that women will speak in their own voices when such matters arise.

Notes

1   All of the media included in this chapter are owned by women except *Media Report to Women*, which, since 1987, has been owned by Communication Research Associates, whose principal owner is Ray E. Hiebert, the husband of Sheila Gibbons. They serve as publisher and editor, respectively. The foundational role that *Media Report* served in supporting women's media enterprises during the 1970s and 1980s, and its continued leadership under a feminist editor, suggested its inclusion in this chapter. The publication retains its global focus on women and media.

2   Anita Anand, personal communication, December 26, 2004.

3   For a fuller history of the Women's Feature Service Project, see Margaret Gallagher (1981), Paula Kassell and Susan J. Kaufman (1989), and Carolyn M. Byerly (1995).

4   The WFS program located in San José, Costa Rica, was called Oficina de Noticias de la Mujer (OIM), and served all of Latin America. OIM became a completely independent operation in the late 1990s.

5   Anita Anand was interviewed in New Delhi, India, on January 5, 2004.

6   This definition includes information from Shree Venkatram, personal communication, March 20, 2004.

7   Angana Parekh was interviewed in New Delhi, India, on January 7, 2004.

8   Rita Henley Jensen submitted answers on August 20, 2003.

9   Sheila Gibbons submitted answers on August 18, 2003.

10   Frieda Werden submitted answers on September 12, 2003.

11   Shamantha D. S. Mani was interviewed in Bangalore, India, on January 9, 2004.

12   Debra Zimmerman was interviewed in New York City, on April 23, 2004.

13   Grace Poore submitted answers on June 5, 2003.

14   Urvashi Butalia, personal communication, April 5, 2004.

15   Ritu Menon was interviewed in New Delhi, India, on January 6, 2004.

11

Conclusion

Our examination of women and media began with an extensive, critical probing of what feminist media scholars have revealed to date about women's historical and contemporary relationship to mainstream media industries. We presented our review of this international body of work by recognizing the enduring trend of male-owned media to omit, marginalize, trivialize, and even pathologize women in content and to limit their numbers and power within the industries. But we also tried to show that women – as media audiences and as citizens – have not stood idly by in the face of these conditions, but that progress *has* been made. Women's active challenges to marginalization by mainstream media have resulted in specific advancements in numerous industries and nations; for example, more women hired and promoted into decision-making, stronger women's representations in some television programs and news stories, and so on. We have acknowledged that progress and constraint are longstanding, uneasy companions in the process of change. In addition, we have explored the ways in which women have circumvented these limitations by establishing alternative media enterprises. With the dialectical nature of women's relationship to media in mind, we have tried to chart new directions for feminist media scholarship, building on the work of others who have sought to better understand not only the losses and gains that mark this relationship, but also the struggle by which men's dominance has been challenged so that women's public voice and presence could be more forcefully heard and seen in order to reshape their societies. In shining a spotlight on the locus of struggle, we have moved inside the work and experiences of women media activists, learning more about their range of goals, activities, and accomplishments.

We are now ready to ask two questions. First, how does women's communicative action, represented by this struggle to speak about matters in their world, function in the process of feminist social change? We want to address this question because women's media activism is always conducted within the context of women's liberation movements whose shared goals are to advance women's rights and status. Formulating an answer will require us to consider the ground we covered in Part II, in order to locate some of the specific ways in which women's activism has served its desired ends. Our second question is: What should be the direction of future feminist media scholarship that seeks to extend itself beyond what we offer here? We therefore suggest new research avenues to pursue, recognizing that other scholars will envision their own projects aimed at correcting, revising, and otherwise building on some of the theoretical and empirical work related to women's media activism that we have provided.

Functions of Women's Media Action

In Chapter 7, we observed that all women who engage in media activism are politically motivated; that is, they want their work to contribute to a world in which women's influence shapes everything from culture to social policy, advancing women in the process. While they have diverged considerably in the strategies that they have adopted in setting about their task – as revealed most clearly in the four paths they have followed in their work – they have used communicative action as their shared method, and some kind of media as their vehicle in shaping what we have called a women's public sphere. That public sphere is understood to be feminist in its orientation, in that it seeks to bring women into fuller social participation in every way. Based on the narratives of our 90 informants, we suggest that women's media activism functions in at least five important ways within feminist movements. Because other feminist scholarship also alludes to these functions in some way, we cite instances in which our findings find broader support.

The ritualistic *function*

First, women's media activism serves a ritualistic function, announcing women's commitment to self-determination in the wider world. Self-determination connotes a publicly stated desire to be free from that which oppresses (e.g., patriarchal constraints in the form of laws that limit women's mobility, marriage and property rights, education or participation in the economic sphere) and the intent to create new laws, customs, opportunities, and possibilities that enable women to be free and to advance. The ritualistic function would obviously be strong in the early stages of a women's movement, when energy is particularly high and leaders may be more militant and outspoken in their messages. In fact, however, we found evidence of this function in both early and continuing stages in several nations.

An excellent example can be seen in relation to issues. Take, for instance, the matter of women's media enterprises – which allows women the maximum control over their messages and images. Donna Allen and her daughter Dana Densmore wrote their treatise "A radical feminist analysis of mass media" in 1972 (reprinted in 2002), at the beginning of the US second-wave feminist movement, announcing women's need to establish their own media. Today, three decades later, that same position is advanced by the Women's Institute for Freedom of the Press (WIFP), based in Washington, DC – which Allen founded and her daughter Martha now directs – in its publications. WIFP bases its assessment on a proliferation of women-owned (and -controlled) media around the world – presently manifest in both traditional media such as books, magazines, and film and music companies, as well as in Internet sites. But, in fact, that same position is advocated by a number of other informants across nations and generations.

In Portland, Oregon, college student Chelsia Rice launched a newsletter in 2002 called *The F-Word*, to write about water conservation and other current issues from a feminist perspective, believing that "the voice of feminist media needs to be amplified because women's rights the world over are being lost." A number of young feminists use radio and alternative magazines (zines) to promote what they see to be their generation's oppositional discourse on women. For example, Californian K. T. Jarmul turned to her campus radio station to play her type of music – women-identified hardcore, metal, and punk rock – and feminist artists such as Sleater-Kinney, The Butchies, Wage of Sin, 7-year Bitch, and singer–songwriters Ani DiFranco, Tori Amos, and Michelle Shocked use their music as their politics. In Belgium, Claudia Wulz and two female colleagues produce their own weekly lesbian-feminist radio program to challenge the heterosexual male standard for "normality."

The connective *function*

Second, women's media activism serves to connect women with a feminist perspective across space and time. Such connectivity has been the subject of considerable feminist work exploring the role and significance of feminist media (Steiner 1983; Anderson & Zinsser 1988; Pinnock 1997; Beasley & Gibbons 2003). Our study emphasized the activism involved in creating women's media enterprises, although we also discerned the possibilities for this role to be fulfilled by mainstream media via informants who intentionally sought a broader public of women in/for their work.

Steiner's (1983) research emphasized the community building that took place in the United States during the nineteenth century through suffrage-era magazines and journals. These publications allowed women in varied locations and of various ages to feel united in a common cause of getting the vote and expanding women's other legal rights. We would argue such connectivity can also be seen in larger timeframes, as when women of the twenty-first century read or watch documentaries about women of earlier eras to develop historical knowledge of feminism and its goals. The connective function of women's media activism was seen in a number of young feminists, such as Red Chidgey in the United Kingdom who, through her Internet website called FingerBang distro, creates "a distribution network of young women's feminist, personal, political and artistic zines, pamphlets and books." The name of her website, a reference to female masturbation, attracts other like-minded young sisters, a contemporary means of achieving what the Sophie's Parlor Radio Collective, based in Washington, DC, managed through their weekly radio program three decades earlier. Feminist scholar Gillian Youngs (2004) refers to the kind of work that Chidgey is doing as cyberfeminism, or the use of virtual space by women who want a low-budget, high-visibility means of communicating with other women. Youngs notes that the Internet transgresses both patriarchal boundaries (that work through social institutions to silence and limit women) and national/international boundaries to achieve its goal.

The educational *function*

Third, women's media activism serves an educational function, pushing new feminist-oriented ideas, analyses, and language into a public sphere that otherwise would have been silent, invisible, or marginal. A number of our informants said that they sought specifically to inform women about something; for example, about their legal rights, health and well-being, or how to stop media stereotypes of women. This educational function can be seen in the media activism of Cameroonian Madeleine Memb's weekly broadcast *Au Nom de la Femme* (*In the Name of the Woman*), which aims to empower women by educating them, as well as in the work of her broadcast journalism colleague Patti Dapaah in nearby Ghana. Canadian feminist Jay Hartling's work in a bilingual Vancouver radio program since 1995 uses her media activism to educate the community about Latin American issues and to build working relationships among Canadians and Latin Americans living in her region.

Elayne Rapping (1994) has argued that feminism placed violence against women on the nation's public – and policy – agendas through made-for-TV films such as *Something About Amelia* (incest), the *Burning Bed* (wife battering), and *When He's Not a Stranger* (date rape). Anti-pornography campaigns, beginning in the 1970s, helped to emphasize connections between graphic images of sexual violence and the real-life experiences of so many women. In relation to news, feminists protested (and eventually stopped) the segregation of classified job listings by "women's" and "men's" categories, the designation of women's marital status through the use of "Miss" and "Mrs." in news stories, and the use of "he" as the standard pronoun (regardless of the sex of the person being referred to).

The social alignment *function*

Fourth, women's media activism has brought gender issues into closer alignment with socioeconomic ones such as class, race, ethnicity, and sexuality; that is, related social characteristics that have long served as the basis for exclusion and marginalization. We found that informants in our study repeatedly talked about how their own work as media activists integrated these elements. The presence of this function was seen in the work of a number of documentary filmmakers. One of these was Anne Lewis, of Austin, Texas, whose films show complex relationships between gender and issues of violence, labor, economics, and environmental degradation, as well as the social movements that address these. Lewis's award-winning films appear on public television and are used widely in classrooms, giving her a broad, diverse audience.

Another example is found in the work of several Indian media activists who transcended their own privileged backgrounds to make documentary films to raise contemporary issues across race, caste, and gender lines. As we saw, Gargi Sen both makes and distributes others' films to bring greater understanding of the rights sought by women, Dalit, and tribal communities, prostitutes, and other groups; Deepa Dhanraj's most recent films have pushed village women's participation in local councils (panchayats); and Sanjana's films have sought to let women and indigenous groups working in political and human rights campaigns speak publicly for themselves, and also to begin to connect the issues and actors among various movements in India – land rights, assaults on women, poverty, globalization, the environment, and other issues. As the lead member of a male–female editorial team, US journalist Patricia Gaston was able to help oversee the production of a series of stories in the early 1990s that connected and analyzed not only many forms violence against women in distinct cultural contexts around the world, but also women's cross-cultural campaign to categorize these crimes as human rights violations. In the process, she said, it was also possible to illustrate that the global was local, happening right in the Dallas – Forth Worth neighborhoods.

The regulatory *function*

Fifth, women's media activism serves a regulatory function, helping to increase the flow of information from the inner workings of women's movements into the wider world. The most commonly cited primary and secondary goal among informants in our study was to increase the amount of information about women to the general public. Women working in media careers saw this as a particularly strong motive for their activism, finding both routine and nonroutine ways of doing this. Journalist Preeti Mehra, based in New Delhi, told us that, by the 1980s, she began to find ways to get women into news stories, both routine events and more dramatic coverage of riots, earthquakes, and disasters. "Women were so marginalized," she remembers, and helping them gain visibility became part of her daily challenge. Former CNN television producer Stacey Cone convinced her managers to let her cover violence against women through documentaries including topics such as court cases in which women had killed their abusive husbands. And former Israeli radio journalist Dalia Liran-Alper, who went on to chair the Women's Status Committee of the Israeli Broadcasting Authority from 1993 to 1998, thereby creating better national broadcasting policy on gender issues, said that the committee's first goal was to disseminate feminist values to the public. The means by which they sought to accomplish this were by increasing women's visibility in broadcast media, limiting sexist portrayals, and expanding the number of women in the profession.

Research by Byerly (1995) found that women pushing for the establishment of the Women's Feature Service project in the mid-1970s identified a major goal to increase news flow about women internationally – in women's own voice. The WFS project, which included five separate programs in developing regions of the world, is carried on today by the surviving Women's Feature Service, based in New Delhi, which is still a woman-owned and -managed international news agency. WFS is not the only such group sharing this goal, as we saw in Shree Venkatram's Unnati Features organization (also in New Delhi), and Rita Henley Jensen's US-based Women's eNews daily online news service.

Future Research

Women's agency through media activism defines the lines and means of struggle over women's right to communicate. As many have observed, the right to communicate is bound up with meaningful democratic participation in the civil society, to which women already belong but do not always have the means to readily enter, because of historical barriers based on sex discrimination. But very little is actually known about the specific ways in which women have challenged such restrictions on their communication in their day-to-day worlds. Such explorations have broad possibilities within and across nations, as our own study sought to identify. Significantly, women's struggles to be heard in their societies on a wide range of matters that concern them, their families, and their world have not been confined to a single nation or region but, rather, seem to be universal in their geographical reach. We have viewed these efforts collectively as a communicative phenomenon and we have posited women's media activism as a phenomenon whose patterns and contours are ready for more extensive description, definition, and theoretical analysis.

We encourage an expansion of theory-building in relation to women's media action. When, some might ask, is the time right for the creation of new feminist theory? Citing Elaine Marks and Isabelle de Courtivron (1980), Teresa de Lauretis (1988b: 138) suggests that:

> [A] new feminist theory begins when the feminist critique of ideologies becomes conscious of itself and turns to question its own body of writing and critical interpretations, its basic assumptions and terms, and the practices which they enable and from which they emerge.

We began this project as precisely such critics of our own field's scholarly practices. We recognized that feminist media research to date had focused disproportionately on women's portrayal and representation, and paid rather less attention to structural and other considerations. It was also clear that much of the published research on women and media is written from a Western (albeit feminist) perspective, and is thus overly preoccupied with issues and events in that region. In addition, little attention has been given to the range of strategies that women use in pursuing their ambitions to discipline and reform existing media or to create their own. Nor has there been a sufficient accounting of the many individuals – both the sung and unsung – who have engaged in media reform or alternative media practice over past decades.

In seeking to move toward a theoretical analysis of what women's media activism has comprised and meant, we have offered an emergent framework, the Model of Women's Media Action. Models are often a starting point for the establishment of theory that emerges through the scholarly process of application, critique, and refinement. The Model of Women's Media Action, which takes account of the tenets and motives that have underpinned women's media activism, has allowed us to organize the strategies and approaches that women have used not only in a single nation or period, but within several nations and within a timeframe of three decades of modern feminism. These approaches, or paths, have explicated the ways in which women's agency, through their activism, has created the spaces to speak both within women's communities and to larger audiences. We see in these paths the embodiment of Jürgen Habermas's model of the democratic public sphere, and its further development through the notion of multiple public spheres that operate both alongside and in overlapping relations to each other. In future research, we hope to see an expanded interest in a wide range of media through which women seek to enter into public debate within those public spheres, and community building that grows out of it. Pilar Riaño (1994) made the argument that if the connections between the media and women's participation in public arenas are to be understood, feminist media scholarship must go beyond consideration of problems in the content and structures of mainstream industries and instead (or at least as well as) also consider women-generated media. She said that:

> ... excessive emphasis placed on issues of access and equity of representation has silenced a more central structural question regarding the absence of voice of subordinated groups in the media. Participatory practices of media production have placed this issue at the center, defining themselves as spaces for grassroots communication, for the building of representations that foster communication of the others (of women, ethnic immigrants, minorities, and homosexuals). These practices, therefore, challenge dominant representations and forms of communication. (Riaño 1994: 122)

Riaño referred to a range of activities intended to give women and other marginalized groups a voice through their own grassroots media, thereby developing what we have earlier referred to as women's, feminist, and other public spheres. The obvious value in strengthening a sense of community within distinct public spheres at the local level is that the members of these spheres gain strength and skills to participate in their own spheres, and, simultaneously, challenge men's control in what is imagined as that larger (dominant) public sphere. Women's media activism, thus, will be further understood for the central role that it plays in women's liberation and the transformation of societies.

Bibliography

Aaron, Michele 2004: *New Queer Cinema: A Critical Reader*. Edinburgh: Edinburgh University Press.

Adler, Margot 1979: *Drawing Down the Moon*. Malden, MA: Beacon Press.

Akhavan-Majid, Roya and Ramaprasad, Jyotika 2000: Framing Beijing: dominant ideological influences on the American press coverage of the Fourth UN conference on women and the NGO forum. *Gazette*, 62(1), 45–59.

Aldana, Celia 2004: Can media regulation help in the search for equality? *Media and Gender Monitor* issue 15, 12.

Alexander, Karen 1993: *Daughters of the Dust* (film review). *Sight & Sound*, 3(9), 20–2.

Alfaro, R. 1988: Producers of communication: What is the proposition? *Group Media Journal*, 7(2), 10–15.

Allan, Stuart 1999: *News Culture*. Buckingham, UK: Open University Press.

Allen, Donna 1968: Up against the media. *The Liberated Voice*, July 10.

—— 1989: From opportunity to strategy: women contribute to the communication future. In Ramona R. Rush and Donna Allen (eds.), *Communication at the Crossroads: The Gender Gap Connection*. Norwood, NJ: Ablex, 59–82.

—— and Densmore, Dana 2002: A radical feminist analysis of mass media. In Martha Leslie Allen (ed.), *Directory of Women's Media*. Washington, DC: Women's Institute for Freedom of the Press, 11–17.

Allen, Martha Leslie (ed.) 2002: *Directory of Women's Media*. Washington, DC: Women's Institute for Freedom of the Press.

Allen, R. 1985: *Speaking of Soap Operas*. Chapel Hill, NC: University of North Carolina Press.

Amnesty International 2004: Colombia: scarred bodies, hidden crimes: sexual violence against women in the armed conflict – facts and figures. October 13;

http://amnestyusa.org/countries/colombia/document.do?id=80 (accessed October 31, 2004).

Ananda, Mitra 2004: Voices of the marginalized on the Internet: examples from a website for women of South Asia. *Journal of Communication*, 54(3), 492–510.

Andermahr, Sonya, Lovell, Terry and Wolkowitz, Carol 2000: *Feminist Counter-Public Sphere*. London: Arnold, 94–5.

Anderson, Bonnie S. and Zinsser, Judith P. 1988: *A History of Their Own*, vol. II. New York: Harper & Row.

Andrae, Thomas 1996: Television's first feminist: *The Avengers* and female spectatorship. *Discourse: Theoretical Studies in Media and Culture*, 18(3), 112–36.

Ang, Ien 1985: *Watching Dallas: Soap Opera and the Melodramatic Imagination*. London: Methuen.

—— 1990: Melodramatic identifications: television fiction and women's fantasy. In Mary Ellen Brown (ed.), *Television and Women's Culture: the Politics of the Popular*. London: Sage, 75–88.

—— 1991: *Desperately Seeking the Audience*. London: Routledge.

Annenberg Public Policy Center 2002: *No Room at the Top?* Philadelphia, PA: University of Pennsylvania.

Anon. 1996: Media must advance the cause of women. *Media Development*, 43(1), 47–8.

Armstrong, Leila 1998: The zeal for Xena: appropriation, discursive elaboration and identity production in lesbian fan fiction. *Whoosh!* 25 (October); http://whoosh.org/issue25/arm1.html (accessed September 7, 2004).

Arnaldo, Carlos A. (ed.) 2001: *Child Abuse on the Internet: Ending the Silence*. New York: Berghahn Books.

Arnheim, Rudolph 1944: The world of the daytime serial. In Paul F. Lazarsfeld and Frank N. Stanton (eds.), *Radio Research: 1942–1943*. New York: Duell, Sloan and Pearce, 34–107.

Arnold, Rebecca 2001: *Fashion, Desire and Anxiety: Image and Morality in the Twentieth Century*. Piscataway, NJ: Rutgers University Press.

Aronson, Amy Beth 2002: *Taking Liberties: Early American Women's Magazines and Their Readers*. Westport, CT: Greenwood Press.

Arthurs, Jane 1994: Women and television. In Stuart Hood (ed.), *Behind the Screens*. London: Lawrence & Wishart, 82–101.

Attile, Martine 1988: The passion of remembrance: background. In Kobena Mercer (ed.), *Black Film: British Cinema*. ICA paper #7. London: British Film Institute/ICA, 53–4.

Baehr, Helen and Dyer, Gillian (eds.) 1987: *Boxed In: Women and Television*. New York: Pandora Press.

Baistow, Tom 1985: *Fourth-Rate Estate: An Anatomy of Fleet Street*. London: Comedia.

Bakker, Isabella 1994: *The Strategic Silence: Gender and Economic Policy*. London: Zed Books.

Ballaster, Ros, Beetham, Margaret, Frazer, Elizabeth and Hebron, Sandra 1991: *Women's Worlds: Ideology, Femininity and Women's Magazines*. Basingstoke, UK: Palgrave Macmillan.

Bam, B. 1994: Women, communication and socio-cultural identity: creating a common vision. *Media Development*, 41(2), 15–17.

Bambara, Toni Cade 1993: Reading the signs, empowering the eye: *Daughters of the Dust* and the black independent cinema movement. In Manthia Diawara (ed.), *Black American Cinema*. London: Routledge, 118–44.

Baron, Larry and Strauss, Murray A. 1989: *Four Theories of Rape in American Society: A State-Level Analysis*. New Haven, CT: Yale University Press.

Basinger, Jeanne 1994: *A Woman's View: How Hollywood Spoke to Women, 1930–1960*. London: Chatto and Windus.

Basu, Amrita (ed.) 1995: *The Challenge of Local Feminisms: Women's Movements in Global Perspective*. Boulder, CO: Westview Press.

Beale, Alison and van den Bosch, Annette (eds.) 1998: *Ghosts in the Machine: Women and Cultural Policy in Canada and Australia*. Toronto, Canada: Garamond Press.

Beasley, Maureen H. 1993: Is there a new majority defining the news? In Pamela J. Creedon (ed.), *Women in Mass Communication*. Newbury Park, CA: Sage, 18–33.

——and Gibbons, Sheila J. 2003: *Taking Their Place: A Documentary History of Women and Journalism*. State College, PA: Strata Publishing, Inc.

Becker, Ron 1998: Primetime TV in the gay nineties: network television, quality audiences and gay politics. *The Velvet Light Trap*, 42, 36–47.

Beetham, Margaret 2001: *Victorian Women's Magazines: An Anthology*. Manchester: Manchester University Press.

Benedict, Helen 1992: *Virgin or Vamp: How the Press Covers Sex Crimes*. Oxford: Oxford University Press.

Bennett, W. Lance 1997: Cracking the news code: some rules that journalists live by. In Shanto Iyengar and Richard Reeves (eds.), *Do the Media Govern? Politicians, Voters and Reporters in America*. Thousand Oaks, CA: Sage, 103–17.

Bennett, W. Lance 2002: Feminists must speak out against loss of media diversity. *National NOW Times*, 34(2), 13.

Bennett, W. Lance, Pickard, Victor W., Iozzi, David P., Schroeder, Carl L., Lagos, Taso and Caswell, C. Evans 2004: Managing the public sphere: journalistic construction of the great globalization debate. *Journal of Communication*, 54(3), 437–55.

Berger, John 1977: *Ways of Seeing*. New York: Penguin.

Berkowitz, Sandra 2003: Can we stand with you? Lessons from women in black for global feminist activism. *Women & Language*, XXVI(1), 94–9.

Berns, Nancy 1999: My problem and how I solved it: domestic violence in women's magazines. *Sociological Quarterly*, 40(1), 85–108.

Bird, S. Elizabeth and Dardenne, Robert W. 1988: Myth, chronicle and story: exploring the narrative qualities of news. In James Carey (ed.), *Media, Myths and Narrative*. Newbury Park, CA: Sage, 67–86.

Bobo, Jacqueline 1988: *The Color Purple*: black women as cultural readers. In E. Deirdre Pribham (ed.), *Female Spectators: Looking at Film and Television*. London: Verso, 90–109.

——and Seiter, Ellen 1991: Black feminism and media criticism: *The Women of Brewster Place*. *Screen*, 32(3), 286–302.

Bonfadelli, Heinz 2002: The Internet and knowledge gaps: a theoretical and empirical investigation. *European Journal of Communication*, 17(1), 65–84.

Bordo, Susan 1995: *Unbearable Weight: Feminism, Western Culture and the Body*. Berkeley, CA: University of California Press.

Boulding, Elise c.1980: *Women: The Fifth World*. New York: Foreign Policy Association, Inc.

——1992: *The Underside of History: A View of Women Through Time*, vol. 2, rev. edn. Newbury Park, CA: Sage.

Bourdieu, Pierre 1984 [1979]: *Distinction: A Social Critique of the Judgment of Taste*, trans. Richard Nice. London: Routledge and Kegan Paul.

Bourne, Stephen 1998: *Black in the British Frame: Black People in British Film and Television 1896–1996*. London: Cassell.

Brennan, Zoe 2004: *The Older Woman in Recent Fiction*. Jefferson, NC: McFarland.

Brown, Mary Ellen 1994: *Soap Opera and Women's Talk: The Pleasure of Resistance*. Thousand Oaks, CA: Sage.

——1990: Motley moments: soap opera, carnival, gossip and the power of the utterance. In Mary Ellen Brown (ed.), *Television and Women's Culture: The Politics of the Popular*. London: Sage, 183–98.

Brunsdon, Charlotte 1981: *Crossroads*: notes on a soap opera. *Screen*, 22, 32–7.

——(ed.) 1986: *Films for Women*. London: British Film Institute.

——1998: Structure of anxiety: recent British television crime fiction. *Screen*, 39 (Autumn), 223–43.

——2000: *The Feminist, the Housewife and the Soap Opera*. Oxford: The Clarendon Press.

——, D'Acci, Julie and Spigel, Lynn (eds.) 1997: *Feminist Television Criticism: A Reader*. Oxford: Oxford University Press.

Buckingham, David 1987: *Public Secrets*: EastEnders *and its Audience*. London: British Film Institute.

Burch, Sally 2002: The right to communicate: new challenges for the Women's Movement. *Women in Action*; Isis International website www.isiswomen.org/pub/wia/wia202/right2com.htm (accessed August 2, 2004).

Burrell, Ian 2004: Radio's golden girl. *The Independent Review*, June 1.

Burt, Elizabeth V. 2000: Preface. In Elizabeth V. Burt (ed.), *Women's Press Organizations, 1881–1999*. Westport, CT: Greenwood Press, xi–xv.

Butler, Alison 2002: *Women's Cinema: The Contested Screen*. London: Wallflower Press.

Buzzanell, Patrice M. 2003: A feminist standpoint analysis of maternity and maternity leave for women with disabilities. *Women & Language*, XXVI(2), 53–65.

Byerly, Carolyn M. 1990: The Women's Feature Service and the making of world news. Unpublished dissertation, School of Communication, University of Washington, Seattle, WA.

——1994: An agenda for teaching news coverage of rape. *Journalism Educator*, 49(1), 59–69.

——1995: News, consciousness and social participation. In Angharad N. Valdivia (ed.), *Feminism, Multiculturalism and the Media*. Thousand Oaks, CA: Sage, 105–22.

——1998: Women, media and structure: feminist research in an era of globalization. Paper presented to the International Association of Media and Communciation Research annual conference, Glasgow, July.

——1999: News, feminism and the dialectics of gender relations. in Marian Myers (ed.), *Mediated Women: Representations in Popular Culture*. Cresskill, NJ: Hampton Press, 383–403.

——2001: The deeper structures of storytelling: women, media corporations and the task of communication researchers. *Intersections*, 1(2), 63–8.

——2004a: Feminist interventions in newsrooms. In Carolyn M. Byerly and Karen Ross (eds.), *Women and Media: International Perspectives*. Malden, MA: Blackwell, 109–31.

——2004b: Women and the concentration of media ownership. In Ramona R. Rush, Carol E. Oukrup, and Pamela J. Creedon (eds.), *Seeking Equity for Women in Journalism and Mass Communication Education*. Mahwah, NJ: Lawrence Erlbaum Associates, 245–73.

——and Warren, Catherine A. 1996: At the margins of center: organized protest in the newsroom. *Critical Studies in Mass Communication*, 13(1), 1–23.

Calhoun, Craig 1992: Introduction: Habermas and the public sphere. In Craig Calhoun (ed.), *Habermas and the Public Sphere*. Cambridge, MA: The MIT Press, 1–48.

Cann, D. and Mohr, P. B. 2001: *Journalist and source gender in Australian television news. Journal of Broadcasting & Electronic Media*, 45(1), 162–74.

Caputi, J. 1999: Pornography of everyday life. In Marian Myers (ed.), *Mediated Women: Representations in Popular Culture*. Cresskill, NJ: Hampton Press, 57–80.

Carstarphen, Meta G. 1999: Getting real love: *Waiting to Exhale* and film representations of womanist identity. In Marian Myers (ed.), *Mediated Women: Representations in Popular Culture.* Cresskill, NJ: Hampton Press, 369–82.

Carter, Cynthia 1998: When the extraordinary becomes ordinary: everyday news of sexual violence. In Cynthia Carter, Gill Branston, and Stuart Allan (eds.), *News, Gender and Power.* London: Routledge, 219–32.

——and Weaver, C. Kay 2003: *Violence and the Media.* Buckingham, UK: Open University Press.

——, Branston, Gill and Allan, Stuart (eds.) 1998a: *News, Gender and Power.* London: Routledge.

——, ——and ——1998b: Setting new(s) agendas: an introduction. In Cynthia Carter, Gill Branston, and Stuart Allan (eds.), *News, Gender and Power.* London: Routledge, 1–12.

Ceulemans, Mieke and Fauconnier, Guido 1979: *Mass Media: The Image, Role and Social conditions of Women – a Collection and Analysis of Research Materials.* Paris: United Nations Educational, Scientific and Cultural Organization (UNESCO).

Chambers, Deborah, Steiner, Linda and Fleming, Carole 2004: *Women and Journalism.* London: Routledge.

Chapman, James 2002: *Saints and Avengers: British adventure series of the 1960s.* London: I. B. Taurus.

Chaudhuri, Maitrayee (ed.) 2004: *Feminism in India.* New Delhi: Kali for Women & Women Unlimited.

Christian, Barbara 1985: Trajectories of self-definition: placing contemporary Afro-American women's fiction. In Marjorie Pryse and Hortense J. Spillers (eds.), *Conjuring: Black Women, Fiction and Literary Tradition.* Bloomington, IN: Indiana University Press, 233–48.

Christmas, Linda 1997: *Chaps of Both Sexes? Women Decision-Makers in Newspapers: Do They Make a Difference?* London: Women in Journalism.

Clark, Danae 1990: Cagney and Lacey: feminist strategies of detection. In Mary Ellen Brown (ed.), *Television and Women's Culture: The Politics of the Popular.* London: Sage, 117–34.

——1996 [1990]: *Cagney and Lacey:* feminist strategies of detection. In Paul Marris and Sue Thornham (eds.), *Media Studies: A Reader.* Edinburgh: Edinburgh University Press, 211–20.

Clover, Carol J. 1992: *Men, Women and Chainsaws: Gender in the Modern Horror Film.* London: British Film Institute.

Cohen, Jean L. 1995: Critical social theory and feminist critiques: the debate with Jürgen Habermas. In Johanna Meehan (ed.), *Feminists Read Habermas.* New York: Routledge, 57–90.

Coles, Joanna 1997: Boy zone story. *The Guardian*, 28 April.

Compesi, R. J. 1980: Gratifications of daytime TV serial viewers. *Journalism Quarterly*, 57, 155–85.

Compton, Laura 2001: Bridgeting the gap: if we can't have a true heroine, an anti-Ally will have to do. *Bitch! Magazine* issue 8; available at www.bitchmagazine. com/archives/08_01bridget/bridget.shtml (accessed September 9, 2004).

Cooke, Kaz 1996: *Real Gorgeous: the Truth about Body and Beauty*. New York: W. W. Norton.

Corner, John 1991: Meaning, genre and context: the problematics of "public knowledge" in the new audience studies. In James Curran and Michael Gurevitch (eds.), *Mass Media and Society*. London: Edward Arnold, 267–306.

Cottingham, Jane 1989: Isis: A Decade of International Networking. In Ramona R. Rush and Donna Allen (eds.), *Communication at the Crossroads: The Gender Gap Connection*. Norwood, NJ: Ablex, 238–50.

Cottle, Simon (ed.) 2004: *News, Public Relations and Power*. London: Sage.

Creeber, Glen 2001: Cigarettes and alcohol: investigating gender, genre and gratification in *Prime Suspect*. *Television and New Media*, 2(2), 149–66.

Creed, Barbara 1993: *The Monstrous Feminine: Film, Feminism, Psychoanalysis*. London: Routledge.

Creedon, Pamela J. 1993: The challenge of re-visioning gender values. In Pamela J. Creedon (ed.), *Women in Mass Communication*, 2nd edn. Newbury Park, CA: Sage, 3–23.

Cresser, Frances, Gunn, Lesley and Balme, Helen 2001: Women's experiences of online e-zine publication. *Media, Culture and Society*, 23(4), 457–73.

Croteau, David and Hoynes, William 1997: *Media/Society: Industries, Images and Audiences*. Thousand Oaks, CA: Pine Forge Press.

—— and —— 2001: *The Business of Media: Corporate Media and the Public Interest*. London: Sage.

Cuklanz, Lisa M. 1996: *Rape on Trial. How the Mass Media Construct Legal Reform and Social Change*. Philadelphia, PA: University of Pennsylvania Press.

—— 2000: *Rape on Prime Time: Television, Masculinity and Sexual Violence*. Philadelphia, PA: University of Pennsylvania Press.

Curphey, Shauna 2003: Women push for media coverage in southern Africa. Women's eNews; www.womensenews.org (accessed September 15, 2003).

Cuthbert, Marlene 1989: "Woman day a come": women and communication channels in the Caribbean. In Ramona R. Rush and Donna Allen (eds.), *Communication at the Crossroads: The Gender Gap Connection*. Norwood, NJ: Ablex, 149–59.

D'Acci, Julie 1987: The case of *Cagney and Lacey*. In Helen Baehr and Gillian Dyer (eds.), *Boxed In: Women and Television*. London: Pandora, 203–25.

—— 1994: *Defining Women: Television and the Case of Cagney and Lacey*. Chapel Hill, NC: University of North Carolina Press.

Damon-Moore, Helen 1994: *Magazines for the Millions: Gender and Commerce in the "Ladies' Home Journal" and the "Saturday Evening Post", 1880–1910*. New York: State University of New York Press.

Daniels, Therese and Gerson, Jane (eds.) 1989: *The Colour Black: Black Images in British Television*. London: British Film Institute.

Darling-Wolf, Fabienne 2004: Virtually multicultural: trans-Asian identity and gender in an international fan community of a Japanese star. *New Media and Society*, 6(4), 507–28.

David, Prabu, Morrison, Glenda, Johnson, Melissa A. and Ross, Felecia 2002: Body image, race and fashion models: social distance and social identification in third-person effects. *Communication Research*, 29(3), 270–94.

Davis, Angela Y. 1981: *Women, Race and Class*. New York: Vintage Books.

Day, Gary and Bloom, Clive (eds.) 1988: *Perspectives on Pornography: Sexuality in Film and Literature*. Basingstoke, UK: Macmillan Press.

de Bruin, Marjan 1998: Gender in Caribbean media: beyond the body count. Paper presented to the 21st General Assembly and Scientific Conference of the International Association for Media and Communication Research, Glasgow, July.

——and Ross, Karen (eds.) 2004: *Gender and Newsroom Cultures: Identities at Work*. Cresskill, NJ: Hampton Press.

de Lauretis, Teresa 1987: Rethinking women's cinema: aesthetics and feminist theory. In Teresa de Lauretis (ed.), *Technologies of Gender: Essays on Theory, Film and Fiction*. Bloomington, IN: Indiana University Press, 127–48.

—— 1988a: Displacing hegemonic discourses: reflections on feminist theory in the 1980s. *Inscriptions*, 3–4, 127–44.

——(ed.) 1988b: *Feminist Studies/Critical Studies*. London: Macmillan.

Desai, Jigna 2004: *Beyond Bollywood: The Cultural Politics of South Asian Diasporic Film*. New York: Routledge.

DiCenzo, Maria 2000: Militant distribution: votes for women and the public sphere. *Media History*, 6(2), 115–28.

Dines, Gail 1997: *Pornography: The Consumption of Inequality*. London: Routledge.

——and Humez, Jean M. (eds.) 1995: *Gender, Race and Class in Media*. Thousand Oaks, CA: Sage.

——and —— (eds.) 2003: *Gender, Race, and Class in Media: A Text Reader*, 2nd edn. Thousand Oaks, CA: Sage.

——, Jensen, Robert and Russo, Ann 1998: *Pornography: The Production and Consumption of Inequality*. New York: Routledge.

Donat, Patricia L. N. and D'Emilio, John 1992: A feminist redefinition of rape and sexual assault: historical foundations and change. *Journal of Social Issues*, 48(1), 9–22.

Dougary, Ginny 1994: *The Executive Tart and Other Myths: Media Women Talk Back*. London: Virago.

Douglas, Susan 1994: *Where the Girls Are: Growing Up Female with the Mass Media*. London: Penguin.

Durham, Meenakshi Gigi 1998: Dilemmas of desire: representations of adolescent sexuality in two teen magazines. *Youth and Society*, 29(3), 369–89.

Dworkin, Andrea 1997: *Life and Death: Unapologetic Writings on the Continuing War Against Women*. London: Virago.

——2000: Pornography and grief. In Drucilla Cornell (ed.), *Feminism and Pornography*. Oxford: Oxford University Press, 39–44.

Edut, Ophira (ed.) 1998: *Adios Barbie: Young Women Write About Body Image and Identity*. Berkeley, CA: Publishers Group West.

——and Walker, Rebecca (eds.) 2000: *Body Outlaws: Young Women Write about Body Image and Identity*. Seattle: Seal Press.

Eldridge, John (ed.) 1995: *News Content, Language and Visuals: Glasgow Media Group Reader*, vol. 1. London: Routledge.

Eliasoph, Nina 1988: Routines and the making of oppositional news. *Critical Studies in Mass Communication*, 5, 313–34.

Elson, Diane 1994: Micro, meso, macro: gender and economic analysis in the context of policy reform. In Isabella Bakker (ed.), *The Strategic Silence: Gender and Economic Policy*. London: Zed Books, 33–45.

Entman, Robert M. 1989: How the media affect what people think: an information processing approach. *Journal of Politics*, 51, 347–70.

European Commission 1999: *Images of Women in the Media*. Brussels: Commission of the European Communities.

Fahmy, Shahira 2004: Picturing Afghan women: a content analysis of AP wire photographs during the Taliban regime and after the fall of the Taliban regime. *Gazette*, 66(2), 91–112.

Fejes, Fred and Petrich, Kevin 1993: Invisibility, homophobia and heterosexism: lesbians, gays and the media. *Critical Studies in Mass Communication*, 20(6), 396–422.

Felski, Rita 1989: *Beyond Feminist Aesthetics: Feminist Literature and Social Change*. London: Hutchinson Radius, 9–10.

Firestone, Shulamith 1970: *The Dialectic of Sex*. New York: William Morrow.

Fiske, John 1987: *Television Culture*. London: Methuen.

Foss, Karen and Foss, Sonja 1989: Incorporating the feminist perspective in communication scholarship: a research commentary. In Katherine Carter and Carol Spitzack (eds.), *Doing Research on Women's Communication: Perspectives on Theory and Method*. Norwood, NJ: Ablex, 65–91.

Fowler, Roger 1991: *Language in the News: Discourse and Ideology in the Press*. London: Routledge.

Franklin, Bob 1997: *Newszak & News Media*. London: Arnold.

Fraser, Nancy 1993: Rethinking the public sphere: a contribution to the critique of actually existing democracy. In Craig Calhoun (ed.), *Habermas and the Public Sphere*. Cambridge, MA: The MIT Press, 109–42.

Fudge, Rachel 2001: The Buffy effect or, a tale of cleavage and marketing. *Bitch!*

Magazine issue 10 (August); www.bitchmagazine.com/archives/08–01buffy/buffy3.shtml (accessed September 19, 2004).

Gaines, Jane 1988: White privilege and looking relations: race and gender in feminist film theory. *Screen*, 29(4), 12–27.

Gajjala, Radhika 2002: An interrupted postcolonial/feminist cyberethnography: complicity and resistance in the "cyberfield." *Feminist Media Studies*, 2(2), 177–93.

Galician, Mary-Lou 2003: *Sex, Love and Romance in the Mass Media: Analysis and Criticism of Unrealistic Portrayals and Their Influence.* Mahwah, NJ: Lawrence Erlbaum Associates.

Gallagher, Margaret 1979: *The Portrayal and Participation of Women in the Media.* Paris: United Nations Educational, Scientific and Cultural Organization (UNESCO).

——1981: *Unequal Opportunities: The Case of Women and the Media.* Paris: United Nations Educational, Scientific and Cultural Organization (UNESCO).

——1988: *Women and Television in Europe.* Brussels: Commission of the European Communities.

——1995: *An Unfinished Story: Gender Patterns in Media Employment.* Reports and Papers on Mass Communication, No. 110. Paris: United Nations Educational, Scientific and Cultural Organization (UNESCO).

——2001: *Gender Setting: New Agendas for Media Monitoring and Advocacy.* London: Zed Books.

Gamman, Lorraine and Marshment, Margaret (eds.) 1988: *The Female Gaze: Women as Viewers of Popular Culture.* London: The Women's Press.

Gandy, Oscar H., Jr. 1998: *Communication and Race: A Structural Perspective.* London: Hodder.

Gans, Herbert J. 1980: *Deciding What's News: A study of CBS Evening News, NBC Nightly News, Newsweek.* London: Constable.

Gauntlett, David 2002: *Media, Gender and Identity: An Introduction.* London: Routledge.

——n.d.: More about *More!* The sexual language of young women's magazines; http://theoryhead.com/gender/more.htm (accessed September 23, 2004).

Geraghty, Christine 1981: The continuous serial: a definition. In Richard Dyer, Christine Geraghty, Marion Jordan, Terry Lovell, Richard Paterson, and James Stewart (eds.), *Coronation Street.* London: British Film Institute.

——1991: *Women and Soap Opera: A Study of Prime Time Soaps.* Cambridge, UK: Polity Press.

——2000: Post-war choices and feminine possibilities. In Ulrike Sieglohr (ed.), *Heroines Without Heroes: Reconstructing Female and National Identities in European Cinema 1945–1951.* London: Cassell, 15–32.

Gerbner, George, Mowlana, Hamid and Nordenstreng, Kaarle 1993: *The Global Media Debate: Its Rise, Fall and Renewal.* Norwood, NJ: Ablex.

Giddens, Anthony 1984: *The Constitution of Society: Outline of the Theory of Structuration*. Cambridge, UK: Polity Press.

Giffard, C. Anthony 1999: The Beijing Conference on Women as seen by three international news agencies. *Gazette*, 61(3–4), 327–41.

Gilbert, Sandra M. and Gubar, Susan 1979: *The Madwoman in the Attic: the Woman Writer and the Nineteenth-Century Literary Imagination*. New Haven, CT: Yale University Press.

Gillespie, Carmen R. 1999: Mammy goes to Las Vegas: showgirls and the constancy of African-American female stereotypes. In Marian Myers (ed.), *Mediated Women: Representations in Popular Culture*. Cresskill, NJ: Hampton Press, 81–90.

Gillwald, Alison 1994: Women, democracy and media in South Africa. *Media Development*, 2, 27–32.

Gilmour, Heather 2004 [1999]: What girls want: the intersections of leisure and power in female computer game play. In Cynthia Carter and Linda Steiner (eds.), *Critical Readings: Media and Gender*. Maidenhead, UK: Open University Press, 328–44.

Gilroy, Paul 1990: It ain't where you're from, it's where you're at. *Third Text*, 13, 3–16.

Giroux, Henry 2002: Public intellectuals, race, and public space. In David Theo Goldberg and John Solomos (eds.), *A Companion to Racial and Ethnic Studies*. Malden, MA: Blackwell, 383–404.

Gledhill, Christine 1988: Pleasurable negotiations. In E. Deirdre Pribham (ed.), *Female Spectators: Looking at Film and Television*. London: Verso, 64–77.

Golden, Catherine J. 2003: *Images of the Woman Reader in Victorian British and American Fiction*. Florida: University of Florida Press.

Gole, Nilufer 1997: The gendered nature of the public sphere. *Public Culture*, 10(1), 61–81.

Gordon, Bette 1984: Variety: the pleasure in looking. In Carole S. Vance (ed.), *Pleasure and Danger: Exploring Female Sexuality*. Boston, London: Routledge and Kegan Paul, 189–203.

Gough-Yates, Anna 2002: *Understanding Women's Magazines: Publishing, Markets and Readerships*. London: Routledge.

——and Osgerby, Bill (eds.) 2001: *Action TV: Tough-Guys, Smooth Operators and Foxy Chicks*. London: Routledge.

Gramsci, Antonio 1971: *The Prison Notebooks*, trans. and ed. Quintin Hoare and Geoffrey Nowell Smith. New York: International Publishers.

Gross, Larry 1994: What is wrong with this picture? Lesbian women and gay men on television. In R. Jeffrey Ringer (ed.), *Queer Words, Queer Images: Communication and the Construction of Homosexuality*. New York: New York University Press, 143–56.

Grosz, Elizabeth 1995: *Space, Time and Perversion*. New York: Routledge.

Gui, Shugin 2003: *Women Through the Lens: Gender and Nation in a Century of Chinese Cinema*. Honolulu: University of Hawaii Press.

GVRD 1998: *Greater Vancouver's "Roots": Defining Our Ethnic Origins*. Report, Greater Vancouver Regional Development, Strategic Planning Department, Vancouver; http://www.gvrd.bc.ca (accessed November 1, 2004).

Gwenllian Jones, Sara 2000: Histories, fictions and *Xena: Warrior Princess*. *Television & New Media*, 1(4), 403–18.

Habermas, Jürgen 1984: *The Theory of Communicative Action, Volume Two: Lifeworld and System: A Critique of Functionalist Reason*, trans. Thomas McCarthy. Malden, MA: Beacon Press.

——1987: *The Theory of Communicative Action, Volume One: Reason and the Rationalization of Society*, trans. Thomas McCarthy. Malden, MA: Beacon Press.

——1993: Further reflections on the public sphere. In Craig Calhoun (ed.), *Habermas and the Public Sphere*. Cambridge, MA: The MIT Press, 421–61.

Hall, Stuart 1980: Coding and encoding in television discourse. In Stuart Hall/Centre for Contemporary Cultural Studies (eds.), *Culture, Media, Language*. London: Hutchinson, in association with CCCS, Birmingham, 197–208.

——1988: New ethnicities. In Kobena Mercer (ed.), *Black Film: British Cinema*. ICA paper #7. London: British Film Institute/ICA, 27–31.

Hallam, Julia 2000: Power play: gender, genre and Lynda La Plant. In Jonathan Bignell, Stephen Lacey and Madeleine Macmurraugh-Kavanagh (eds.), *British Television Drama: Past, Present and Future*. London: Palgrave, 140–9.

Hantzis, Darlene M. and Lehr, Valerie 1994: Whose desire? Lesbian (non)sexuality and television's perpetuation of hetero/sexism. In R. Jeffrey Ringer (ed.), *Queer Words, Queer Images: Communication and the Construction of Homosexuality*. New York: New York University Press, 107–21.

Harcourt, Wendy (ed.) 1999: *Women@Internet: Creating New Cultures in Cyberspace*. London: Zed Books.

Harrington, C. Lee 2003: Lesbian(s) on daytime television: the Bianca narrative on *All My Children*. *Feminist Media Studies*, 3(2), 207–28.

——and Bielby, Denise D. 1995: *Soap Fans: Pursuing Pleasure and Making Meaning in Everyday Life*. Philadelphia: Temple University Press.

Hartley, John 1996: *Popular Reality: Journalism, Modernity, Popular Culture*. London: Edward Arnold.

Hartsock, Nancy C. M. 1983: *Money, Sex and Power: Toward a Feminist Historical Materialism*. Boston, MA: Northeastern University Press.

Haskell, Molly 1973: *From Reverence to Rape: The Treatment of Women in the Movies*. New York: Holt, Rinehart and Winston.

Hayward, Anthony and Rennert, Amy (eds.) 1996: Prime Suspect: *The Official Book of the Award-Winning Series*. London: Carlton Books.

Herman, Edward and McChesney, Robert 1997: *The Global Media*. London: Cassell.

Hermes, Joke 1995: *Reading Women's Magazines: An Analysis of Everyday Media Use*. London: Polity Press.

Hernandez, Debra Gersh 1995: Are women being annihilated by the media? *Editor & Publisher*, July 1.

Hernandez, Zoila 1992: Mujer y Sociedad: writing for a mass audience. In Gaby Kuppers (ed.), *Companeras: Voices from the Latin American Women's Liberation Movement*. London: The Latin American Bureau, 146–52.

Herzog, Hannah 1944: What do we really know about daytime serial listeners? In Paul F. Lazarsfeld and Frank N. Stanton (eds.), *Radio Research: 1942–1943*. New York: Duell, Sloan and Pearce.

Hesse-Biber, Sharlene 1997: *Am I Thin Enough Yet?: The Cult of Thinness and the Commercialization of Identity*. Oxford: Oxford University Press.

Hill, Annette 2001: "Looks like it hurts": women's responses to shocking entertainment. In Martin Barker and Julian Petley (eds.), *Ill Effects: The Media/Violence Debate*, 2nd edn. London: Routledge, 135–49.

Hill Collins, Patricia 1990: *Black Feminist Thought*. New York: Routledge.

—— 1995: Pornography and black women's bodies. In Gail Dines and Jean M. Humez (eds), *Gender, Race and Class in Media (A Text Reader)*. Thousand Oaks, CA: Sage, 279–86.

Hinds, Hilary 1992: Fruitful investigations: the case of the successful lesbian text. In Sally Munt (ed.), *New Lesbian Criticism: Literary and Cultural Readings*. New York: Columbia University Press, 153–82.

Hiriart, Berta 1992: Mujer/fempress: Latin American women's news agency. In Gaby Kuppers (ed.), *Companeras: Voices from the Latin American Women's Liberation Movement*. London: The Latin American Bureau, 163–6.

Hobson, Dorothy 1982: *Crossroads: The Drama of a Soap Opera*. London: Methuen.

—— 1990: Women audiences and the workplace. In Mary Ellen Brown (ed.), *Television and Women's Culture*. Newbury Park, CA: Sage, 61–71.

—— 2002: *Soap Opera*. Malden, MA: Blackwell.

Holland, Patricia 1987: When a woman reads the news. In Helen Baehr and Gillian Dyer (eds.), *Boxed In: Women and Television*. New York: Pandora, 133–49.

—— 1998: The politics of the smile: "soft news" and the sexualisation of the popular press. In Cynthia Carter, Gill Branston, and Stuart Allan (eds.), *News, Gender and Power*. London: Routledge, 17–32.

Holmlund, Chris 2002: *Impossible Bodies: Femininity and Masculinity at the Movies*. London: Routledge.

hooks, bell 1991: *Yearnings: Race, Gender and Cultural Politics*. London: Turnaround.

—— 1992: *Black Looks: Race, Representation*. London: Turnaround.

—— 1996: *Reel to Reel: Race, Sex and Class at the Movies*. New York: Routledge.

—— 2000: *Feminism Is For Everybody: Passionate Politics*. London: Pluto Press.

Humm, Maggie 1988: Is the gaze feminist? Pornography, film and feminism. In Gary Day and Clive Bloom (eds.), *Perspectives on Pornography: Sexuality in Film and Literature*. Basingstoke, UK: Macmillan Press, 83–100.

—— 1997: *Feminism and Film*. Edinburgh: Edinburgh University Press.

Inness, Sherrie A. 1999: *Tough Girls: Women Warriors and Wonder Women in Popular Culture*. Philadelphia, PA: University of Pennsylvania Press.

International Institute of Communications 1996: *Media Ownership and Control in the Age of Convergence*. Luton, UK: University of Luton Press.

Isis International – Manila; www.isiswomen.org/organization/index.html (accessed September 10, 2004).

Islam, Needeya 1995: "I wanted to shoot people" – genre, gender and action in the films of Kathryn Bigelow. In Laleen Jayamanne (ed.), *Kiss Me Deadly: Feminism & Cinema for the Moment*. Sydney: Power Institute of Fine Arts, 91–125.

Iyengar, Shanto 1991: *Is Anyone Responsible? How Television Frames Public Issues*. Chicago: The University of Chicago Press.

Jagger, Alison M. 2004: Arenas of citizenship: civil society, state and the global order. In Barbara S. Andrew, Jean Keller, and Lisa H. Schwartzman (eds.), *Feminist Interventions in Ethics and Politics*. Lanham, MD: Rowman & Littlefield.

Jain, Devaki 1996: Panchayat Raj: Women changing governance.Gender in Development website; www.sdnp.undp.org/gender/resources/mono5.html (accessed February 4, 2004).

Jayamanne, Laleen (ed.) 1995: *Kiss Me Deadly: Feminism & Cinema for the Moment*. Sydney: Power Institute of Fine Arts.

Jenkins, Henry 1992: *Textual Poachers: Television Fans and Participatory Culture*. New York: Routledge.

Jenkins, Philip 2003: *Beyond Tolerance: Child Pornography on the Internet*. New York: New York University Press.

Jigna, Desai 2004: *Beyond Bollywood: The Cultural Politics of South Asian Diasporic Film*. New York: Routledge.

Jennings, Ros 1995: Design and design: Ripley undressed. In Tamsin Wilton (ed.), *Immortal, Invisible: Lesbians and the Moving Image*. London: Routledge, 193–206.

Johnson-Odim, Cheryl 1991: Common themes, different contexts. In Chandra Mohanty Talpede, Ann Russo, and Lourdes Torres (eds.), *Third Women and the Politics of Feminism*. Bloomington, IN: Indiana University Press, 314–27.

Jones, Nicholas 1996: *Soundbites & Spin Doctors: How Politicians Manipulate the Media and Vice Versa*. London: Indigo.

Joseph, Ammu 2000: *Women in Journalism Making News*. Delhi, India: Konark Publishers.

—— 2004a: Another face of violence. *The Hindu*, August 15, 2004; www.thehindu.

com/thehindu/mag/2004/08/15/stories/2004081500460200.htm (accessed October 31, 2004).

—— 2004b: NWMI's (Network of Women in Media in India) second national meeting; www.nwmindia.org/ (accessed February 9, 2004).

—— 2004c: Southern Africa strikes a blow for gender equality at the Gender and Media Summit. *Media Report to Women*, 32(4), 1–3.

—— 2004d: The gender (dis)advantage in Indian print media. In Marjan de Bruin and Karen Ross (eds.), *Gender and Newsroom Cultures: Identities at Work*. Cresskill, NJ: Hampton Press, 145–62.

—— 2004e: When violence is not news. Indiatogether.org newsletter; www.indiatogether.org/2004/dec/ajo-medviol.htm (accessed December 5, 2004).

—— and Sharma, Kalpana 1994a: Appendix D: lessons from Ahmedabad. In *Whose News: The Media and Women's Issues*. Thousand Oaks, CA: Sage, 318–22.

—— and —— 1994b: *Whose News: The Media and Women's Issues*. Thousand Oaks, CA: Sage.

Juffer, Jane 1998: *At Home With Pornography: Women, Sex and Everyday Life*. New York: New York University Press.

Kahn, Kim Fridkin and Goldenberg, Edie N. 1991: Women candidates in the news: an examination of gender differences in US Senate campaign coverage. *Public Opinion Quarterly*, 55, 180–99.

—— and —— 1997: The media: obstacle or ally of feminists? In Shanto Iyengar and Richard Reeves (eds.), *Do the Media Govern? Politicians, Voters and Reporters in America*. Thousand Oaks, CA: Sage, 156–64.

Kaplan, E. Ann (ed.) 1983: *Women and Film: Both Sides of the Camera*. New York: Methuen.

—— (ed.) 2000: *Feminism and Film*. Oxford: Oxford University Press.

Kapoor, Priya 2003: Gendered sites of conflict: Internet activism in reproductive health. *Feminist Media Studies*, 3(3), 368–71.

Kassell, Paula and Kaufman, Susan J. 1989: Planning an international communications system for women. In Ramona R. Rush and Donna Allen (eds.), *Communication at the Crossroads: The Gender Gap Connection*. Norwood, NJ: Ablex, 222–37.

Katz, James E. and Rice, Ronald E. 2002: *Social Consequences of Internet Use: Access, Involvement and Interaction*. Cambridge, MA: The MIT Press.

Kaul, Malvika 2004 (July): Raw deal for women journalists; http://indiatogether. org/2004/jul/wom.rawdeal.htm (accessed November 12, 2004).

Keane, John 1991: *The Media and Democracy*. Cambridge, UK: Polity Press.

Keller, Kathryn 1994: *Mothers and Work in Popular American Magazines*. Westport, CT: Greenwood Press.

Kellner, Douglas 1989: *Critical Theory, Marxism and Modernity*. Baltimore, MD: Johns Hopkins University Press.

Kemp, Amanda, Madlala, Nozizwe, Moodley, Asha and Salo, Elaine 1995: The dawn of a new day: redefining South African feminism. In Amrita Basu (ed.), *The Challenge of Local Feminisms: Women's Movements in Global Perspective*. Boulder, CO: Westview Press, 131–62.

Kendall, Lori 2000: "Oh no! I'm a nerd!" Hegemonic masculinity on an online forum. *Gender & Society*, 14(3), 256–74.

Kerber, Linda K. 1997: *Toward an Intellectual History of Women*. Chapel Hill, NC: University of North Carolina Press.

——and Sherron De Hart, Jane (eds.) 2000: *Women's America: Refocusing the Past*. New York: Oxford University Press.

Kern-Foxworth, Marilyn 2004: Women of color on the frontline in the mass communication professions. In Ramona R. Rush, Carol E. Oukrup, and Pamela J. Creedon (eds.), *Seeking Equity for Women in Journalism and Mass Communication: A 30-Year Update*. Mahwah, NJ: Lawrence Erlbaum Associates, 205–22.

Kielbowicz, Richard and Scherer, Clifford 1986: The role of the press in the dynamics of social movements. *Research in Social Movements, Conflict and Change*, 9, 71–96.

Kilbourne, Jean 1999: *Deadly Persuasion: Why Women and Girls Must Fight the Addictive Power of Advertising*. New York: The Free Press.

——2000: *Can't Buy My Love: How Advertising Changes the Way We Think and Feel*. New York: Touchstone.

Kitzinger, Jenny 1992: Sexual violence and compulsory heterosexuality. *Feminism and Psychology*, 2(3), 399–418.

——2004: Media coverage of sexual violence against women and children. In Karen Ross and Carolyn M. Byerly (eds.), *Women and Media: International Perspectives*. Malden, MA: Blackwell, 13–38.

Komter, Aafke 1991: Gender power and feminist theory. In Kathy Davis, Monique Leigenaar, and Jantine Oldersma (eds.), *The Gender of Power*. London: Sage, 42–64.

Kramarae, Cheris 1981: *Women and Men Speaking: Frameworks for Analysis*. Rowley, MA: Newbury House.

——1995: A backstage critique of virtual reality. In Steven G. Jones (ed.), *Cybersociety: Computer-Mediated Communication and Community*. Thousand Oaks, CA: Sage, 36–56.

Krishnan, Prabha and Dighe, Anita 1900: *Affirmation and Denial: Constructions of Femininity on Indian Television*. New Delhi: Sage.

Kuhn, Annette 1975: Women's cinema and feminist film criticism. *Screen*, 16(3), 107–12.

——1984: Women's genres: melodrama, soap opera and theory. *Screen*, 25(1), 18–28.

Kuppers, Gaby (ed.) 1992: *Companeras: Voices from the Latin American Women's Liberation Movement*. London: The Latin American Bureau.

Kurian, Priya A. and Munshi, Debashish 2003: Terms of empowerment: gender, ecology and ICTs for development. *Feminist Media Studies*, 3(3), 352–5.

Kwan, Mei-Po 2003: Gender troubles in the Internet era. *Feminist Media Studies*, 3(3), 371–4.

Lægran, Anne Sofie and Stewart, James 2003: Nerdy, trendy or healthy? Configuring the Internet café. *New Media and Society*, 5(3), 357–77.

Lafky, Sue 1991: Women journalists. In David Weaver and G. Cleveland Wilhoit (eds.), *The American Journalist: A Portrait of US News People and Their Work*, 2nd edn. Bloomington, IN: Indiana University Press, 160–81.

——1993: The progress of women and people of color in the US journalistic workforce: a long, slow journey. In Pamela J. Creedon (ed.), *Women in Mass Communication*, 2nd edn. Newbury Park, CA: Sage, 87–103.

Lafuente, María Suárez 2003: Women in pieces: the filmic re/constructions of Josefina Molina. *European Journal of Women's Studies*, 10(4), 395–407.

Lamas, Marta 1992: Debate Feminista: a bridge between academia and activism. In Gaby Kuppers (ed.), *Companeras: Voices from the Latin American Women's Liberation Movement*. London: The Latin American Bureau, 160–2.

Lane, Christina 2000: *Feminist Hollywood: From* Born in Flames *to* Point Break. Detroit: Wayne State University Press.

Lant, Antonia 1991: *Blackout: Reinventing Women for Wartime British Cinema*. Princeton, NJ: Princeton University Press.

Lauer, Nancy Cook 2002: Studies show women's role in media shrinking. Women's eNews; www.womensenews.org/article.cfm/dyn/aid/915/context/archive (accessed May 5, 2004).

Lauzen, Martha D. 2000: *Status of Women in the Industry: the Real Story on Reel Women: Behind the Scenes Employment in the Top 250 Films of 1999*. New York: New York Women in Film and Television; http://nywift.org/resources/status_lauzen.html (accessed September 29, 2004).

——2002: *Boxed In: Women On Screen and Behind the Scenes in the 2001–2002 Prime-time Season* (Executive Summary); http://moviesbywomen.com/stats2002.html (accessed November 6, 2004).

Lavie, Aliza and Lehman-Wilzig, S. 2003: Whose news? Does gender determine the editorial product? *European Journal of Communication*, 18(1), 5–29.

Lee, Francis L. F. 2004: Constructing perfect women: the portrayal of female officials in Hong Kong newspapers. *Media, Culture and Society*, 26(2), 207–25.

Lee, Sarah 1999: Private uses in public spaces: a study of an Internet café. *New Media and Society*, 1(3), 331–50.

Lees, Sue 1995: Media reporting of rape: the 1993 British "date rape" controversy. In David Kidd-Hewitt and Richard Osborne (eds.), *Crime and Media: The Post-Modern Spectacle*. London: Pluto Press, 107–30.

Lemish, Dafna 2000: The whore and the "other": Israeli images of female immigrants from the former USSR. *Gender & Society*, 14(2), 339–49.

——2004: Exclusion and marginality: portrayals of women in Israeli media. In Karen Ross and Carolyn M. Byerly (eds.), *Women and Media: International Perspectives*. Malden, MA: Blackwell, 39–59.

——and Drob, Gil 2002: "All the time his wife": portrayals of first ladies in the Israeli press. *Parliamentary Affairs*, 55(1), 129–42.

Lerner, Gerda 1986: *The Creation of Patriarchy*. New York: Oxford University Press.

Lesage, Julie 1984: Political aesthetics of the feminist documentary film. In Thomas Waugh (ed.), *"Show Us Life": Toward a History and Aesthetic of the Committed Documentary*. Metuchen, NJ: Scarecrow Press; reprinted in Charlotte Brunsdon (ed.), *Films for Women*. London: British Film Institute, 14–23.

Levitin, Jacqueline, Plessis, Judith and Raoul, Valerie 2003: *Women Filmmakers Refocusing*. New York: Routledge.

Liebes, Tamar and Livingstone, Sonia 1994: The structure of family and romantic ties in the soap opera: an ethnographic approach to the cultural framing of primordiality. *Communication Research*, 21, 717–41.

——and——1998: European soap opera: the diversification of a genre. *European Journal of Communication*, 13(2), 147–80.

Liebler, Carol and Smith, Susan J. 1997: Tracking gender differences: a comparative analysis of network correspondents and their sources. *Journal of Broadcasting and Electronic Media*, 41 (Winter), 58–68.

Lipson, Joanne 2002: Equality and difference in women's media: in fighting a past of inequality do we envision a future of division? In Julia Beizer, Ann Keller, and Joanne Lipson (eds.), *Media Democracy: Past, Present and Future*. Washington, DC: Women's Institute for Freedom of the Press, 57.

Liran-Alper, Dalia 1994: Media representation of women in politics – are they still "domineering dowagers and scheming concubines"? Paper presented to the International Association of Media Communication Research annual conference, Seoul, July.

——1999: The future of media in the hands of women? The Women Status Committee at the Israeli Broadcasting Authority. Paper presented at International Association for Media and Communication Research, Leipzig, Germany.

Lisanti, Tom and Paul, Louis 2002: *Film Fatales: Women in Espionage Films and Television 1963–1973*. Jefferson, NC: McFarland.

Liswood, Laura A. 1995: *Women World Leaders: Fifteen Great Politicians Tell Their Stories*. London: Pandora.

Lotz, Amanda 2001: Postfeminist television criticism: rehabilitating critical terms and identifying postfeminist attributes. *Feminist Media Studies*, 1(1), 105–21.

Lovell, Terry 1981: Ideology and "Coronation Street," In Richard Dyer, Christine Geraghty, Marion Jordan, Terry Lovell, Richard Paterson, and James Stewart (eds.), *Coronation Street*. London: British Film Institute.

Lünenborg, Margaret 1996: *Journalists in Europe: an International Comparative Study* (transl.). Wiesbaden: Westdeutscher Verlag.

Luther, Catherine A. and Nentl, Nancy J. 2001: Japanese teenage girls: their ad-inspired social comparison behaviour and perceptions of women's roles. *Gazette*, 63(1), 25–40.

Mackie, Erin 1997: *Market à la Mode: Fashion, Commodity and Gender in the "Tatler" and the "Spectator."* Baltimore, MD: The Johns Hopkins University Press.

MacKinnon, Catherine A. 2000: Only words. In Drucilla Cornell (ed.), *Feminism and Pornography*. Oxford: Oxford University Press.

Malhotra, Sheena and Rogers, Everett 2000: Satellite television and the new Indian woman. *Gazette*, 62(5), 401–29.

Malik, Sarita 1994: Beyond identity: British Asian film. *Black Film Bulletin*, 2(3), 12–13.

——2002: *Representing Black Britain: Black and Asian Images on Television*. London: Routledge.

Manatu, Norma 2002: *African American Women and Sexuality in the Cinema*. Jefferson, NC: McFarland.

Mani, Lata 1992: Cultural theory, colonial texts: reading eyewitness accounts of widow burning. In Lawrence Grossberg, Cary Nelson, and Paula Treichler (eds.), *Cultural Studies*. New York: Routledge, 392–408.

Mankekar, Purnima 1999: *Screening Culture, Viewing Politics: Television, Womanhood and Nation in Modern India*. Durham, NC: Duke University Press.

Manning, Paul 2001: *News and News Sources: A Critical Introduction*. London: Sage.

Marks, Dorrit K. (ed.) 1996: *Women and Grass Roots Democracy in the Americas: Sustaining the Initiative*. Miami, FL: North–South Center Press (University of Miami).

Marks, Elaine and de Courtivron, Isabelle 1980: *New French Feminisms: An Anthology*. Amherst, MA: University of Massachusetts Press.

Martin, Michèle 2002: An unsuitable technology for a woman? Communication as circulation. In Eileen R. Meehan and Ellen Riordan (eds.), *Sex and Money: Feminism and Political Economy in the Media*. Minneapolis, MN: University of Minnesota Press, 49–59.

Martin, Stana 2002: The political economy of women's employment in the information section. In Eileen R. Meehan and Ellen Riordan (eds.), *Sex and Money: Feminism and Political Economy in the Media*. Minneapolis, MN: University of Minnesota Press, 75–87.

Masi de Casanova, Erynn 2004: "No ugly women": concepts of race and beauty among adolescent women in Ecuador. *Gender & Society*, 18(3), 287–308.

Massoni, Kelley 2004: Modeling work: occupational messages in *Seventeen* magazine. *Gender & Society*, 18(1), 47–65.

Mata, Marita 1994: Being women in the popular radio. In Pilar Riaño (ed.), *Women in Grassroots Communication: Furthering Social Change*. Thousand Oaks, CA: Sage, 192–212.

Mathew, George 2004: The silent revolution. Women's Feature Service (e-wire), ref: OPID412, April 19.

Mattelart, Michèle 1986: *Women, Media and Crisis: Femininity and Disorder*. London: Comedia; reprinted in Charlotte Brunsdon, Julie D'Acci, and Lynn Spigel (eds.) 1997: *Feminist Television Criticism: A Reader*. Oxford: Oxford University Press.

Mayer, Vicki 2003: Living televovelas/telenovelizing life: Mexican American girls' identities and transnational televnovelas. *Journal of Communication*, 53(3), 479–95.

Mayne, Judith 1988: *L.A. Law* and prime-time feminism. *Discourse*, 10(2), 30–47.

Mazierska, Ewa 2001: Wanda Jakubowska's cinema of commitment. *European Journal of Women Studies*, 8(2), 221–38.

McChesney, Robert W. and Nichols, John 2002 (January 7): Making of a movement; www.thenation.com/doc.mhtml?l=20020107&s=mcchesney (accessed November 7, 2004).

McCracken, Ellen 1992: *Decoding Women's Magazines: From "Mademoiselle" to "Ms."* Basingstoke, UK: Palgrave Macmillan.

McDonald, Myra 1995: *Representing Women: Myths of Femininity in the Popular Media*. London: Hodder Arnold.

McLaughlin, Lisa 1993: Feminism, the public sphere, media and democracy. *Media, Culture and Society*, 15(4), 599–620.

—— 1998: Gender, privacy and publicity in "media event space." In Cynthia Carter, Gill Branston, and Stuart Allan (eds.), *News, Gender and Power*. London: Routledge, 71–90.

—— 1999: Beyond "separate spheres": feminism and the cultural studies/political economy debate. *Journal of Communication Inquiry*, 23(4), 327–54.

—— 2002: Something old, something new: lingering moments in the unhappy marriage of Marxism and feminism. In Eileen R. Meehan and Ellen Riordan (eds.), *Sex and Money: Feminism and Political Economy in the Media*. Minneapolis, MN: University of Minnesota Press, 30–48.

McMillin, Divya 2003: Television, gender, and labor in the global city. *Journal of Communication*, 53(3), 496–511.

McNair, Brian 2002: *Striptease Culture: Sex, Media and the Democratisation of Desire*. London: Routledge.

——, Hibberd, Matthew and Schlesinger, Phillip 2003: *Mediated Access: Broadcasting and Democratic Participation in the Age of Mediated Politics*. Luton, UK: University of Luton Press.

McQuail, Denis 1992: *Media Performance: Mass Communication and the Public Interest*. Newbury Park, CA: Sage.

———1994: *Mass Communication Theory: An Introduction*, 3rd edn. London: Sage.

McRobbie, Angela 1978: Jackie: *Ideology of Adolescent Femininity*. Birmingham: University of Birmingham.

———1991: *Feminism and Youth Culture: from* Jackie *to* Just Seventeen. Boston: Unwin Hyman.

———2000: *Feminism and Youth Culture*, 2nd edn. Basingstoke, UK: Palgrave Macmillan.

Media Watch 1995: *Global Media Monitoring Project: Women's Participation in the News*. Ontario: National Watch on Images of Women/Media Watch.

Meehan, Eileen R. 2002: Gendering the commodity audience: critical media research, feminism and political economy. In Eileen R. Meehan and Ellen Riordan (eds.), *Sex and Money: Feminism and Political Economy in the Media*. Minneapolis, MN: University of Minnesota Press, 209–22.

———and Riordan, Ellen (eds.) 2002: *Sex and Money: Feminism and Political Economy in the Media*. Minneapolis, MN: University of Minnesota Press.

Meister, Melissa 1998: The importance of Sapphic subtext in *Xena: Warrior Princess*; available at www.whoosh.org (accessed September 19, 2004).

Melin-Higgins, Margareta 2004: Coping with journalism: gendered newsroom culture in Britain. In Marjan de Bruin and Karen Ross (eds.), *Gender and Newsroom Cultures: Identities at Work*. Cresskill, NJ: Hampton Press, 197–222.

———and Djerf-Pierre, Madeline 1998: Networking in newsrooms: journalist and gender cultures. Paper presented to the International Association of Media and Communication Research annual conference, Glasgow, July.

Mercer, Kobena 1988: Recoding narratives of race and nation. In Kobena Mercer (ed.), *Black Film: British Cinema*. ICA paper #7. London: British Film Institute/ICA, 4–14.

Merck, Mandy 1986: Lianna and the lesbians of art cinema. In Charlotte Brunsdon (ed.), *Films for Women*. London: British Film Institute, 166–75.

Michielsens, Magda 1991: *Women in View: How Does BRTN Portray Women? An Audience Survey*. Brussels, BRTN/Commission of the European Communities.

Milkie, Melissa A. 2002: Contested images of feminity: an analysis of cultural gatekeepers' struggles with the "real girl" critique. *Gender & Society*, 16(6), 839–50.

Miller, Alan V. (compiler) 1991: *Our Own Voices: A Directory of Lesbian and Gay Periodicals, 1890s–1990s*. Toronto: Canadian Gay and Lesbian Archives.

Miller, Katherine 2005: *Communication Theories: Perspectives, Processes and Contexts*, 2nd edn. New York: McGraw-Hill.

Mills, Kay 1990: *A Place in the News: From the Women's Pages to the Front Page*. New York: Columbia University Press.

———1997: What difference do women journalists make? In Pippa Norris (ed.), *Women, Media and Politics*. New York: Oxford University Press, 41–56.

Mills, Sara 1999: Discourse competence: or how to theorize strong women speakers. In Christina Hendricks and Kelly Oliver (eds.), *Language and Liberation: Feminism, Philosophy and Language*. Albany, NY: State University of New York Press, 81–127.

Mitchell, Caroline 2004: Dangerously feminine? Theory and praxis of women's alternative discourse. In Karen Ross and Carolyn M. Byerly (eds.), *Women and Media: International Perspectives*. Malden, MA: Blackwell, 157–84.

Mitra, Ananda 2004: Voices of the marginalized on the Internet: examples from a website for women of South Asia. *Journal of Communication*, 54(3), 492–510.

Modleski, Tania 1979: The search for tomorrow in today's soap operas: notes on a feminine narrative form. *Film Quarterly*, 33(1), 12–21.

—— 1982: *Loving With a Vengeance: Mass-Produced Fantasies for Women*. London: Methuen.

Mohanty, Chandra Talpade 1991: Introduction: cartographies of struggle: Third World women and the politics of feminism. In Chandra Talpade Mohanty, Ann Russo, and Lourdes Torres (eds.), *Third World Women and the Politics of Feminism*. Bloomington, IN: Indiana University Press, 1–50.

——, Russo, Ann and Torres, Lourdes (eds.) 1991: *Third World Women and the Politics of Feminism*. Bloomington, IN: Indiana University Press.

Moorti, Sujata 2000: Inflamed passions. Fire, the woman question and the policing of cultural borders. *Genders Online Journal*, 32; www.gendersorg/g32/g32_moorti.html (accessed September 20, 2004).

—— 2002: *The Color of Rape: Gender and Race in Television's Public Spheres*. Albany, NY: State University of New York Press.

Moritz, Marguerite J. 1994: Old strategies for new texts: how American television is creating and treating lesbian characters. In R. Jeffrey Ringer (ed.), *Queer Words, Queer Images: Communication and the Construction of Homosexuality*. New York: New York University Press, 122–42.

Morley, David 1980: *The "Nationwide" Audience: Structure and Decoding*. London: British Film Institute.

Mufune, Jennifer 2003: Women: gender and media baseline study: monitoring the media in southern Africa. World Association of Christian Communication (WACC) website; www.wacc.org.uk/modules.php?name=News&file&sid=190 (accessed October 18, 2003).

Mulvey, Laura 1975: Visual pleasure and narrative cinema. *Screen*, 16(3), 6–19.

—— 1989: *Visual and Other Pleasures*. Basingstoke, UK: Macmillan Press.

Myers, Marian 1997: *News Accounts of Violence against Women: Engendering Blame*. Thousand Oaks, CA: Sage.

Na, Misu 2001: The home computer in Korea: gender, technology and the family. *Feminist Media Studies*, 1(3), 291–306.

Nagrath, Sumati 2001: The bottom line: keeping the women out. *Intersections*, 1(2), 69–73.

Nassanga, L. G. 1997: Women, development and the media: the case for Uganda. *Media, Culture and Society*, 19(3), 471–6.

National Institute of Mental Health 1994: *Eating Disorders*. Rockville, MD: NIH Publication no 94–3477.

National Telecommunications and Information Administration 1999: Falling through the net: defining the digital divide; www.ntia.doc.gov/ntiahome/digitaldivide/ (accessed November 11, 2002).

Neale, Stephen 2000: *Genre and Hollywood*. London: Routledge.

Negra, Diane 2001: *Off-White Hollywood: American Culture and Ethnic Female Stardom*. London: Routledge.

Negrine, Ralph 1998: *Parliament and the Media*. London: Cassell.

Neves, Helena 1994: Speech to the *Prix Niki* conference. Lisbon, March.

Newcomb, Horace and Alley, Robert S. 1983: *The Producer's Medium*. New York: Oxford University Press.

Nightingale, Virginia 1996: *Studying Audiences: The Shock of the Real*. London: Routledge.

Nochimson, Martha 1992: *No End to Her: Soap Opera and the Female Subject*. Berkeley: University of California Press.

Norris, Pippa 1997a: Women leaders worldwide: a splash of color in the photo op. In Pippa Norris (ed.), *Women, Media and Politics*. Oxford: Oxford University Press, 149–65.

——(ed.) 1997b: *Women, Media and Politics*. New York: Oxford University Press.

——2001: *Digitial Divide, Civic Engagement, Information Poverty and the Internet Worldwide*. Cambridge, UK: Cambridge University Press.

North, Louise C. 2004: Naked women, feminism, and newsroom culture. *Australian Journal of Communication*, 31(2), 53–67.

NOS Gender Portrayal Department 1995: Interviewtechnieken in acualiteitenprogramma's (Interview techniques on male and female guests in Dutch current affairs features). Hilversum: NOS.

Nunn, Heather and Biressi, Anita 2003: *Silent Witness*: detection, femininity and the post-mortem body. *Feminist Media Studies*, 3(2), 193–204.

Nussbaum, Martha C. 2003: Genocide in Gujarat: the international community looks away. *Dissent* magazine (online edition), Summer; www.dissentmagazine.org/menutest/articles/su03/nussbaum.htm (accessed December 10, 2003).

Opoku-Mensah, Aida 2004: Hanging in there: women, gender and newsroom culture. In Marjan de Bruin and Karen Ross (eds.), *Gender and Newsroom Cultures: Identities at Work*. Cresskill, NJ: Hampton Press, 107–20.

Organ, Christine L., Brown, Charlene J. and Weaver, David 1979: Characteristics of managers of selected US daily newspapers. *Journalism Quarterly*, 56(4), 803–9.

O'Sullivan, Tim, Hartley, John, Saunders, Danny, Montgomery, Martin and Fiske, John 1994: Model (entry). In *Key Concepts in Communication and Cultural Studies*, New York: Routledge, 185.

Ouellette, Laurie 1999: Inventing the Cosmo girl: class identity and girl-style American dreams. *Media, Culture and Society*, 21(3), 359–83.

Owen, Sarah A. 1999: Vampires, post modernity and post feminism: *Buffy the Vampire Slayer*. *Journal of Popular Film and Television*, 27 (Summer), 24–31.

Parameswaran, Radhika 2002: Local culture in global media: excavating colonial and material discourses in *National Geographic*. *Communication Theory*, 12(3), 287–314.

Parmar, Pratibha 2000 [1993]: That moment of emergence. In E. Ann Kaplan (ed.), *Feminism and Film*. Oxford: Oxford University Press, 375–83.

Penley, Constance (ed.) 1988: *Feminism and Film Theory*. London: Routledge.

—— 1991: *Brownian Motion: Women, Tactics and Technology*. In Constance Penley and Andrew Ross (eds.), *Technoculture*. Minneapolis, MN: University of Minnesota Press, 135–61.

Phegley, Jennifer 2004: *Educating the Proper Woman Reader: Victorian Family Literary Magazines and the Cultural Health of the Nation*. Columbus, OH: Ohio State University Press.

Phillips, Anne 1991: *Engendering Democracy*. Cambridge, UK: Polity Press.

Pingree, Suzanne and Hawkins, Rosemary P. 1978: News definitions and their effects on women. In Laurily Keir Epstein (ed.), *Women and the News*. Mamaroneak, NY, Hasting House.

Pinnock, Don 1997: Writing Left: the journalism of Ruth First and *The Guardian* in the 1950s. In Les Switzer (ed.), *South Africa's Alternative Press: Voices of Protest and Resistance, 1880–1960*. Cambridge, UK: Cambridge University Press, 308–30.

Pitt, Lisa 2003: Masculinities@work: gender inequality and the new media industries. *Feminist Media Studies*, 3(3), 378–82.

Plou, Dafne 2004 (June 5): Women: the right to communicate: women in the information society. World Association of Christian Communication (WACC) website; www.wacc.org (accessed August 14, 2004).

Pollock, Griselda 1977: What's wrong with images of women? *Screen Education*, 24, 25–34.

Powers, Kirsten A. 2005: More women on Op-Ed, please. *The Washington Post*, Saturday, March 26, p. A13.

Press, Andrea L. 1990: Class, gender and the female viewer: women's responses to *Dynasty*. In Mary Ellen Brown (ed.), *Television and Women's Culture: The Politics of the Popular*. London: Sage, 158–82.

Pribham, E. Deirdre 1988: *Female Spectators: Looking at Film and Television*. London: Verso.

Radway, Janice 1984: *Reading the Romance: Women, Patriarchy and Popular Literature*. Chapel Hill, NC: University of North Carolina Press.

Rai, Usha 1999: Women media practitioners. In *Changing Lenses: Women's Perspectives on Media*. Manila, the Philippines: Isis International – Manila.

——— 2004: Women in journalism – then and now. *Media and Gender*, the Hoot website; www.thehoot.org (accessed August 2, 2004).

Rao, Anupama (ed.) 2003: *Gender & Caste*. New Delhi: Kali for Women.

Rapping, Elayne 1994: *Media-tions: Forays into the Culture and Gender Wars*. Boston, MA: South End Press.

——— 1995: Daytime enquiries. In Gail Dines and Jean M. Humez (eds.), *Gender, Race and Class in Media*. Thousand Oaks, CA: Sage, 377–82.

Reese, Stephen D. 1990: The news paradigm and the ideology of objectivity: a socialist at *The Wall Street Journal. Critical Studies in Mass Communication*, 7, 390–409.

Rege, Sharmila 2004: Dalit women talk differently: a critique of "difference" and towards a dalit feminist standpoint position. In Maitrayee Chaudhuri (ed.), *Feminism in India*. New Delhi: Kali for Women & Women Unlimited, 211–27.

Reichert, Tom and Lambiase, Jacqueline (eds.) 2003: *Sex in Advertising: Perspectives on the Erotic Appeal*. Mahwah, NJ: Lawrence Erlbaum Associates.

Rense, Rip 1991: Color blind. *Emmy*, 13(1), 33–7.

Riaño, Pilar 1991: Myths of the silenced: women and grassroots communication. *Media Development*, 2, 20–2.

——— (ed.) 1994: *Women in Grassroots Communication: Furthering Social Change*. Thousand Oaks, CA: Sage.

Riaño-Alcalá, Pilar, Colorado, Marta and Perez, Berta Alicia 2001: Four Latin American women in the downtown Eastside of Vancouver: health, housing and immigration. Report; www.sfu.ca/~fisls/four_latin_american_women.doc (accessed November 1, 2004).

Rich, B. Ruby 1986 [1983]: Anti-porn: soft issue, hard world. In Charlotte Brunsdon (ed.), *Films for Women*. London: British Film Institute, 31–43.

——— 1992: In the eyes of the beholder. *The Voice*, January 28.

Right to Communicate Overview n.d.: Right to Communicate website; www.righttocommunicate.org/printContent.atm (accessed August 2, 2004).

Riordan, Ellen 2002: Intersections and new directions: on feminism and political economy. In Eileen R. Meehan and Ellen Riordan (eds.), *Sex and Money: Feminism and Political Economy in the Media*. Minneapolis, MN: University of Minnesota Press, 3–15.

——— 2004: The woman warrior: a feminist political economic analysis of *Crouching Tiger, Hidden Dragon*. In Karen Ross and Carolyn M. Byerly (eds.), *Women and Media: International Perspectives*. Malden, MA: Blackwell, 81–103.

Roach, Colleen 1990: The movement for a New World Information and Communication Order: a second wave? *Media, Culture and Society*, 12, 283–307.

Robertson, Nan 1992: *The Girls in the Balcony: Women, Men and the New York Times*. New York: Fawcett Columbine.

Robins, Melinda 2002: Are African women online just ICT consumers? *Gazette*, 64(3), 235–49.

Robinson, Gertrude J. 2005: *Gender, Journalism and Equity: Canadian, US and European Perspectives*. Cresskill, NJ: Hampton Press.

——and Saint-Jean, Armande 1997: *Women's Participation in the Canadian News Media: Progress Since the 1970s*. Unpublished report, McGill University, Montreal.

Rodgerson, Gillian and Wilson, Elizabeth (eds.) 1991: *Pornography and Feminism: The Case Against Censorship*. London: Lawrence & Wishart.

Rodino, Michelle 2003: Mobilizing mother. *Feminist Media Studies*, 3(3), 375–8.

Rommes, Els 2002: Creating places for women on the Internet: the design of a "women's square" in a digital city. *European Journal of Women's Studies*, 9(4), 400–29.

Root, Jane 1986: *Open the Box: About Television*. London: Channel 4 and Comedia series no. 34.

Ross, Karen 1995a: Gender and party politics – how the press reported the Labour leadership campaign, 1994. *Media, Culture and Society*, 17(3), 499–509.

——1995b: Skirting the issue: political women and the media. *Everywoman*, 199, 16–17.

——1995c: Women and the news agenda: media-ted reality and Jane Public. Discussion Papers in Mass Communication. Leicester, UK: University of Leicester.

——1996: *Black and White Media: Black Images in Popular Film and Television*. London: Polity Press.

——1997a: Two-tone telly: black British audiences and television. *Communications: the European Journal of Communication Research*, 22(1), 93–108.

——1997b: *Watching Women: Election '97*. London: Fawcett Society.

——1998: Making race matter: an overview. In Bob Franklin and David Murphy (eds.), *Making the Local News: Local Journalism in Context*. London: Routledge, 228–40.

——2000: *Women at the Top 2000: Cracking the Public Sector Glass Ceiling*. King-Hall Paper no. 9. London: Hansard Society.

——2001: Women at work: journalism as en-gendered practice. *Journalism Studies*, 2(4), 531–44.

——2002: *Women, Politics, Media: Uneasy Relations in Comparative Perspective*. Cresskill, NJ: Hampton Press.

——2004a: Political talk radio and democratic participation: caller perspectives on *Election Call*. *Media, Culture and Society*, 26(6), 785–801.

——2004b: The Global Media Monitoring Project. *Media and Gender Monitor 14*, February 14, 2–3.

——2004c: Women framed: the gendered turn in mediated politics. In Karen Ross and Carolyn M. Byerly (eds.), *Women and Media: International Perspectives.* Malden, MA: Blackwell, 60–80.

——2005: Women in the boyzone: gender, news and herstory. In Stuart Allan (ed.), *Journalism: Critical Issues.* Buckingham, UK: Open University Press, ch. 21.

——and Nightingale, Virginia 2003: *Media and Audiences: New Perspectives.* Buckingham, UK: Open University Press.

——and Sreberny, Annabelle 2000: Women in the House: media representations of British politicians. In Annabelle Sreberny and Liesbet van Zoonen (eds.), *Gender, Politics and Communication.* Cresskill, NJ: Hampton Press, 79–110.

——and Sreberny-Mohammadi, Annabelle 1997: Playing house – gender, politics and the news media in Britain. *Media, Culture and Society,* 19(1), 101–9.

Ross, Leone 1993: Home boy rides into town. *The Voice,* November 23.

Rowe, Kathleen K. 1990: *Roseanne*: unruly woman as domestic goddess. *Screen,* 31(4), 408–19.

Rubin, A. W. 1985: The uses of daytime television serials by college students: an examination of viewing motives. *Journal of Broadcasting and Electronic Media,* 29, 241–58.

Rush, Ramona R. 2001: Three decades of women and mass communications research: the ratio of recurrent and reinforced residuum hypothesis (R^3) revisited. Paper presented at Donna Allen Memorial Symposium, Freedom Forum, Roslyn, VA.

Russell, Diana E. H. 1998: *Dangerous Relationships: Pornography, Misogyny and Rape.* London: Sage.

——and Harmes, Roberta A. (eds.) 2001: *Femicide in Global Perspective.* New York: Teachers College Press.

Ryan, Mary P. 1992: Gender and public access: women's politics in nineteenth century America. In Craig Calhoun (ed.), *Habermas and the Public Sphere.* Cambridge, MA: The MIT Press, 259–88.

Sakamoto, Kazue 1999: Reading Japanese women's magazines: the construction of new identities in the 1970s and 1980s. *Media, Culture and Society,* 21(2), 173–93.

Salmon, Catherine and Symons, Donald 2001: *Warrior Lovers: Erotic Fiction, Evolution and Female Sexuality.* London: Weidenfeld and Nicolson.

Sancho-Aldridge, Jane 1997: *Election '97.* London: Independent Television Commission.

Sanders, Karen 2003: *Ethics and Journalism.* London: Sage.

Sanders, Marlene and Rock, Marcia 1988: *Waiting for Prime Time: The Women of Television News.* New York: Harper & Row.

Santa Cruz, Adriana 1989: Alternative communication and Latin American women.

In Ramona R. Rush and Donna Allen (eds.), *Communication at the Crossroads: The Gender Gap Connection.* Norwood, NJ: Ablex, 251–64.

Sassen, Saskia 1998: *Globalization and its Discontents.* New York: The New Press.

Scodari, Christine 1998: No politics here: age and gender in soap opera cyber-fandom. *Women's Studies in Communication,* 21(2), 168–87.

———2004: *Serial Monogamy: Soap Opera, Lifespan and the Gendered Politics of Fantasy.* Cresskill, NJ: Hampton Press.

Selwyn, Neil 2004: Reconsidering political and popular understandings of the digital divide. *New Media and Society,* 6(3), 341–62.

Sen, Ashish 2004: Media reform in India: legitimising community media. World Association of Christian Communication (WACC) website; www.wacc.org.uk/modulesphp?name=News&file=print&sid=1491 (accessed February 26, 2004).

Sen, Ilina 2004: Women's politics in India. In Maitrayee Chaudhuri (ed.), *Feminism in India.* New Delhi: Kali for Women & Women Unlimited, 187–210.

Sen, Jai, Anand, Anita, Escobar, Arturo and Waterman, Peter 2004: *World Social Forum: Challenging Empires.* New Delhi: The Viveka Foundation.

Shade, Leslie Regan 1999: Whose right to communicate? Conference paper presented at Citizens at the Crossroads: Whose Information Society, London, Canada, October 21–24, 1999; available at http://courseweb.edteched.uottawa.ca/cmn2180/rightspaper.htm (accessed August 18, 2004).

Shohat, Ella 1997: Framing post-third-worldist culture: gender and nation in Middle Eastern/North African film and video. *Jouvert,* 1(1); http://social.chass.ncsu.edu/jouvert/viii/shohat.htm (accessed September 10, 2004).

Sieghart, Mary Anne and Henry, Georgina 1998: *The Cheaper Sex: How Women Lose Out in Journalism.* London: Women In Journalism.

Singh, Supriya 2001: Gender and the use of the Internet at home. *New Media and Society,* 3(4), 395–416.

Siochrú, Seán Ó. and Girard, Bruce, with Mahan, A. 2002: *Global Media Governance: A Beginner's Guide.* Lanham, MD: Rowan & Littlefield.

Skidmore, Paula 1995: Telling tales: media power, ideology and the reporting of child sexual abuse. In David Kidd-Hewitt and Richard Osborne (eds.), *Crime and Media: The Postmodern Spectacle.* London: Pluto Press, 78–106.

———1998: Gender and the agenda: news reporting of child sexual abuse. In Cynthia Carter, Gill Branston, and Stuart Allan (eds.), *News, Gender and Power.* London: Routledge, 204–19.

Slide, Anthony 1996: *The Silent Feminists: America's First Woman Directors.* Lanham, MD: Scarecrow Press.

Smith, Conrad, Fredin, Eric S. and Nardone, Carroll Ann Ferguson 1993: Television: the nature of sex discrimination in local television news shops. In Pamela J. Creedon (ed.), *Women in Mass Communication,* 2nd edn. Newbury Park, CA: Sage, 171–82.

Smith, Dorothy 1990: *Texts, Facts, and Femininity: Exploring the Relations of Ruling.* London: Routledge.

Smith-Shomade, Beretta E. 2002: *Shaded Lives: African-American Women and Television.* Piscataway, NJ: Rutgers University Press.

Soothill, Keith and Walby, Sylvia 1991: *Sex Crime in the News.* London: Routledge.

Sparks, Colin 2002: Empowering women and men through participatory structures. *Media Development,* 49(1), 3–6.

Spears, G. and Seydergaart, K., with Gallagher, M. 2000: *Who Makes the News? Global Media Monitoring Project 2000.* London: World Association for Christian Communication.

Spender, Dale 1995: *Nattering on the Net: Women, Power, and Cyberspace.* North Melbourne, Australia: Spinifex Press.

Spilker, Hendrik and Sørensen, Knut H. 2000: A ROM of one's own or a home for sharing? Designing the inclusion of women in multimedia. *New Media and Society,* 2(3), 268–85.

Spivak, Gayatri Chakravorty 1988: Can the subaltern speak? In Cary Nelson and Lawrence Grossberg (eds.), *Marxism and the Interpretation of Culture.* London: Macmillan, 271–313.

Squire, Corrine 1994: Empowering women? *The Oprah Winfrey Show. Feminism and Psychology,* 4(1), 63–79.

Sreberny-Mohammadi, Annabelle 1994: Women talking politics. In *Perspectives on Women in Television.* Research Working Paper 9. London: Broadcasting Standards Council, 60–79.

——and Ross, Karen 1996: Women MPs and the media: representing the body politic. In Joni Lovenduski and Pippa Norris (eds.), *Women in Politics.* Oxford: Oxford University Press, 105–17.

Stacey, Jackie 1994: *Star Gazing: Hollywood Cinema and Female Spectatorship.* New York: Routledge.

Stafford, Nikki 1998: *Lucy Lawless: Warrior Star of* Xena. Toronto: ECW Press.

Staiger, Janet 2000: *Perverse Spectators: The Practices of Film Reception.* New York: New York Press.

Steeves, H. Leslie 1987: Feminist theories and media studies. *Critical Studies in Mass Communication,* 4(2), 95–135.

——2004: Trends in feminist scholarship in journalism and communication: finding common ground between scholars and activists globally. In Ramona R. Rush, Carol E. Oukrup, and Pamela J. Creedon (eds.), *Seeking Equity for Women in Journalism and Mass Communication.* Mahway, NJ: Lawrence Erlbaum Associates, 289–312.

——and Wasko, Janet 2002: Feminist theory and political economy: toward a friendly alliance. In Eileen R. Meehan and Ellen Riordan (eds.), *Sex and Money:*

Feminism and Political Economy in the Media. Minneapolis, MN: University of Minnesota Press, 16–29.

Steiner, Linda 1983: Finding community in nineteenth century suffrage periodicals. *American Journalism*, 1 (Summer), 3–4, 7, 9.

——1998: Newsroom accounts of power at work. In Cynthia Carter, Gill Branston, and Stuart Allan (eds.), *News, Gender and Power*. London: Routledge, 145–59.

Stephenson, Mary-Anne 1998: *The Glass Trapdoor: Women, Politics and the Media During the 1997 General Election*. London: Fawcett Society.

Sterne, Jonathan and Stabile, Carol 2003: Using women as middle men: the real promise of ICTs. *Feminist Media Studies*, 3(3), 364–8.

Streitmatter, Rodger 1994: *Raising Her Voice: African-American Women Journalists Who Changed History*. Lexington, KY: The University Press of Kentucky.

Stuart, Andrea 1994: Blackpool illumination. *Sight & Sound*, 4(2), 26–7.

Sylvester, Judith and Huffman, Suzanne 2002: *Women Journalists at Ground Zero: Covering Crisis*. Lanham, MD: Rowman & Littlefield.

Tasker, Yvonne 1993: *Spectacular Bodies: Gender, Genre and the Action Cinema*. London: Comedia/Routledge.

——1998: *Working Girls: Gender and Sexuality in Popular Cinema*. London: Routledge

Tavris, Carol 1992: *The Mismeasure of Woman*. New York: Simon and Schuster.

Taylor, Helen 1989: *Scarlett's Women: Gone with the Wind and its Female Fans*. London: Virago.

Taylor, M. and Quayle, E. 2003: *Child Pornography: An Internet Crime*. London: Brunner-Routledge.

The Hindu 2003: Campaign for relief to acid attack victims. December 28; www.thehindu.com/2003122812130300.htm (accessed October 31, 2004).

The Times of India 2004: 25-year-old woman commits suicide. January 7, p. 3.

Thomas, Lyn 2002: *Fans, Feminisms and "Quality" Media*. London: Routledge.

Thomas, Richard 1996: Blair's bad hair day. *The Guardian*, November 7.

Thornham, Sue (ed.) 1999: *Feminist Film Theory: A Reader*. Edinburgh: Edinburgh University Press.

Tinkler, Penny 1995: *Constructing Girlhood: Popular Magazines for Girls Growing Up in England, 1920–50*. London: Taylor & Francis.

Tuchman, Gaye 1978a: Introduction: the symbolic annihilation of women by the mass media. In Gaye Tuchman, Arlene Kaplan Daniels, and James Benet (eds.), *Hearth and Home: Images of Women in the Mass Media*. New York: Oxford University Press.

——1978b: *Making the News*. New York: The Free Press.

——, Daniels, Arlene Kaplan and Benet, James (eds.) 1978: *Hearth and Home: Images of Women in the Mass Media*. New York: Oxford University Press.

Tufte, Thomas 2000: *Living with the Rubbish Queen: Telenovelas, Culture and Modernity in Brazil.* Luton, UK: University of Luton Press.

Tunstall, Jeremy 1977: *The Media are American.* London: Constable.

Turan, Kenneth 1992: *Daughters* recaptures power of Gullah past. *The Los Angeles Times,* March 6.

Turkle, Sherry 1995: *Life on the Screen: Identity in the Age of the Internet.* New York: Simon and Schuster.

Turow, Joseph 1994: Hidden conflicts and journalistic norms: the case of self-coverage. *Journal of Communication,* 44(2), 29–46.

UNESCO 1980: *Women in the Media.* Paris: United Nations Educational, Scientific and Cultural Organization (UNESCO).

United Nations 1948: Universal Declaration of Human Rights. Office of the High Commissioner for Human Rights website; www.unhchr.ch/udhr/lang/eng.htm, Article 19 (accessed August 2, 2004).

—— 1976: Project Request, July 1. New York: UN Fund for Population Agency (UNFPA).

—— 1995: *United Nations and the Advancement of Women 1945–1995.* New York: UN Department of Public Information.

—— 1996: *World Investment Report on Transnational Corporations and Competitiveness, 1995.* New York: UN Conference on Trade and Development (UNCTAD), Division on Transnational Corporations and Investment.

University of Loughborough 1992: *Election Study for* The Guardian. Loughborough, UK: University of Loughborough.

—— 1997: Election study for *The Guardian,* post election review. *The Guardian,* May 2.

Urban, D. 1996: Uses of local media in consolidation of democracy. In Dorrit K. Marks (ed.), *Women and Grass Roots Democracy in the Americas: Sustaining the Initiative.* Miami, FL: North–South Center Press (University of Miami), 119–24.

van Zoonen, Liesbet 1989: Professional socialization of feminist journalists in the Netherlands. *Women's Studies in Communication,* 12(3), 1–23.

—— 1998: One of the girls? The changing gender of journalism. In Cynthia Carter, Gill Branston, and Stuart Allan (eds.), *News, Gender and Power.* London: Routledge, 33–46.

—— 2001: Feminist Internet studies. *Feminist Media Studies,* 1(1), 67–72.

—— 2002: Gendering the net: claims, controversies and cultures. *European Journal of Communication,* 17(1), 5–23.

Vares, Tiina 2002: Framing "killer" women films: audience use of genre. *Feminist Media Studies,* 2(2), 213–29.

Vetten, Lisa 1998: Reporting on rape in South Africa. *Women's Media Watch Newsletter,* 3, 5–8.

Venkatram, Shree c.2002: *Women in Print.* New Delhi: Unnati Features.

Virmani, Shabnam 2001: Women making meaning: telling stories about reality in India. *Feminist Media Studies*, 1(2), 233–43.

Wagner, Sally Roesch 1996: *The Untold Story of the Iroquois Influence on Early Feminists*. Aberdeen, SD: Sky Carrier Press.

Wakeford, Nina 2003: The embedding of local culture in global communication: independent Internet cafés in London. *New Media and Society*, 5(3), 379–99.

Walker, Alice 1981: Coming apart. In *You Can't Keep a Good Woman Down*. New York: Harcourt Brace Jovanovich, 41–53.

Walker, Nancy A. 2000: *Shaping Our Mothers' World: American Women's Magazines*. Mississippi: University Press of Mississippi.

——(ed.) 1998: *Women's Magazines, 1940–1960*. Basingstoke, UK: Palgrave Macmillan.

Wallace, Michelle 1970: *Black Macho and the Myth of the Superwoman*. New York: Dial Press.

Waller-Zuckerman, Mary-Ellen 1998: *A History of Popular Women's Magazines in the United States, 1792–1995*. Westport, CT: Greenwood Press.

Walsh Childers, Kim, Chance, Jean and Herzog, Kristin 1996: Sexual harassment of women journalists. *Journalism & Mass Communication Quarterly*, 73(3), 559–81.

Warner, W. L. and Henry, S. E. 1948: The radio day time serial: a symbolic analysis. *Genetic Psychology* Monographs, 37, 71.

Warschauer, M. 2003: *Technology and Social Inclusion: Rethinking the Digital Divide*. Cambridge, MA: The MIT Press.

Weaver, David H. 1992: A secret no more. *Washington Journalism Review*, September, 23–7.

——1997: Women as journalists. In Pippa Norris (ed.), *Women, Media and Politics*. New York: Oxford University Press, 21–40.

Weibel, Kathryn 1977: *Mirror Mirror: Images of Women Reflected in Popular Culture*. New York: Anchor Books.

Weisbrot, Robert 1998: Xena: Warrior Princess: *The Official Guide to the Xenaverse*. London: Bantam Books.

White, Michelle 2003: Too close to see: men, women and webcams. *New Media and Society*, 5(1), 7–28.

Williamson, Judith 1994: *Decoding Advertisements: Ideology and Meaning in Advertising*. New York: Marion Boyars.

Wilson, T. 1993: *Watching Television: Hermeneutics, Reception and Popular Culture*. Cambridge, UK: Polity Press.

Winship, Janice 1980: *Advertising in Women's Magazines*. Birmingham: University of Birmingham.

——1987: *Inside Women's Magazines*. London: Oram Press/Pandora List.

——1990: *Women's Magazines*. Buckingham, UK: Open University Press.

Wober, Mallory 1981: *Television and Women: Viewing Patterns and Perceptions of Ideal Actual and Portrayed Women's Roles*. Report.

Wolf, Naomi 1992: *The Beauty Myth: How Images of Beauty are Used against Women*. New York: Anchor/Doubleday.

Women's Feature Service 2003: *Annual Report for the Period October 16, 2002 to October 15, 2003*. New Delhi: Women's Feature Service.

Women in Journalism 1996: *Women in the News: Does Sex Change the Way a Newspaper Thinks?* London: Women in Journalism.

Women's Broadcasting Committee 1993: *Her Point of View*. London: WBC and Bectu.

Women's Communication Centre 1996: *What Women Want*. London: WCC.

World Association for Christian Communication 2000: *Global Media Monitoring Project 2000*. London: WACC.

Wykes, Maggie 1998: A family affair: the British press, sex and the Wests. In Cynthia Carter, Gill Branston, and Stuart Allan (eds.), *News, Gender and Power*. London: Routledge, 233–47.

——and Gunter, Barrie 2004: *The Media and Body Image: If Looks Could Kill*. London: Sage.

Yearwood, Gladstone 1992: Towards a theory of a black cinema aesthetic. In Gladstone Yearwood (ed.), *Black Cinema Aesthetics: Issues in Black Filmmaking*. Athens, OH: Ohio University Press, 9–18.

Young, Lola 1996: *Fear of the Dark: "Race", Gender and Sexuality in the Cinema*. London: Routledge.

Youngs, Gillian 2001: The political economy of time in the Internet era: feminist perspectives and challenges. *Information, Communication and Society*, 4(1), 14–33.

——2004: Cyberspace: the new feminist frontier? In Karen Ross and Carolyn M. Byerly (eds.), *Women and Media: International Perspectives*. Malden, MA: Blackwell, 157–84.

Yuen Carrucan, Jasmine 2000: The politics of Deepa Mehta's *Water*. *Bright Lights Film Journal*, 28 (April); www.brightlightsfilm.com/28/water.html (accessed July 3, 2005).

Zeilizer, Barbie 1993: Journalists as interpretive communities. *Critical Studies in Mass Communication*, 10(2), 219–37.

Zilliacus-Tikkanen, Henrika 1997: *The Essence of Journalism from a Gender Perspective* (transl.). Helsinki: Ylesradio Publications A1.

Zoch, Lynn M. and VanSlyke Turk, Judy 1998: Women making news: gender as a variable in source selection and use. *Journalism & Mass Communication Quarterly*, 75(4), 762–75.

Appendix: Research Participants

The following people took part in the cross-cultural study on women's media activism:

Margot Adler, broadcast journalist, National Public Radio, USA
Agenda (Magazine) Collective, South Africa
Lubna Yousif Ali, print journalist and proofreader, Sudan
Martha Allen, director, Women's Institute for Freedom of the Press, USA
Anita Anand, therapist in private practice (former director, Women's Feature Service), India
Sash Banerjee, board member, Point of View, India
Virginie Barré, freelance journalist and member, l'Association des Femmes Journalistes, France
Nupur Basu, broadcast journalist and documentary filmmaker, NDTV, India
Suzanne Francis Brown, freelance print journalist, and teacher at the Caribbean Institute of Media and Development, Jamaica
Jo Campbell, print journalist and editor, Ecotopics International News Service, USA
Libay Linsangan Cantor, media campaigns associate, Isis International – Manila, the Philippines
Red Chidgey, FingerBang distro, UK
Inja Coates, Media Tank, USA
Stacey Cone, faculty member, University of Iowa (former producer with CNN), USA

Angela Cuevas de Dolmetsch, attorney, Women's Peace Boat, and radio and television producer, "Looking at the World Through Women's Eyes," Colombia

Patience (Patti) Dapaah, development journalist, Ghana

Rajashri Dasgupta, print journalist and co-founder of Network of Women in Media, India

Bishakha Datta, program director and filmmaker, Point of View, India

Dorothy Dean, elected official (formerly with women's music productions and newsletters), USA

Deepa Dhanraj, documentary filmmaker, India

Aliza Dichter, director of programs, Center for International Media Action, USA (formerly with Media Channel)

Nombuso Dlamini, Soul Beat Africa, South Africa

Jennifer Drew, co-chair of Object and member of London3rdWave, UK

Margaret Gallagher, independent researcher and author, UK

Tanushree Gangopadhyay, print journalist, India

Patricia Gaston, national desk editor, *The Washington Post*, USA (formerly with *The Dallas Morning News*)

Nomusa Gaxa, print journalist, South Africa

Sheila Gibbons, editor, *Media Report to Women*, USA

Vasanthi Hariprakash, freelance print journalist, India

Jay Hartling, producer, *America Latina al Dia* radio program, USA

Ulrike Helwerth, Deutscher Fraunet (National Council of German Women's Organizations), Germany

Natacha Henry, print journalist and member of l'Association de Femmes Journalistes, France

Katharine (K. T.) Jarmul, broadcast journalist, KCSB-FM radio station, USA

Rita Henley Jensen, print journalist and founder and director of Women's eNews, USA

Ammu Joseph, freelance journalist, author, and co-founder of Network of Women in Media, India

Sonal Kellogg, print journalist, India

Abhilasha Kumari, sociologist and academic researcher, India

Trella Laughlin, creator and producer of the *Let the People Speak!"* television program, USA

Jill Lawrence, co-originator and former member, Sophie's Parlor Radio Collective, USA

Anne Lewis, documentary filmmaker, USA

Margaret Lewis, Sheffield Women's Forum Media Action Group, UK

Dalia Liran-Alper, former chair, Women's Status Committee, Israeli Broadcasting Authority, Israel

Anjali Mathur, print journalist and co-founder of Network of Women in Media, Bombay [Mumbai] chapter, India

Preeti Mehra, print journalist, The Hindu Business Line, India (formerly with Women in Media in Bombay [Mumbai])

Madeleine Memb, producer of the *Au Nom de la Femme* radio program and member of the International Association of Women in Radio and TV, Cameroon

Ritu Menon, Women Unlimited and co-founder of Kali for Women Press, India

Kristie Miller, print journalist, USA (former board member, Chicago Tribune board of directors)

Colleen Lowe Morna, director, Gender Links, South Africa

Mildred Mulenga, print journalist, Pan African News Agency, Zambia

Jeroo Mulla, head, Social Communications Media Department, Sophia Polytechnic Institute, India

Laxmi Murthy, Saheli Women's Group, Editor for India Resource Center, and member of the International Federation of Journalists, India

Sakuntala Narasimhan, *Femina* magazine and columnist for Women's Feature Service, India

Hilary Nicholson, program coordinator, Women's Media Watch, Jamaica

Louise North, print journalist and workshop leader on women and media issues, Australia

Crystal Oderson, senior political writer, South African Broadcasting Corporation, South Africa

Anghana Parekh, print journalist and director of Women's Feature Service, India

Seeta Pena Gangadharan, co-founder, Center for International Media Action, USA

Grace Poore, documentary filmmaker and director, Shakti Productions, LLC, Malaysia and USA

Janne Poort-van Eeden, videomaker and Women Peacemakers Program, Education Office, International Fellowship of Reconciliation, the Netherlands

Jennifer Pozner, print journalist and founder of Women in Media and News, USA (former writer for *Sojourners* and Fairness and Accuracy in Media Newsletter)

M. Radhika, print journalist and chair of the Network of Women in Media in India, Bangalore chapter, India

Sasha Rakoff, founder and director, Object, UK

Moira Rankin, co-originator and former member, Sophie's Parlor Radio Collective, USA

Sandhya Rao, former director, Hengasara Hakkina Sangha women's rights organization, India

Chelsia Rice, chair and editor for the Women's Resource Center, Portland Community College, and writer for *The Alliance* newspaper, USA

Joan Ross-Frankson, Women's Environmental Development Organization, USA (formerly with Sistren, Jamaica)

Howedia Saleem Jabir, print journalist with the *Khartoum Monitor* (English), and member of the Center for Arab Women's Training and Research and ENGEAD Center, Sudan

Judy Sandison, editor of new media (Special News Services), South African Broadcasting Corporation, South Africa

Boden Sandstrom, former member of the Sophie's Parlor Radio Collective, and president of City Sound Productions, USA

Sanjana, member of Pedestrian Pictures collective and documentary filmmaker, India

Vicki Semler, director, International Women's Tribune Center, USA

Gargi Sen, member, Magic Lantern Foundation film collective, India

Ramesh Sepehrrad, president, National Committee of Women for a Democratic Iran, Iran and USA

Geeta Seshu, officer in the Bombay [Mumbai] Union of Journalists and member of the BUJ's Women's Committee; and lecturer, Research Centre for Women's Studies, SNDT University, India

D. S. Shamantha Mani, freelance development media professional and project director of the Saarathi Resource Center for Communications, India

Kalpana Sharma, Bombay [Mumbai] bureau chief of *The Hindu* newspaper, and co-founder of Network of Women in Media, India

Gretchen Luchsinger Sidhu, development communications consultant, and former reporter and editor for Women's Feature Service, USA

Akhila Sivadas, director, Center for Advocacy and Research, India

Judith Smith, director, Women's Media Watch, South Africa

Patricia Solano, editor, *Quehaceres* newspaper, Centro de Investigación para la Acción Femenina, Dominican Republic

Sureka Sule, print journalist and fellow at the Ministry of Water Resources, and member of Women in Media, India

Sandhya Taksale, print journalist and member of Women in Media, India

A. E. Tijhoff, member, *de Natte Vinger* (The Wet Finger), the Netherlands

Sue Valentine, Internet journalist, South Africa

Shree Venkatram, print journalist, and founder and director of Unnati Features, India

Sylvia Vollenhoven, print journalist, South Africa

Frieda Werden, co-founder and producer, Women's International News-gathering Service (WINGS), Canada

Claudia Wulz, co-producer of lesbian-feminist radio programs, the Netherlands

Debra Zimmerman, executive director, Women Make Movies, USA

Jane Zondo, journalist and producer, Channel Africa, South Africa

Name Index

Abbott, Dorothy 221
Abzug, Bella 197
Adler, Margot 155, 159, 163–4
Aldana, Celia 195–6
Alexander, Karen 86
Alfaro, R. 152
Allan, Stuart 39, 54
Allen, Donna 94, 106, 134, 193, 209, 210, 218, 233
Allen, Martha Leslie 106, 186, 193–4, 233
Anand, Anita 114, 211, 212–14
Ananda, Mitra 204
Andermahr, Sonya 167
Anderson, Bonnie S. 208, 234
Andrae, Thomas 24
Ang, Ien 22, 58–9, 62
Arnaldo, Carlos A. 70
Arnheim, Rudolph 57
Arnold, Rebecca 50
Aronson, Amy Beth 49
Arthurs, Jane 91
Attile, Martine 86

Bakker, Isabella 229
Ballaster, Ros 50

Balme, Helen 71
Basinger, Jeanne 19
Basu, Amrita 2
Beale, Alison 77
Beasley, Maureen H. 162, 193, 234
Becker, Ron 35
Beckett, Margaret 46
Beetham, Margaret 49
Benedict, Helen 43
Benet, James 17, 40
Bennett, W. Lance 39, 92, 121
Berger, John 20
Berkowitz, Sandra 102
Berns, Nancy 43
Bhaiya, Abha 138
Bielby, Denise D. 62
Biressi, Anita 25
Blackwood, Maureen 86
Boaden, Helen 93
Bobo, Jacqueline 29, 31, 61, 63
Bonfadelli, Heinz 71–2
Bordo, Susan 53
Bose, Brinda 227
Boulding, Elise 2, 101, 104, 113
Bourne, Stephen 29, 32

Branston, Gill 78
Brown, Mary Ellen 22, 57, 60
Brunsdon, Charlotte 21, 22, 24, 58, 63, 85
Burch, Sally 114
Burrell, Ian 94
Burt, Elizabeth V. 172
Butalia, Urvashi 227–8
Butler, Alison 83, 84
Buzzanell, Patrice M. 102
Byerly, Carolyn M. 6, 7, 76, 77, 78, 79, 81, 92, 101, 103, 113, 119, 122, 123, 155, 163, 212, 213, 237

Caputi, J. 37
Carstarphen, Meta G. 30
Carter, Cynthia 37, 41, 78
Caswell, C. Evans 121
Ceulemans, Mieke 17
Chadha, Gurinder 86, 87, 88, 90
Chambers, Deborah 82, 161
Chance, Jean 81
Chapman, James 24
Chaudhuri, Maitrayee 2, 4, 227
Clover, Carol J. 27, 64
Cohen, Jean L. 119
Colorado, Marta 147
Compesi, R. J. 57
Compton, Laura 52
Cottingham, Jane 105, 106
Cottle, Simon 39
Craft, Christine 81–2
Creed, Barbara 21
Cresser, Frances 71
Cresson, Edith 37
Croteau, David 32, 39
Cuklanz, Lisa M. 42, 43
Cuthbert, Marlene 106

D'Acci, Julie 62
Damon-Moore, Helen 49
Daniels, Arlene Kaplan 17, 40

Dash, Julie 87–8
Davenport, Katherine 220
David, Prabu 68
Davis, Angela Y. 4
de Courtivron, Isabelle 238
de Lauretis, Teresa 84, 238
Densmore, Dana 134, 209, 233
Desai, Jigna 90
Djerf-Pierre, Madeline 79, 80
Douglas, Susan 25
Drob, Gil 44
Durham, Meenakshi Gigi 50

Edut, Ophira 50
Elson, Diane 158, 171, 179, 187
Engels, Friedrich 6
Entman, Robert M. 39
Escobar, Arturo 114
Estrich, Susan 80

Fahmy, Shahira 42
Fauconnier, Guido 17
Felski, Rita 116
Fielding, Helen 52–3
Firestone, Shulamith 6
First, Ruth 116
Fiske, John 107
Fleming, Carole 82, 161
Fowler, Roger 44
Franklin, Bob 39
Fraser, Nancy 117, 118–19
Frazer, Elizabeth 50
Fudge, Rachel 27

Gaines, Jane 21
Gajjala, Radhika 73
Galician, Mary-Lou 53
Gallagher, Margaret 7, 17, 47, 75, 101, 113, 122, 124, 126, 162, 185, 186, 189–90
Gamman, Lorraine 63
Gans, Herbert J. 47

Gauntlett, David   52, 68
Geraghty, Christine   22–3, 58
Gerbner, George   196
Gibbons, Sheila J.   162, 193, 211, 219, 234
Giddens, Anthony   188
Gillespie, Carmen R.   29
Gillwald, Alison   66, 79
Gilmour, Heather   72
Gledhill, Christine   21
Goldenberg, Edie N.   44
Gole, Nilufer   99, 119
Gough-Yates, Anna   25, 50
Gramsci, Antonio   167
Gross, Larry   34
Grosz, Elizabeth   21
Gunn, Lesley   71
Gunter, Barrie   50
Guy, Alice   83
Gwenllian Jones, Sara   28

Habermas, Jürgen   117–21, 238–9
Hall, Stuart   66
Hantzis, Darlene M.   32, 33, 34
Harcourt, Wendy   69
Harrington, C. Lee   34, 62
Harris, Leslie   87
Hartley, John   107
Hartsock, Nancy C. M.   102
Haskell, Molly   19
Hayzer, Noeleen   12–13
Heaton, Louis   32
Hebron, Sandra   50
Hegel, Georg   6
Henry, Georgina   81
Henry, S. E.   57
Hepburn, Katharine   56
Hermes, Joke   67
Hernandez, Debra Gersh   48
Hernandez, Zoila   123
Herzog, Hannah   57
Herzog, Kristin   81

Hesse-Biber, Sharlene   53
Hibberd, Matthew   48
Hill Collins, Patricia   4
Hill, Annette   65
Hinds, Hilary   33
Hobson, Dorothy   22, 58, 59, 60
hooks, bell   29
Hoynes, William   32, 39
Humm, Maggie   18–19, 20

Inness, Sherrie A.   25, 26, 28
Iozzi, David P.   121
Iyengar, Shanto   39

Jain, Devaki   139
Jayamanne, Laleen   21
Jennings, Ros   27
Johnson, Melissa A.   68
Johnson-Odim, Cheryl   5
Jones, Nicholas   39
Joseph, Ammu   79, 92, 158, 159, 172, 174, 182

Kahn, Kim Fridkin   44
Kanwar, Roop   173
Kaplan, E. Ann   19, 63, 85
Kapoor, Priya   72–3
Kasbekar, Kiron   136
Katz, James E.   70
Kaul, Malvika   174
Kelber, Mim   197
Keller, Kathryn   51
Kemp, Amanda   5, 119
Kerber, Linda K.   4, 121–2
Kielbowicz, Richard   113
Kilbourne, Jean   37, 49, 50, 53–4
Kinsey, Michael   80
Kitzinger, Jenny   41, 42
Komter, Aafke   79
Kramarae, Cheris   102
Kuhn, Annette   63
Kuhn, Maggie   223

Kumar, Radha 227
Kurian, Priya A. 70
Kwan, Mei-Po 70

Lægran, Anne Sofie 71
Lafuente, María Suárez 19–20
Lagos, Taso 121
Lamas, Marta 123
Lambiase, Jacqueline 52
Lant, Antonia 19
Lauer, Nancy Cook 78
Lauzen, Martha D. 78
Lavie, Aliza 92
Lawrence, Carmen 46
Lee, Ang 77
Lee, Francis L. F. 46
Lee, Sarah 71
Lees, Sue 42
Lehman-Wilzig, S. 92
Lehr, Valerie 32, 33, 34
Lemish, Dafna 41, 44, 161
Lesage, Julie 83–4
Levitin, Jacqueline 84
Liebler, Carol 47, 92
Lipson, Joanne 208
Liran-Alper, Dalia 44, 159, 160–1, 237
Lisanti, Tom 24
Lovell, Terry 61, 167
Lünenborg, Margaret 77
Luther, Catherine A. 52, 67

Mackie, Erin 49
Madlala, Nozizwe 5, 119
Malhotra, Sheena 31
Malik, Sarita 29, 30, 86
Manatu, Norma 30
Mani, Lata 173
Mankekar, Purnima 22, 23, 29
Manning, Paul 39, 47
Marks, Elaine 238
Marshment, Margaret 63

Martin, Michèle 76
Marx, Karl 6
Masi de Casanova, Erynn 68
Massoni, Kelley 51
Mata, Marita 152
Mayer, Vicki 60
McChesney, Robert W. 93
McCracken, Ellen 50, 52
McLaughlin, Lisa 62, 102, 118, 120, 121, 145
McMillan, Terry 30
McMillin, Divya 62, 102
McNair, Brian 48, 52
McQuail, Denis 22, 188
McRobbie, Angela 50
Meehan, Eileen R. 69, 102
Mehra, Preeti 10–11, 12, 159, 168, 236–7
Melin-Higgins, Margareta 79, 80
Mercer, Kobena 87
Michielsens, Magda 41
Milkie, Melissa A. 51, 53
Miller, Alan V. 82
Mills, Sara 102–3
Mitchell, Caroline 145, 219–20
Mitra, Ananda 73, 121
Modleski, Tania 63
Mohanty, Chandra Talpade 4–5
Montgomery, Martin 107
Moodley, Asha 5, 119
Moorti, Sujata 89, 91
Moritz, Marguerite J. 32, 33
Morley, David 66
Morrison, Glenda 68
Mowlana, Hamid 196
Mukherjee, Rina 174
Mulvey, Laura 20–1, 64, 85
Munshi, Debashish 70
Myers, Marian 43

Na, Misu 70
Nagrath, Sumati 77, 94

Naylor, Gloria   31
Neale, Stephen   19
Negra, Diane   30
Nentl, Nancy J.   52, 67
Nichols, John   93
Nochimson, Martha   61
Nordenstreng, Kaarle   196
Norris, Pippa   39, 44, 70, 78
North, Louise C.   79, 160, 167–8
Nunn, Heather   25

O'Neill, Terry   92
O'Sullivan, Tim   107
Opoku-Mensah, Aida   79, 177
Osgerby, Bill   25
Ouellette, Laurie   52
Ove, Horace   86
Owen, Sarah A.   27

Parameswaran, Radhika   26, 29, 30
Parmar, Pratibha   88
Paul, Louis   24
Penley, Constance   21, 85
Perez, Berta Alicia   147
Phegley, Jennifer   49
Pickard, Victor W.   121
Pinnock, Don   116, 234
Pitt, Lisa   77
Plessis, Judith   84
Powers, Kirsten A.   80
Pozner, Jennifer   92, 186, 198–9
Pribham, E. Deirdre   63

Quayle, E.   70

Radway, Janice   65
Rai, Usha   231
Rao, Anupama   137, 227
Rao, Meera   138
Raoul, Valerie   84
Rapping, Elayne   162, 235
Rege, Sharmila   102
Reichert, Tom   52

Rense, Rip   91
Riaño, Pilar   1, 122–3, 147, 151–2, 239
Rice, Ronald E.   70
Rich, B. Ruby   89
Riordan, Ellen   76–7, 102
Roach, Colleen   196
Roberts, Cokie   163
Robertson, Nan   158
Robins, Melinda   72
Robinson, Gertrude J.   78
Rock, Marcia   158
Rodino, Michelle   70
Rogers, Everett   31
Root, Jane   40
Ross, Felecia   68
Ross, Karen   30, 39, 44, 46, 48, 66, 67, 79, 81, 86, 124
Ross, Leone   87
Rubin, A. W.   57
Rush, Ramona R.   78
Ryan, Mary P.   118

Sakamoto, Kazue   51, 52
Salo, Elaine   5, 119
Sanders, Karen   39
Sanders, Marlene   158
Saunders, Danny   107
Savio, Roberto   213
Scherer, Clifford   113
Schlesinger, Phillip   48
Schroeder, Carl L.   121
Scodari, Christine   70
Seiter, Ellen   31
Selwyn, Neil   72
Sen, Gargi   129, 132, 137, 140–1, 142, 236
Sen, Ilina   106, 137, 138
Sen, Jai   114
Sepehrrad, Ramesh   11–12, 187, 205
Shade, Leslie Regan   114
Sharma, Kalpana   158, 160, 172, 174
Sherron De Hart, Jane   4

Shiva, Vandana 227
Shohat, Ella 87
Sieghart, Mary Anne 81
Sims, Monica 93
Singh, Supriya 71, 72
Smith, Dorothy 37
Smith, Judith 185, 187, 191–2
Smith, Susan J. 47, 92
Smith-Shomade, Beretta E. 30
Soothill, Keith 42
Sørensen, Knut H. 71
Spender, Dale 70
Spilker, Hendrik 71
Spivak, Gayatri Chakravorty 119
Stabile, Carol 70
Stacey, Jackie 64
Steeves, H. Leslie 102
Steinem, Gloria 164
Steiner, Linda 82, 116, 161, 234
Sterne, Jonathan 70
Stewart, James 71
Stuart, Andrea 87

Tasker, Yvonne 25
Taylor, Helen 63
Taylor, M. 70
Thomas, Lyn 61
Thornham, Sue 21
Tottenberg, Nina 163
Trotter, Amanda 165
Tuchman, Gaye 17, 40
Tufte, Thomas 60
Tunstall, Jeremy 39
Turan, Kenneth 88
Turkle, Sherry 70

Unwurah, Ngozi 86

van den Bosch, Annette 77
Van Peebles, Mario 87
van Zoonen, Liesbet 70, 71
VanSlyke Turk, Judy 47, 48, 92
Vares, Tiina 65

Vaughan, Genevieve 221
Venkatram, Shree 41, 47–8, 54–5,
    127, 211, 215–16, 237
Vetten, Lisa 43, 44
Virmani, Shabnam 123

Wade, Rebekah 91
Wagner, Sally Roesch 4
Wakeford, Nina 71
Walby, Sylvia 42
Walker, Alice 5, 30, 63
Walker, Rebecca 50
Waller-Zuckerman, Mary-Ellen
    49
Walsh Childers, Kim 81
Warner, W. L. 57
Warren, Catherine A. 81, 163
Warschauer, M. 70
Wasko, Janet 102
Waterman, Peter 114
Waters, Sarah 33
Weaver, C. Kay 37, 41
Weaver, David H. 80
Weisbrot, Robert 28
Wertheimer, Linda 163
White, Michelle 71
Williams, Brenda 82
Williamson, Judith 49
Wilson, T. 61
Winship, Janice 50
Winterson, Jeanette 33
Wober, Mallory 66
Wolf, Naomi 49
Wolkowitz, Carol 167
Wykes, Maggie 50

Young, Lola 29–30, 32
Youngs, Gillian 70, 151, 234–5
Yuen Carrucan, Jasmine 88–9

Zilliacus-Tikkanen, Henrika 77
Zinsser, Judith P. 208, 234
Zoch, Lynn M. 47, 48, 92

Subject Index

"16 Days of Activism Against Gender Violence" campaign 181

abortion 134
abuse *see* incest; violence
acid attacks *see* violence
advertising 17, 38, 49, 50, 52, 53, 67, 93, 101, 102, 112, 122, 136–7, 146, 157, 162, 189, 192, 199, 200, 202, 235
Afghanistan 214
   Taliban regime 42
Africa 17, 41, 72, 79, 103, 104, 108, 113, 177, 212
ageism 28, 29, 61
agency, personal 62–3
agency, of women 163–4, 188, 237
AIDS *see* HIV/AIDS
Amnesty International 11, 146, 182, 205
AOL Time Warner 76
apartheid 109, 116, 143, 170, 179
Arabs Union 126, 178
Asia 17, 72, 86, 212
Associated Press news service 42, 162
Australia 22, 79, 108, 159
   Labor Party 46

backlash, anti-feminist 25
Bangladesh 143, 180, 214
Barbados 106, 192
beauty 68, 216
Belgium 108, 132, 145, 148–9, 234
   Tribunal on Crimes against Women, Brussels 105
Bertelsmann 76
Bolivia 123
book publishing 9, 101, 110, 111, 209, 210, 227–8, 233
Bosnia 175–6
Brazil 60, 114, 115
Britain *see* United Kingdom
Bulgaria 217

Cameroon 108, 159, 164, 235
Campaign for Communication Rights in the Information Society (CRIS) 114–15, 190, 197
Canada 89, 108, 132, 145, 211, 226, 235
capitalism 75, 76, 102, 116, 171, 187
career advancement 75, 104, 111, 157, 162, 209, 224–5
   "glass ceiling" 75, 77, 167
   media training 188–92, 198

see also discrimination;
    marginalization
Caribbean Association for Feminist
    Research and Action
    (CAFRA) 192
Caribbean Gender Equity Fund 192
Caribbean Institute for Media and
    Communications (CARIMAC)
    181, 192
Caribbean, the 113, 180, 181, 212
Chile 196
    Fempress/mujer magazine/news
        service 105–6
China 117
    4th International NGO Forum for
        Women, Beijing, 1995 226
    Beijing Declaration and Platform
        for Action, 1995 114
    Beijing Platform for Action 221
civil rights movement 134, 179
class, socioeconomic 131, 144, 152,
    235
Colombia 108, 132, 145
    civil war 125, 146
colonialism 86, 170, 173
commodity audience 69
communicative action 116–21, 232
    theory of 117–18
Cosmopolitan magazine 52
Costa Rica 221
counter spheres 118, 119
crime reporting 216
culture, high/low 64–5
cyberfeminism 151, 234

Decade for Women (UN) *see* United
    Nations Decade for Women
democracy 157, 171, 180, 195, 237
Denmark 104
development journalism 214, 222
dialectical process 6
discourse competence theory 102–3

discrimination 11, 157, 160, 164
    culture of 177–9
    in employment 161–2, 202
    lawsuits 81–2, 217, 218
Disney Corporation 76
Dominican Republic 108, 187, 201

Earth Summit, Rio de Janeiro, 1992 198
economics 144, 201, 236
Ecuador 68
education 130, 144, 147, 165, 180,
    214, 222
Egypt 198, 224
empowerment, women's 53, 68, 151,
    202, 203, 226, 235
ethnicity 21, 28, 119, 135, 196, 235
ethnographic research 58, 60, 62, 65,
    73, 112
Europe 38, 101, 104, 108, 208, 214
European Commission 41
e-zine 71, 83, 91, 147–8, 150–1, 233,
    234

fandom 58, 60, 74
fashion 50–1, 53, 68, 216
female feticide 158, 203
female genital mutilation 175–6, 178,
    223
feminism, second-wave 83, 84, 133,
    149, 158
Feminist International Radio Endeavor
    (FIRE), Costa Rica 221
feminist, definition of 3, 100, 108
film, documentary 157, 179–80
film, woman's 19, 63
film, women and 63–4
Finland 77
France 108, 126, 159, 160, 186, 189
    Agence Femmes Information
        (AFI) 106
    l'Association des Femmes
        Journalistes (AFJ) 172

gay and lesbian issues 82, 131, 176, 195, 196
Gender and Media Baseline Study, Southern Africa, 2003 41, 55, 127, 190–1
Gender and Media Network Southern Africa (GEMSA) 177
gender inequality/imbalance 77–8, 157, 168, 190, 219
Germany 41, 108, 132, 135
European Organization Against Fundamentalism 11
National Council of German Women's Organizations 135
Ghana 108, 159, 164, 235
"glass ceiling" *see* career advancement
Global Fund for Women 221
Global Media Monitoring Project (GMMP) 40–1, 123–4, 126, 189–90, 192
globalization 136, 142, 180, 236
Guinea 164

harassment *see* violence
health care 110, 130, 138, 144, 152, 165, 175, 177, 201, 235
Hindu fundamentalism 173
historical materialism, feminist theory of 102
HIV/AIDS 144, 177, 201, 202, 222, 225
homophobia 31, 88, 144, 148
Hong Kong 46
horror movies 64
human rights 134, 141, 142, 143, 163, 175, 182, 222, 236
Hungary 125

incest 23, 130, 162, 225, 226, 235
India 4, 31–2, 54–5, 62, 70, 72–3, 79, 88–9, 94, 102, 106, 108, 109, 123, 125, 132, 135–43, 158–9, 160, 165, 168–9, 173, 174, 177, 179–82, 186, 201–4, 208, 214, 215, 216, 222, 225, 226, 228
All-India Radio, Bangalore 222
Bombay Union of Journalists 173–4, 175
Campaign and Struggle Against Acid Attacks on Women (CSAAAW) 143
caste system 137, 172–3, 236
Chipko Movement 138
Dalit movement 102, 129, 136, 137, 140, 236
Doordarshan state-owned television network 23, 121, 136
English-language newspapers 41–2, 47–8
Gujarat 141, 168–9, 172–3
Hengasara Hakkina Sangha 203–4, 222
Hindi-language newspapers 41–2, 47–8
Kali for Women book publishers 227–8
Karnataka 139, 142, 143, 222
Kashi Sanskrit Raksha Sangharsh Samiti (KSRSS) Party 88–9
Magic Lantern Foundation, New Delhi 129, 140–1
Network of Women in Media in India (NWMI) 11, 92, 136, 174–5
panchayat (local council) 139, 194, 236
Panchayat Raj Act 1993 139
Pedestrian Pictures, Bangalore 141–3
Point of View (POV) 202–3
Press Institute of India 174, 175
Saarathi Resource Center, Bangalore 221–2
sati (widow-burning) 158, 173

tribal communities   129, 236
Unnati Features   127, 215–16, 237
Women and Media Group
   (WMG)   136, 172–3
Women in the Media, Bombay/
   Mumbai   10–11
Women Unlimited (WU)   228
Women's Feature Service (WFS)
   123, 137, 180–1, 211–15, 237
women's movement   137–8
Yugantan collective   138
Zubaan publishing company   228
Indonesia   225
information communication
   technologies (ICTs)   197
Inter Press Service (IPS)   212–13
International Association of Women in
   Radio and Television   164, 221
International Fellowship of
   Reconciliation (IFOR)   143
International Women's Day, March 8,
   2004   12
International Women's Tribune Center
   197
International Women's Year, 1975
   104, 113
Internet   8, 9, 11, 18, 57, 69–71, 73,
   107, 110, 111, 121, 125, 127, 131,
   150–1, 204, 208, 209, 220–1, 233,
   234–5
Iran   11–12, 108, 186, 204
Isis International   105, 119, 196–7
Islamic community   119, 224
Israel   41, 108, 142
   Israeli Broadcasting Authority
      160–1, 237
   Women in Black   102
Italy   105, 196, 212

Jamaica   106, 108, 159, 181, 186,
   191–2
   Woman Speak! magazine   106

Women's Media Watch (WMW)
   181
Japan   51–2, 67–8

Kenya   104, 176

labor issues   51, 144, 152, 160, 168,
   171, 199, 203, 236
Ladyfest women's film festivals   150
Latin America   17, 94, 101, 104, 113,
   123, 135, 212
lawsuits   156, 158, 161–2, 168
Lebanon   212, 224
Leninism   135, 149
lesbian identity   29, 32–5, 61, 91, 131,
   133, 145, 148–50, 152, 225
   see also gay and lesbian issues
lesbian-feminism   149
liberal feminism   149

magazine publishing   48–55, 56,
   67–8, 73, 81, 110, 157, 209, 233
   Victorian women's   7–8, 9, 49
Malaysia   108, 211, 225
Mali   197
marginalization, of minority
   groups   119–20, 195, 203, 235,
   239
marginalization, of women   19, 37,
   40, 47, 70–1, 86–7, 88, 157, 161,
   186, 188, 204, 226, 231, 236
   in the newsroom   169, 190–1
marriage, arranged   88, 178
martial arts   25, 26, 65
Marxism   102, 135, 149
mass communication theory   58
mass media, globalization of   77
media advocacy   3, 101, 110, 111, 187,
   190, 198–200, 201, 202–5, 217,
   222
media conglomerates   76–7, 94, 122,
   228

media economics   76–7
media education   198
media enterprises, women-owned
    see women's media enterprises
media globalization   11
media industries   75–94
media monitoring   3, 10, 110,
    188–92
media ownership   8–9, 39, 69, 75,
    76–7, 91, 93, 94, 122, 189, 210–11
media reform   2, 10, 18, 62, 93, 100,
    198
media structure   2, 9, 101, 163–4
melodrama   31
mergers and acquisitions   92
Mexico   104, 105–6, 113, 123, 176,
    211, 224
Middle East   104, 108, 113, 212
middle-classness   23, 57, 64
Model of Women's Media Action
    (MWMA)   9, 10, 94, 99–128, 238
    advocate change agent   126–7, 130,
        185–206
    media profession to politics
        125–6, 155–82, 130
    politics to media   125, 129–52
    women's media enterprises   127–8,
        130, 208–29
Morocco   224
movements, feminist   100–1
music   122, 133, 147–8, 149, 152, 209,
    233, 234

national development   213, 225
Nepal   214
Nepal, Asian Girls Peace Camp   143
Netherlands, the   67, 71, 108, 132,
    187
    de Natte Vinger   200
    International Fellowship of
        Reconciliation (IFOR)   125, 143
    Viva magazine   59

Women Peacemakers and the
    Media   125
New International Economic
    Order   212
new technology   56, 68–73, 139–40,
    148
New World Information and
    Communication Order   196, 212
news agency, women's   211–18
News Corporation   76
news media   2, 7–8, 9, 17–18, 39,
    47–8, 56, 66, 93, 111–12, 209
    and gender   39–41, 65–7
    as men's domain   65–6
newspaper journalism   10–11, 37–48,
    78–80, 81, 91, 110, 131, 135, 163,
    179–81, 190, 210
newsroom, activism in   82–3
newsroom, masculine/macho   78–80,
    167–8
nonaligned (developing) nations   196
North America   17, 104, 180, 225
North–South divide   70, 72, 105, 114,
    115, 147, 196, 229
Norway   71, 72, 176
NOS Gender Portrayal Department
    41

Pakistan   224
    Revolutionary Association of
        Women in Afghanistan   11–12
Pan African News Agency (PANA),
    Southern Africa   169
patriarchy   23, 38, 43, 47, 50, 61, 75,
    84, 90, 122, 146, 151, 233, 234–5
    women's complicity in   166–71
peacemaking   125, 131, 143–6, 214
Peru   152
    Mujer y Sociedad supplement   123
    NGO Calandria   195
Philippines, the   105, 108, 186, 196,
    214

Depthnews Women's Service   212
  Sappho Society   196
  Task Force Pride   196
political activism   11–12
political economy   75–94, 102
  feminist   134, 187
pornography   18, 38, 70, 89, 159, 162,
  200, 224, 235
postcolonial theory   102
poverty   130, 131, 147, 166, 199, 201,
  215, 236
power relations   2, 20, 43, 99, 102,
  115, 128, 135
Press Foundation of Asia   212
professional change organizations
  171–5
property rights   202
prostitution   29, 32, 152, 203, 225,
  236
psychoanalysis   20–1, 85
public broadcasting system   93
public policy   101, 111, 222
public sphere
  dominant   91, 118, 120, 130, 131,
    181, 209, 210, 225, 235, 239
  feminist   9, 116, 118, 120, 130,
    150–1, 157, 181, 209, 210, 225,
    239
  Habermas's formulation   117–18,
    119
  official   118
public spheres, multiple   118, 119,
  146–8, 238–9

race   119, 131, 135, 144, 145, 152,
  195, 196, 235, 236
race studies   102
racial equality   134
racism   23, 31, 88, 144, 148, 150, 159,
  164, 165, 171, 192, 199
radical feminism   149, 151
radio stations, noncommercial   93

radio, lesbian-feminist   234
Radio-Television News Directors
  Association and Foundation   78
rape   23, 38, 42, 43, 80, 118, 130, 138,
  152, 158, 175–6, 202, 203, 225
  date rape   118, 162, 235
  see also violence

SAWnet   *see* South Asian Women's
  Network
self-determination   103, 233
sexism   31, 54, 88, 118, 159, 171
sexist media imagery   10, 38, 52, 101,
  112, 136–7, 146, 157, 160, 162,
  199, 200
sexist practices, women's complicity
  in   168
sexuality   21, 28, 150, 152, 235
Slovenia   195
soap opera   8, 18, 21, 22–3, 29, 31, 39,
  56, 57–63
social class   119, 135, 196
social justice   143–6
South Africa   5, 44, 66, 79, 81, 108,
  109, 116, 119–20, 143, 160,
  169–70, 178–9, 187, 208
  Agenda magazine collective   159,
    165
  Center for the Study of Violence
    and Reconciliation   43
  Femina magazine   44
  Gender Links   126–7, 170, 190–1
  Media Institute for Southern Africa
    (MISA)   190
  South African Broadcasting
    Corporation (SABC)   170–1
  South African News Editors' Forum
    (SANEF)   55, 190
  South African Police Service
    (SAPS)   44
  Violence Against Women
    coalition   192

South Africa (*cont'd*)
　Women's Media Watch (WMW)
　　170, 185, 191–2
South Asia　88, 90, 108, 121, 214, 225–6
　Global Reproductive Health Forum
　　(GRHF)　72–3
South Asian Women's Network
　　(SAWnet)　73, 121, 204
Spain　19–20
Sri Lanka　143, 214, 225, 226
stereotyping　7, 29, 30, 32, 35, 40,
　　48–9, 50, 52, 53, 60, 62, 84, 85, 90,
　　99, 101, 104, 161, 163, 219, 235
structuration theory　188
subaltern theories　119
Sudan　108, 159, 160
　Azza magazine　126, 178
　Khartoum Monitor　178
　Umma Party　178
suffrage publications　82, 116, 234
Sweden　104
Switzerland　71–2, 105, 115, 176, 196,
　　197, 198

Tanzania Media Women's Association
　　(TAMWA)　177
Tasmania　79, 167
　Women Tasmania Media Award
　　168
telecommunication industries　122
television, drama　78
television, news　38
television, noncommercial　93
television, situation comedy　78
textual analysis　63–4, 73–4, 85
theory, feminist　238
theory, need for　102–7
"third cinema"　86
Tunisia　115, 178, 197
　Center for Arab Women's Training
　　and Research (CAWTAR)　178
Turkey　119

Uganda　105, 196
UNESCO　*see* United Nations
　Educational, Scientific, and
　Cultural Organization
UNIFEM　*see* United Nations Fund
　for Women
United Kingdom　3, 22, 33–4, 42, 45,
　　46, 49, 51–2, 54, 68, 81, 82–3,
　　86–7, 88, 91, 103, 108, 109, 116,
　　126, 132, 159, 186, 199
　Advertising Standards Authority
　　(ASA)　200
　British Broadcasting Corporation
　　(BBC)　93–4
　Channel 4 television　34, 86
　Conservative Party　45
　FingerBang distro　150–1, 234
　London3rdWave　200
　Object　199, 200
　Sex Discrimination Act 1975
　　161–2
　Sex Disqualification (Removal) Act
　　1919　161–2
　Sheffield Women's Media Action
　　Forum　200
　Women in Journalism　45, 92
　Workshop Declaration, 1981　86
United Nations (UN)　1, 104, 216
　UN Children's Fund (UNICEF)
　　181
　UN Commission on Human Rights
　　198
　UN Commission on the Status of
　　Women　104
　UN Conference on Human Rights
　　176
　UN Decade for Women, 1976–85
　　104, 113, 114, 163, 211–12
　UN Development Fund for Women
　　(UNIFEM)　192
　UN Economic and Social Council
　　104

UN Educational, Scientific, and Cultural Organization (UNESCO)   17, 136, 212
UN Fourth Conference on Women, Beijing, China, 1995   117
UN Fund for Population   212
UN Fund for Population Development   198
UN Fund for Women (UNIFEM)   12, 216
UN General Assembly   104, 113
Universal Declaration of Human Rights   113, 221
United States   3, 4, 19, 22, 32–3, 38, 49, 58–9, 70, 72–3, 76, 78, 80, 82, 87–8, 101, 108, 109, 116, 119, 132, 133, 134, 141, 144, 145, 148, 149, 150, 159, 160, 163, 166, 169, 172, 175–7, 181, 186, 193, 198, 211, 214, 220, 221, 222, 223, 224, 233–4, 236
Amazon magazine   82, 133
American Resurrection   92
Annenberg Public Policy Center   78, 162
Bitch! magazine   83, 151
Center for International Media Action (CIMA)   194–5
Civil Rights Act 1964   162
CNN news network   122, 166, 237
Ecotopics International News Service online magazine   163
E-Zan electronic newsletter   12, 205
Fairness and Accuracy in Reporting (FAIR)   93, 198
Federal Communications Commission (FCC)   92, 193
Feminist Radio Network   149
Hollywood   21, 26, 61, 64, 122
KCSB-FM radio station, California   148

KMBC radio station, Kansas City   81–2
KPFK community radio station   220
MacArthur Foundation   127, 215–16
Media Access Group   93
Media Education Foundation   93
Media Report to Women bulletin   105–6, 210, 218–19
Media Tank   92, 194
Michigan Women's Music Festival   164
Ms. magazine   199
National Advisory Council on Violence Against Women   182
National Committee of Women for a Democratic Iran (NCWDI)   11–12, 205
National Organization for Women   92, 119, 127, 193, 194, 217
National Public Radio   155, 163, 220
Network of South Asian Incest Interventionists   226
Olivia Records   133, 149
Paid My Dues magazine   133
Seneca Falls Convention, 1848   4
September 11, 2001, attacks   224
SHaKTI Productions   225–6
Sophie's Parlor Radio Collective   149–50, 220, 234
The Dallas Morning News   175
The New York Times   73, 158
The Washington Post   80, 162, 176
Women In Media and News (WIMN)   92, 194, 198
Women Make Movies (WMM), New York   223–5
Women's eNews   127, 216–18, 219, 237

United States (*cont'd*)
  Women's Environmental and
    Development Organization
    (WEDO) 197–8
  Women's Forum Against
    Fundamentalism in Iran
    (WFAFI) 11–12, 204–5
  Women's Institute for Freedom of
    the Press (WIFP) 106, 134,
    193–4, 208, 209, 210, 233
  Women's Resource Center, Portland,
    Oregon 134
  women's shelter movement 144

Viacom 76
Vietnam 150
violence 31, 38, 40, 42, 54, 143, 144,
    145–6, 152, 175–6, 181–2, 199,
    218, 201, 203, 225, 235, 236, 237
  acid attacks 142–3, 180
  child abuse 59, 80
  disappearance of women 152
  domestic 23, 135, 144, 151, 182,
    202, 225–6
  dowry deaths 158, 175–6, 180
  family 138, 160
  harassment 75, 80–82, 165
  maltreatment of women in Iran
    205
  sadism 38
  sex crimes 42–4, 54
  sexual harassment 11, 81, 118,
    152, 157, 160, 162, 163, 166, 174,
    175, 203
  sexual violence 8, 44, 135, 151,
    162, 182, 226, 235
  torture 152, 175–6
  and transgender love 223
  widow-burning *see* India, sati
  wife battering/beating 130, 162,
    176, 203, 225, 226, 235
  women watching 64–5

see also female feticide; female
  genital mutilation; incest; rape;
  war
Vivendi 76

war 110, 131, 145–6, 161, 214
woman, as audience/spectator 19,
  56–74
woman, as bad girl (whore) 41, 161
woman, as decision-maker 44–7
woman, as good mother (or caretaker)
  161
woman, as sex object/symbol 17, 41,
  145, 146, 190
woman, as victim 8, 41, 42–4, 54, 64,
  161, 190, 199, 225–6
woman, as victor 64
woman, as virgin 161
woman, traditional domestic role
  17
Women and Development (WAND)
  organization, Barbados 106,
  192
women, African American 87
women, African Caribbean 29–30,
  32
women, commodification of 37,
  49–50
women, ethnic minority
  filmmakers 85–9
women, in movie industry 83–5
women, in politics 44–6, 160
women, in public office 146
women, media professionals 9,
  125–6
women, Mexican American 60
women, news coverage about 10, 101
women, objectifying, in news
  discourse 38–42
women, of color 3, 8, 26, 28, 31, 43,
  61, 63, 68, 85–90, 127–8, 148, 165,
  170, 179, 199, 217, 226

women, pseudo-emancipated image
of 228
women, third world 3, 4–5
women, watching crime 64–5
women, working-class 43, 57, 144
Women's International Network of
AMARC 221
Women's International Newsgathering
Service (WINGS) 220–1
women's liberation 1, 3, 7, 101, 212,
232
women's lived experience 73–4, 101,
130, 132, 152, 158, 161, 162, 235
women's media activism 94, 100–1,
235, 237–9
cross-cultural study on 107–12
functions of 232–7
women's media enterprises 2, 10, 101,
103, 106, 115, 134, 231, 233, 234
women's media production, feminist
critiques of 89–91
women's movements 1–2, 9, 37–8

women's rights 34, 111, 116, 133,
134, 165, 179, 221, 233
to communicate 112–16
women-owned media *see* women's
media enterprises
World Association for Christian
Communication (WACC) 41,
123–4, 189
World Forum on Communication
Rights 195
World Plan of Action, 1975 104, 105,
113, 117
World Social Forum (WSF), 2002
114, 115
World Summits on the Information
Society (WSIS), 2003, 2005 115,
197
WSIS Gender Caucus 197

Zambia 108, 159, 169
Zimbabwe 125
zine *see* e-zine

DATE DUE

NOV 21 '07			
NOV 21 '08			